D1084312

HISTORIÆ NATURALIS CLASSICA, XXXII

HISTORIÆ NATURALIS CLASSICA

EDIDERUNT

J. CRAMER ET H. K. SWANN

TOMUS XXXII

VOLES, MICE
AND LEMMINGS

BY

CHARLES ELTON

REPRINT 1965

BY J. CRAMER · WEINHEIM

WHELDON & WESLEY, LTD · STECHERT-HAFNER SERVICE AGENCY, INC.

CODICOTE, HERTS.   NEW YORK, N.Y.

VOLES, MICE
AND LEMMINGS

BY

CHARLES ELTON

REPRINT 1965

BY J. CRAMER · WEINHEIM

WHELDON & WESLEY, LTD · STECHERT-HAFNER SERVICE AGENCY, INC.

CODICOTE, HERTS.   NEW YORK, N.Y.

QL 752
E 45
1965 x

599.32
E51

VOLES, MICE
AND LEMMINGS

CAPTAIN GEORGE CARTWRIGHT visiting his fox-traps in the eighteenth century, in the country south of Hamilton Inlet, Labrador. He has a silver fox hung on to his bandolier, and in the background is another fox in a trap, and in the distance a bear. This picture is taken from his Journal, published in 1792.

VOLES, MICE
AND LEMMINGS

PROBLEMS IN
POPULATION DYNAMICS

BY

CHARLES ELTON
DIRECTOR OF THE BUREAU OF
ANIMAL POPULATION, OXFORD

OXFORD
AT THE CLARENDON PRESS
1942

OXFORD UNIVERSITY PRESS
AMEN HOUSE, E.C. 4
LONDON EDINBURGH GLASGOW NEW YORK
TORONTO MELBOURNE CAPETOWN BOMBAY
CALCUTTA MADRAS
HUMPHREY MILFORD
PUBLISHER TO THE UNIVERSITY

PREFACE

THE materials of this book have been assembled slowly for sixteen years with the help of a great many people, most of whom I can only thank here collectively. The first part is a panorama of vole and mouse plagues in those countries for which records are available. The second part describes the vole and mouse fluctuations that occur in Great Britain and Scandinavia, and the methods developed at Oxford for the study of population dynamics in the field and laboratory. The third and fourth parts contain the history of similar fluctuations in Northern Labrador and Ungava that have an important influence upon the fur trade and the life of natives.

It is only possible here to acknowledge those, who, by supplementing the gaps in our national system of subsidizing free research, enabled me to live and work continuously with less than the normal burden of University teaching: Oxford University (more especially since 1936); the Hudson's Bay Company (1925–31); Mr. Charles V. Sale (1928–31); the Empire Marketing Board (1928–31); the New York Zoological Society (1931–3); the Leverhulme Research Fellowship Trustees (1933–5); the Christopher Welch Trust (1936); and Corpus Christi College (since 1936). Mr. Sale, by his foresight and energy while he was Governor of the Hudson's Bay Company between the years 1925 and 1931, played such a large part in enabling me to start these investigations, that I wish to dedicate this book to him. Mr. Copley Amory, who created the Matamek Conference on Biological Cycles, in Canada in 1931, helped also very materially to promote this research.

My special obligations to the Hudson's Bay Company and to the Moravian Missions, for allowing me to draw so much unpublished information from their records, will be obvious in Parts III and IV, where (especially in Chapter XIII) a more detailed acknowledgement is given of this and other help received during the study of Labrador and Canadian wild-life cycles. The Hudson's Bay Company, the Department of Scientific and Industrial Research, the Leverhulme Research Fellowship Trustees, and the Carnegie Institution of Washington, have all contributed towards the expenses of this work.

There is a Chinese proverb that says: 'The bits of fur from under the legs of many foxes will in the end make a robe.' I hope that the numerous different lines of evidence brought together in this book will leave in the reader's mind the realization that there is a general phenomenon of world-wide extent for which quite new methods of research are being developed.

C. E.

18 *December* 1941.

CONTENTS

PART I

VOLE AND MOUSE PLAGUES

CHAPTER I

ANCIENT HISTORY, AND A PROPHECY

'Voici le vrai, le grand, l'éternel coupable, redouté depuis l'origine du monde.'

1

THESE words of Charles Gérard sound like the beginning of some judge's sentence upon a habitual criminal, perhaps because Gérard was not only a naturalist but also a lawyer at the court of Nancy. His two vocations led him to search the archives for information about wild animals, and his *Essai d'une faune historique des mammifères sauvages de l'Alsace* (1871)[6] contains one of the best descriptions of field-mouse plagues that exist.

It is an impressive picture of insurgent subterranean activity, of devastation breaking like a flood upon the crops. All man's vigilance and care are taxed by the multitude of small, swift, flitting forms that infest the ground and devour all living plants. Poison, ploughing, fumigation, trenches, and prayers, all these can scarcely stop the destruction. Gérard remembered an outbreak that happened in 1822, when he was a boy. In that year Alsace was absolutely in the power of mice. 'It was a living and hideous scourging of the earth, which appeared perforated all over, like a sieve.'

There is also a description of the chief actor, a kind of police report from which he could be recognized and his character defined. According to it the vole wears a livery entirely suitable to his surroundings: his coat is a short jacket of russet over a dull brown waistcoat; his clothing is completed by white small-clothes, altogether a fine costume for a life in the fields. He makes up for any poverty in his surroundings by an unquenchable activity. He takes no notice of the sun, but works morning, noon, and night. With such incessant activity, and a taste for almost every kind of crop, it is not surprising that the vole makes a success of his life.

But the resources of nature are not equal to a continual pressure of this magnitude. The plague abates, and for some years the land is able to recover. Gérard speaks of the abatement, but has no theory about the cause. Each plague of voles followed something of the same course. The biggest outbreaks were usually recorded, together with other disasters, in the country's annals. They came in 1271, 1278–9, 1366, 1378, 1468, 1538, 1593, 1617–19, 1652, 1685, 1719, 1742, 1794, 1801–2, 1818, 1822, 1856, and 1861. There is no regularity in these occurrences: they average about three to a century, or one to a generation. Some came at closer intervals. But they were so spaced out that few of the people living at any time during the last 700 years can have failed to experience at least one great plague of this kind.

2

The field-mouse that makes these plagues in Europe is the Continental vole (*Microtus arvalis*), known in France as *campagnol*, in Germany as *Feldmaus*, in Holland as *Veldmuis*, in Italy as *Topo campagnolo*, in Denmark as *Sydmarkmus* (Southern field-mouse), and in Russia as обыкновенная полевка.

There are of course other, subsidiary, species that scourge these countries, but seldom with the thoroughness and rapacity of *arvalis*. There is *Microtus agrestis*, which is the only species on the mainland of Great Britain and in Norway. In these countries its occasional plagues take their place with the best, or worst, that voles can achieve. On the Continent *agrestis* seems to play second fiddle to *arvalis* (the Germans call it *Ackermaus*).

The Continental vole was, it seems, once an inhabitant of Great Britain, since an island race (*Microtus orcadensis*) that seems to be a relict colony of *arvalis* occurs in Orkney. By an odd chance, our name of 'vole' is an Orkney word that got into English books a hundred years ago. But though it be incorrect, it is a good, compact, hard-hitting word that well expresses the square, well-whiskered face of the field-mouse.

In later chapters there is more information about other voles and mice that have these cycles of irruption and decrease. Sometimes they make a composite outbreak with *arvalis*, at other times they fluctuate without relation to this species. Our concern is to chart the distribution of these plagues, something of their history and kinds of periodicity, and then to describe how research on populations is being employed to give a deeper analysis of the problem.

The literature is peculiar and immense. To comprehend the history of European mouse plagues one has to read, among other and less peculiar works, a fauna of Alsace by a French notary; a vole plague report by a learned Indian civil servant and oriental scholar who retired to become a landowner in Scotland; a folk-lore essay written by a classical scholar and head of an Oxford college; a painstaking collection of classical references about animals by a school-teacher in Germany; and part of the works of Aristotle.

3

The earliest vole plague that we know about is the one which God of the Old Testament sent to punish the Philistines for carrying off the ark of the covenant.

Et ebullierunt villae et agri in medio regionis illius, et nati sunt mures, et facta est confusio mortis magnae in civitate.

'Mice were generated and "boiled over" the towns and fields in the midst of that region, and there was a confusion of great death in the land.' (Vulgate, 1 Kings v. 6.)

According to Elliott, this part of the story is given in the Septuagint and the Vulgate, but is missing from the English Bible,[4] which, however, gives the sequel. 'But the hand of the Lord was heavy upon them of Ashdod, and he destroyed them and smote them with emerods, even Ashdod and the coast thereof.' (Authorized Version, 1 Sam. v. 6.)

The priests of the Philistines announced that the ark must be returned, with a golden offering to appease the wrath of God: 'Five golden emerods, and five golden mice, according to the number of the Lords of the Philistines; for one plague was on you all, and on your lords' (vi. 4). They placed the golden emerods and the images of the 'mice that mar the land' in the ark and carried them beyond their frontiers.

In spite of sweeping changes in God and circumstances, Authority has for several thousand years continued to act in much the same way, even to the present day. The Bible story is, if you like, a parable. The affair runs always along a similar course. Voles multiply. Destruction reigns. There is dismay, followed by outcry, and demands to Authority. Authority remembers its experts or appoints some: they ought to know. The experts advise a Cure. The Cure can be almost anything: golden mice, holy water from Mecca, a Government Commission, a culture of bacteria, poison, prayers denunciatory or tactful, a new god, a trap, a Pied Piper. The Cures have only one thing in common: with a little patience *they always work*. They have never been known entirely to fail. Likewise they have never been known to prevent the next outbreak. For the cycle of abundance and scarcity has a rhythm of its own, and the Cures are applied just when the plague of voles is going to abate through its own loss of momentum.

Aristotle remarked:[13]

'The phenomena of generation in regard to the mouse are the most astonishing both for the number of the young and for the rapidity of recurrence in the births. . . . The rate of propagation of field mice in country places, and the destruction that they cause, are beyond all telling. In many places their number is so incalculable that but very little of the corn-crop is left to the farmer; and so rapid is their mode of proceeding that sometimes a small farmer will one day observe that it is time for reaping, and on the following morning, when he takes his reapers afield, he finds his entire crop devoured. Their disappearance is unaccountable: in a few days not a mouse will be there to be seen. And yet in the time before these few days men fail to keep down their numbers by fumigating and unearthing them, or by regularly hunting them and turning in swine upon them; for pigs, by the way, turn up the mouse-holes by rooting with their snouts. Foxes also hunt them, and the wild ferrets in particular destroy them; but they make no way against the prolific qualities of the animal and the rapidity of its breeding. When they are superabundant, nothing succeeds in thinning them down except the rain; but after heavy rains they disappear rapidly.'

Aristotle's measured and balanced description of the rise and fall of a mouse population might be taken for a text for the present book. For it contains most components of the problem of natural fluctuations. The

other ancient stories are more concerned with the human disasters caused
by them: some are embroidered perhaps too fancifully with mice, but at
any rate they show that plagues of mice were in the chroniclers' minds,
and that they were ranked with fire, pestilence, war, massacre, or flood as
one of the calamities of mankind. Harting[8] says, 'the classics are full of
wonderful stories about mice'. This is true, but almost any one of them
can be matched by well-attested happenings in modern times.

One of the best of the ancient tales is told by Herodotus. We read in the
Bible that (probably about the year 686 B.C.[11]) 'did Sennacherib King of
Assyria come up against all the fenced cities of Judah, and took them'
(2 Kings xviii. 13). The Bible confines itself to saying: 'And it came to
pass that night, that the angel of the Lord went out, and smote in the
camp of the Assyrians an hundred fourscore and five thousand: and when
they arose early in the morning, behold, they were all dead corpses. So
Sennacherib king of Assyria departed . . .' (xix. 35–6).

Herodotus has more than this to say.[4] The disaster was brought about
by field-mice 'which pouring in upon the soldiers, devoured their quivers,
bowstrings, and the handles of their shields, so that next day when they
fled bereft of their arms, many were slain' (*Euterpe*, ii. 141). Elliott,[4] from
whom this translation is taken, tells us that 'the event was commemorated
by a statue of Sethón, the Egyptian king, in the temple of Vulcan, with a
mouse in his hand, which Herodotus himself saw'. Some historians now
believe that the Assyrians may have died from bubonic plague or some
other rodent-carried disease, and that the story telescopes these happenings into a single night. The defeat of the Assyrians by Jove-sent mice
may not be a strictly true historical event. In fact Professor F. S. Bodenheimer tells me that vole plagues do not occur near Jerusalem where the
Assyrian cohorts camped, though there are other rodents in the neighbourhood that might have played a part. But the story shows the respect
which a historian of ancient times could have for field-mice.

4

This respect for mice was well founded and widespread, not only over
the Mediterranean and Aegean, but farther afield. The industrious
Harald Lenz[9] has provided us with references to a number of classical
stories about animals, and among these are passages that refer to field-
mice. I am indebted to Professor E. Fraenkel for finding and translating
for me many of the passages that I have drawn upon for the following
notes. It may be noted that Lenz gives much condensed paraphrases, and
not actual quotations, and that one or two of his references to mice are
incomplete or incorrectly placed.

Diodorus Siculus (3. 30. 2) states that: 'In Italy it came to pass that the
field-mice in the plains appeared in such numbers that the inhabitants
were driven away.' Strabo (3. 4. 18) describes how, in the land of the
Iberians (that is, in Spain), plague-like diseases often arose, on account of
the numbers of mice. There was a multiplication of this sort when the

Romans were in Cantabria. 'People engaged in catching the mice were paid a reward for delivering a fixed measure', and the Romans were only saved with difficulty. There was famine in everything, particularly in corn.

Theophrastus recorded (Pliny, *Nat. Hist.* 8. 222) that mice in the island of Gyaros drove out the people. Pliny himself has some observations on mouse plagues (10. 186). He says that mice often increased until the harvest was utterly destroyed, and that they diminished again remarkably quickly, though no one knew how it was that such a multitude died. 'For neither are dead ones found, nor is there anyone who has dug up a mouse in winter in his field.' The Troas was subject to these invasions, and the inhabitants of that country had even been driven out by the mice. 'Their appearance takes place in dry seasons. It is said that when they are about to die, a worm is generated in their heads.'

Another story comes from farther east. It is given by Aelian (17. 17), and quoted, with commentary, by Jacoby.[8b] 'Amyntas relates . . . that in the Caspian country . . . mice at certain times appear in prodigious numbers.' They swam the rivers, which in that region are formidable in size and strength. They ate down the corn, climbed up the trees and devoured the fruit, and also nibbled the branches. The Caspians defended themselves against the invasions of mice by preserving the birds of prey 'which in their turn fly in clouds and devour them'.

The fear of mice gave rise to religious ceremonies which were expressed particularly in the cult of Apollo. This god (already held responsible for a great many other serious tasks, such as town-planning, preservation of cattle, protection from locusts, wolves and mildew, and partly for the sun) was invested with power over mice. 'In Chrysa stands the temple of Apollo Smintheus. At the foot of the statue of the god lies the mouse, a work of the Parian Skopas' (Strabo).[9]

The god's special name meant 'mouser', supposedly derived from σμίνθος = a mouse. Skopas was a sculptor as famous as the mice. It was like employing Eric Gill to make the statue on Broadcasting House in London, symbolic of controlling force. The mouse of Apollo can be matched by other images of the sort in former days, mentioned by Frazer in the *Golden Bough*:[5] the bronze scorpion at Antioch, the bronze fly and gnat at Constantinople, the bronze grasshopper and golden leech at Naples, the golden locust in Arabia, the bronze snake and dormouse in Paris, the golden mice and emerods of the Philistines, and the brass serpent of the Israelites. Apollo's temple went one better than the others, by keeping tame mice in the sanctuary and a colony of white mice beneath the altar,[5] all attesting a close regard for mouse plagues.

The use of this word 'plague' requires an explanation. We use it in two senses. First as an increase in population, and in this sense an 'outbreak' of mice; just as we say a 'plague' of flies or locusts or caterpillars. The other use is for a definite disease, bubonic plague (which sometimes takes to the lungs, as pneumonic plague). This is a fatal fever, caused by the spread of a bacillus, the *Pasteurella pestis*, which lives in some fleas and can attack many animals that these fleas may bite. There is a confusion of words, yet each is useful, and the logical basis is correct—a multiplication of organisms in the mammalian or the ecological body. There comes a further complexity from the fact that plague disease is carried by many rodents, among them rats and mice, which multiply to form rat or mouse 'plagues', die of bubonic plague, and often communicate the epidemic to man.

The Greeks may have been to some slight extent aware of this connexion, when they gave the already over-departmentalized Apollo another burden, calling him Apollo Loimios, or Plague Apollo.[11] This title may not have been universal, but it is known to have been used at Lindus in Rhodes.

5

The researches of Frazer, Lenz, Powell, and other scholars have left no doubt about the importance of mice in the religions of those days. In medieval times this cult existed, whether derived or formed anew we do not know, in several parts of Europe. There is St. Gertrude, patron of towns in North Brabant in Holland, who is still invoked against field-mice. An eighteenth-century statue of this saint, standing in the eleventh-century church of Nivelles, not far from Brussels, has a long-tailed mouse or rat creeping up the robe; while in a Brussels church one mouse creeps up the pastoral staff of the saint and another lies at her feet.[11]

In Germany the goddess Holda, who ruled in Carniola and Hanover, was offered presents of flax and corn to keep the crops from mice.[11] In some parts of Bohemia the people always preserve any white mouse they find, making it a comfortable nest to live in.[5]

Such customs often grew into regular festivals, like the Apolline feast of Sminthia. A similar sort of ceremony occurs among the Huzuls of the Carpathians, who hold a weasel festival on St. Matthew's or on St. Catherine's Day, because they believe the bites of weasels bring disease to their cattle.[5] You may still find in the Outer Hebrides farmers who are afraid of the pigmy shrew: if one runs across a sleeping beast, there will be illness that can only be cured by passing a dead shrew over its body again. And who shall say that the fear that women have of mice running up their skirts is not a relic of St. Gertrude's rites, themselves derived from Apollo, who was perhaps descended from the Egyptian sun-god, Horus, giver of life? Or perhaps it is a relic of the Pied Piper of Hamelin, who went off with all the children.

Another curious survival of this kind of superstitious fear is recorded[8a] for the village of St.-Géniès-de-Malgoires, in the south of France. The last rat-catcher in this village lived in 1892. The people thought him to be a sorcerer, and no one would sit at the table with him, or drink from his cup. In 1480, at Nîmes, not far from this village, the Church was reading denunciations of 'the rats and moles and other such creatures' that devastated the land in that year.

Where prayers failed (that is, I suppose, if they were put forth too early in the mouse cycle), there were exorcizings to be done. Here is a Greek one.[11] 'Take a sheet of paper and write on it as follows: "I adjure you, ye mice here present, that ye neither injure me, nor suffer another mouse to do so. I give you yonder field" (here you specify a field, perhaps a neighbour's) "but if I catch you here again, by the mother of the gods, I will rend you in seven pieces." Write this and stick the paper on an unhewn stone in the field before sunrise, taking care to keep the written side uppermost.' This formula was still used, in Latin, in the sixteenth century. But, as Gérard remarks, to cut all the mice in seven pieces is more easy to say in Latin than to carry out in French. They exorcize rats still in the Ardennes, and Frazer relates that one American farmer wrote an 'open letter' to the rats and pinned it up in his barn.

6

There is a pleasant mixture of cajolery and warning in these threats, a rather precarious bluff. There is also usually a spice of bargaining and persuasion, which reminds one of international political conferences. The Celebes farmer runs round his patch saying to the rats: 'Pruner is your name. Creep not through my rice. Be blind and deaf. Creep not through my rice. If you must creep through rice, go and creep through other rice.'[5] The hairy Ainus of a certain village in Japan were reputed to take extreme precautions about the rats. Besides offering them libations and sacred sticks whittled at the top into shavings, they carried no cats in any boats that passed along that shore, lest the rats should be offended.[1]

Sterner measures were sometimes used. The Church would, in extreme cases, excommunicate the field-mice—a somewhat empty dishonour. The Moslems of one East Indian island where the mice destroy the rice performed a more subtle and rather mysterious rite. On Friday, after service in the mosque, the priests took four pairs of mice and married them together with full religious rites. Each pair was put in a little boat filled with rice and fruits, and they were all carried down to the shore with wedding procession in the wake, and launched to their later death at sea.[5]

7

Many astonishing stories have been written about the plagues of mice that have ravaged Europe during the last thousand years. One of the best is given in Stow's *Chronicle*, from which Elliott[4] quotes the record that 'about Hallowtide last past (1581) in the marshes of Danesey Hundred, in a place called South Minster, in the county of Essex . . . there sodainlie appeared an infinite number of mice, which overwhelming the whole earth in the said marshes, did sheare and gnaw the grass by the rootes, spoyling and tainting the same with their venimous teeth in such sort, that the cattell which grazed thereon were smitten with a murraine, and died thereof; which vermine by policie of man could not be destroyed, till at last it came to pass that there flocked together such a number of owles, as all the shire was able to yield, whereby the marsh-holders were shortly delivered from the vexation of the said mice. The like of this was also in Kent.'

In January 1622 the agent of the Grand Duke of Tuscany was writing:[10] 'A new portent: so many voles are breeding in Puglia that we cannot kill them. And so they are eating up all the crops. I call them the Curse of God, because *once again* they have fallen upon this unhappy province.' Fifty years ago a Scottish farmer in the Border hills wrote,[2] in more circumstantial but no less despairing manner, about his losses:

'For the year 1890–91 the shortness of lambs, owing to the mice having the ground sore destroyed, £250. For the year 1891–92: lightness of clip, £31; 410 sheep wintered away, £143. 10; grass taken to lamb 600 ewes on, £210; hay grown on the farm, which the sheep are eating, which they would not require but for the mice, £160. But it is impossible to estimate the damage; and unless the mice depart soon, and the grass come again in the spring (what was eaten in 1890-91 has not grown again), the most of the sheep will be to take away and keep away till the mice plague gets past. . . . It is impossible for anyone to believe the ground is so sore destroyed unless they see it. They have missed nothing, everything cropped to the earth. The future is a terrible looking to.'

These tales could be multiplied, like the mice, until they would spoil and taint the reader's mind with too oppressive a sense of disaster, so that the dulled appreciation would in the end accept the plagues as acts of God, best slipped from the memory. They are, indeed, real Facts of Nature: not just part of the weary Nemesis that comes from man's interference with his surroundings. The fluctuations are a part of the orchestral variations that all animal communities undergo from year to year.

Although the farmer and forester suffer, and sometimes health is endangered, there are other points of view. For instance, much of the world's trade in furs is built out of mice and voles and lemmings. Northward, beyond the line where crops will flourish, the mice themselves become a crop, harvested by fox and trapper and trader in succession. Rising above the bread-and-butter zone of thought, we can see in these fluctuations the expression of natural forces worthy of study for their own interest and significance. They give a hint of the biological *shape* of the world we live in. Beyond this again there is a realm of pleasant personal feelings that come from the contemplation of those delicate small warm bodies, the free busy life under hedge or crossing stems of grass, the subterranean energy and skill that beat us so often at our own games. Walt Whitman wrote that 'A mouse is miracle enough to stagger sextillions of infidels'.

8

Research, to be worth its salt, should be able to forge from these different points of view a clear description and understanding of the populations of mice that would have in it something more than an unthinking assertion of the power of man to stifle the progress of his competitors. It would contribute to our insight into ourselves, and show how we stand in relation to the other life of a teeming globe.

The practical problem in this research remains what it has been for several thousand years: how to anticipate and check a multiplication whose onset is unexpected because its causes are unknown. The general situation is the same, whether the mouse plague is destroying alfalfa in Nevada, spruce-trees in Argyll, peach orchards in Italy, or the wheat-fields of Canada; whether it is killing a child from food poisoning in a Liverpool slum, Russians from bubonic plague by the Volga, or Japanese from river-fever in Formosa; whether it brings the foxes inland for the Nascopie Indian of Labrador to trap, or the short-eared owl to nest on the Scottish hills; and whether it interests the student of statistical epidemiology, the scientist at work on his knees among grass tussocks, or the naturalist who hears the rustle of many small active feet in a Lapland pine forest at night.

During the last hundred years the control, or attempted control, of field-mice has fallen gradually out of the hands of the local god into those of the local government. As Powell[11] remarks: 'If Apollo Smintheus is made into a Government Department, the Minister or Chief Secretary will take the place of his priest Chryses, and the god's double function will continue.'

With this change has grown up a volume of research which I shall attempt partly to sift in the ensuing chapters. Although it is scattered and the records are usually unrelated in different countries, yet it pertains to a world-wide problem. If we could imagine ourselves able to see great stretches of the earth's surface at one time, we should notice the ground in many places to have a troubled appearance, with quite large patches of ruined orchard or plantation or spoiled crops. In other regions hundreds of men would be seen laying traps in the snow so that they might strip the fur off foxes and martens fat with mice.

9

The head-quarters of the Central Field-Mouse Staff Office of a World State (CENMOSO for short), if it existed, would be compiling reports in some such style as these:

August 1928. Charles French, Fur Trade Commissioner of the Hudson's Bay Company in Winnipeg, Canada, reports great increase of field-mice (*Microtus drummondi*) in the Mackenzie River valley, and expects this to affect the numbers of fur-bearing animals.

January 1929. Norman M. Ross, Chief of the Tree Planting Division, Department of the Interior, Forest Nursery Station, Indian Head, Saskatchewan, Canada (by Canadian National Parks Branch inquiry), reports a great many complaints about the numerous field-mice this year from fruit-growers, who say that the mice are doing much damage to young fruit-trees, by girdling them under the snow. F. H. Gisborne, District Forest Inspector for British Columbia, Kamloops, B.C., Canada (by Canadian National Parks Branch inquiry), reports a great many complaints about the numerous field-mice this year from fruit-growers who say that the mice are doing much damage to young fruit-trees.

November 1929. A. D. Middleton (by Oxford Rodent Investigation) has received reports from Forestry Commission officials and other observers, that voles (*Microtus agrestis*) were extremely numerous in the late summer

in various parts of the north and west of Scotland, where they have been
destructive to forest plantations by ringing the trunks and also attacking
the roots and branches of young trees.

December 1929. The *New York Tribune* (Paris edition, quoted by Central
News) states that the island of Flores in the Dutch Indian Archipelago is
suffering from a terrible famine caused by a plague of mice, which have
destroyed crops. The inhabitants of all villages have fled to the woods.

August 1930. The Oxford University Expedition to · Norwegian Lapland
(Finmarken and Troms) reports that field-mice (*Microtus*) are extremely
numerous both on the margins of upland streams (*M. ratticeps*) and in the
lower valley hayfields (*M. agrestis*). Red-backed mice (*Clethrionomys
rufocanus* and *rutilus*) are excessively abundant in the pine woods at
Punta, while incipient lemming (*Lemmus lemmus*) migrations have been
encountered at a number of points on the route.

February 1931. A. D. Middleton (by Oxford Rodent Investigation) has
received reports from Forestry Commission officials and other observers
that marked increase in voles (*Microtus agrestis*) took place during 1930
in the Scottish Border and in certain parts of the English Lake District.
Voles had by the spring of 1930 become greatly reduced in numbers in
some parts of the north and west of Scotland, where they were very abundant
in 1929, e.g. at Glenfinart and Benmore in Argyllshire, also at Ratagan and
Loch Maree, in west Ross-shire. Damage to young trees in these areas has,
therefore, temporarily ceased.

July 1931. P. A. Buxton reports that a bad vole plague hit part of Palestine
in the summer of 1930, and continued until early 1931. The voles (*Microtus
guentheri*, mainly) affected some 150,000 acres of farm-land on the plain of
Esdraelon. The Government estimates that they destroyed 65 per cent. of
the wheat, barley, and other crops. Several thousand pounds were spent
on control measures, in which poisoned grain was used. This has also killed
some useful snakes and jackals that ate the mice.

Autumn 1931. The Hauptstelle für Pflanzenschutz[12] (Central Station for
Plant Protection) at Landsberg (Warthe) in the east of Prussia, reports
that following general rarity of field-mouse damage throughout 1929, a
more marked increase in voles (*Microtus arvalis*) was observed by the late
summer of 1930. These observations imply correspondingly higher damage
to farm-crops.

Summer 1931. N. Tinbergen[14] (Zoological Laboratory, Leiden University)
reports that whereas 35 out of 36 stations recorded abundance of voles
(*Microtus arvalis*) in Holland in the summer of 1930, decrease occurred
throughout 1931, when only 1 out of 55 stations reported abundance, 6 no
change in numbers, and the rest scarcity. The food of long-eared owls in
five districts contained 86 per cent. *Microtus* in the winter of 1930–1, and
only 30 per cent. in the winter of 1931–2. The percentages of house
sparrows in the food in these two years were 2 per cent. and 30 per
cent.

October 1931. The Italian Royal Ministry of Agriculture and Forestry has
dispatched Athos Goidanich[7] to investigate two plagues of voles (*Pitymys
savii*) which had been destroying the roots and girdling the stems of peach-
trees in the commune of Cesena in Puglia. At this time a thousand dead
trees were counted.

March 1932. A Reuter message from Basrah, Iraq, states that a great plague of field-mice is threatening the villages of the Western Desert, according to reports by Bedouins. Special smoke cartridges and poison bait are being distributed to deal with the menace.

June 1933. Dr. H. L. Paddon, of the International Grenfell Association Mission, at North West River, Labrador, reports: 'Mice were legion last winter. . . . In such years the foxes simply will not come to trap.'

10

These are all real stories, taken more or less at random from records in the Bureau of Animal Population. Perhaps in a hundred years' time there will be a newspaper notice of this kind:

'2040. St. Gertrude's Day. The staff of CENMOSO will meet to celebrate the publication of Volume 50 of *Rodent Almanack*, whose use by primary producers all over the world in connection with the forecasting and prevention of outbreaks is too well known to require detailed description. After dinner and the Rodent Rhythm Dance, members will be entertained by a television showing of the lemming migration in Gudbrandsdal, and of the flowering of the bamboo and its associated rodent outbreaks in Chittagong, Burma.'

Is this fantastic? Let us quote the remarks of a Soviet ecologist, Fenyuk, who is defining the measures necessary for the control of mouse plagues in the U.S.S.R.:

'For timely control of rodents one needs prognostications of their population dynamics and warning signals of local increases in their numbers, i.e. one needs a developed network, considerably wider than at present exists, of census service observation posts, the work of which would be coordinated from one centre. . . . Considering how specific the importance of mass increases in mouse-like rodents is in plague enzootic districts, I think it necessary to urge the creation of a network of zoological observation posts affiliated to the peripheral posts and stations of the anti-plague organisations. The centre uniting the observers' work might be the Saratov Institute of Microbiology and Epidemiology for the South-East of the U.S.S.R.'

The following chapters will give some idea of how far the world has moved towards such organized study of rodent fluctuations, and what has been found out at different centres about the principles underlying these phenomena.

REFERENCES

1. BATCHELOR, J. (1901). 'The Ainu and their folk-lore.' London. pp. 508–9.
2. BOARD OF AGRICULTURE (1892). 'Reports on the plague of field mice or voles in the South of Scotland.' London. p. 18. (Reprinted in the Report of the Departmental Committee, see No. 4.)
3. CHAPPELLIER, A. (1932). 'Les rongeurs de France. . . .' Arch. Hist. Nat. 9: 58.
4. ELLIOTT, W. (1878). 'Some account of the plague of field mice in the Border farms, in 1876–7, with observations on the genus *Arvicola* in general.' History [Proc.] of the Berwickshire Naturalists' Club, 8: 447–72. [Reprinted also in 'Report of the Departmental Committee appointed by the Board of Agriculture to enquire into a plague of field voles in Scotland. . . .' Parliamentary Blue-book, C 6943, Appendix 3. London.]

4 a. Fenyuk, B. K. (1937). ['The influence of agriculture on the numbers of mouse-like rodents, and the biological foundations of rodent control.'] Rev. Microbiol., Saratov, 16: 487–92. (In Russian. Translation in the Bureau of Animal Population, Oxford.)

5. Frazer, J. (1912). 'The golden bough. Part 5. Spirits of the corn and of the wild.' 2: 276–84.

6. Gérard, C. (1871). 'Essai d'une faune historique des mammifères sauvages de l'Alsace.' Paris. pp. 220–9.

7. Goidanich, A. (1933). 'Arvicole danneggiatrici di peschi.' L'Italia Agricola, 70: 79–84.

8. [Harting, J. E.] (1893). Zoologist, 17:187–8.

8 a. Hughes, A. (1924). 'Les campagnols dans le Gard.' Progr. Agric. Vitic. 81: 405–6.

8 b. Jacoby, F. (1929). 'Die Fragmente der griechischen Historiker.' 122, F 3. Berlin.

9. Lenz, H. O. (1856). 'Zoologie der alten Griechen und Römer.' Gotha. pp. 151–5.

10. Martelli, G. (1919). 'Contributo alla conoscenza della vita e dei costumi delle arvicole in Puglia.' Portici. p. 195.

11. Powell, U. K. (1929). 'Rodent-gods in ancient and modern times.' Folk-Lore, 40: 173–9.

12. Schander, R., Goetze, G., & Schleusener, W. (1931). 'Berichte über das Auftreten der Krankheiten und Beschädigungen der Kulturpflanzen im Bereich der Hauptstelle für Pflanzenschutz in Landsberg (Warthe): Vegetationsperiode 1929–30.' pp. 52–4.

13. Thompson, D'A. W. (transl. by, 1910). 'The works of Aristotle. Vol. 4. Historia Animalium.' Oxford. p. 580b.

14. Tinbergen, N. (1933). 'Die ernährungsökologischen Beziehungen zwischen Asio otus otus L. und ihren Beutetieren, insbesondre den Microtus-Arten.' Ecol. Monogr. 3: 445–92.

CHAPTER II

FRANCE

1

THE history of vole and mouse plagues in Europe reads like the story of an unending war. Not continuous fighting: rather a series of pitched battles with intervals of armistice while both sides pause to lick their wounds. As with a war, especially when it is fought over many hundred miles of open country, the story is not easy to piece together afterwards. Action is often hurried and much goes unrecorded, and that which is noted down may be lost. Nearly always the records are scattered and local and hard to get hold of, at any rate in England, where an abnormal freedom from such devastation has permitted only a languid interest in this literature.

The accounts of these plagues abound in military metaphors, which testify to the serious threat that mice can offer to country people. We read of invasions, advances, attacks on crops, squadrons of mice, campaigns, victories, and defeats. Everything takes place on a huge scale. It is difficult for us in this quiet country to realize that an area of farm-land equal in size to all the plantings made by the British Forestry Commission during the last eighteen years may be ravaged by mice; that the damage runs into millions; that hundreds of villages turn out to make war on the pests; and that this happens, not just once in a generation, but sometimes twice or more in ten years.

France suffers probably more than the other countries of Europe from plagues of field-mice, although Germany and Italy cannot be far behind. For this reason the records are rather copious, though by no means easily accessible. It is only certain regions that are commonly affected. These are defined by the general geological anatomy of France. From the intractable central mountain massif on which the Atlantic winds lay down much rain, long rivers run to the north, west, and southern seaboards, through rich agricultural plains lying on sedimentary rocks. Brittany, forming the north-west angle of France, is, however, made of old hard rocks and chiefly given to pasture. It is in the plains and low hills of Ouest, Loire, Normandy, the Paris basin, Picardy, Nord, Champagne, and Est that the vole populations especially flourish.

Half the area of France is cultivated, and a third of this is grown with crops among which wheat predominates. Wheat and also oats cover very large parts of the northern region, especially in the Paris basin. There is another sixth of the country grass-grown for stock. The vole and mouse plagues are chiefly remarkable in the growing crops: they are not so important either in Brittany or the mountain core of France, where grasslands are the chief agricultural resource.[12] The intensity of cultivation, induced by a widespread peasant ownership of comparatively small hold-ings, makes the damage worse when it comes.

There are several works of authority that one turns to. Danysz, of the Institut Pasteur in Paris, is famous as the discoverer of the Danysz 'virus', a bacteriological culture used in the control of voles. He also made, in 1913, an important summary of the distribution of French vole plagues.[12] For most of the years between 1913 and 1931 one may consult the *Rapports phytopathologiques* assembled by Marchal and his colleagues in Government research institutes.[29-42] Mainly concerned with insect and fungus pests, these annual summaries give also brief but valuable notes on vole damage in various departments. Guénaux's book[19] condenses much of the previous published information about voles, and adds some new records (as does Chappellier more recently[8a]). It also usefully defines the actions of other mammal pests in France. In more recent years Regnier, Pussard, and other workers of the Government Station Entomologique at Rouen have with admirable versatility made ecological studies of the life of voles, and also of the literature on French outbreaks. This station also manufactures the Danysz 'virus' for general use by farmers, and has played an important part in the organization of campaigns.

These major works afford a partial key to a host of smaller writings, mostly buried in local agricultural publications. The literature must really be almost endless, for one notices a number of further French references in the German bibliography of Schander and Meyer.[63]

2

As Regnier and Pussard point out,[53] Rouen has been before now a centre of interest in voles. There is a thirteenth-century manuscript in the municipal library of Rouen which relates the following story. The head of St. Valentin, martyred in Rome in the third century, was later brought to Jumièges, a famous abbey near Rouen. Some time in the twelfth century the land was ridden with field-mice. The saint appeared twice to one of the priests and commanded that, in order to abate the plague, his head should be carried through the fields. A procession was organized, and 'upon seeing the relic, the field-mice fled in great haste, and their squadrons ran down the Chemin des Îles and threw themselves into the Seine, where they were drowned'. The people afterwards revered the saint as protector against the mice. We shall have to examine, later on, the question of how far beyond this point research has carried us.

Although there are other species that damage the crops, chief actor is the Continental vole, *Microtus arvalis*. This species inhabits the greater part of Europe and part of Asia, chiefly between the 45° and 55° north lines of latitude. North-westward it gives place to *Microtus agrestis*, which, however, lives also in company with it in northern France and in Germany. *Agrestis* is seldom a pest in France, where it seems to have somewhat different habits from English *agrestis*, living in woods and plantations, and less in pure grass-land.[53]

Southwards *arvalis* gives place, at any rate as a major pest, to species of *Pitymys*, another vole. *P. subterraneus* is harmful in south-east France,[20, 47] while *P. savii* is very harmful in Italy (see Chapter IV). Chappellier[8a] also mentions an outbreak of *subterraneus* in Marne in 1928–9, and it may be that this species, from its strictly underground habits, does more damage generally than is realized. It attacks the roots of vegetables, trees, and even vines. In the mountains of Auvergne, Pyrenees, and Savoy there is still another vole, *Arvicola monticola*, which sometimes causes serious damage in the fields. Chapellier's book[8] gives excellent descriptions of all these species, with coloured pictures of some.

Our immediate object of study is *Microtus arvalis* in the northern and western plains of France. We are here on the western edge of an area of *arvalis* damage that covers Germany, Belgium, Austria, Czechoslovakia, Hungary, Poland, Russia, northern Italy, and country eastwards to a little known extent in Asia. These are some of the richest farming lands of Europe.

Although *arvalis* is less often a pest in the mountain regions, it does live quite high up. It comes, for instance, in Haute Savoie, also round Lucerne and Geneva, and it has been recorded as doing damage round Basel.[17]

Another species occasionally comes into the picture. This is the wood-mouse or long-tailed field-mouse (*Apodemus sylvaticus*), whose activities may be confused with those of the voles. Its French name is 'mulot'—a word derived from low German 'mul', and allied to our 'mole' and the German 'Maulwurf'. But the older writers in agricultural journals often used it indiscriminately to mean either *Apodemus sylvaticus* or *Microtus arvalis*—just as ancient chroniclers did, before the word 'campagnol' was introduced from Italy. I cannot find, however, that this general use was continued after Danysz wrote about field-mouse plagues just before the War of 1914. In practically all the notes written since then 'mulot' means definitely the wood-mouse. However, Chappellier,[8a] in the course of a questionnaire inquiry about rodent pests in France in 1937, found that it is still often used for *Microtus* in ordinary parlance among people in the country north of the Loire. But with this knowledge of the possible confusion in the names, it is usually fairly easy to work out which species is referred to in the older records.

With its long tail, large delicate ears and big eyes adapted to life in the dark, and its bounding gait, there can be no confusion with the square whiskery face, small ears and beady eyes, and partly diurnal ways of a vole.

There are other names for *Apodemus*, mostly found in natural history books,[8] rather than in the agricultural literature we are concerned with: 'souris de bois', 'rat-mulot', and 'rat sau eur'. In Luxembourg[18] it is 'Besch-maus' and 'Sprenger'; in Germany 'Waldmaus'. Many of its names refer to the woodland habit of the species (as also in Italy: 'rato selvatico'; and in Norway and Denmark: 'skovmus'). This definition is broadly true, for although it is common enough in gardens and on the edge of cultivation, *Apodemus sylvaticus* does not seem to grow large permanent populations out in the open fields.

The names of the voles (*Microtus*) are in most countries significant of an open habitat. 'Vole' comes from Old Norse 'völlr', which means 'field'. The word hung on in Orkney dialect and was by chance transferred to English zoological literature over a century past, as another name for short-tailed field-mouse. In Norway it is 'markmus', in German and Luxembourgeois 'Feldmaus', in French 'campagnol des champs', in Dutch and Flemish 'Veldmuis', and so on.[8] Only, in France, our own *agrestis* has a partiality for woods.

3

There are only two records of large outbreaks of *Apodemus* in France, both, as we might expect, in the heavily wooded country of Est. Of the one that Danysz mentions,[11] in the spring and summer of 1893, we know little. It affected various parts of Est.

The other, in 1923, gives clearer records. Early in that year Ardouin-Dumazet reported[2] to the Académie d'Agriculture that great damage was being done by field-mice in some parts of Est and southern Champagne, especially in the departments of Aube and Haute-Marne. Later three others were also affected: Marne, Meurthe-et-Moselle, and Haute-Saône. This region is on the Lorraine Plateau which is formed of the hills between the Paris basin and the high Vosges. We are here in country with many remnants of ancient forests, such as Chateauvillain, Clairvaux, and Haye.

Vayssière, an investigator from Rouen, went to the mulot area.[64, 65] He was struck by the unusual nature of the damage. Rye was the crop that had chiefly been attacked. Many of the stems still stood, but the heads of corn had in many cases been nipped off.

Lienhart,[24] writing in *L'Est Républicain*, 17 July 1923, described what occurred:

> 'At dusk, parties of mulots made their way into the fields of ripe corn. They went leaping along. In less time than it takes to say it, a mouse, with the help of its paws and its long tail which is prehensile, climbed right up the stalk, and when it got to the top, cut it off with one swift bite. The head of corn fell to the ground, where the mulot retrieved it promptly. The head has its seeds removed and these are carried to stores in the neighbouring wood. . . .'

Vayssière confirms this account and he says that no vole could do damage of this peculiar kind. The damage started near the forests, but later on it spread more widely. Evidently there was either a great multiplication of mice inside the woods or else some unfavourable condition drove them out. It is certain that no such large mulot outbreaks on farmland have been recorded in the less heavily wooded places like Normandy. A vast campaign was organized and repressive measures used until the plague abated. Guénaux[19] mentions the wood-mouse as a pest in plantations and forest nurseries.

Apodemus plagues in France are infrequent invasions from the woods.

They happen perhaps once in a generation, and in a small part of France. With voles it is very different. Many departments are attacked; the multiplication happens repeatedly, at quite short intervals. And there is little sign that it has been permanently prevented by measures used in the last forty-five years.

4

Although there must be many field-mouse outbreaks that were never reported in the journals, nevertheless there is a large flourishing literature which we may accept as a fair sample from which to gauge the distribution of the outbreaks. Danysz[12] gives a map that shows the chief zone of vole plagues. I have checked this over a longer period by counting the number of vole plagues recorded for each department. Admitting that there is no common standard of intensity or widespreadness, that occasionally some other species than *arvalis* is the cause, and that a good many plagues must have been unrecorded, the results agree sufficiently with Danysz's general chart to suggest that the figures must have a broad value.

TABLE 1

Vole plagues in France, 1792-1899

Date	District, &c., and references
1792	Charente, Charente-Inférieure, Vendée (52, 53)
1801–2	Charente, Charente-Inférieure, Deux-Sèvres, Gironde, Loire-Inférieure, Maine-et-Loire, Vendée. Most of the crops were lost, and there was over 3 million francs damage in Vendée alone, where a Commission from Paris made an investigation (10, 14, 19, 53, 56). Also in Alsace-Lorraine (53)
1816–17	Vendée, over 3 million francs damage (53)
1822	'Partial or general' (10). Bas-Rhin (Alsace) (19)
1832, 1856, 1863, 1867	'Partial or general' (10)
1865	Aisne (9)
1870	Picardy (14). Aisne (9)
1872	'Partial or general' (10)
1879	Aisne (9)
1880	'Partial or general' (10). Aisne (9). Aube, Somme (50). Pas-de-Calais (14, 50)
1881	Aisne. 13 million francs damage (4, 52, 19). Haute-Marne (4). Seine-et-Marne (16). Somme (23)
1882	Aisne, Eure-et-Loire, Marne, Seine-et-Marne, Somme (19)
1885	Seine-Inférieure (53)
1892–3	Damage in millions of francs (10, 12). Seine-et-Marne; most departments of Est (*Microtus* and *Apodemus*) (11)
1898–9	Somme (53)

For reference, these figures are also summed in two tables (1 and 2), to which additions may doubtless be made by anyone sufficiently enthusiastic to burrow through the early files of such periodicals as the *Revue de Viticulture*, *La Vie Agricole et Rurale*, *Journal d'Agriculture Pratique*, and many more. The first table summarizes the rather threadbare records that exist for the years before 1900. The second gives the more abundant records for 1900–35: these are full enough to reflect real fluctuations in intensity. A sketch-map showing the French departments is given in Fig. 1. Although the meaning of the records must vary a good deal, it is believed that most of them are widespread outbreaks within a department,

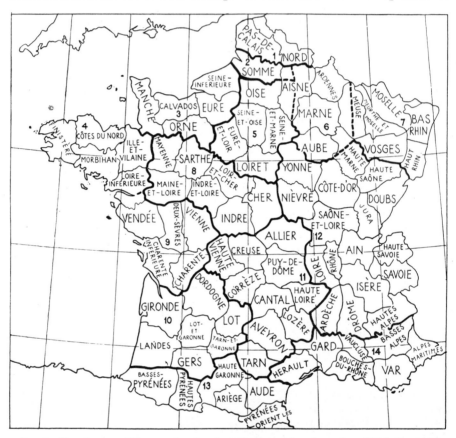

Fig. 1. Sketch map of France, showing departments and main regions (thick lines). The regions are only roughly indicated, and for reasons of clarity on the map follow as nearly as possible the department boundaries. They are numbered as follows:

1. Nord. 2. Picardy. 3. Normandy. 4. Brittany. 5. Paris Basin. 6. Champagne. 7. Est. 8. Loire. 9. Ouest. 10. Aquitaine. 11. Massif Central. 12. Jura, Rhône Valley. 13. Pyrenees. 14. Mediterranean.

Regnier and Pussard (reference no. 53) are of the opinion that the outbreaks reported for the Central Massif region and some other southern places may be caused by other voles than *M. arvalis*. The distribution of outbreaks in other regions corresponds in a general way with the sketch-maps given by these authors, and by Danysz (No. 12), of the main areas of *arvalis* infestation. The present map is, however, built up from the assembly of detailed records and is probably more accurate.

and not simply 'back-yard' infestations. There is reasonable justification for treating them as 'outbreak units', since also the departments are mostly of a similar order of size to one another.

The map (Fig. 2) defines more closely the chief theatres of vole activity, to which a general reference has already been made. The zone of eruptive populations runs in a horseshoe shape, from the western seaboard (mainly northward of Bordeaux), up through the country of the Loire, the rich· eastern part of Normandy, the Paris basin, Picardy and Nord, turns east through Champagne to Est (including Alsace and Lorraine), and dips

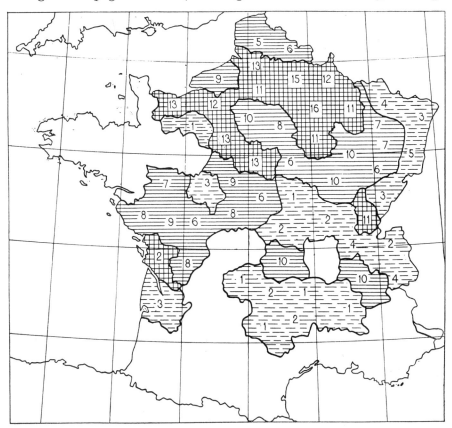

Fɪɢ. 2. Distribution of vole outbreaks in France 1900–35, mapped from the data in Table 2. Four zones are shown: departments with none recorded; with 1–5 recorded; with 6–10 recorded; and with 11–16 recorded. The main belt of frequent and heavy outbreaks falls into Picardy (Somme), Champagne, parts of the Paris basin and Normandy; with another high spot in Charente-Inférieure. Between these two, and extending eastwards below the main area, is a region of moderately frequent infestation. For a note on the southern areas of distribution see Fig. 1.

down through Burgundy to the valleys of the Saône and Rhône. The curve of this danger zone flanks the central mountains on three sides, avoids the rough lands of Brittany and western Normandy, and fades out rather vaguely to the south. It weakens a little in the Loire, giving emphasis to two separate centres of action, one in the west, the other in the north and east. There are rather isolated centres in Puy-de-Dôme and Isère. The intensity is startling in such departments as Marne and Aisne, which seldom have been entirely free from voles.

On the margins of this zone are departments which at long intervals take part in the general pullulation. Probably some of these are really more frequently infested than the map suggests. Such errors are inherent in the method by which the map is made. We are not concerned here to give a microscopist's or a theodolite surveyor's standard of precision, but rather to sketch the broad distribution of this western arm of strong *arvalis* fluctuation.

5

We have now to study the recurrence of these outbreaks, how they run their course, and the factors that control their rise and fall. After that we shall have to consider how much effect the gigantic human efforts at control, applied with all the tense organization and fervour of a French community in peril, have had; to what extent the controllers rode their storm or harnessed it; and the influence of these operations upon the general character of the vole fluctuations. It may be opportune to say that, although the facts that follow are the product of compilation, a point of view is put forward that differs from that of most French investigators.

After ransacking the French literature, several impressions are left in the mind. For one thing, the general surveys published by various people are not always general surveys: in reality there is often much local limitation in the information drawn upon. The result is a series of partial surveys dependent on the accidents of personal experience, library, or contact with other regions. This situation needs explaining, because the reader might otherwise conclude that the facts used here are complete, like the figures of the Registrar-General. We are using, rather, a random sampling method, which gives representative, but not complete, records from most of the vole plague zone.

Another thing that strikes one is the absence of any national intelligence system, co-ordinating on a standard plan the information from each 'department' (the equivalent of our 'county'). With the exception of the summaries by Marchal and others, action from Paris has mainly been limited to occasional outbursts of Government commissions (manned, often enough, by some of the best brains in the country) and to the manufacture and distribution of supplies to check the pest. Local interest is, however, intense, and finds a written outlet in numerous communications to papers and the agricultural journals. It is from the general works already mentioned and from these somewhat random sources that maps and tables have to be constructed. There is no material obstacle, though there may be plenty of mental ones, to prevent a small central staff from following and mapping in detail vole plagues all over France, and publishing periodic reports, as has been done in several German states. Such a staff would (untimely thought!) add to the list (that already includes disease, food, drugs, and the white-slave traffic) of things that argue for treatment of Europe as a natural biological unit.

Generally speaking each vole plague has been considered as an isolated event, with its own cycle of destruction, public excitation, desperate measures, final relief (from one cause or another), and dismissal from thought. Such a staccato consciousness of the phenomenon is not justified by the history shown in Tables 1 and 2. There is no need to expand these tables much, except to bring out certain general features. During the period from 1790 to 1935—145 years—there were at least twenty epochs of vole abundance amounting to serious plague proportions. Some of them covered several years together. The earlier plagues leave no specially valuable facts that the later ones cannot supply. The one in 1801 is note-worthy for the two reasons that it almost wiped out the crops in many parts of western France, and that the disturbance was sufficient to bring to the spot a commission of learned men appointed by the French Academy under the Revolutionary Government. The dispatch of Government com-missions has long been known to exercise a soothing influence similar to that of the doctor's medicine and bedside manner, and their observations are often of the greatest scientific value. Other outbreaks happened in 1816–17, 1822, and 1832. Reports are more frequent after 1850. The main periods were 1856, 1863–5, 1870–2, 1880–1, 1885, 1892–3, 1898–9, 1903–4, 1909, 1912–13, 1918–23, 1925–8, and 1930–1: quite a formidable list, com-prising 13 groups in 80 years, or, taking the latter half of the period, 8 in 40 years. The average interval in the later period was 5 years, but the approximate intervals were actually 6, 5, 6, 3, 6, 7, 5.

6

These figures indicate some recurrence at short intervals, but they are subject to an important fallacy. The table does not prove that every department in the vole plague zone had an outbreak every time. It only shows that 'somewhere in France' there were outbreaks at recurrent intervals that have not been far apart. A good many, but not always the same, departments were ravaged badly at each recurrence, while some of them suffered more than half the times.

There are obvious signs of recurrence in the earlier period from 1850 to 1889, but based on scarcer literature. There must have been a great many increases in the vole population that passed without much notice, not justifying complaint. Or the complaints, as is not uncommon, got pigeon-holed and were never published. These smaller increases would be very important for an ecologist studying recurrence, yet unimportant for the administrator and even perhaps to the farmer. As to all this we are in the dark, but the matter must be kept in the mind, lest too high a standard of negative evidence should be inferred.

Three epochs of vole abundance stand out in the present century. In 1903–4 millions of acres were ravaged, and vast loss occurred through injury or destruction of the crops. At least twenty-one departments suffered this plague, which began to develop seriously in 1903, reached its climax in 1904, and was followed by comparative quiescence for another four years.

In 1909 there were serious local outbreaks, especially in the Aisne region,

3

but the big one grew in 1912 and reached its zenith the following year. In 1913 over 1,200,000 acres of land were attacked by voles. It was reckoned that they caused a total loss of at least 80 million francs—of which 65 millions were to wheat, and 12 millions to forage crops.[19] In January 1914, a special Government credit of 750,000 francs was granted for vole control.[62] The scale was astronomical.

During the War there seems to have been a lull in voles. Their powers of increase remained unfulfilled, except in a few places. One of these was in the zone of trenches on the Western Front. Mr. D. Munro gives me this information: when he was with the British Army at a place near Péronne, in the winter battle-fields of 1917–18, voles were swarming. Men sleeping out on ground-sheets at this time often found that voles had taken cover under them during the night, attracted apparently by the warmth, for the ground was frozen hard. Even the War did not suppress the field-mice living under its cloud.

This local abundance lasted until March 1918, at least. It has more than a casual interest, because immediately after the War was over, in 1918, voles broke out once more, partly in the region that had been regained from the German Army, in the seven departments of Aisne, Ardennes, Marne, Nord, Oise, Pas-de-Calais, and Somme. But they also increased outside this zone. It seems quite reasonable to suppose that the re-cultivation and growth of devastated lands may in some way have encouraged the already ascending cycle of the voles in this part of France. The plague went on and spread in 1919 and 1920, but other departments, out of the zone of war, also began to experience voles again. Although the continuous history of the next six years is not easy to sort out from the records, several things seem certain. Nearly every year from 1918 to 1927 not less than half a dozen departments were having serious losses from voles. By 1923 the situation had reached its old alarming state and very many departments were damaged.

After 1923 there seems to have been a lull again, but not for long. The plague surged up again on a large scale in 1926. Monsieur R. Regnier has kindly given me some notes on the situation then. The outbreak of 1926 covered more than a million acres of France. It affected Normandy, Picardy, Nord, Artois, Ardennes, Beauce (in Eure-et-Loire), Brie (in Seine-et-Marne), Berry (in Indre), Gâtinais (on the edges of Seine-et-Marne, Loiret, and Yonne), Deux-Sèvres, Anjou (that is in Maine-et-Loire), Vendée, the two Charentes, Vienne, and even Isère.

We must make some allowance for a progressive increase in records and of general interest in the vole problem. Even so, it looks as if the French farmer had a worse time from voles during the ten years after the War than he had ever had before. That is, taking France as a whole, the aggregate vole abundance was high and disappearance only temporary. Within this ten-year period one can distinguish four peaks, in 1918–19, 1921, 1923–4, 1925–8.

If we look back over the history of French vole plague control we may distinguish two eras. The first runs to the end of last century. Before this many methods of control were tried and practised; but the use of bacterial cultures hardly counted much, although Danysz, in 1893, discovered the disease that is now in use for controlling voles.

This culture came into widespread use in the later plagues, and has been especially praised and used since 1922, partly under the influence of the Rouen supplying station. Accompanying the introduction of disease into the vole populations has been an apparent increase in their power of recovery after control has been applied. The two trends may not in reality be connected, but both seem to have occurred. And Table 2, if we accept it as a valid picture of vole history in France, does not give an encouraging impression. Relief has been too short-lived to justify the name of control.

The French voles might take as their motto 'Resurgam', as did the rat, Mr. Samuel Whiskers, who was hero of one of Beatrix Potter's animal tales. This periodic upwelling of voles, the transfer of so large a share of human husbandry into the tissues of field-mice, is a process of terrific power. And yet we really know so far very little about the process. There are several bare descriptions of the reappearance: how one year a few patches of abundance are noticed, coalescing to larger ones by the late summer and autumn, and how the plague grows serious next year and sometimes lasts over a third season. But Danysz stated that the plague does not usually keep its maximum intensity in one region for two years in succession. Apart from the natural rhythm of decrease and recovery which operates in nearly all animal populations, we cannot at present suggest reasons for the widespread regional character of the outbreaks. It is sometimes thought that dry seasons precede the plagues. There are casual observations in support of this theory, but there is no analytical study, no clue to the way dry weather acts on the vole population, or any sure evidence that it is a master influence at all.

Agreeing with this rather vague hypothesis is the fairly wide evidence that *arvalis* flourishes most on dry clay soils, often on calcareous clay. It is less dominant on sand or rock, as one would expect from its burrowing habits.

Regnier and Pussard[53] have made a thorough field study of *arvalis* from which one gets a clear idea of the ordinary life of the vole. When it is not in sexual season the vole is sociable, but lives in separate pairs for breeding, which happens from February to July. With a gestation of twenty days, litters that average five to six young (though less in the earlier months of breeding life), maturity reached at about five weeks, up to half a dozen litters in a season, and a life that can reach more than two years in span, *arvalis* is a formidable engine.

7

Calculations of vole increase are often wild enough, and the values for breeding rates are seldom accurate. The most conservative estimate is that of Regnier and Pussard, who give 738 descendants as the maximum possible from one pair in a single season. This takes no account of death, which walks easily through a vole population day by day. The higher figures, which range up to 4,000 or more, can probably be ignored as fanciful. But it seems likely that a pair that starts in spring may often live until its grandchildren are born in the middle of summer.

This mounting population feeds in the ordinary way on various herbs and grasses. *Arvalis* is even beneficial during the periods of lower numbers, for it makes winter food stores that include large amounts of weeds.[54] In Normandy it collects the bulbs of 'gernotte' or 'avoine à chapelets', a noxious grass (*Arrhenatherum elatius* var. *bulbosum*). Even in plague times, after the harvest of corn is over, the voles collect bulbs of gernotte and grape hyacinth (*Muscari*), rhizomes of *Convolvulus*, stolons of mint (*Mentha arvensis*), and roots of sow-thistle (*Sonchus*), which they store in chambers a few inches below the ground.

These stores begin to be drawn upon later in winter, so that the voles can stay indoors during the worst weather, without starvation. At the same time sexual activity revives.

It does not seem to be known how much the voles live normally on crops as well as upon the weeds and wild pasture and field-side plants; that is, whether they turn to crops only after the wild food has become exhausted. Regnier[51b] certainly states that they are chiefly found in undisturbed or uncultivated land from which they spread into the crops. Guénaux[19] also says that they multiply on waste grass-land bordering crops. Anyhow, when the numbers grow to the high density of a plague, voles eat nearly everything that is green, though probably trees and vines are left as a last resource. In 1904 during the western outbreak 'they devoured wheat, barley and oats, cut down the forage plants before the mower, ate the beetroots, attacked young greens, then the grapes on the vines, and gnawed, when hard pressed, even the bark of trees'.[22]

The usual story is that corn and clover fields and meadows are devastated. According to Duflos,[15] in 1912 round Toul (in Meurthe-et-Moselle) they attacked first of all the wheat and oats. After the harvest, they turned to potatoes and root-crops, and meanwhile had multiplied as well in hayfields. During the winter of 1912–13 many voles moved from the fields and occupied the woods, where they began to attack the bark of the trees; young pines and hornbeams (many of which were killed), also laburnums and bladder-sennas. But common fir and acacias they did not touch. The next stage in the cycle is sometimes sheer destruction of all living plants in the fields. The people who describe this condition run short of vigorous phrases: 'the earth is perforated and looks like a cullender', 'it appears blasted and sterile', and so on. Or else control is sometimes achieved. But usually the situation ends in natural decrease of the voles through unknown limiting causes, not unconnected with the shortage of food and the great crowding of their numbers.

8

One would very much like to know what densities of population French *arvalis* climb to at the top of their curve of increase. Observation on this matter exists, but only in scraps that do not always have a sound basis of ecological proof. The only definite statements I have found are these: De Céris[5] speaks of 20,000 voles to a hectare during the Charente plague of 1904. That is over 8,000 to an acre, or about 2 on each square yard! The figure seems to rest on counts made after treatment with Danysz cultures, which, it was claimed, destroyed 95 per cent. of the voles on an area of 1,200–1,300 hectares. Regnier and Pussard[53] counted over 15–20 holes to the square metre, on ground plagued with voles. This was in Normandy in 1923.

There are other European records that deal with astronomical figures but do not say what area the voles were collected from. Duchaussoy[14] gives some examples of the kind. In 1792 the abbey of Dommartin, whose land was infested with voles, offered a denier for each one brought in. Within two months 53,114 had been caught, not counting those killed by the farm people. In 1818, in the district of Offenbach, in Germany, 47,000 voles and mice were caught in three days. In 1822, in some districts of Saverne, not far from Strasbourg, the people killed over 2 million in a fortnight. A farmer in Pas-de-Calais in 1881 counted a hundred underground stores of corn, made by voles, on an area of less than an acre. Each store had nearly a litre of corn in it.

Whatever the actual density or the total biomass of voles may be, these must reach above the level at which a whole mixed community of animals could maintain itself. For the removal by voles of nearly all the visible vegetation must destroy the base of life for other species, except those that live in the small crevices of the soil or depend on carrion. The rarity of such absolute erosion of the vegetation in any natural community of plants and animals reminds us that we are witnessing still another situation brought about by the creation of artificial conditions, as a result of which unwished-for and greatly increased oscillations man has introduced a further artificial innovation still: 'biological control', which fills the next chapter. It will be worth the reader's while to carry in his mind a query whether the initial mistake that has led to the flourishing of such a formidable pest at these unusual levels does not lie in an omission to plan agricultural habitats according to deeper principles, just as the blind growth of human aggregations has set up epidemiological oscillations difficult to remove by secondary cures.

REFERENCES

Note. Where title is omitted it is some variant of 'La lutte contre les campagnols', 'Les campagnols', &c.

1. ANON. (1924). La Nature, 62 (Suppl. 'Informations'): 177–8.
2. ARDOUIN-DUMAZET (1923). 'Les mulots dans les départements de l'Aube et de la Haute-Marne.' C. R. Acad. Agric. France, 9: 612–13.

3. Brugière, P.-L. (1914). La Vie Agricole et Rurale, 5 (Année 3, No. 26): 724–5.

4. de Céris, A. (1881). J. Agric. Prat., Paris, 2: 790.

5. de Céris, A. (1904). J. Agric. Prat., Paris, 7: 273.

6. de Céris, A. (1905). J. Agric. Prat., Paris, N.S. 9 (Année 69): 594–5.

7. de Céris, A., & Sagnier, H. (1901). J. Agric. Prat., Paris, 17: 225.

7 a. de Céris, A., & Sagnier, H. (1909). J. Agric. Prat., Paris, 18: 394.

8. Chappellier, A. (1932). 'Les rongeurs de France et la lutte contre les rongeurs nuisibles.' Arch. Hist. Nat. 9: 1–138.

8 a. Chappellier, A. (1937). 'Enquête sur les rongeurs de France.' Ann. Epiphyt. Phytogen. 3: 619–50.

9. Chavée-Leroy (1882). 'Les mulots dans l'Aisne.' J. Agric. Prat., Paris, 1: 13.

10. Danysz, J. (1893). Rev. Scientifique, 52: 338–40.

11. Danysz, J. (1893). 'Destruction des campagnols et des mulots par les cultures artificielles de microbes pathogènes.' J. Agric. Prat., Paris, 2: 920.

12. Danysz, J. (1913). 'Les campagnols.' (Publ. Institut Pasteur: Service de Parasitologie Agricole.) Paris (Laval).

13. Donon, D. (1910). J. Agric. Prat., Paris, 20: 86.

14. Duchaussoy, H. (1888). 'Le campagnol des champs.' Bull. Mens. Soc. Linn. Nord de la France, 9: 358–61.

15. Duflos, A. (1914). 'L'invasion de campagnols dans le Toulois en 1912–13.' La Vie Agricole et Rurale, 5 (Année 3, No. 9): 237.

16. Fasquelle, C. (1881). J. Agric. Prat., Paris, 2: 914.

17. Fatio, V. (1869). 'Faune des vertébrés de la Suisse. vol. 1. Histoire naturelle des mammifères.' Geneva and Basel.

18. Ferrant, V. (1931). 'Faune du Grand-Duché de Luxembourg. Part 4. Mammifères.' Luxembourg (P. Worré-Mertens).

19. Guénaux, G. (1919). 'Zoologie agricole. Animaux nuisibles et animaux utiles à l'agriculture. Mammifères, Reptiles, Batraciens.' Encyclopédie Agricole. Paris (Baillière).

20. Hughes, A. (1924). 'Les campagnols dans le Gard.' Progr. Agric. Vitic. 81: 405–6.

21. Jaguenaud, G. (1921). J. Agric. Prat., Paris, 35: 77–9.

22. 'L. B.' (1904). J. Agric. Prat., Paris, N.S. 8 (Année 68): 625–6.

23. Leblond, A. (1884). J. Agric. Prat., Paris, 1: 161.

24. Lienhart, R. (1923). 'Nos récoltes de céréales menacées par les mulots.' L'Est Républicain. 17 July 1923. (Nancy). [Not seen: quoted in part by Vayssière, Ref. 65.]

25. Loir, A., & Legangneux, H. (1920). 'Nos ennemis les rats.' Mus. Hist. Nat., Le Havre.

26. Malpeux, L. (1919). La Vie Agricole et Rurale, 15: 273–5.

27. Marchal, P. (1919). C. R. Acad. Agric. France, 5: 872–3.

28. Marchal, P. (1924). J. Agric. Prat., Paris, 42: 120.

29. [Marchal, P., & Prillieux, E.] (1915). Ann. Epiphyt. 2: 10–12.

30. [Marchal, P., & Prillieux, E.] (1916). Ann. Epiphyt. 3: 10–11.

31. [Marchal, P., & Foex, E.] (1918). Ann. Epiphyt. 5: 19–20.

32. [Marchal, P., & Foex, E.] (1919). Ann. Epiphyt. 6: 16–19.

33. [Marchal, P., & Foex, E.] (1921). Ann. Epiphyt. 7: xxiv–xxv.

34. [Marchal, P., & Foex, E.] (1922). Ann. Epiphyt. 8: xxiii–xxv.

35. [Marchal, P., & Foex, E.] (1923). Ann. Epiphyt. 9: xxii.

36. [Marchal, P., & Foex, E.] (1924). Ann. Epiphyt. 10: xxvii–xxviii.

37. [Marchal, P., & Foex, E.] (1925). Ann. Epiphyt. 11: 431.

38. [Marchal, P., & Foex, E.] (1928). Ann. Epiphyt. 13: 403–4.

39. [Marchal, P., & Foex, E.] (1929). Ann. Epiphyt. 14: 436–7.

40. [Marchal, P., & Foex, E.] (1930). Ann. Epiphyt. 15: 335–6.

41. [Marchal, P., & Foex, E.] (1931). Ann. Epiphyt. 17: 22–3.

42. [Marchal, P., & Foex, E.] (1932). Ann. Epiphyt. 18: 21–2.

43. Marsais, G. (1904). Ann. Sci. Agronom. 2: 1–15.
44. Maurette, F. (1933). 'Toute la France. . . .' (Hachette).
45. Paillot, A. (1925). Ann. Epiphyt. 11: 483–5.
46. Perrier, L. (1914). La Vie Agricole et Rurale, 5 (Année 3, No. 11): 297–300.
47. Picard, M. (1918). Ann. Epiphyt. 5: 260–2.
48. 'R. C.' (1932). J. Agric. Prat., Paris, 57: 397.
49. Rabaté, E. (1914). J. Agric. Prat., Paris, 27: 47–9, 78–80.
50. Raquet (1881). J. Agric. Prat., Paris, 1: 43.
51. Regnier, R. (1924). 'Une grave invasion de campagnols dans le département de la Seine-Inférieure.' Bull. Soc. Amis Sci. Nat. de Rouen, Ser. 6, vols. 58/9 (1922/3): 164–8.
51 a. Regnier, R. (1928). Ann. Epiphyt. 13: 469–74.
51 b. Regnier, R. (1932). 'Quand et comment il faut détruire les campagnols.' J. Agric. Prat. 58: 149–51.
52. Regnier, R., & Pussard, R. (1925). Rev. Bot. Appliquée Agric. Colon. 5: 746–54, 854–63.
53. Regnier, R., & Pussard, R. (1926). 'Le campagnol des champs (Microtus arvalis Pallas) et sa destruction.' Ann. Epiphyt. 12: 385–522.
54. Regnier, R., & Pussard, R. (1926). 'La constitution des magasins de réserve du Microtus arvalis Pallas (campagnol des champs). . . .' C. R. Acad. Sci., Paris, 183: 92–4.
55. Regnier, R., & Pussard, R. (1926). C. R. Acad. Sci., Paris, 183: 451–2.
56. Richard, Fourcroy, Nizard, & Teissier (1802). 'Sur les ravages exercés par les campagnols et les mulots, et sur les moyens de détruire ces animaux.' C. R. Acad. Sci., Paris, 1er ventôse, Année X (not seen by me).
57. Rozeray, A. (1913). J. Agric. Prat., Paris, N.S. 25 (Année 77): 566–7.
58. Sagnier, H. (1905). Bull. Soc. Nat. Agric. France, 65: 378–9.
59. Sagnier, H. (1912). J. Agric. Prat., Paris, N.S. 24 (Année 76): 326–7.
60. Sagnier, H. (1912). J. Agric. Prat., Paris, N.S. 24 (Année 76): 359.
61. Sagnier, H. (1913). J. Agric. Prat., Paris, 26: 614.
62. Sagnier, H. (1914). J. Agric. Prat., Paris, 27: 69.
63. Schander, R., & Meyer, R. (1923). 'Zur Bekämpfung der Feldmäuse.' Arch. Naturgesch. 98 (Abt. A): 1–130.
64. Vayssière, P. (1923). 'Les mulots (Mus Sylvaticus L.) dans l'Est de la France.' C. R. Acad. Agric. France, 9: 648–55.
65. Vayssière, P. (1923). 'Les mulots et les campagnols dans nos départements de l'Est.' Rev. Scientifique, 61: 520–4.

CHAPTER III

BIOLOGICAL CONTROL OF VOLES IN FRANCE

1

WHAT happens to French voles after they have reached the climax of their cycle in population is still a mystery, about which two entirely different views have been expressed. Those who have planned and conducted wide and powerful measures of repression are inclined to attribute to them the decrease in numbers so energetically sought. Or at any rate, they believe that their effort must have loaded against the voles a scale already tipping from equilibrium. Other observers point out that voles can decrease suddenly in places where no considerable repression has been undertaken, and that there are therefore natural forces making for decrease after a certain density has been reached. One view asserts 'we killed the voles', the other 'they would in any case have died'. Some have thought that the influence of repression was still more shadowy and that it claimed dead voles that really disappeared from natural causes. So Rabaté[34] in 1914: 'In fact, the big outbreaks disappear suddenly, through causes little understood, as in November 1905 (in Charente-Inférieure). . . . The general disappearance seems to be caused by a microbe infection, epidemic, swiftly spreading, and interesting to investigate further; but as regards voles, nothing yet has been determined on this matter.'

Nowadays the first view is the one that almost entirely prevails. But through the history of the subject a curious change is evident—a gradual shift during forty-five years, from a fresh scientific curiosity about vole fluctuations, towards an official doctrine built out of general impressions and opinions, thinly bound together by scientific evidence. In 1893 Danysz, the greatest authority upon French vole repression before the World War, discoverer and developer of the 'Danysz virus', and a man of impressive penetration, could write:[6] 'It is very probable that all the great outbreaks come to an end through epidemics that result in the death of almost all the voles in a particular region; also one has never observed two big outbreaks during two successive years in the same region.'

The history of the change from this theory is interesting to follow. For many years before 1892 various methods had been tried for destroying voles, and every few years some new device is still invented and tested. The French voles are born to trouble and end their lives unpleasantly in a variety of ways.[10, 14, 37, 42] They can be killed directly or by the use of dogs. They can be trapped or caught in pits filled with water. They can be fumigated underground with gases (as hydrogen cyanide) or with quickly vaporizing liquids such as carbon disulphide or chloropicrin. Predators, as owls and hawks, cats and foxes and weasels, can receive a dispensation for the duration of the plague, or longer. Mostly these measures obviously fall far short of practical control, and some of them are too expensive or laborious. The two things above all relied upon have been poison and bacterial cultures. Of poisons various brands are used, according to fashion or the practical experience of different regions. The chief have been strychnine, zinc phosphide, barium carbonate, and arsenious oxide. In 1932 arsenic was forbidden in vole control.[3] Zinc phosphide is also dangerous to man. Strychnine has certain drawbacks whose seriousness is plain in the light of recent research. It kills various other animals and birds, including some of the species that are prized as game (in France an appreciably important food supply), and others that are thought to benefit farmers and vine-growers because they destroy insect pests. Regnier and Pussard remarked[36] that poisons could not be used in Normandy, where game is abundant and cattle commonly kept on the farms. In 1904 the laying down of strychnine in Charente-Inférieure destroyed a certain number of rooks and magpies (regarded as pests themselves), but also larks and greenfinches.[1] Again in 1913 in Charente many small birds were killed by strychnine.[22, 23] It was suggested, however, that these deaths could be prevented in the following way. Voles come out especially towards the evening, when the birds are preparing to sleep. By putting poisoned baits out late in the day it is ensured that voles will have removed them all before next morning. Similarly birds pick up frozen baits which voles avoid, and the right day should be chosen.[23, 33]

Severin[44] describes the delight with which farmers in the Vermandois (on the edge of Oise and Aisne) discovered dead rooks killed by the strychnine bait put out in 1927–9. He states that it is not harmful to game, an idea held by others. But Chapellier has done some experiments that prove this belief to be wrong.[2] He gave various doses of strychnine sulphate to hens and partridges, and found that they were killed by large doses, while the partridges were often paralysed by smaller doses—a state that would leave them vulnerable to enemies. Rooks and magpies died quickly.

It seems that the use of poisons has several disadvantages, partly the danger to man and beast and bird ; and also their relatively high cost both to buy and to distribute in the fields. From this conclusion we are led back to the original question of disease.

2

Perrier has remarked[32] that the idea of a germ which would spread a fatal disease among harmful animals is 'très séduisante'—very alluring. In theory, disease is infinitely superior to poison, since poison only kills the individual, while disease propagates and destroys the species. This antithesis is broadly true, though there are exceptions to it. For instance arsenic remains unchanged in the body of a dead animal and can kill a chain of others that practise cannibalism. And there are, as we shall see, diseases whose chief reaction comes from poisoning the individual and that do not have powers of spread.

Pasteur was the first to take up this idea for the control of a rodent pest. He started artificial epidemics with cultures of *Pasteurella* among rabbits infesting a region in Champagne. Then he proposed to introduce the disease into Australia. But because the bacillus was similar to that of fowl cholera, Australian authorities at the last moment blocked the plan. This enterprise forms a remarkable story that has been described by the biographers of Pasteur.

The next step happened in Germany in 1892, where Loeffler[21] isolated from an epidemic among white mice in his laboratory at Greifswald a microbe that he called *Bacillus typhi-murium*, or the germ of mouse typhoid. He tried this on various rodents, and chose for his chief field trial a vole plague in Thessaly. The results of this experiment were conflicting: that is, he and the Greek inhabitants were satisfied, while the Turkish peasants and an English Commission were unbelieving. The discussion of this incident comes in Chapter IV. We only have to note here that Loeffler returned to Germany convinced that the cultures were valuable. They were afterwards used in that country for some years with varying success. The ultimate failure was due to an unforeseen development.

In February 1893, the year after Loeffler's discovery, Danysz,[5] working under the Institut Pasteur in Paris, examined an epidemic among wild voles and wood-mice in the commune of Charny (Seine-et-Marne). When the animals were brought into captivity they went on dying, and Danysz found in them a microbe that produced similar symptoms when he inoculated it into other mice. This was the origin of the 'Danysz virus' from which a vast descendant army of bacteria has been bred for vole control in France and elsewhere.

During the next ten years other investigators, in Russia, Denmark, and other countries, were finding rodent diseases and trying to adapt them for repression work. Mereshkowsky,[29] working in St. Petersburg in 1895, got cultures from an epidemic of marmots (*Spermophilus = Citellus*) in Samara; Issatschenko[17] in 1898 from an epidemic among wild brown rats (*Rattus norvegicus*) in St. Petersburg; Neumann in 1902 from the urine of a sick child at Aalborg—it was the forerunner of the well-known 'Ratin' strain used for killing rats;[47] and Laser in 1892 from *Apodemus agrarius* in Europe.[20]

Everything seemed rather promising, and the years from 1892 to 1914 saw a great wave of experiments, interlocking creditably or otherwise with rapid commercial exploitation of mouse and rat 'Viruses'. Not only were the German and French farmers attacking voles, but all the great towns of the world were trying to keep down rats, impelled by another bacteriological discovery of the same period—the carriage of bubonic plague by rats.

3

The classification and relationship of these different rodent microbes has now to be explained. Arrangement on a secure plan has only lately become possible, through the careful analysis of bacterial reactions. All the rodent diseases that have been mentioned (except Pasteur's rabbit one) are varieties of mouse typhoid, related to human typhoid and paratyphoid, but quite distinct from them. As they are real bacteria, with visible and stainable bodies that will grow and multiply on culture media, it is incorrect to call them 'viruses', a name now reserved for ultra-microscopic organisms. The German and French literature has, however, preserved the older term, and it is also widely entrenched in various trade-names, among which the 'Liverpool Virus' is familiar.

I will follow here the authority of Topley and Wilson's text-book,[45] in which the typhoid-paratyphoid and dysentery groups are called *Bacterium*. In the literature of bacteriology the typhoid-paratyphoid group alone has also been known for long as *Salmonella*, and this name is likely to stick in general parlance, beside the other. There is one point to be remembered in the study of German works: they call typhoid 'Typhus', which is our name for a totally different disease that is the German 'Fleckfieber'.

The typhoid and paratyphoid bacteria are two important subdivisions of *Salmonella*, and with them come the various mouse-typhoid strains. Fortunately strains of these bacteria keep many characters firmly and breed true for countless generations. Only through this is it possible now to say what Loeffler or Danysz really found. The characters are determined by two methods, both ultimately a kind of chemical test. First are the different kinds of media on which the strains will grow. Secondly, there are antigenic relationships shown by the ways that one strain will react to blood-serum that has been made by the proteins of another strain to produce certain specific antibodies.

In one respect, however, cultures do not keep a constant quality. Their virulence changes, and can often be exalted or attenuated by laboratory treatment. There is a peculiar phenomenon, the change of 'smooth' to 'rough' colonies, that is always accompanied by loss of virulence, and it seems that smooth colonies can also sometimes lose their virulence without becoming rough. This phenomenon is of obvious importance for the practical use of cultures.

The types of interest for rodent control fall into two distinct groups. They are practically all intestinal parasites of man or animals, some harmless, others deadly. First is *Bacterium typhi-murium*, Loeffler's culture from white mice in cages in 1892. It is sometimes called the 'Breslau bacillus'. The same clan includes human paratyphoid B and another species that is a dangerous secondary invader in hog cholera. Besides these are a number of food-poisoning bacteria that have been found in epidemics among sheep, guinea-pigs, chickens, pigeons, parrots, turkeys, canaries, ducks, and even carried in ducks' eggs. Most important here is the species *Bacterium aertrycke* that causes serious food poisoning in man. It is quite certainly the same as Loeffler's *typhi-murium*, and the latter name is commonly used for it. For that reason its use in rat and vole control has been strongly discouraged in recent years. In France it has been forbidden.[14] In England and America it is frowned upon. There are several fairly conclusive reports of human infection from strains used for rat control.[28, 43] The result has been a general tendency to abandon the

use of Loeffler's organism and to concentrate on the Danysz one, whose
reputation, until fairly recently, has been distinctly less dangerous.

4

We come now to *Bacterium enteritidis* var. *Danysz*. This looks just like
typhi-murium, but differs in important stable characters as definite as
those separating the African from the Indian elephant. As with these
elephants, both species are destructive or useful, according to the circumstances that direct their power; both are destructive in similar fashion;
both are somewhat alike in habits and could live on much the same kind
of food.

Enteritidis (often called 'Gaertner's bacillus') belongs to a sub-group
that has in it also the germs of human typhoid, fowl typhoid, and bacillary
white diarrhoea of poultry. *Enteritidis* itself has within the species several
varieties, divided by their biochemical reactions. Of these the 'Danysz
Virus' is one, known to bacteriologists as *Salmonella enteritidis* var. *Danysz*.
But French vole investigators increase the darkness of the subject by
calling this variety *typhi-murium*—a name really preoccupied by Loeffler's
organism. It is as if an explorer announced the shooting of an Indian
elephant in the Congo! We can easily see that not the least obstacle to
comprehension of the literature about vole and rat control is this confusion
about the names.

Included now in the Danysz variety of *enteritidis* are Neumann's cultures, originally taken from a sick child in Denmark, but since adapted for
killing rats, under the commercial name of 'Ratin'. Mereshkowsky's and
Issatschenko's bacteria also come in the *enteritidis* species, as do 'Liverpool
Virus' and 'Raticide' and a tail of others.[47] Laser's organism does not
seem to have been typed.

Varieties of *enteritidis* cause disease in man and animals. Such are
Chaco fever in man; a kind of Japanese enteric; and types that have been
found in cattle or in the eggs of poultry. *Enteritidis* itself, the type of the
species without additional name, is a famous food poisoner of man, a fact
to which a large and sound body of medical research is absolute witness.
These bacteria, like many others, are killed by heating at 100° C.: that
is, they are destroyed by cooking. But the toxins they produce are not
destroyed unless the cooking is very long. For this reason meat on which
the bacteria have left their toxins can cause outbreaks of 'food-poisoning'
in people that eat it.[41]

However, the toxin alone practically never kills the patient, although
the symptoms can be very bad. It takes a living colony to kill, which
after entering the body can multiply, in the same way that typhoid spreads
by general infection.

It was for long believed that the strains of *enteritidis* used against the
rat were harmless to man and his domestic animals. Such belief was an
essential sponsor for the use of the cultures in dwellings and cattle sheds
and fields. Research on this matter has especially been done in Denmark.

where Ratin has been in common use. Kristensen and Bojlén[19] report thirteen undoubted infections of man by the Ratin strain, distributed in ten separate outbreaks. In other countries a growing indictment is also being made.

Another established fact is the widespread natural occurrence of both *typhi-murium* (= *aertrycke*) and *enteritidis* (French 'typhi-murium') strains in rats and house-mice,[30] to which some outbreaks of human food poisoning have been traced, and many others attributed on suspicion.

Jones and Wright[18] studied an epidemic in Liverpool that attacked five members of a family and caused one child to die. From all five were isolated definite cultures of *typhi-murium*. Six house-mice taken in the house were studied. One was carrying this *Bacterium*, obtainable from the mouse's droppings. The used tin of dried milk from which the child had been fed had in it some mouse pellets. The *Bacterium* was isolated again from one of these. In this example there was no suggestion that any 'Rat Virus' had been used.

This is the sort of evidence from which food-poisoning research builds up its case against rats and mice, and the cumulative effect is impressive enough. It should be said, though, that many outbreaks have nothing to do with any rodents: these are only part of the story, the part of special interest here.

Epidemics of *typhi-murium* and *enteritidis* are common enough in laboratory stocks of rats and mice.[30] They have usually been regarded as an infuriating loss that must be cut, rather than an opportunity for research. But in 1919 Topley conceived the idea of using such organisms to stage an experimental study of epidemics in cage mice. From this idea has grown a great investigation, recently summarized by Greenwood and others.[13] It has also taken root in other countries, especially in New York where Webster has done the main research. This field of work is mentioned here from its theoretical importance, and also because it ranks as one of the useful contributions of the *Salmonella* group to human welfare.

5

We come then to this point. The two kinds of *Salmonella* from which so much was hoped for rodent control when they were discovered over forty years ago are now proved to be dangerous to man and animals. Both cause food poisoning, which may be fatal. Both are carried naturally by rats and mice. One is still used on an enormous scale to kill voles in France, and also to kill rats and mice in towns and farms in many parts of the world.

There is another side to the subject that has not yet been mentioned. Many authorities believe that these cultures are not only full of danger but often also quite ineffective. Thus Bruce White[47] says:

'In field practice results have been as discrepant as in the laboratory: Danysz and Issatschenko both claimed highly satisfactory results with their respective organisms, and Bahr (1909, 1918, 1923), basing his opinions on results obtained by the systematic use of Ratin in a large number of Danish provincial towns, and pleading with the conviction of experience, presents the 'Ratin system' as the ready-to-hand remedy against the rat pest. Against these claims must, however, be measured the results of others who, working with one or other of these organisms, found that the rats either avoided the bait, merely migrated, or eating the bait did not disappear: in similar contrast with Loeffler's favourable results in the use of *B. typhi-murium* for mouse extermination are those of various observers, including Messerschmidt (1921), who found the method of little or no avail.'

Our judgement of the biological control of voles in France, towards which this preamble is directed, will be influenced accordingly by two criteria. First, does biological control cause the voles to disappear, and, if not, what does ? This is a consideration of the effectiveness of control. Secondly, is there danger to the health of man and animals from the wide use of this method of control ? Having cleared the ground, we now turn to the history of this amazing venture. For it is one of the greatest attempts to apply, on a noble scale, a purely biological method for the control of pests. In its type of inspiration, in its scale (and cost), it ranks with the Hawaiian efforts in biological control of insect pests, the use of cochineal insects and the *Cactoblastis* moth to kill Australian prickly pear, and the introduction of the fish *Gambusia* into Europe for the control of malaria mosquito larvae.

6

1892 and 1893 were two of the disastrous years when voles overran great parts of the farm-lands of France, making heavy loss, especially in the north and east departments.[6] One of the repercussions of this destruction of the crops was the setting up by the Paris Bourse de Commerce of a parasitological laboratory, with which Danysz was associated.[6, 7] This laboratory worked in conjunction with the Institut Pasteur.

In this year Danysz[5] isolated his mouse-typhoid strain from a natural disease of voles and mice. He describes it as a spontaneous epidemic in the fields and barns of a village in Seine-et-Marne, arising apparently from the high abundance at this time. He found that the first cultures would scarcely harm a rat, but that with successive inoculations into a string of mice the virulence could be exalted, until the microbe would easily kill rats, black or brown.[7, 32]

In later years Danysz[8] returned to the development of cultures suitable for rat control, and he published in 1900 a report on his laboratory and field trials. This report only concerns us directly here in that it describes what is perhaps the first artificial experiment in the epidemiology of mouse typhoid in a population whose size was known.

Having by elaborate technical improvements exalted the virulence of the bacteria so that they would kill cage mice in 36 to 60 hours instead of 4 to 7 days, and would kill rats in 5 to 12 days, he tried his cultures 'in the field', particularly on farms. In half of the trials (the number of which he did not state) the rats vanished completely. In a fifth of the trials no result was found. In the others some decrease was apparent. The doubt that still hung over these field trials led to a definite experiment, aided by the Paris Service Sanitaire.

On 2 February 200 brown rats (*Rattus norvegicus*) were put into an enclosed section of sewer, measuring 160 by 3 metres. On 12 February they seemed healthy still—the criterion was general observation and the absence of any corpses. On that day twenty tubes of culture placed on bread were given to the rats.

On the 20th disease appeared. More culture was introduced. The place was visited every day until 2 March, and 80 dead rats were found at various times, of which 40 were given autopsy. All the 40 showed the expected symptoms, and one is allowed to assume that the bacteria of Danysz were isolated. Owing to cannibal practices, the other 120 rats were mostly eaten and formed a debris that gave no chance of census. Only 8 survived: these accidentally escaped. Throughout this trial, food, as corn and carrot, was plentiful.

The essential soundness of the experiment is that it concerned a population whose size was known at the beginning and at the end. Its other crudenesses seem less material when we remember how early in the days of bacteriology it was performed.

We turn back now to another series of field trials with the Danysz bacteria, in which no population census was undertaken. Here the investigators relied on general observation in recording changes. The first experiments were done in 1893, in widely different parts of France.[6, 7, 32]

Number one was a trial at Merchines (in the department of Meuse), in which Danysz had the assistance of Julian Krantz of the Merchines École Agricole. Using cultures from the Seine-et-Marne epidemic only a month before, they distributed infected bread over a sample area. This was a field of lucerne, surrounded by vast fields of corn. The bread was put on an area of about one hectare (that is $2\frac{1}{2}$ acres). After four days dead voles were found on the experimental field and round about it. From the blood of some of these the original bacterial strain was recovered.

One month after introduction of the disease 32 voles were caught, about 600 metres distant from the lucerne field. Some of these were visibly ill. They all died in cages within 9 days, and the same bacteria were recovered from them. At the end of April (that is after 6 weeks altogether) part of the lucerne was cleared away. On this ground dead voles were numerous: some of them were partly eaten. Danysz even obtained his bacteria from this old 'debris', and they were still virulent to mice. During the whole removal of lucerne only 2 live voles were seen, and these died in captivity 4 days later, with the same disease. These results were thought to be conclusive.

Number two was carried out by D. Dickson, a schoolmaster at Berthonval (in the department of Pas-de-Calais). According to Danysz the general experience was quite similar to the other. Dickson, incidentally, fed the corpses of diseased voles to hens, ducks, dogs, cats, and other animals, with no ill results. Apparently Danysz, too, did some experiments on farms round Paris that satisfied him also.

7

Danysz continued his field trials in some other places; but by this time the news of his success had spread among the French farmers, who began to clamour for a share of the magic cultures. We have to remember that these were years of disaster to farming, when any chance was snatched at, and it was no time to plan long, quiet experiments in which the real operation of vole diseases could be traced and understood. However, Danysz persisted with a few more tests, which he described in an extraordinary report issued in 1894 in a rather inaccessible journal.[7]

In this report he described briefly the history of French vole plagues (summarized with little change in his later monograph); recorded the virulence of his ordinary cultures, by feeding and inoculation, to most French rodents except the brown rat; gave the technique of raising their virulence for rat control; and noted the results of these vole control tests. But his ideas went soaring farther. If rodents, why not insects? Epidemics of fungi might play as useful a part in killing beetles and other pests as *Salmonella* for the voles. He reviewed the history of this work, of which Metchnikoff was the real founder, and expressed high hopes for the future. These hopes have partly fallen, just as the dream of rodent control by diseases has been scarcely realized as yet.

The third trial was at the village of Payns in Aube, in the summer of 1893. Here was a valley flat of sandy soil, 10–15 kilometres long, flanked by marly hills and cut across by the Seine to form a naturally limited region in which voles had pullulated in 1892. The fields of rye, with a little oats and wheat and meadow-land as well, had been eaten up by voles. The village people hoped for relief in 1893, but a warm dry spring brought further increase, and so the municipal council asked Danysz to come down and wave his magic wand.

No census work was done before the test. We may assume that the vole population was at any rate conspicuous, but must bear in mind that it may have been ripe for natural decrease. On 22 August 20 hectares were treated with a vast bait consisting of 12,000 pieces of bread soaked in diluted culture. A fortnight later dead voles were found at various points. A few days after that a field of 35 ares (about 4,235 square yards), riddled with vole runs on the scale of about 10 holes to a square metre, was dug or ploughed. No live animals were found at all. After another week, only 50 holes had been reopened by the remaining voles, which another small treatment finally removed. These results cost 3 fr. 15 c. per hectare, and were 'complètement satisfaisants'.

The method seemed good enough. But a fourth trial was done at the hamlet of La Borde, near Bar-sur-Seine in Aube, where Danysz was also asked to operate. He arrived in September 1893 and found some 50 hectares of fields strongly infested. Traps set overnight caught not only *Microtus arvalis* but also some *Apodemus sylvaticus.* The tough clay soil had 5 to 15 holes per square metre. Danysz reckoned 1 vole to every 5 holes, giving up to 30,000 voles per hectare, an estimate of whose validity we cannot judge.

With twenty people working for three days, 80,000 bits of treated bread were scattered on the fields, but during these three days very heavy rain was falling, which may have interfered with the testing value. The cost was 3 fr. 10 c. per hectare. Danysz, by this time, was besieged to send out cultures to other ravaged areas, and so could not stay to examine the results of the experiment at La Borde. However, Danguy of the department of agriculture wrote a report that Danysz quotes. A fortnight after treatment only three mice were recovered, living still, but paralysed, in the lucerne fields of the experiment. In neighbouring lucerne, untreated, a good many voles were noted, alive and well. In some treated stubble many dead voles were found, some partly eaten. The proof stops here.

Although the experiments were obviously done with honesty and good purpose, they do not by any means satisfy the requirements of epidemiology. There is no proof that the vole populations were free from mouse-typhoid infection to begin with. After all, the Danysz cultures came from a natural outbreak only a month before, in another area. There is no proof that the deaths in the population were all due to disease, or that there was no migration. There might have been other, undetected, factors in the mortality, of which mouse typhoid was only the most conspicuous. Strictly speaking, the experiments only made out a prima-facie case for biological control. But it is also possible, and I think quite likely, that the disease did everything that was claimed for it.

8

The next public testing of mouse typhoid for vole control took place in 1904. The quiescent period of eleven years was perhaps chiefly due to the infrequency of serious plagues of voles in France. But in 1903–4 the country was once more attacked in serious fashion.

In 1904 there was a great revival of interest in the Danysz bacteria, by means of which it was hoped that the agricultural situation might be saved from ruin. The thing was, however, first tested carefully and with every desire to know the real efficiency of biological control. The following summary is put together out of the publications of Danysz, Perrier, and Marsais.[10, 27, 32]

The vole plague had hit Charente intensely in 1903, when 50,000 hectares of corn and forage crops were devastated. The French Ministry of Agriculture sent Marsais to the spot to study the situation. A test was planned by Lapparent, inspector-general of agriculture, and Roux of the Institut Pasteur. For Roux was clear that laboratory results alone gave no certain promise of successful results, and that field trials were necessary as well. Danysz co-operated in the supply of cultures, while Chamberland, who had as assistants Arthaud-Berthet and Perrier, also of the Institut Pasteur, drew up a report that is quoted in full by Danysz.

The site of this huge experiment covered 1,200 hectares (about 3,000 acres) of ravaged land in the communes of Aigre, Oradour, and Mons (Charente). In some degree the bounds of this area, defined by a river, a railway, and some roads, could be considered natural barriers to the movements of the voles. But these barriers were only partial. Within the area there had been heavy damage, which apparently was still going on in January 1904 when operations started. Nearly all the crops had been attacked: cereals, hayfields, pasture, lucerne, and sainfoin, vines (especially little vineyards set among other crops), Jerusalem artichokes, and even trees. The industry of this rich milk and butter country was hard hit. Everywhere the holes and runways of voles were obvious. Beyond these two facts, the wide and continuing damage, and the numerous runs, we are not given any absolute evidence of the population density before the experiment was launched. This was on 27 January 1904.

The bacteria of Danysz were grown in Paris, in beef broth and peptone, and when the colonies were twelve to fifteen hours old they were rushed to the ground with all possible speed, and used next morning, or at latest on the second day after arrival. Each litre of the broth culture was mixed with 4 litres of water, to which five spoonsful of salt were added. The mixture was poured on cubes of bread, or on oats when bread ran short. That bread ran short was not surprising, for altogether 4 tons of bread was used, to which were added 8 tons of oats and a little wheat.

Men in line 6 feet apart paced the fields and threw a piece of bread right and left at each pace, putting, however, a little more down in the places where the damage was mounting badly. This sowing of mouse typhoid was done on eleven days between 27 January and 8 February, in fact on every week-day during the period. The work required 600 man-days of labour.

The commission did not neglect to test their cultures before distribution in the fields. From each consignment of culture some was fed on bread to three white mice. All except one of these test animals died in three to six days of the disease, confirmed by autopsy and culture.

On 7 February, that is after a space of twelve days, the first examination of the ground was made. The fields by now had an abandoned look; plants were recovering a little, and spiders' webs had covered some of the runway holes. This appearance spoke for widespread death or emigration. Search was made in several spots, by digging, or turning over stacks of hay. Under one old stack were 48 voles, all dead but 1: the autopsy of 6 taken at random proved their infection from the *Salmonella*. Several other discoveries of bodies, with only a few live voles near them, gave the same verdict. Often small groups of voles were found in their nests, dead. This examination was taken by the investigators as proof that the experiment had quite succeeded. It is not easy to assess from the report of Chamberland how representative the examinations were. The evidence amounts to this: coincidence of disappearance with the application of control, and deaths from the introduced disease in the samples that were recovered a fortnight later.

9

Another test is also mentioned. Untreated fields were examined, and in particular a fallow field some 500 metres outside the road limits of the main experimental area. Here they found by digging 170 square metres 23 voles, from which they deduced 1,350 voles to a hectare. No dead were found.

Elsewhere, in a field conveniently surrounded by vineyards, they counted 12,480 holes. The ground was then raked over. Two days afterwards 1,304 new holes had been made by the voles. The field was then given bacterial culture in the usual way, and after eight days the ground was again raked smooth. Two days afterwards only 37 holes had appeared. From this experiment a 95 per cent. mortality was deduced.

Early in March 1904 Metchnikoff went from Paris to examine Aigre, and the farmers agreed that voles had greatly diminished and that very few had been found by workmen on the treated fields. In neighbouring places there were, however, 'still a few'.

It can be said of these field trials that they lack several important elements of proof, mainly because of the absence at that date of any convenient method of measuring the density of voles. Even so, one wishes that the investigation had used more controls on untreated fields, so as to measure a possibility of natural decrease having been in progress during the experiment. The crude method of counting reopened holes would alone have supplied much evidence. On the other hand, it is difficult to imagine how any voles could have escaped the intense barrage of bacteria that was showered upon their surroundings for eleven days. There must have been enough to poison every vole directly, without the development of epidemic spread at all. In other words, the epidemic hypothesis was hardly tested in this experiment, which might equally have been carried out as a study of the effects of strychnine or zinc phosphide, so far as vole control was concerned! An interesting point that Chamberland brings out is that the voles had destroyed so much of the plant life that formed their food that they eagerly attacked the baits. This might not always happen if natural food were abundant.

The effect of the Aigre experiment on professional and public opinion was immediate. The Chambers voted a credit of 295,000 francs to allow the Institut Pasteur to manufacture and distribute the 'Virus' free to farmers all over France. By 1 July 1904, some 120,000 litres of culture had been distributed to the ravaged areas, especially to Eure-et-Loir, Charente, Charente-Inférieure, Loiret, Deux-Sèvres, Marne, Vendée, Seine-et-Oise, Aube, and Côte-d'Or. The stuff cost a little less than 2 francs per litre, with transport extra. The total cost of it is given as 215,008 fr. 20 c.!

A few other field experiments are reported from this time. Mostly they seem to have been like the one at Aigre, though less elaborate. None throw much light on the question whether an introduced epidemic of mouse typhoid would spread in a vole population. The chief question really was of the relative cost of poisoning voles with ordinary poisons or with the toxins of *Salmonella*. By using bacteria the manufacture of poisons for distribution is done by bacteria, living as it were in the status of domestic animals, just as we may keep a horse to draw the plough or bees to collect honey. They have the further power of multiplying inside each vole, so that the task of destruction is surely done. And there was the great advantage that man and his animals took no harm from the bacteria—this was at any rate believed by the practical men of that time, and may have been also true.

10

It can easily be understood how each big outbreak of voles in France aroused scientists to a new, feverish burst of interest and research. Equally, the dying down of the plague saw a recession of interest and a period when research was apt to turn to other problems. So, after 1904, practically no serious experimental testing of the kind I have described for 1893 and 1904 was done.

That does not mean that bacterial cultures were abandoned by the practical man. On the contrary, until quite recent years large quantities of the Danysz culture were manufactured by the Institut Pasteur in Paris[10, 46] (or at temporary out-stations like those at Verdun, Suippes, and Strasbourg in 1921,[24] and at Lille and Colmar in 1928[26]). In 1923 the Station Entomologique at Rouen, a branch of the Agricultural Service, became the main centre for manufacture.[37] This change was perhaps an indication that the methods were sufficiently well standardized to pass safely out of the hands of the research bacteriologist. However, various changes in technique were made from time to time,[37] the latest of which is the experiment of growing the *Salmonella* on grains of rye instead of in broth or on any ordinary medium.[4] Other important improvements concerned the length of time that the cultures would be kept fresh and ready for use. The diluted cultures perfected by Regnier and Pussard allowed the stuff to be kept fresh for several days instead of only one.[37]

Various other investigations have been made since 1919, notably by Regnier and Pussard,[37] and by Chappellier.[3, 4] From these inquiries we can learn a little of the conditions of a vole's ordinary life at different seasons, how he runs and eats and mates and nests: all vital facts for understanding how he is likely to die from epidemic.

It is known, for instance, that the disease spreads easily in the nest, where in winter the voles live in quite large groups, usually eight to twelve, but sometimes up to fifteen or twenty. Regnier and Pussard[38] therefore worked out what seemed the best months to apply biological control. It is after the harvest that the voles begin to store their collection of roots and tubers underground for winter use. Also breeding is at an end and the numbers at their highest for the season. After January the groups dissolve and the new breeding season brings the first pregnancies in February. Since farm work is still a heavy call until October, and the weather may turn after November to rain and snow, the recommendation is that work on vole control should be done if possible in late October and early November: the sooner the better.

In this fashion biological control of voles, the harnessing of *Salmonella* for the welfare of agriculture, would seem to have settled quietly into the national life of France. But the matter cannot be left without some further probing. There are several important questions that require answers.

11

In the literature on vole control we notice a constantly recurring note of disappointment at the results of treatment with the bacteria. This does not, it is true, come from the inventors and manufacturers of the cultures, who, we may assume, are likely to be both more skilled and more enthusiastic in their use. Some of these contrary reports may now be considered. From August 1909 to February 1912 a heavy outbreak hit the Aisne. It seems to have moved gradually over the whole department, spreading outward from a central zone around St. Quentin.[10, 15]

Guerrapain and Demolon reported that the bacterial method of control had been generally ineffective in the Aisne (although success was claimed for it in some other places).[15] The failure was put down to wrong handling of the control operations by the peasants.[39]

Rabaté, who was director of the Agricultural Service of Charente-Inférieure, found that bacterial control varied and was only local in its effects, although he admitted its power to give a temporary relief. 'The necessity for these repeated treatments has already much discouraged the farmers of Saintonge, who came to the following rather paradoxical conclusion: that the use of poisons and virus, in reducing the density of rodents, makes the environment more favourable, more healthy for those that resist, and so the treatments ensure the repetition and prolongation of the outbreak.' These reflections were induced by personal experience of the two outbreaks in 1903–4 and 1912–13.

Again, Sagnier[40] and Perrier[32] record how the cultures failed to achieve control of a big outbreak in the eastern departments, for which a grant of a quarter of a million francs had been allotted. The reasons for failure were not known, but Sagnier suggested bad weather, inefficient operation, or cultures of weak virulence. These doubtful results led the French Ministry of Agriculture, in search of every possible cure for the plague, to test the usefulness of 'Ratin' for voles. The Ratin strain is now known to be the same as *Bacterium enteritidis* var. *Danysz*, i.e. the 'Danysz Virus'. But this identity was then unrealized.

The test was done at La Jarrie, in Charente-Inférieure, from 15 February to 9 March 1913. Here a commission, headed by Grosjean, inspector-general of agriculture, chose an area of 12,500 hectares (about 31,000 acres) of vole-infested ground. After the treatment squads of workmen dug up 24 sample blocks of ground, making a total area of 9,275 square metres. They found 324 dead and 178 live voles, that is about two dead to one alive. Only four blocks showed over 90 per cent. of deaths. As there was also thought to be some emigration, the commissioners voted that Ratin was not effective, though it should not be left from account. Rougier and Bernard tried the same test in the department of Isère, and claimed complete mortality on the experimental plot.[32]

These and several other reports[1, 10, 12] give a distinct impression that by 1913, anyhow, the biological method of control was often effective, in the sense that voles vanished shortly after treatment; but that there were also important failures for which no obvious explanations could be given. And several writers agree that the best results are got when voles are at a high density, and failure more common when they are not so thick on the ground.[32, 37]

12

One can follow this history in its ramifications after 1919,[37] up to the present time, without discovering anything very fresh, apart from the details of manufacture and administration, and the ecological investigations that have been mentioned. No deep analysis of epidemiology has been attempted, perhaps because the cultures are really used so intensively that their action is almost the same as direct poisoning of all the voles. Practice has drifted far from the original conception of introducing disease at a few points from which a spreading epidemic would develop. The reason for this abandonment of real epidemic control is fairly clear. We know a good deal about the life of bacteria outside the body while they still grow in test-tubes in an incubator. They can be counted, fed, and watched, and have become the object of a fairly exact science. But the body of a vole, or of any animal, is still by comparison a well of mystery. We throw in a stone and listen for a distant splash. In spite of the laws of immunity, based on experiments, and a tiny nucleus of cage experiments in epidemiology, we know very little indeed about the chances of an introduced culture of bacteria spreading successfully in a wild population. Such fundamental knowledge has still to be discovered. Therefore it is natural that the practical man has preferred to grow his *Salmonella* in conditions that are controlled and partly understood (in the laboratory and outside an animal), rather than trying to find out how to make them spread in the dimly known conditions of nature.

There has therefore been a failure to gain the primary advantage that bacterial control might have over poisons, namely, its power of enormous multiplication in the field. The reason why the method is now employed is on the ground that it gives a *slight* power of spread (e.g. in nest colonies) that reduces cost, and that it is *believed to be* harmless to anything but rodents. The proof that *enteritidis* together with its *Danysz* variety are dangerous food poisoners to man and animals has changed this situation, seriously challenging the justification for bacterial control. For, as we have seen, there is no important difference, antigenically or chemically, between Neumann's 'Ratin' strain and the Danysz 'Virus'. The Ratin investigations suggest that the French cultures should be dangerous to man and to some animals. But here we meet with a remarkable conflict of evidence.

There is unanimity among all vole-control investigators in France that Danysz bacteria are harmless to man and other animals than voles and rats.

Consider this description by Danysz[9] that he wrote for the *British Medical Journal* in 1909:

'It should be noted that in 1903–4, nearly 600,000 litres of cultures of the Danysz bacillus were distributed in France, in different departments, for the purpose of destroying field mice; that for more than ten years some hundreds of litres of virus have been distributed every week for the destruction of rats, and that consequently more than a million persons have handled this virus without taking any special precaution, and that in spite of that, no appreciable case of illness has resulted, either in man or among domestic animals.'

Consider also the way that the French country people handled the stuff! For each 1,000 hectares about 1,000 litres of culture was used. Grain was put on the floor of 'a schoolroom, a barn, or the large room of an inn', and the culture poured on to it, and mixed in thoroughly by means of spades. Then the village people (including children) were organized to distribute this mixture in the fields. They handled it with bare hands, in baskets, &c. It stuck on hands and clothes, and many birds and animals ate it. . . . Yet no disaster followed.[9]

Although it was many years before the danger from 'Ratin' was exposed, yet one can scarcely believe that the Institut Pasteur's investigators would have passed unnoticed any serious outbreak of disease in the village populations.

13

It is well known, of course, that the virulence of *Salmonella* varies according to the conditions of its culture, the animals that it passes through from time to time, and unpredictable changes from the virulent 'smooth' to the avirulent 'rough' condition of the colonies. But if we are to seek in low virulence an explanation of the apparent specificity of the *Danysz* strain, it is very difficult to see how the state of virulence could so long have kept to a standard level. There is some evidence that the Danysz cultures, as used in vole control, will not very easily kill even rats,[8, 35] and this gives a certain colour to this explanation. On the whole, were it not for the rather clear decision of bacteriological tests, one would suspect that the strain has a real specificity for voles and mice. It may quite possibly be that these tests (cultural reactions to sugars, agglutination of antibodies) do not give always a test of specific virulence. And it is interesting to remember that the Danysz dynasty of *Salmonella* did come originally from wild voles and mice.

Throughout the French reports there is constant reiteration of the harmlessness of the strain to man and various birds and animals. Danysz, in the whole-heartedness of his belief, swallowed a stiff dose and took no harm.[37] In 1893 Dickson fed the bodies of voles dead from mouse typhoid to hens and ducks and cats and dogs, with no ill results.[6] Chamberland in 1904 reported that birds and domestic animals consumed the baits in great quantities and did not suffer.[10]

The immunity of man, so powerfully stated by Danysz, is reaffirmed by Regnier and Pussard[37] from their campaigns in Normandy in 1923–6. And yet the same statements were made about *Bacterium typhi-murium* during German campaigns in 1899[31] and 1903;[16] and about the 'Ratin' strain used widely in Danish cities. Both these have since been conclusively condemned as dangerous.

This mystery still remains, for the present. Until it is cleared, the use of Danysz cultures outside France is scarcely advisable. French experience thinks it worth the risk, and it may be so, when fields are ravaged and made bare by voles. At times even French medical opinion has wavered, for the cultures were not permitted against rats in the trenches during the Great War.[11]

14

There remains still another problem about which comparatively little has been written, because almost no research has been done upon it. Between 1900 and 1935 innumerable local populations of voles in France have reached high abundance and then died down to scarcity before increasing a few years later. Of the causes of decrease we know, except in one instance, none except various methods of repression by man. The one instance is the 1893 epidemic studied by Danysz. Of the natural causes of increase we are otherwise ignorant completely. And yet there *is* natural decrease, often on a vast scale. In 1913, one of the great vole-plague years, over a million acres were attacked. There were most active repressive measures, achieving a degree of temporary success.[22] The cold winter of 1913–14 had not much effect, for voles went on causing damage right into February and March. There was then, in the beginning of spring (the worst time for control operations), a definite decrease, which Marchal and Prillieux attributed to bad weather and natural disease.[23]

This decrease cleared 10,000 hectares in the north which had been very bad in February. On 50,000 hectares of Oise the same thing occurred, also in Est, Burgundy, Normandy, and the Loire valley, e.g. in Vendée, Deux-Sèvres, Charente, and Charente Inférieure.

In 1925 the voles overran the northern and eastern departments. This outbreak reached its climax in the early part of the year, and then subsided, only to increase again by autumn. Control was intensely tried but did not satisfy the central office.[25]

In the course of this book much evidence will be brought forward to show that wild rodent populations fluctuate naturally and often undergo sudden decrease after periods of abundance. This decrease happens even in regions where absolutely no artificial control is undertaken, as in Norway and in northern Labrador. Voles are peculiarly subject to these fluctuations, and it is likely, indeed almost certain, that the French voles have their own rhythm of increase and decrease, which may be profoundly altered by human interference. But it does not necessarily follow that the interference is only beneficial to man. If one looks back at the tables (Nos. 1 and 2) showing intensity of vole outbreaks in France, one does not see the permanent reduction that should result from these vast measures of repression. On the contrary there is more than a suggestion that the situation became materially worse for many years in which mouse typhoid was introduced. Can it be that interference before the natural period of decrease would occur is in the long run likely to prolong the plague, by partly preventing natural epidemic or other factors from coming into play ?

It would be rash to dogmatize on this suggestion, just as it is unwise to accept all the results of artificial biological control without careful testing. If natural decrease still plays a major part in stopping vole plagues in France, it deserves more study than it has yet received. It is of great moment to decide whether biological (and other) control is master or companion of a subsiding outbreak. Further research might also reveal organisms of disease more rampant and deadly than mouse typhoid, and by continuing the original pioneer investigations of Danysz, carry to satisfactory conclusion the exploratory work of forty-five years.

There is another aspect of biological control that is never referred to, yet is not to be avoided. Mouse typhoid kills a vole like this.[37] After four days' incubation, symptoms develop. The vole lies still towards the end and shivers. It crumples up with its paws together in front. The breathing becomes slower, it cannot hear a noise. On the fifth or sixth day it dies, and *post mortem* shows congestion of the blood-vessels round the intestines, swollen lymph glands on the wall of the gut, congestion of the spleen, and degeneration of the liver. One is rather used to the assertion of man's right to live, but a million deaths like this in voles can only be justified on any ground if the method is really effective. We have here another, less commonly held, reason for further inquiry.

REFERENCES

Note. Where title is omitted it is some variant of 'la lutte contre les campagnols', 'les campagnols', &c.

1. DE CÉRIS, A. (1905). J. Agric. Prat., Paris, 9: 594–5.
2. CHAPPELLIER, A. (1932). 'Le blé et le maïs "empoisonnés" au sulfate neutre de strychnine sont-ils dangereux pour les oiseaux de basse-cour et pour le gibier ?' Ann. Epiphyt. 17: 387–407.
3. CHAPPELLIER, A. (1932). 'Les rongeurs de France et la lutte contre les rongeurs nuisibles.' Arch. Hist. Nat. 9: 1–138.
4. CHAPPELLIER, A. (1936). 'Essai sur l'action, sur différents rongeurs, du *Bacillus typhi murium* cultivé dans les grains de seigle. . . .' Ann. Epiphyt. Phytogen. 1: 341–8.
5. DANYSZ, J. (1893). 'Destruction des campagnols et des mulots par les cultures artificielles de microbes pathogènes.' J. Agric. Prat., Paris, 57: 920–1.
6. DANYSZ, J. (1893). Rev. Scientifique, 52: 338–40.
7. DANYSZ, J. (1894). 'Destruction des animaux nuisibles à l'agriculture (rongeurs et insectes) par les maladies contagieuses.' Ann. Sci. Agronom., Année 10, 1: 410–91.
8. DANYSZ, J. (1900). 'Un microbe pathogène pour les rats (*Mus decumanus* et

Mus rattus), et son application à la destruction de ces animaux.' Ann. Inst. Pasteur, 14: 193–201.

9. DANYSZ, J. (1909). 'Some reflections regarding the free use of bacteriological cultures for the destruction of rats and mice.' Brit. Med. J. 1909, part 1: 209–10.

10. DANYSZ, J. (1913). 'Les campagnols.' (Publ. Institut Pasteur: Service de Parasitologie Agricole.) Paris (Laval).

11. DANYSZ, J. (1916). C. R. Soc. Biol. Paris, 68: 470–1.

12. DUFLOS, A. (1914). 'L'invasion de campagnols dans le Toulois en 1912–13.' La Vie Agricole et Rurale, 5: 237.

13. GREENWOOD, M., HILL, A. BRADFORD, TOPLEY, W. W. C., & WILSON, J. (1936). 'Experimental epidemiology.' Medical Research Council, Special Rep. Ser. No. 209: 1–204.

14. GUÉNAUX, G. (1919). 'Zoologie agricole. Animaux nuisibles et animaux utiles à l'agriculture. Mammifères, Reptiles, Batraciens.' Encyclopédie Agricole. Paris (Baillière).

15. GUERRAPAIN & DEMELON (1912). 'Enquête sur l'invasion des campagnols dans l'Aisne, de 1909 à 1912.' Bull. Off. Renseign. Agric., Paris, 11: 897–902. (Not seen: cited by Schander & Meyer, No. 42; and by Danysz, No. 10, p. 38.)

16. HILTNER, L. (1903). 'Bericht über die von der Agrikulturbotanischen Anstalt durchgeführten Versuche zur Bekämpfung der Feldmäuse.' Prakt. Bl. Pflanzenb. 1: 97–102 and 112–16.

17. ISSATSCHENKO, B. (1898). 'Über einen neuen für Ratten pathogenen Bacillus.' Zbl. Bakt. 23: 873–4.

18. JONES, E. R., & WRIGHT, H. D. (1936). '*B. aertrycke* food poisoning due to contamination of food with excreta of mice.' Lancet, part 1: 22–3.

19. KRISTENSEN, M., & BOJLÉN, K. (1931). 'Ratininfektion hos Mennesket.' Hospitalstidende, 74: 489–502.

20. LASER, H. (1892). 'Ein neuer, für Versuchsthiere pathogener Bacillus aus der Gruppe der Frettchen-Schweineseuche.' Zbl. Bakt. 11: 184–9.

21. LOEFFLER, F. (1892). 'Über Epidemien unter den im hygienischen Institute zu Greifswald gehaltenen Mäusen und über die Bekämpfung der Feldmausplage.' Zbl. Bakt. 11: 129–41.

22. [MARCHAL, P., & PRILLIEUX, E.] (1915). Ann. Epiphyt. 2: 10–12.

23. [MARCHAL, P., & PRILLIEUX, E.] (1916). Ann. Epiphyt. 3: 10–11.

24. [MARCHAL, P., & FOEX, E.] (1922). Ann. Epiphyt. 8: xxiii–xxv.

25. [MARCHAL, P., & FOEX, E.] (1925). Ann. Epiphyt. 11: 431.

26. [MARCHAL, P., & FOEX, E.] (1929). Ann. Epiphyt. 14: 436–7.

27. MARSAIS, G. (1904). Ann. Sci. Agronom. 2: 1–15.

28. MAYER, G. (1905). 'Über die Verschleppung typhöser Krankheiten durch Ameisen und die Pathogenität des Loeffler'schen Mäusetyphusbazillus für den Menschen.' Münch. Med. Wschr. 52 (2): 2261–2.

29. MERESHKOWSKY, S. S. (1895). 'Ein aus Zieselmäusen ausgeschiedener und zur Vertilgung von Feld- resp. Hausmäusen geeigneter Bacillus.' Zbl. Bakt. 17: 742–56.

30. MEYER, K. F. (1928). 'Communicable diseases of laboratory animals.' In 'The newer knowledge of bacteriology and immunology', ed. by E. O. Jordan and I. S. Falk. Chicago. pp. 632–8.

31. NÄF, A. (1900). 'Die Feldmäuse und deren Bekämpfung durch den Löfflerschen Mäusetyphusbazillus.' (Not seen: cited by Schander & Meyer, No. 42.)

32. PERRIER, L. (1914). La Vie Agricole et Rurale, 5 (Année 3, No. 11): 297–300.

33. PRIOTON, C. (1914). 'Les campagnols, la noix vomique, et les petits oiseaux.' Progr. Agric. Viticole, 61: 251–2.

34. RABATÉ, E. (1914). J. Agric. Prat., Paris, 27: 47–9 and 78–80.

35. REGNIER, R. (1928). Ann. Epiphyt. 13: 469–74.

36. REGNIER, R., & PUSSARD, R. (1924). C. R. Acad. Agric. France, 10: 736–42.

37. REGNIER, R., & PUSSARD, R. (1926). 'Le campagnol des champs (*Microtus arvalis* Pallas) et sa destruction.' Ann. Epiphyt. 12: 385–522.
38. REGNIER, R., & PUSSARD, R. (1926). 'Détermination de l'époque favorable au traitement dans la lutte contre les campagnols par le virus Danysz.' C. R. Acad. Agric. France, 12: 761–6.
39. SAGNIER, H. (1912). J. Agric. Prat., Paris, 24: 265.
40. SAGNIER, H. (1913). J. Agric. Prat., Paris, 25: 549–50.
41. SAVAGE, W. C. (1929). 'Bacterial food poisoning.' In 'A system of bacteriology in relation to medicine' (Medical Research Council), 3: 407–13.
42. SCHANDER, R., & MEYER, R. (1923). 'Zur Bekämpfung der Feldmäuse.' Arch. Naturgesch. 98 (Abt. A): 1–130.
43. SCHIBAYAMA, G. (1907). 'Über Pathogenität des Mäusetyphusbazillus für den Menschen.' Münch. Med. Wschr. 54 (1): 979–80.
44. SEVERIN, C. (1934). 'L'emploi de la strychnine dans le Vermandois contre les campagnols et les corbeaux.' J. Agric. Prat., Paris, 62: 301–3.
45. TOPLEY, W. W. C., & WILSON, G. S. (1936). 'The principles of bacteriology and immunity.' London. Part 2, ch. 27.
46. VAYSSIÈRE, P. (1923). 'Les mulots (*Mus sylvaticus*) dans l'Est de la France.' C. R. Acad. Agric. France, 9: 648–55.
47. WHITE, P. BRUCE (1929). 'The Salmonella group.' In 'A system of bacteriology in relation to medicine' (Medical Research Council), 4: 132–3.

CHAPTER IV

GERMANY, HOLLAND, ITALY, AND THE BALKANS

1

ONLY a polyglot with the great libraries of Europe at command could write a complete history of vole plagues in Europe. It would be folly for one who has neither of these advantages to attempt the task. There are not yet for vole-plague history any of those monumental studies upon which the epidemiologist relies for his knowledge of the great outbreaks of disease. No Creighton or Hirsch has ransacked the annals of Europe as a whole in order to chart the outbreaks of mice and voles. There is not even any current review of the question, such as we find for insect outbreaks in the *Review of Applied Entomology*. What we find instead is a mass of separate records that tend to repeat themselves at different times, in different countries, and with more than one kind of rodent. All are stamped with much the same hall-marks as the accounts of French vole plagues already noticed. These records erect a question-mark, but do little more. Accompanying them we find also a spate of practical experiments and instructions that show a gradual evolution of new empiric methods for destroying rodents, some of doubtful value, others of great temporary effectiveness.

Amongst this dark confusing drift of published description and comment and advice one can distinguish certain glowing points that represent real biological research or at any rate illuminating ideas. It is with these positive contributions that the following chapters will be chiefly concerned. They are really a series of sketches, each of which is intended to bring out certain aspects of the general problem.

The best general commentary on rodent damage to crops and trees in Europe is that of Hans Sachtleben,[22] of the Biologische Reichsanstalt für Land- und Forstwirtschaft at Berlin-Dahlem. There must be in this institute the fullest library on the subject on the Continent, and no worker should neglect the annual lists of references to this literature contained in its *Bibliographie der Pflanzenschutzliteratur*.[32] This periodical, though it gives only references and no reviews, is the nearest approach to a central channel in Europe for this sort of information on the practical aspects of control, although mammals occupy only a small fraction of the whole, which primarily handles the literature of insect outbreaks.

The Continental vole, that is *Microtus arvalis*, breaks out in all the countries of central Europe, from Belgium and Germany to Austria, Czechoslovakia, Hungary, Poland, and also in Russia. The general history that was related for France would apply, with various differences of emphasis, to all these other countries too.

The German situation can be illustrated by four examples. The first is chosen because of its enormous range and power, the destruction it did to crops, and its undoubted influence upon the result of the Great War. The second shows the serious destruction that can be done in forests. The third and fourth carry us a little further towards biological interpretation.

2

The description of the great vole and mouse plague in 1917 and 1918 comes through Schwartz,[24, 25] another official of the Biologische Reichsanstalt. This institution has for many years formed a central channel through which reports of insect and rodent outbreaks in Germany have been collected and mapped and published. The great increase was first remarked in the late summer of 1917, but the damage did not seriously begin until the end of September. In the next few months it mounted rapidly. The outbreak happened chiefly in various parts of the northern plain of Germany, that is in Brandenburg (the province in which Berlin stands), Hanover, Mecklenburg, Silesia, Braunschweig ('Brunswick'), and Schleswig-Holstein. The eastern section of the plain, Pomerania, West Prussia, Posen (this follows the former map of Germany) Hamburg and Lübeck, had a marked multiplication of field-mice but not extensive damage. Still farther away, in East Prussia, no important increase was noted. The outbreak therefore, with or without agricultural damage, extended over the northern plain between the Baltic and the central mountains, for several hundred miles from east to west. This country forms the central part of that general Northern Plain of Europe which stretches from France to Poland and on into Russia, the whole of it more or less subject to vole plagues.

On the southern edge of this plain, where it begins to turn into mountains, there was also serious damage in the province of Saxony and in the Thuringian mountains: for instance in the Erfurt region, where field-mice spoiled the crops. Elsewhere the plague had not yet developed fully. Some of these other regions were to suffer in the following year.

The outbreak was not of course universal in this huge area. For one thing the voles were limited by the type of soil, flourishing most on one of a medium, loamy kind, and less on sand or heavy clay. Also they were thought to increase more on dry than on damp ground. The chief species that made this plague was *Microtus arvalis*; but here and there *agrestis* took part, also two species of field-mice, *Apodemus sylvaticus* and *agrarius*; and in Schleswig-Holstein the harvest-mouse (*Micromys minutus*). In many places the large water-vole (*Arvicola terrestris*) did damage, especially in gardens.

The attacks on crops were multifarious. Clover and lucerne everywhere suffered most, but meadows and pastures were also invaded. The autumn corn harvest was not seriously affected because the good weather allowed it to be collected early. But the winter seed of rye and wheat was often destroyed. This was especially serious in Mecklenburg, Braunschweig, and Saxony, where sugar-beet was also eaten. The latter suffered in Posen and West Prussia too, but in these provinces the general damage was not great.

Almost everywhere potatoes were destroyed—a very serious loss in a country that grows such large quantities, utilizing in this way the poorer soils. Voles ate the tubers in the fields and also in the winter stacks; and the coincidence of voles with an outbreak of caterpillars annihilated a part of the supply.

Then, with the onset of winter weather, many voles and mice took up quarters in the barns and farm buildings and more damage followed. They also attacked young seedlings, ate out the hearts of cabbages, and devoured cauliflowers, parsley, carrots, lettuce, radishes, and other garden produce. But before the winter was out, the plague abated. The progress of this decrease is interesting. By the spring a large part of the Northern Plain was free from serious damage. The voles had diminished. Those parts of it that had only suffered mildly in 1917 also reported the same recession. There was no new large area of outbreak in the north. Some provinces, including Silesia and Mecklenburg, still had patches of vole plague in 1918, Silesia right through the summer. Parts of Saxony and the Thuringian states got distinctly worse in the spring of 1918, but these (except for some districts in the Erz Mountains) were also clear by the end of the year.

But meanwhile a huge new increase was taking place in the south of Germany: in Baden, Württemberg, and Bavaria. The voles were numerous from January 1918 onwards, and it was thought that the mild dry winter and spring down here had favoured increase, likewise dry early-summer weather. Damage was serious during the year; but there was decrease in the winter of 1918–19. In 1919 only a few parts of Germany were affected. The serious plague had passed. The War was over too. And one can hardly doubt that the great destruction of food by voles and mice had an appreciable influence on the War's decision.

Schwartz makes some suggestions about the causes of decrease. On the one hand there was evidence of natural mortality: a spontaneous epidemic at Rubow (Mecklenburg); heavy rains in Mecklenburg in October 1917 and in Erfurt in the summer of 1918; sudden melting of the snow in January 1918. On the other hand, there were very widespread human measures of control. Though some carbon disulphide and phosphorus compounds were used, poisons were presumably hard to get during the war-time scarcity of chemicals, and chief reliance was put on Loeffler's bacillus— *Bacterium typhi-murium*, which we have seen causes dangerous food poisoning in man, its use being forbidden in France and discouraged in most other countries.

Schwartz notes that the shortage of labour and a certain reluctance on the part of country people to handle the stuff made bacterial control rather difficult to organize effectively. We shall not be far wrong in assuming that much of the decrease was natural and coincided with control measures which mostly killed voles that were fated in any case soon to die.

3

The next example concerns the forests of Germany. In 1878–9 there was a great increase of rodents with consequent damage to all kinds of trees, which led Bernard Altum, a professor at the Forest Academy of Ebers-walde and an authority on research in forest zoology, to send an elaborate questionnaire inquiry round to foresters all over the kingdom of Prussia. From the 336 replies he received, together with specimens of rodents and of damaged trees, he wrote a very full report.[2] The questionnaire, inci-dentally, was a model of its kind, witnessing the already highly developed state of forestry research in Germany fifty years ago. Information was sought about the type and extent of damage, its distribution, and the species of animals causing it. At the same time, the men were to send in specimens of tree damage, and also samples of the voles and mice (but not shrews, which are insectivorous).

The serious damage was concentrated especially in forests of Schleswig-Holstein and East Prussia, though it affected also a good many others scattered over the old Kingdom of Prussia, which included more or less the whole Northern Plain, the Rhine, and certain neighbouring provinces. Because so much of this plain is covered with glacial drift which often gives poor soils, there is a good deal of forest growing. Recent figures give about one-quarter forest, a quarter grazing, and the rest those cultivated fields that the 1917–18 vole plague ravaged.

In these forests also the chief destroyer was the Continental vole, *Micro-tus arvalis*, which was killing trees and shrubs by gnawing the bark. The bank-vole, *Clethrionomys* (= *Evotomys*) *glareolus*, also assisted in this destruction, but *Microtus agrestis* (the chief agent of tree damage in Great Britain) does not seem to have done very much harm. The voles swarmed chiefly in places where tall or matted grass or fallen leaves gave sufficient cover. The foresters reported generally: no cover, no voles. Another class of damage was that mice ate the seed crop. The wood-mouse (*Apodemus sylvaticus*) was chiefly responsible for this: it attacked a few smooth-barked trees such as ash and holly, but mostly ate acorns and beech mast and other seeds. In this it was a little joined by the bank-vole; but it was not believed that *arvalis* often attacked the seeds. Two other mice, *Apodemus agrarius* and the house-mouse (*Mus musculus*), did little harm except perhaps to beech and oak in store.

Forty different species of tree and shrub were damaged, some much more than others. Above all the beech, then these others in order of fre-quency: hornbeam, oak, willow, spruce, aspen, maple, pine, birch, hazel, alder, larch, rowan, elm, and a tail of others including some shrubs like blackthorn and elder. There was much local difference in the emphasis of attack, and Altum concluded agnostically that 'the mouse's fancy varies'. He noted that acacia, greatly relished by hares, was not touched by mouse-like rodents. Fallen trees and shrubs were more attacked than standing ones (just as, he says, the roe-deer, which does not usually bark trees, will gnaw fallen aspen eagerly). But the general damage to living trees was very severe.

Sixty-eight forests reported seed destruction: chiefly acorns, but also beech mast and the cones of spruce and pine. This seed was partly wild and partly sown. In some places no seed at all was raised.

4

The power of field-mice to check the regeneration of woodlands by eating seeds and nuts has been directly demonstrated in Great Britain by Watt and Moore. Watt[31] proved by experiment that except in very full years of the beech crop the whole of the mast is destroyed before it can even produce seedlings. This destruction is chiefly due to wood-mice. Moore[15] has shown by experiment a similar state of affairs in oak woods in Somerset, where voles or mice (it is not quite certain which) and birds such as pigeons destroy the acorns.

'Many of the woods on clay soils in south-western England are composed of pedunculate oak (*Quercus robur*), generally with an understory of hazel (*Corylus Avellana*). Natural regeneration of oak in these woods is sparse in some places and lacking in others. Ash comes in freely in many places. These woods can be renewed, therefore, only by planting or sowing, unless ash is desired. As oak plantations are expensive and the growth is rather slow, these woods, after cutting, are being replaced by coniferous plantations, or allowed to revert to ash. This is unfortunate for two reasons: first, a certain amount of oak is needed, and if not grown must be imported; secondly, an oak wood, with its associated vegetation, is better cover for game than a plantation of conifers; hence it gives a higher value to the shooting rights.'

The deep influence of vole and mouse abundance upon farming and forestry stands out clear enough.

The artificial control of these outbreaks is a great deal harder in forests than it is on agricultural land, and for this reason we find most forest zoologists placing much reliance on the natural enemies of rodents: predators such as the fox and owls and hawks. Also in forests (unless they are dedicated to the preservation of game) there are fewer obstacles to a policy of protecting predators. In Germany generally, the form of repressive measures against rodents on agricultural land, and also to some extent in forests, has hovered between the use of bacterial cultures and of more direct artificial poisons. This subject, however, cannot be followed deeply here; the works of Schander and Meyer,[23] Sachtleben,[22] and Hiltner[7, 8, 9] may be consulted.

The enormous scale of such organized repression—the 'Feldmausbekämpfung' of numerous official leaflets and reports—has tended to draw away research from the primary and moving cause: the voles. We hear much of the damage, of the organization and technique of poisoning, and much of the ultimate abatement of the plague, but very little about the voles themselves. One would like to know their real numbers, their ecology and length of life, their reproductive efficiency in the field, and the natural causes of mortality among their populations. Apart from the industrious and valuable breeding experiments of Rörig and Knoche[21] on the Continental vole, we are left with a very small sifting of research.

In the chapters dealing with French vole plagues and the use of poisons (bacterial or otherwise) in control, it was suggested that we know too little about the natural causes that terminate vole increase. This introduces the third illustration, which comes from Blasius,[3] a German naturalist who watched the end of a huge outbreak of voles in the early twenties of the nineteenth century—long before any really wide control was practised, and certainly before bacteria were dreamed of.

'During the twenties, the Lower Rhine was repeatedly visited by such a plague. The ground in the fields was so undermined in places that you could scarcely set foot on the earth without touching a mousehole, and innumerable paths were deeply trodden between these openings. On fine days it swarmed with voles, which ran about openly and fearlessly. If they were approached, from six to ten rushed to the same hole to creep in. . . . All seemed to be strong and healthy, but mostly rather small, for the greater part were probably young ones. Three weeks later I revisited the place. The number of voles had actually increased, but the animals were apparently in a sickly state. Many had mangy places or sores, over the whole body, and even in those which appeared sound, the skin was so loose and delicate that it could not be roughly handled without destroying it. When I visited the place for the third time, four weeks later, every trace of voles had disappeared. . . . People said that the whole race had suddenly disappeared from the earth as if by magic. Many may have perished from a devastating pestilence, and many may have been devoured by their fellows, as happens in captivity [he also mentions 'buzzards' earlier on]; but people also spoke of the innumerable hosts that had swum across the Rhine at several places in broad daylight. No extraordinary increase was noticed anywhere over a wide area; but they seem to have disappeared everywhere at the same time, without reappearing elsewhere. . . . It was fine autumn weather, apparently favourable to them to the last moment.'

5

This example proves that a vole outbreak in Germany can end by a natural decrease in the population. We come now to the very interesting records kept by Hiltner for the upland plateau that forms Bavaria. When the Agrikulturbotanische Anstalt was set up at Munich in 1902, one of its first tasks was to deal with a plague of voles in Bavaria. From that year until 1916 Hiltner, who was one of its chief officials, collected all the records of field-mouse outbreaks (entirely or mainly *arvalis*) and analysed them in a series of very lucid reports.[7, 8, 9] In 1914 he summarized the whole history of the previous twelve years, giving maps for nine of them. These maps show the distribution of outbreaks in various parts of Bavaria. No doubt, as in all agricultural staff maps of the kind, there are many considerations that make them unsuitable as exact indicators of vole population density. There is probably more than one species of rodent implicated; an 'outbreak' may be large or small; the intelligence system cannot spread an entirely even net. But the strength of the Institute's figures lies in the fact that it was engaged throughout upon the large-scale distribution of materials for vole repression, so that any farmer who was in trouble would

5

tend to apply for help. And we may assume a thoroughness of organization that has always been an attribute of the staffs of German governments. Then the maps do not stand alone: they are supported by the detailed reports already mentioned. Finally, the whole series of observations was in charge of the same man.

The 1914 report was followed by several more that brought the published story up to the end of 1916. Besides the maps and descriptions, Hiltner provides certain statistics. The most useful are the numbers of consignments of counter-vole materials of all kinds (poisons, cultures, and so on) sent out to the infested areas. Comparison with the maps shows that the dots on them represent these figures, and therefore that each unit was a particular place, not just a particular parcel (for several might have gone to one place). Assuming that there was something like a uniform demand in proportion to the vole damage each year, the figures illustrate (though they do not exactly define) the changes in damage and therefore in concentration of voles. With this thought in mind we shall not attribute too much importance to small differences in the figures shown in Table 3.

TABLE 3

Periodicity of vole plagues in Bavaria from 1902 to 1916 (autumn situation)

The figures in the main part of the table represent the number of consignments of anti-vole materials of all kinds sent out in the second half of each year by the Agrikulturbotanische Anstalt of Munich. For 1902–4 Hiltner's notes have been converted roughly into symbols: + means serious outbreaks, (+) means locally serious, − means none or comparatively few.

		N. Bavaria				S. Bavaria				
Year	Pfalz	Unter-franken	Mittel-franken	Ober-franken	Ober-pfalz	Schwaben	Ober-bayern	Nieder-bayern	Total (omitting Pfalz)	Total
1902	+	+	−	−	−	+	+	−	..	..
1903	−	−	+	−	+	+	+	+	+	..
1904	−	(+)	−	−	−	(+)	(+)	−	..	..
1905	76	7	2	5	3	15	59	12	103	179
1906	0	5	5	0	11	19	61	16	117	117
1907	11	207	138	12	81	106	159	138	841	852
1908	24	6	4	3	13	11	73	47	157	181
1909	141	4	2	0	3	6	25	2	42	183
1910	38	115	112	41	59	197	268	111	903	941
1911	15	14	96	31	93	83	170	215	702	717
1912	34	9	5	7	4	21	111	6	163	197
1913	23	42	17	5	8	18	101	7	198	221
1914	17	5	19	16	77	29	151	113	410	427
1915	47	43	45	18	16	96	175	54	447	494
1916	8	78	16	3	5	30	189	13	334	342

It is necessary to look only for the major trends. In this table only the figures for the second half of the year are given: the others are in Hiltner's reports, but the autumn situation (at the end of the breeding cycle) gives the best general comparisons from year to year. Conditions in the first three years of the series are roughly indicated by symbols derived by me from his text reports. Because Pfalz ('the Palatinate') is separate geographically from the rest of Bavaria the totals are given with and without it.

6

The marked periodicity stands out plainly, and was commented upon by Hiltner himself in 1916, though it is rather remarkable that he noticed it only after fourteen years' research. We may perhaps attribute this partly to the fixed belief prevalent among biologists up to that time and after, that all over-multiplication of animals was 'unusual', rather than part of the natural ecosystem of the world. Nevertheless, Hiltner was the first man in Central Europe to discover that wild voles had an unexplained periodicity, and his underlying idea has not yet received very much attention in Germany, even at the present day. The reason for specifying central Europe was that Robert Collett, as will be shown in Chapter X, was fully aware before 1910 of the periodicity of Norwegian mouse-like rodents. That the idea was in the air about this time is shown by Seton's[26] and Hewitt's[6] accounts of the periodicity of Canadian fur-bearing animals and rodents in 1912 and 1921 respectively. It is almost certain that all these were quite independent realizations, just as was Lotka's highly theoretical deduction of the same idea that he published in its completed form in 1926.[10a]

Hiltner's discovery came out with the title, 'On a new remarkable fact concerning the regularity in progress of field-mouse plagues in South Germany'. A good deal of his discussion was about the regional order in which the periodic vole plagues developed in Bavaria, since it appeared that Pfalz (the Palatinate), for instance, was liable to break out before the rest of the country. This might have made possible a very valuable forecast of impending damage. Unfortunately, after behaving three times successively according to this rule, Pfalz fell out of step on the fourth occasion, and Hiltner in a later report withdrew with complete scientific honesty that part of his theory. He thought it possible, however, that the war-time figures were not so reliable and perhaps contained some fallacy in this respect.

But the main facts are undeniable. Field-mouse plagues in the different regions of Bavaria do not come up absolutely together, but they tend very strongly to do so, or to reach their peaks within one or two years of one another. This, in a country covering some 29,000 square miles (a little bigger than Ireland, or more than half England and Wales) is an impressive cycle in populations of voles. The history of it is carried through another stage by the reports of Schwartz, already summarized, which fix the next year of vole plague in Bavaria as 1918.

Unfortunately Hiltner was not able, in the aftermath of the War, to continue publishing his special studies on voles. But the annual reports of the Biologische Reichsanstalt,[33] covering Germany as a whole, enable us to get a rough picture of later cycles in Bavaria. Most of this Bavarian information evidently came originally from the same institute in which Hiltner's work was done. I shall deal only with the autumn situation in each year, although the spring position of the voles was of great importance to the farmers. Often there was a recession during the winter and spring, but not always. In certain cases the plague reached its climax in the spring: but always after a serious development during the previous half-year. The general trends, however, stand out most clearly if we take a year-to-year interval for comparison.

7

In 1919 there was a marked subsidence of the plague, except in Ober-bayern, Niederbayern, and Unterfranken, where important centres existed in the autumn. By 1920, although voles had by no means disappeared and were still doing local damage, it was considered that there was no general serious outbreak. But in 1921 a serious outbreak occurred throughout Bavaria which partly lasted through 1922, though in this year Pfalz, Oberpfalz, and Oberfranken were largely clear, and Mittelfranken, Unter-franken, and Schwaben were not universally affected, and even so, often only moderately. Niederbayern seems to have been the worst. In 1923 only south-east Bavaria was badly damaged, chiefly in Oberbayern and parts of Niederbayern. In 1924 the country, except for parts of Ober-bayern, was largely free.

During the next few years the story does not stand out so clearly, because the official reports grow more and more telegraphic in their descriptions. In 1925 there were a few local outbreaks, and in 1926 there were quite a number, amounting to a moderate plague, at any rate in Oberbayern, Oberpfalz, Mittelfranken, and Schwaben. In 1927, except for parts of Ober- and Niederbayern, the country was mostly free from damage. 1928 saw a complete recession, with few complaints. But in 1929 and 1930 there were very serious outbreaks in many parts of Bavaria, which again dimi-nished in 1931, except in Oberbayern and Pfalz. So far as one can judge from the rather limited reports, there was little damage in 1932 and 1933, but voles increased greatly in 1934 in many parts of Bavaria. 1935 was marked by frequent but local outbreaks. In 1936 there was still damage of the same type, but not comparable with the heavy outbreak in north and central Germany. By 1937 voles were very abundant again in Bavaria, and the late summer and autumn saw a serious plague.

While there may be a good many dangers in attempting to construct a periodic system from records of this nature, it should be said that I have made no attempt to force them by preconceived notions into such a system. The facts at any rate suggest a prima-facie case for deeper analysis of the full archives pigeon-holed in Munich, in order to find out whether or not Hiltner's hypothesis is really substantiated, as the series seems to show. For if we take the years of greatest vole infestation in Bavaria generally, they run as follows: 1903, 1907, 1910, 1915, 1918, 1921, 1926, 1929 and

1930, 1934, and 1937. These years are nearly all clear-cut in the intensity of vole damage, 1926 being the only one for which there is a slight element of doubt, as it was not nearly so bad as some of the others. The intervals between these years are 4, 3, 5, 3, 3, 5, 3 or 4, 5 or 4, and 3: the average being 3·9 years. This figure is extraordinarily like the period which will be shown to occur in Norwegian lemmings and voles, British voles, Labrador voles, and Canadian Arctic lemmings. Whether this be a coincidence one cannot at present say. The German records need a much more thorough analysis; but at any rate the recurrence of peak years at short intervals is obviously true.

We might recount the stories of many other vole plagues in German farm-lands and forests, but they would not differ remarkably from the ones already described in this chapter. One rather complete one is given by Poppe,[20] who organized with the help of a natural-history society a special inquiry into a field-mouse plague in the country between the Ems and the Elbe in 1899. There are a good many more.

8

Although much is very obscure, certain features of these outbreaks are established. The chief species is *Microtus arvalis*, both in fields and forests. With it goes a set of other rodents that usually increase less formidably. In forests, especially, these others matter, and nearly all the destruction of tree seeds is caused by them. These are the actors; the stage is the whole of Germany wherever a possible habitat of food and cover and soil exists. The increase can happen simultaneously over half Germany or even more; but this does not always happen, and there is much local difference. In Bavaria at any rate the outbreaks have recurred very regularly every three to five years.

About the nature of the cycle of increase and decrease we are still profoundly ignorant. Sachtleben[22] remarked as lately as 1932: 'On the causes of mass increase of field-mice no systematic research has yet been carried out.' There has been a good deal of theory about the influence of weather conditions upon multiplication and survival, in fact the official view appears usually to be that dry warm weather is associated with unusual increase of voles. No proper study of this subject has been published and the theory still lacks proof.

The only really solid contribution to this part of the problem was made by Rörig and Knoche,[21] who published in 1916 some very thorough experiments and observations upon captive Continental voles which they had induced to breed. This contribution adds much to the scientific background in giving sex ratios, breeding rates, and something about the length of reproductive life. When survival rates at different ages in the laboratory and (by ringing voles) in the field have been worked out for *arvalis*, these reproductive figures will be found of great value. Unfortunately, by themselves, they only tell us at what rate a vole population might increase if there was no steady loss of voles from those natural deaths that create the typical death-curve for the species. It follows that all estimates of the type that Rörig and Knoche made are much too high. They give an unattainable maximum limit, rather than a model of what really happens in the field. The reproductive potential itself is, however, very high, as their figures show.

We know also very little about the densities that vole populations reach. This ignorance is due to the lack hitherto of good census techniques: the only measures available were the number of holes, and other rough indications of the numbers present. Rörig and Knoche tended to think that vole numbers are usually over-estimated and that several hundred on an acre could cause the kind of damage that is met with. A factor here is that voles destroy more than they eat. And these authors determined from their captive specimens that a vole weighing about 32 grams would eat 3·6 grams of dry food in twenty-four hours. That means it would eat its own weight of dry food in nine days. The aggregate destruction caused by only a few hundred voles may therefore be very considerable in a single season.

Then the decrease: here again we know only a few things. Sachtleben says:[22] 'About the influence of enemies, parasites and diseases little is known in detail.' There can be little doubt that natural decrease happens. After all, it happened before there were any serious counter-pest methods used, as in the outbreak quoted from Blasius earlier on, in which the epidemic may have been caused by a kind of 'ringworm' (favus). The development of bacterial cultures in vole repression during recent years has introduced a new complexity. Rörig and Knoche made this pertinent comment in 1916: 'Since the discovery in 1892 by Loeffler of *Bacillus typhi murium*, the agricultural journals always assume that it is responsible, when a wholesale death of voles takes place; but it is not proved that some disease other than this, or other than favus, is not the cause. . . .'

9

There are several rather curious possibilities which are worth mentioning, although they are at present only theoretical ideas. One is that the natural causes still operate, as they have always done, in bringing the outbreak to an end. It might be, then, that the introduced cultures and other poisons either help the process, have very little influence, or actually retard it. They might help it by killing voles that would otherwise survive the crash, or they might kill them sooner. By killing them sooner, some crops will be saved or breeding prevented or reduced. But these voles would have been destined in any case to die, either from old age, from normal death factors, or from the periodic onset of high mortality that sometimes makes the crash. Purely on this count, the sooner suppression is begun, the more benefit is derived from artificial killing rather than from the eventual natural crash. But this brings in the third possibility: the crash may only happen at a certain stage of the cycle of increase. Partial reduction of the population may prolong the plague at a lower, though still formidable level.

There is a still further possibility: the introduction of counter-pest diseases may have affected the normal parasites of voles in such a way as to reduce the force of the voles' own natural diseases, e.g. by upsetting the normal levels and time-relations of density through the cycle. The casual manner in which *Salmonella* cultures have been strewn over the countries of Europe for forty years or more is astonishing in itself; but that this should have been done without first investigating the normal diseases and parasites of small rodents is more astonishing still.

We cannot say which of these possibilities is true until more research has been done on vole populations. But it is fairly reasonable to suppose that the tremendous organized destruction by farmers does often give considerable temporary assistance to whatever natural causes of mortality are also working within the population. If so, there is another consideration that is worth careful study. The repression of voles by man is only a particular case of the general predator-prey relationship that Lotka and Volterra and Nicholson have studied mathematically. They show how in such a system oscillations inevitably tend to develop. In the case of voles and man there is great expenditure and activity against the voles when they are thick on the ground. When they are scarce the effort is relaxed almost completely. Here we have a direct parallel with the predator which increases in density, following the upward trend in the population of its prey, and catches more in a given time because searching is quicker and easier. When the preys are scarce the predator is less efficient in catching them, and starves or goes away or changes its food habits.

An important feature is that the human excitement and propaganda and organized control may affect the whole country at once and so synchronize gradually the increase and decrease of voles over a large region which previously had independent areas with peaks in different years. If there is any truth in this idea, it is of some economic significance, because the loss of crops over a wide area becomes concentrated into a single year, instead of being spread out over different years and avoiding a sudden and smashing agricultural catastrophe.

10

The importance of voles as enemies to the economic welfare of man is apt to draw attention away from the equally important interrelationships that they have with other animals. Predatory animals flourish when voles are abundant, multiplying until they in turn suffer a crash which kills them by starvation or otherwise, or sends them wandering elsewhere. The influences of such an overmastering increase of rodent life must be manifold, bringing complicated effects of which we know very little: on the composition of natural and semi-natural vegetation, on insect and molluscan life, and on the soil. We know most about the effects on predators, which have been studied a good deal in the hope that they might provide some means of controlling outbreaks. There is a large literature on the subject, but it is too large and the research too full of critical and undecided issues to be treated properly here. Some mention is made of predators in the works of Altum[1, 2] and of Rörig and Knoche[21] already cited. On the whole, it seems that while predator populations are deeply influenced by changes in quantity of rodent food supply, they are seldom a master factor in bringing rodent outbreaks under control, although their influence is by no means negligible. Whether the reduction they cause only contributes to prolongation of the outbreak, by preventing the rodent populations from reaching the density at which other things such as disease can cause a crash, is a question that cannot yet be answered. But the question is by no means a wild one to ask, even though it seems paradoxical.

As regards the effect of voles on predators, I shall describe one particularly neat investigation done in Holland. In 1930–2 N. Tinbergen, a Dutch zoologist of Leiden University, organized an inquiry[30] into the food of the long-eared owl (*Asio otus*). It had a double scope. On the one hand, numerous pellets of owls were collected from beneath their roosting-trees, while at the same time a questionnaire about vole abundance was circulated to a thousand observers in Holland. By these methods Tinbergen was able to trace the connexion between reported changes in vole numbers and changes in the character of the owls' food. The best replies to the questionnaire, sifted out and mapped, showed that 1930 was a year of abundance for voles (*Microtus*) almost throughout the country, while in 1931 voles were very scarce. The following list shows the food of long-eared owls (from analyses of pellets in five areas) in two successive winters:

	Winter 1930–1. per cent.	Winter 1931–2. per cent.
Vole (*Microtus*) . .	86	30
Wood-mouse (*Apodemus*) .	7	15
Other mammals . .	2	7
House sparrows . .	2	30
Other birds . . .	3	18

In 1930–1 the owls had been living mostly on voles; but in 1931–2 voles had dropped considerably, and other species took their place. The turnover to sparrows is especially interesting. Nearly ten times as many birds were found in owl pellets during the second winter.

This year of vole abundance coincided, as Tinbergen points out, with abundance also in Germany, Hungary, Luxembourg, and Great Britain; but this may have been partly due to chance. Examples of this sort make us suspect that the vole is a dominating factor in disturbing periodically the relationships of European plant and animal communities, and as such it deserves wide research from this general point of view.

11

These outbreaks of field-mice in France and Germany are formidable examples of the power of small rodents to compete with man for the possession of his staple crops. But they are only particular examples of a continual struggle that goes on, with fluctuating intensity, in most of the other European countries; for instance, Belgium, Poland, U.S.S.R., Hungary, Austria, Czechoslovakia, Italy, and the Balkans.[22] In the first six of these the Continental vole is the chief breaker-out; but, as in France and Germany, other species often join in the destruction. From five of these six countries information is hard to find, or difficult to translate. What little I have seen offers no new idea in research. U.S.S.R., and outlying extensions of the problem in Asia Minor and Palestine are subjects for Chapters V and VI. Italy and the Balkans require special notice because different species come in, and because they supply some good data for interpretation.

There is a fairly rich literature about plagues of field-mice in Italy, containing most interesting observations. I have read only some of these works, by means of translations kindly done by several friends. The Italian vole problem falls naturally into two divisions. In the north, that is especially in the rich plain of the Po that contains nearly half the people of Italy and has special crops such as maize and rice, the Continental vole (*Microtus arvalis*) is paramount. In Malenotti's[11] official brochure on vole suppression, which was issued by an institute at Venice, *arvalis* is the only species mentioned.

Down in the south of Italy *arvalis* no longer occurs, and its dominant place in the population is taken by another vole, *Pitymys savii*. We have already seen how *Pitymys subterraneus* in much the same way tends to take the place of *Microtus arvalis* as a pest in southern France. In Spain also, several other species of *Pitymys* cause serious damage.[22]

In the south of Italy the agriculture is also different, wheat (for macaroni) generally taking the place of maize and rice; while there is much greater cultivation of olives and vines, which do not flourish so well in the cold winters of the northern plain. In this southern region *Pitymys* is often joined by *Apodemus sylvaticus* and by a southern species of vole, *Microtus musignanoi*.

Of destruction by voles in Venetia, Malenotti writes:

'The voles feed on seed and also on solid moist food, and their method of collecting their food varies as need dictates. The cereals in bud and the leguminosae growing in meadowland are bitten up and carried into the nest, as are also the leaves of other plants . . . the voles penetrate into the stems of the artichoke direct from their underground runs without any external opening; they are even able to build their nests inside the big globes of beetroots after having hollowed them out very thoroughly and eaten them right to the peel; in dealing with the ripe corn, they cut it off at the foot, chop up the stalk in fragments and drag the ears into the nest. They carry off the seed of the grassy crops and heap it up in the nest, except that they turn it into the open again if, contrary to expectation, it germinates.'

For Apulia in the south of Italy Martelli[12] gives a huge list of plants that voles attack. Among these are wheat, oats, barley, millet; grasses; peas, vetches, and beans; mustard, cabbages, turnips, radishes, potatoes, lettuce, celery, fennel, and chicory; beetroots, pumpkins, water-melons, gherkins; sunflowers (including stems and seeds); young leaves of palm-trees; tomatoes; also tendrils, green bark, and grapes of vine, the fruit of pear, apricot, peach, and cherry; seeds of almond; acorns of oak and holm-oak; olives; leaves and fruit of hawthorn; and leaves and green berries of acacia. Damage to bark of trees is rather unusual, judging from Goidanich's report[4] on an outbreak of voles in peach orchards in Forli, northern Italy, where the heavy damage to roots and stems was thought to be exceptional. The chief authority for southern vole plagues is Martelli's impressive monograph[12] on the disastrous outbreak in south-east Italy (chiefly in the province of Foggia) in 1916, when some 2 million acres of agricultural land were ravaged, at a loss of 200 million lire. Besides his report, we have a series of papers by Mori[16-19] and by Splendore,[27-9] concerned with the pathological causes of the eventual crash that helped to end the outbreak.

12

This was not the first outbreak in the south of Italy. Apulia, of which the province of Foggia is the northern part, has suffered at intervals for hundreds of years. In 1622 (the first known dated record) voles were called 'God's curse', a term which argues a fairly long history of destruction before that time. In 1783 there was a plague, which was said to have been ended by an outbreak of very large fleas; after the voles had gone, a whole huge tract had to be resown. In 1790–1 there was much damage to trees such as lemons. 1797 and 1807 were very bad. In 1821–2 rich families were nearly ruined by voles, and the price of grain soared very high. In 1866 the grain harvest was cut to a quarter by voles; in 1876–7 resowing was useless, as the plague continued badly; in 1879 a province was ravaged; in 1881 there was bad, though less serious damage; and in 1911 a great number of districts in Foggia were attacked.

Then came the wave in 1916, following marked increase the year before. We can imagine the dislocation caused by destruction acting on nearly 2 million acres of land. Pastures suffered as well as arable land, and shepherds had to take their sheep away. Decrees were passed; active suppression of voles was made compulsory. Plenty of causes were suggested for the increase, but Martelli admitted that nothing really was known, and remarks: 'Who has ever followed the development of these Apulian voles?' (i.e. their populations).

Martelli's report laid a solid basis for the study of *Pitymys savii*, its habits, food, breeding capacity, enemies; and the means of destroying it. He recognized an important principle that is not very often discussed:

the effect of agricultural rotation in keeping down vole populations. Where there is long rotation there are more chances for a plague to develop.

But it is his observations on the end of the plague that are of chief interest here. It seems that the farmers in Apulia have long known of the epidemic that ends the outbreak. It was known in Capitanata as 'La Tignola', in the dialect of Lecce as 'Russa', and in the dialect of Bari as 'La Rogna'.[16] These special names suggest that the tradition must have been quite old. Martelli says that the people used to watch for the disease: it was supposed to be present when the ears of the voles had ulcers, and if the skin came off readily when the vole was trodden on and squashed. In 1916 they tried squashing voles and were surprised to find that the symptoms were not there, and they refused to believe the official report that mortality had begun. There is a curious resemblance here to the traditional knowledge which Wu Lien-Teh says the Buriats of Mongolia possess about sick marmots: they were wont to test by the flow of blood from a cut in the marmot's foot whether it had bubonic plague. If it had, they avoided taking the skin.

13

When we read the reports of two pathologists, Splendore and Mori, we find them also in disagreement about the nature of the disease. Splendore received consignments of more or less healthy *Pitymys* from Cerignola, some of which died on the way to his laboratory, and others while they were kept there. His studies, done in the Laboratory of Agricultural Entomology in Rome University, revealed a cocco-bacillus to which he assigned certain properties by experiment. Then he went to the outbreak area and found the same disease, and some mortality in the field. He at once thought of the possibility of introducing this disease to stem the vole plague, and did certain experiments with this end in view.

An enclosure, 100 square metres in extent, was prepared, and in it 90 healthy voles were put, which lived without harm for 20 days. Six *Pitymys* infected with the cocco-bacillus were introduced, and a mortality soon broke out and destroyed the whole 96. Another 100 healthy voles were then put in. These also died in due course. Although the principle was interesting and sound, the execution lacked a good many elementary controls. For instance, would the 'healthy voles' have died in any case after a month? Also, one wishes to know how far the organism Splendore found was a primary and not a secondary invader.

Anyhow, a number of voles artificially infected were disseminated in infested fields in various places, and this action was said to be followed by wide decrease, and dying voles produced the supposed lethal organism again. Here again controls are not described. Further laboratory work disclosed several more types of bacteria, and the final verdict of Splendore is the naming of *Bacterium pitymysi*, of which varieties I, II, III, and IV are distinguished. Some of these organisms he recovered also from fleas.

It does not seem that this bacteriological work has left any very clear evidence of what was going on, except to show that voles were dying with various symptoms and infecting organisms, and that there might be a useful line to be explored if the 'Russa' or other diseases of *Pitymys* could be kept in the laboratory for application sooner than they would break out naturally.

Splendore's conclusions were criticized by Mori, who did a good deal of similar work on the same vole populations. He isolated quite a different bacterium, similar to that causing erysipelas in man and pigs. He also made observations on the abundance of vole ectoparasites. His vole disease was transmitted experimentally to other voles; to house-mice; less certainly to rats; but would not infect *Apodemus* and various domestic birds and animals (which, however, did not include the pig). Like Splendore, he took the disease immediately into the field.

This short précis of the Italian work in 1916 illustrates both the interesting possibilities for research and the technical difficulties of doing it satisfactorily. It might be said of nearly all the research upon this problem in continental Europe that what it has possessed in enthusiasm it has lacked in continuity, depth, and precision.

But the Italian observations are interesting because biological control by *Salmonella* cultures is very little used there. Malenotti says (1931):[11] 'Unfortunately the use of biological methods in the destruction of voles has never been shown to give reliable results, that is, guaranteed in any particular instance. Therefore we cannot recommend them.' We have, therefore, in Italy, populations of voles fluctuating without much direct interference with their natural bacterial flora, and providing evidence of natural epidemics which play a part (probably quite important) in terminating outbreaks. The chief reliance in Italy for large-scale artificial vole-killing is on poisoning by means of zinc phosphide mixed with baits of maize.

14

So far in this survey of Europe we can distinguish several distinct regions, in each of which a particular vole is dominant in damaging crops. There is the zone of *Microtus arvalis* covering most of Europe. North and west of this, in Great Britain and Scandinavia, *Microtus agrestis* is dominant. South of *arvalis* is a Mediterranean régime, in southern France, the Pyrenees, Spain, and peninsular Italy, where *Pitymys* begins to replace *arvalis*. In the different countries there is, again, a wide range of fashion in the campaigns against voles: France with Danysz 'virus' and various poisons; Germany with Loeffler's 'virus' (now abandoned) and poison; Italy avoiding *Salmonella*, but experimenting with local diseases, and chiefly pinning its faith on zinc phosphide; Russia, as we shall see, seeking for more subtle methods of control by removing cover and tightening up agricultural practices, as well as using various poisons on a large scale.

We have now briefly to consider a fourth region, in which a large vole, *Microtus guentheri*, is important. *Arvalis* comes a good way south in Europe, as in northern Italy and Dalmatia, also in Rumania and at any rate as far down as Constantinople.[14, 22] Farther south, in Thessaly, *M.*

hartingi takes its place; this form is closely related to the one (*M. guentheri*) that also plagues Asia Minor and Palestine.[5]

At the time of the great outbreak of voles on the Scottish Border in 1892 (which is described in Chapter VII) public attention was drawn to a similar plague which was ravaging the wheat-fields in Thessaly, in the north of Greece. Loeffler, who had just invented his method of killing field-mice by means of mouse-typhoid cultures, was called in by the rich Greek land-owners of Thessaly to try the new method there. He left a vivid account[10] of the plague and the measures taken against it. Just afterwards a British Commission, consisting of two members of the Government Committee on the Scottish vole plague, Maxwell and Harting, went out to find out how successful Loeffler's method had been.

This is Loeffler's description, somewhat abridged:

'The whole of Thessaly is really one vast plain bordered by mountains, and divided by the range of hills just mentioned into the plain of Larissa and the plain of Trikala. It is traversed from west to east by the river Peneios. . . . The soil is extremely fertile, heavy, and in many places reddish loam, which is often inundated by the Peneios in winter over a large extent of country. . . . This vast fertile plain is for the most part the property of large landowners. . . . The population is scanty. . . . The comparatively small number of inhabitants is of course insufficient to cultivate these extensive flats. Very large districts, perhaps more than two-thirds of the country, lie fallow. The fallow lands are used to pasture large flocks of sheep, goats, and herds of oxen. About every three years the same tracts of land come into cultivation. . . . In these extensive fallow fields the voles can multiply undisturbed. Last year the harvest was a good one. . . . The field voles, which have always been plentiful in Thessaly (the ancient Greeks had their Apollo Smintheus or Myoktonos, the Mouse-destroying God), multiplied on account of the good harvest. . . . At the end of February [1892] . . . they appeared in larger numbers than for twenty-five years. . . . At the beginning of March [1891] the voles were only beginning to troop from the slopes of the hills and the fallow-lands of the cultivated fields . . . when the . . . sun dried up the fallow-fields at the end of May 1891, as happens every year, the mice invaded the cultivated fields . . . and caused such terrible ravages in a short time that last year scarcely any harvest was gathered. . . . The country people were mostly indifferent about the vole-plague. The Turkish inhabitants of the country regarded it as a visitation of God, which must be submitted to. . . . The notions of the Turks were well illustrated by their sending messengers to Mecca to fetch holy water, with which to sprinkle the fields, and thus, as they supposed, exorcise the mice.'

As a matter of fact the action of the Thessalian landowners was not very different, except that they sent to Greifswald to ask Loeffler to sprinkle the fields with bread soaked in mouse typhoid. Local epidemics were un-doubtedly produced by this treatment, and Loeffler returned in triumph, after having eaten a dinner given in his honour by the Mayor of Larissa. 'The Greek journals of all parties were unanimous in expressing their approval of my method, and their gratitude.' On 26 May 1893 he received a telegram from the President of the Vole Committee at Larissa: 'Résultats excellents partout, pays reconnaissant à vous. Anastassiades.' Loeffler concluded: 'We now possess in the *Bacillus typhi murium*, a micro-organism which will infallibly kill this destructive rodent. The bacillus can be used in practice with the greatest ease, as it injures no other animal. . . . Greifswald, 9th June, 1892.'

15

The British Committee on voles was less enthusiastic over the results of this experiment.[13] Maxwell and Harting visited Thessaly in January 1893. At the first place they went to (curiously enough called Volo) everyone agreed that Loeffler's bacillus was a good poison, and harmless to other animals and to man. 'But they were equally unanimous in the conclusion that in spite of its application the voles were still as numerous as ever on some parts of the land. In fact we were informed that on that very morning a steamer was to leave Volo, hired by the Turkish landowners to bring holy water from Mecca, with which to sprinkle the infested district.' At Larissa itself the same opinions about the bacillus prevailed, except that Anastassiades was satisfied that some 7,500 acres of his own land had been cleared of voles. (The reason put forward by Loeffler for the unusual multiplication—a very good harvest of grain—does not agree with the circumstantial accounts of the migration of voles from the fallow land.)

Finally, we have the opinions expressed[13] by Pasteur and Metchnikoff, when they were consulted by Herbert Maxwell.

'M. Pasteur, while admitting freely the efficacy of the virus in destroying those individual mice which should actually swallow it, had some difficulty in understanding how, in the open country, a sufficient number of these animals could be made to partake of it so as to make an appreciable impression on the plague. Moreover, without throwing the slightest doubt on Professor Loeffler's skill or accuracy, or on the importance of his discovery of the bacillus of mouse typhus, M. Pasteur pointed out that there was nothing in the reports to prove either the final extirpation of the hordes of voles, or if such had taken place, the connection between the employment of the virus and the disappearance of the voles. It was usual, he said, for these outbreaks to diminish either from natural causes or from epizootic disease, as suddenly as they arose; and it had not been established that Professor Loeffler's operations had done more than synchronise with the abatement of the plague.'

REFERENCES

1. ALTUM, B. (1872). 'Forstzoologie. 1. Säugethiere.' Berlin.
2. ALTUM, B. (1880). 'Unsere Mäuse in ihrer forstlichen Bedeutung. . . .' Berlin. pp. 1–76.
3. BLASIUS, I. H. (1857). 'Naturgeschichte der Säugethiere Deutschlands und der angrenzenden Länder von Mitteleuropa.' Braunschweig, p. 386. (Translation taken from Parliamentary Rep. (C. 6943, 1893) on 'A plague of field voles in Scotland', Appendix 6, p. 85.)
4. GOIDANICH, A. (1933). 'Arvicole danneggiatrici di peschi.' L'Italia Agricola, 70: 79–84.
5. HARTING, J. E. (1893). 'Observations on the common field vole of Thessaly.' Zoologist, 17: 139–45.

6. HEWITT, C. GORDON (1921). 'The conservation of the wild life of Canada.' New York, ch. 9.

7. HILTNER, L. (1903). 'Bericht über die von der Agrikulturbotanischen Anstalt durchgeführten Versuche zur Bekämpfung der Feldmäuse.' Prakt. Bl. Pflanzenb. 1, No. 9: 97–102, and No. 10: 109–12. (And similar papers in the same journal: (1907), 5, No. 5: 50–1; (1908), 6, No. 2: 18–20; (1910), 8, No. 10: 114–17; (1911), 9, No. 9/10: 121–2; (1915), 13, No. 1: 6–10, and No. 9: 124–8.)

8. HILTNER, L. (1914). 'Über die Verbreitung und die Bekämpfung der Feldmäuse in Bayern in den Jahren 1902–1913.' Landwirtschaftliches Jahrbuch für Bayern, 4 (No. 5): 437–78.

9. HILTNER, L. (1916). 'Über eine neue auffallende Tatsache bezüglich der Gesetzmässigkeit beim Fortschreiten der Feldmäuseplagen in Süddeutschland.' Prakt. Bl. Pflanzenb. 14, No. 12: 137–40.

10. LOEFFLER, F. (1892). 'Die Feldmausplage in Thessalien und ihre erfolgreiche Bekämpfung mittels des Bac. typhi murium.' Zbl. Bakt. 12: 1–17. (Translation taken from Parliamentary Rep. (C. 6943, 1893) on 'A plague of field voles in Scotland', Appendix 6, pt. 2; also in Zoologist (1892), 16: 310–28.)

10 a. LOTKA, A. J. (1925). 'Elements of physical biology.' Baltimore.

11. MALENOTTI, E. (1931). 'Istruzioni pratiche per la lotta contro le arvicole.' Verona.

12. MARTELLI, G. (1919). 'Contributo alla conoscenza della vita e dei costumi delle arvicole in Puglia.' Portici. pp. 1–316.

13. MAXWELL, H. E. (1893). 'Memorandum by the Chairman upon a visit to Thessaly in January 1893.' In Parliamentary Rep. (C. 6943) on 'A plague of field voles in Scotland', Appendix 8, pp. 92–3.

14. MOHR, E. (1938). 'Die freilebenden Nagetiere Deutschlands.' Jena.

15. MOORE, B. (1933). 'Oak woodlands on clay soils in South-western England and scarcity of natural regeneration of oak.' Forestry, 7: 85–92.

16. MORI, N. (1918). 'Di una malattia infettiva delle arvicole, determinata dal B. murisepticus, probabilmente identica alla cosidetta "Russa" dei Leccesi. Esperimenti di lotta contro le arvicole ed i sorci delle abitazioni coi germi di tale malattia.' Ann. Staz. Mal. Best. Napoli, 4, No. 1: 3–21.

17. MORI, N. (1918). 'Le infestioni di topi campagnoli in Capitanata. Cause del loro manifestarsi e del loro estinguersi.' Ann. Staz. Mal. Best. Napoli, 4, No. 1: 113–30.

18. MORI, N. (1918). 'Sulle malattie infettiva-contagiose riscontrate nei topi campagnoli che allignano nelle terre di Puglia.' Ann. Staz. Mal. Best. Napoli, 4, No. 2: 133–51.

19. MORI, N. (1918). 'Di una forma di pediculosi osservata nelle arvicole in Capitanata.' Ann. Staz. Mal. Best. Napoli, 4, No. 2: 175–8.

20. POPPE, S. A. (1902). 'Über die Mäuseplage im Gebiet zwischen Ems und Elbe und ihre Verhinderung.' (Verein für Naturkunde an der Unterweser, Bremerhaven.) pp. 1–67.

21. RÖRIG, G., & KNOCHE, E. (1916). 'Beiträge zur Biologie der Feldmäuse.' Arb. Kaiserl. Biol. Anstalt für Land- und Forstwirtsch. 9, No. 3: 333–420. (Quotation, p. 344.)

22. SACHTLEBEN, H. (1932). 'Rodentia, Nagetiere.' In Reh, L. 'Handbuch der Pflanzenkrankheiten, vol. 5, pt. 2: 858–926. (Quotations, p. 891.)

23. SCHANDER, R., & MEYER, R. (1923). 'Zur Bekämpfung der Feldmäuse.' Arch. Naturgesch. 98, Abt. A: 1–130.

24. SCHWARTZ, M. (1918). 'Das Auftreten der Feldmäuse in Deutschland 1917 und 1918.' Mitt. Deutsch. Landwirtschafts-Gesellsch. 20. July, pp. 418–20.

25. SCHWARTZ, M. (1918). 'Die Ausbreitung der Feldmäuse in Deutschland im Sommer und Herbst 1918.' Mitt. Deutsch. Landwirtschafts-Gesellsch. 28. December, pp. 711–12.

26. SETON, E. T. (1912). 'The Arctic prairies. . . . ' London, ch. 14.
27. SPLENDORE, A. (1916). 'Per la lotta contro le arvicole.' R. C. Accad. Lincei (Rome), 25, pt. 2 (No. 1): 46–9.
28. SPLENDORE, A. (1916). 'Per la lotta contro le arvicole.' R. C. Accad. Lincei (Rome), 25, pt. 2 (No. 6): 218–24.
29. SPLENDORE, A. (1916). 'Ancora per la lotta contro le arvicole.' R. C. Accad. Lincei (Rome), 25, pt. 2 (No. 12): 516–21.
30. TINBERGEN, N. (1933). 'Die ernährungsökologischen Beziehungen zwischen *Asio otus otus* L. und ihren Beutetieren, insbesondere den *Microtus*-arten.' Ecol. Monogr. 3: 443–92.
31. WATT, A. S. (1923). 'On the ecology of British beechwoods, with special reference to their regeneration.' J. Ecol. 11: 1–48.
32. 'Bibliographie der Pflanzenschutzliteratur'. (Annual Reports issued by Biologische Reichsanstalt für Land- und Forstwirtschaft, Berlin—Dahlem.)
33. 'Krankheiten und Beschädigungen der Kulturpflanzen im Jahre. . . .' (Reports for various years, 1919–31, in Mitteilungen aus der Biologischen Reichsanstalt für Land- und Forstwirtschaft, Berlin—Dahlem.) For 1919, vol. 18: 74–80 (1920). For 1920, vol. 23: 35–41 (1922). For 1921, vol. 29: 109–25 (1926). For 1922, vol. 30: 43–6 (1927). For 1923, vol. 30: 193–7 (1927). For 1924, vol. 30: 285–90 (1927). For 1925, vol. 32: 66–70 (1927). For 1926, vol. 40: 55–8 (1930). For 1927, vol. 37: 103–7 (1928). For 1928, vol. 41: 25–8 (1931). For 1929, vol. 43: 22–4 (1932). For 1930, vol. 44: 21–3 (1932). For 1931, vol. 48: 22–5 (1934).
34. Reports as in 33, continued, mostly on monthly basis, in Nachrichtenblatt für den Deutschen Pflanzenschutzdienst, issued by the Biologische Reichsanstalt für Land- und Forstwirtschaft, Berlin—Dahlem, vols. 12–17, which cover the years 1932–7.

CHAPTER V
PROBLEMS OF THE STEPPE: SOVIET RESEARCH

'With a stroke of their chisel-like teeth they fell the stalks of wheat and oats and eat the tender parts, together with some of the grain. It is so easy to cut down the stalks that they destroy many times as much as they need for food.'

VERNON BAILEY, 1900.

1

BEFORE the Revolution in 1917 it would have been comparatively easy to find out and describe what was known about vole and mouse plagues in Russia. There were a few historical records, mostly published in rather obscure agricultural journals, a little museum work on the distribution of species, and a few field investigations by specialists, which often lay on the shelf, unpublished for many years. Schmidt,[27] for instance, remarked in 1899 that field-mice sometimes 'increase so enormously that they become a real scourge to agriculture. In the autumn of 1890, for instance, they completely destroyed the winter corn in the southern part of Moscow Province. Happily this happens rarely.'

The Soviet régime has wrought a great change in research and practical treatment of the problem. It does not need any political disquisition to show that a country which has begun its new era of history by losing over 20 million people through famine and disease (much of which was animal-borne), which has set up an ideal of agricultural and economic self-sufficiency, and whose social and political structure gives it no motive for bolstering up prices by the limitation of production, is bound to have an intense interest in the problems of ecology.

Few scientists outside Russia seem to be aware of the phenomenal growth of ecological research under the auspices of the U.S.S.R., especially during the last ten years. Even considered only as a scheme of organization on paper, these new developments take one's breath away. Ecological stations for research in the U.S.S.R. probably outnumber all those in the rest of the world put together. A whole generation of well-trained workers is growing up and beginning to produce research of a high order. A recent paper by Carpenter[1] forms a very useful guide to the organization of this work. Although this author concentrates primarily on animal community research, his bibliography of Russian ecology runs to more than 500 titles.

To anyone who has investigated the huge literature that is coming out in annually increasing volume, it may seem absurd to devote a chapter to what really deserves a monographic study by itself. But there are several reasons for giving to this subject an essay and not a book. Something must be said about these reasons, for they emphasize what is going to be a very important feature of future ecological research on rodent populations, and on ecology generally.

There are several serious difficulties in the way of mastering the Russian work on ecology, of which research on mouse-like rodents is one of the

6

corner-stones. These difficulties might be described as obstacles of time and size and politics. Nearly all the research is published in the Russian language and incidentally, in the Cyrillic character. Although there are usually summaries in English, German, or French, they only enable one to find out the bare contents: a summary of such critical and often elaborate work amounts only to a statement of conclusions, without providing proofs. Very few people in Great Britain know Russian, and I belong at present to the majority. I have, accordingly, relied on translations of the more important works, made by Miss N. Waloff and Mr. J. D. Jackson for the Bureau of Animal Population. By this means I have been able to follow the main trends of research, but not to survey the whole field—a task inevitably limited by expense and time. However, the Bureau is slowly building up a library of translations, from which it is hoped that 'bourgeois scientists' (as it is the fashion to call us in Russia) will be able to get more in touch with this huge channel of ideas and facts.

There is, in addition, an obstacle imposed by the tendency for Soviet research reports to be longer than necessary, and to repeat the subject-matter overmuch in different places for the benefit of different sections of the huge organization that they serve. This repetition is, however, a characteristic of government publications on vole plagues over the world generally.

It follows from this situation that if we are not just blandly to ignore Russian research in ecology, we shall have to develop contact and discussion, and especially translation and summary, combined with teaching the Russian language to the next generation of ecologists. To the best of its power, the Bureau of Animal Population has followed this plan during the last seven years, and accordingly has what is at present (and one hopes only at present) a unique library of Russian ecological reports on mammal ecology. This policy continues, although the political isolation of the U.S.S.R. imposes limits to the effectiveness of co-operation.

The size of the constellation of Soviet Republics is another serious obstacle to comprehension of their activities in research. A vast region, covering more than 8 million square miles, reaching from Arctic lands, through forest and steppe to the salt deserts of the Caspian, encompassing the high mountains of Ural and Caucasus and eastern Siberia, with corresponding range of climate and crops—its ecological problems are almost infinite. (A recent scientific paper in Russian has summaries in English and in Chinese; while another has summaries in French and Georgian, the latter printed in Armenian script.)

Fortunately, there have been several monographs in recent years which draw together the research on mouse-like rodents, and on these I have chiefly relied in the following essay, which does only bare justice to the subject.

2

It will be convenient to describe Russian vole and mouse plagues under five headings, which will enable us to visualize how the study of the subject is being built up there. First, the different regions and the kind of human problems involved, with which is connected the second aspect—the important species of mouse-like rodents that cause serious trouble, or have been the objects of recent research. The last two things are practically synonymous, since the official Soviet (Marxist) theory of ecological research is that its aim is solely to minister to the power of man and his ability to achieve security, ameliorate social and economic conditions, and develop natural resources for his own benefit.[11]

The third heading is the history of regional outbreaks and the fourth is research upon the causes of fluctuations. Finally, there is something to be said about the lines along which rodent control is progressing.

Two recent summaries of Soviet research on the ecology of mammals give a very good panorama of the broad front along which research is being pushed. Formozov[4] describes the progress of research during twenty years (that is, the life of the U.S.S.R.) on game-birds and on mammals other than mouse-like rodents, which are treated in a similar review by Kalabukhov.[9]

Formozov's paper is mentioned here because it illustrates the extent to which Soviet organizations are using the weapon of ecological research as part of their general policy, to try and solve many other field problems besides those caused by mouse-like rodents. A similar drive is being made along other lines such as insect outbreaks and the fisheries, and in the study of climate, vegetation, and soils.

Among the many subjects reviewed by Formozov are the habitat limits of moles; fur-bearing predators (including the sable, marten, ermine, mink, steppe polecat, red fox, arctic fox, and raccoon-like dog; also the sea-otter and seals); fur-bearing rodents (squirrels, the steppe marmot, beaver, introduced muskrat and nutria, hare); resources of other kinds (walrus, white whale and other dolphins, reindeer, elk, various kinds of wild deer, European bison, aurochs, mountain sheep, and steppe antelope).

Many of these problems also interlock to some extent with those caused by various rodents, particularly where they concern predators such as the fox, wolf, weasel, and polecat. For instance, the steppe polecat is both an energetic destroyer of the suslik or ground squirrel (which carries bubonic plague) and a valuable source of fur.

Perhaps one of the most startling examples of interaction between different ecological sectors was when the inhabitants of part of the province of Astrakhan were encouraged to trap water-voles (*Arvicola amphibius*), with the idea of providing during a serious agricultural depression an extra resource in the form of fur. The immediate result was that more than 800 peasants caught tularaemia, from which a few of them died. This infectious disease of rodents (chiefly hares and rabbits) was not previously known to be carried by water-voles at all, but became epidemic among human beings as soon as they began to handle these animals on a large scale. Similar outbreaks, probably or certainly caused by water-voles carrying tularaemia, were discovered also in three other parts of the U.S.S.R. (Riazan, Uralsk, and Obdorsk) about the same time (1926–8). This history was summarized by Roubakine[25] in a report of the Health Section of the League of Nations.

3

In trying to study the geographical distribution of mouse-like rodents and the economic problems they create in Russia, we are faced with many difficulties about places and their names. The Union of Soviet Republics continually dazzles with the scale and complexity of its vast programmes of development, and inevitably confuses the foreigner by the changes that occur in administrative and internal political arrangements. The map is like a piece of shot-silk tapestry: new patterns appear and shift and fade before we can fix them in our minds. It is best for the present purpose to consider only the broad geographical regions which form the permanent background.

The U.S.S.R. falls into several main zones, running more or less from east to west, except for the great north and south forested barrier of the Ural Mountains. There is a succession of Arctic tundra, northern conifer forest, deciduous forest (much cleared by now for farming and industry), steppe, and desert. The open steppe is several hundred miles across from north to south, and stretches from Ukraine in the south-west, far into central Asia, where it merges gradually into salt-steppe, semi-desert and mountain, to revive again in the loess-lands of Transbaikalia, Manchuria, and parts of China.

This steppe is the counterpart of the North American prairie, the Argentine pampas, the South African high veld, and the grass plains of south-eastern Australia. All these regions have found one of their chief uses to man in the cultivation of wheat, a crop which is attacked by many mouse-like rodents. We shall describe, in the next chapter, plagues of field-mice in the wheat-steppes of Palestine, Australia, the United States, and Canada. In Russia also they are a serious national problem.

The steppe begins not far south of Moscow, on a rich black soil called *chernozem*, and passes gradually into the semi-desert country of the Kirghiz Steppe (Kazakhstan) in the south-east, and the high mountains of the Caucasus in the south. These mountains, lying between the Black Sea and the Caspian, are 700 miles long and reach over 18,000 feet, and they repeat up their slopes some of the life zones north of them, with forest and alpine regions, also important cultivation and mountain pastures.

To the east and west, between the main range of the Caucasus and the two great inland seas, corridors of low land connect the main part of Russia with Transcaucasia, a varied country, much of it mountainous, comprising several federated Soviet republics that include the Georgians, Armenians, and some Turks.

Round the Caspian and east of it lies much dry salt steppe, semi-desert, and (in Turkestan south of the Kirghiz Steppe) large areas of sheer desert. In Siberia there is an important additional zone of wooded steppe, between the northern taiga or coniferous forest and the open steppe. This region, mostly situated on the chernozem, is agriculturally rich and fertile; it falls mostly into the administrative provinces of Omsk and west Siberia, but occurs also in parts of the Buriat-Mongolian Republic and eastern Siberia. In these central and eastern countries there are important areas of mountain, some of them forested, others partly or completely desert.

The U.S.S.R. is therefore seen as a country of continental scale, its richest agricultural land lying between gigantic belts of cold desert and natural forest in the north, and of temperate desert and high mountain in the south. Whether for wheat-growing (which occupies about a quarter of the Soviet agricultural land) or for grazing stock, these steppe lands are of paramount importance. Second to them come the valuable cultivated regions of the cleared deciduous forest belt in the north, the Caucasus and Transcaucasus mountains and valleys, the wooded steppes of Siberia, and huge areas of grazing in the desert margins of the Caspian and central Asia.

Each region has a characteristic association of rodents which attacks its crops: usually some species of marmot or squirrel, and several species of mouse-like rodents. We shall not give much space to the first group here, although they are of enormous importance in the Soviet economy and have been the objects of much research. In many ways ecological investigations, especially on the several species of steppe marmots or ground squirrels known to the Russians as susliks (*Citellus*), have gone parallel with those on voles and mice, since these are often found damaging the same crops, and common measures have to be taken against them.

Citellus has another significance in that it is one of the most important reservoirs of bubonic plague on the steppes of south-east European Russia, and this disease also affects voles and mice and other small rodents there. The other important species in the first group is *Eutamias asiaticus*, a large ground squirrel or 'chipmunk' which causes a great deal of damage in Siberia, chiefly where farm-lands adjoin the forest.[26]

Those who wish to follow the subject of ground squirrels farther will find it well treated by Sachtleben,[26] Vinogradov and Obolenskii,[32] and Kalabukhov,[9] who give a rich bibliography of other work on the group. The close connexion between the development of research on *Citellus* and that on voles is shown by the fact that several Russian workers have published ecological analyses on both, e.g. Kalabukhov's census studies by means of marking methods.

4

There are four general surveys of the distribution of rodent pests. Vinogradov and Obolenskii published in 1926 the results of extensive inquiries made in the years 1921–4; and again in 1930, the results of further inquiries for 1925–8.[32] I have not read the first report, but the second gives a clear picture of the state of knowledge about ten years ago.

The basis of their inquiry was a questionnaire, rather an elaborate one, sent out by the Department of Entomology of the Institute of Plant Protection in Leningrad, to a great number of agricultural, administrative, and research people. The answers were collated and evidently sifted critically and used with caution, and checked by the existing published research material.

The third report is by Sviridenko[29] in 1934. Its main purpose was to analyse fluctuations, but there is also much useful information about the distribution of species in different regions. Another large report, historical survey and discussion, is that by Vinogradov[31] in 1934. A few extra facts are supplied by Plyater-Plokhotskii[19, 20, 21] for the Far East of Siberia, by Formozov[5, 6] and his colleagues for the pastures of the Caucasus region and Kazakhstan, and by Kolesnikov[13] for Turkestan.

The areas attacked by voles and mice in certain years are staggeringly great; in the autumn and early spring of 1925–6 over $2\frac{1}{2}$ million acres in the North Caucasus steppes;[32(1)] in 1927 over 300,000 acres of fields and about 4,000 acres of orchards in the Ural Region;[32(2)] in the autumn of 1927 over 600,000 acres of Ukraine;[32(3)] in November 1932 *nine and a half million acres in North Caucasus alone*, while 'mice did not have a wide distribution in the eastern part of Transcaucasia . . . the area infested in Armenia, Georgia, and Azerbaidjan was only about 50,000 hectares . . . .'.[29(1)]

That an infestation of over 120,000 acres could be referred to as if it was comparatively unimportant gives one some idea of the immense scale of this outbreak, of which even the North Caucasus and Transcaucasus ones were only a part. For the 1932–3 outbreak affected also many other parts of European Russia, including the Crimea, upper, middle, and lower Volga, Ukraine, Moscow Region, Central Chernozem Region, White Russia, and South Ural Region. It also occurred in Kazakhstan, western and part of eastern Siberia.[29, 32] 'The total area infested by rodents in U.S.S.R. in December 1932 was above 10,000,000 hectares [nearly 25 million acres], out of which more than half (5,600,000 hectares) was in its European, and for the greatest extent, southern part. The wave of mass increase of mouse-like rodents reached its maximum in the autumn-winter period of 1932, and then fell off visibly.'[29(2)]

To this astronomical multiplication and its threat to the Soviet self-sufficiency in food supplies, we may reasonably attribute some of the great impetus given to ecological research on mouse-like rodents in that country during the last few years. (The wheat supply affects also the amount of land that can be spared for cotton-growing in central Asia—another vital factor in Soviet independence.) But the outbreak could be matched by earlier ones, and it is not unusual for the infested areas to run into many hundred thousand acres.

The problem facing the Government was a very serious one. Kalabukhov wrote in 1937: [9(1)]

'For organization of control of a whole series of rodent pests, it was necessary to determine their distribution in the different habitats, to establish the regularity of variations in their numbers, and to investigate a whole series of other peculiarities in their lives. . . . Within the territory of a whole series of areas and regions, especially on the border lines of the Soviet Union, not only was the part played by pests unknown, but the fauna of rodents itself was also unknown.'

A list of the species of mouse-like rodents chiefly concerned is given below, together with their Russian names:

Microtinae (voles and lemmings):

Microtus arvalis	Common ('Continental') vole	Обыкновенная полевка
Microtus michnoi	Eastern vole	Полевка Михно
Microtus oeconomus	Vole	Полевка экономка
Chilotus (*Microtus*) *socialis*	Social vole	Общественная полевка
Stenocranius (*Microtus*) *gregalis*	Vole	Стадная полевка
Arvicola amphibius	Water-vole	Водяная крыса
Lagurus lagurus	Steppe lemming	Степная пеструшка

Murinae (Rats and mice):

Mus musculus	House-mouse	Домовая мышь
Apodemus (*Sylvaemus*) *sylvaticus*	Wood-mouse, long-tailed field-mouse	Лесная мышь
Apodemus (*Sylvaemus*) *flavicollis*	Yellow-necked field-mouse	Желтогорлая мышь
Apodemus fulvipectus	Long-tailed field-mouse	Лесная мышь
Apodemus agrarius	Long-tailed field-mouse	Полевая мышь
Apodemus (*Alsomys*) *major*	Large Asiatic field-mouse	Большая азиатская лесная мышь
Micromys minutus	Harvest-mouse	Мышь-малютка

To these fourteen voles and mice must be added one or two species of rats, several hamsters (*Cricetinae*), two gerbilles (*Gerbillinae*), and a jerboa (*Dipodinae*). This is a rich list of species, a fact no doubt attributable to the wide extent and variety of Russian habitats and the suitability of many of them for burrowing rodents, also probably to their position partly outside the impoverishing influence of the Great European Ice Ages—which contributed, however, the outblown loess-dust in which so many of the steppe species now live.

The list indeed becomes less formidable when we consider separate regions. But even so, it is to be remembered that it represents only the species that cause great damage to crops by their mass increase. In central and western Europe (with no social vole or steppe lemming, and only one hamster) there are far fewer harmful species as well as fewer species altogether; while Great Britain (with no Continental vole or hamster) by comparison presents an extremely simple fauna; Ireland (with no voles at all) is in this respect a paradise.

Some of the species can be dismissed shortly, since little is recorded yet about them. *Microtus michnoi* (in company with *Apodemus agrarius* and *Micromys minutus*) is a serious pest to crops in the Far Eastern Republic of Siberia.[19] *Microtus oeconomus* (which ranges from a little west of the Urals across to the Pacific) is abundant and apparently an important pest in parts of eastern Siberia.[32(4)] It is found in and near wooded country (as in the region of Yenisei).[26] *Stenocranius gregalis* is important in the Ural Region,[29(3)] and in western Siberia,[32(5)] where it has a wide habitat range from semi-desert to forest margin and attacks cereal crops. *Stenocranius gregalis raddei* is a subspecies of some importance in the region of the Buriat-Mongolian Republic.[32(5)] The water-vole (*Arvicola amphibius*) has attracted most attention by its association with tularaemia, already mentioned, but is also a resource as well. In the region of Tomsk, Siberia, 4 million skins were taken in 1927 ;[32(6)] and Vinogradov and Obolenskii mention that 56,580 skins of water-voles were collected in the province of Saratov on the lower Volga in 1928.[32(7)]

Of the mice, *Apodemus fulvipectus* is only important in the Caucasus, where it is found right out on the open steppes.[29(4)] *A. major* is another wood-mouse that is harmful in parts of Siberia.[32(8)] Although the harvest-mouse (*Micromys minutus*) is widespread in Europe and Siberia, its chief damage seems to be in the Urals,[32(8)] in the forest-steppe of western Siberia,[32(2)] and in the Far Eastern Republic.[21]

Microtus arvalis once more stands out as far the most powerful field-mouse pest in European Russia. Its outbreaks are recorded[29, 32] for the Central Industrial Region (which is also an important agricultural area north of the main steppe, mostly on cleared forest-land) ; in the steppes of central Chernozem, upper, middle, and lower Volga, Ukraine, Crimea, and North Caucasus (both east and west) ; in the foot-hills and mountains of the north slope of the Caucasus ; in the mountains of Little Caucasus and also in Transcaucasia (as in Georgia) ; in the Ural Mountains. *Arvalis* ranges also far into central Asia : it was found by Formozov and Voronov[6] to be an important element in the steppe pastures on the table-lands of western Kazakhstan (Kirghiz Steppe), and by Kolesnikov[13] damaging plantations of the new rubber-yielding plant, *Scorzonera*, in Turkestan. According to Sachtleben[26] it also comes in Persia and west Siberia. This species is therefore seen to be the dominant rodent competitor for man's crops over a vast region that includes the whole of Europe north of the Mediterranean lands, Balkans and Asia Minor, and south of the northern conifer forest belt. And it extends far into central Siberia and central Asia. Farther east still its place seems to be taken by *Microtus oeconomus, M. michnoi*, and other species.

Another important species, but with a much more restricted distribution, is the social vole, *Chilotus socialis*. It requires, according to Sviridenko,[29(5)] a semi-desert climate for its optimum multiplication. *Socialis* takes a prominent part in outbreaks in the extreme south of European Russia :[29, 32] Ukraine, Crimea, North Caucasus (at any rate in the eastern part), Daghe-stan (east of the Caspian), and eastern Transcaucasus. Being above all a dry-steppe inhabitant it is not abundant in the mountains or in the wetter northern zones. Its distribution limits do not seem to be exactly known, but there are records of its occurrence also on the steppes lying north of the Caspian Sea.

5

Arvalis and *socialis* overlap in their range, and in some regions both are important pests. Sviridenko states that *arvalis* flourishes most in the damper zones of the steppe, and *socialis* in the drier zones, and that this difference is shown by the tendency for outbreaks in the region where the range of the two species overlap to consist mainly of *arvalis* in the wetter years and *socialis* in the drier ones. It is difficult to know how far this theory is true, since the evidence for it is not presented in a very objective and critical way. But it sounds reasonable, and is carried a stage farther by some interesting field studies done by Naumov in Ukraine.

During 1934 and 1935 Naumov[15, 16] tabulated the vegetation and soil conditions on a large number of sample areas, covering altogether about 350 acres of steppe at Berdiansk, in southern Ukraine. The country was mostly ploughed, or the vegetation deeply altered by grazing; but there were patches of fallow and virgin ground, which, in varied topography of field, ravine, and hill slope, provided the elements of a natural experiment. Much of the land that was not ploughed was predominantly grass. On these sample habitats all the rodents were dug out of the burrows and counted, the samples being spread over a period of twenty months. The chief species were *Microtus arvalis* (728 caught), *Lagurus lagurus* (452), and *Mus musculus hortulanus* (176). The social vole was scarce (26) and the chief comparison was of *arvalis* and the steppe lemming (*lagurus*). The densities in different samples (where the habitat was occupied at all) varied from 0·2 to 36 per hectare in *arvalis*, and from 0·3 to 12·9 in *lagurus*. The highest values for each species are equal to about 14 and 5 per acre: really very low figures, showing that the populations were at a comparatively low ebb in those years (which incidentally were very dry years), after the great outbreak of 1932–3.

Perhaps for this reason, the habitat differences stood out rather clearly. *Arvalis* chiefly lived in the lower, damper ground of the ravines and valleys, with abundant weeds (such as thistles, &c.) and grass cover; whereas *lagurus* was able to live along the slopes and watersheds. Naumov believed that the minor seasonal changes in this basic distribution proved that each species has a type of habitat in which it survives permanently, but from which it spreads when population conditions are favourable to occupy other stations. In so far as this microhabitat patchwork exists, it will tend to increase the chances of outbreaks developing, since the climatic optima of different species of voles and mice differ, and when one is up the other will be down, or at any rate will not increase so much as its neighbours, which will then invade its territory.

Whatever validity this theory may be found to have, Naumov's observations establish a different pattern from the one we are used to imagining. When several species of rodents live together, it does not follow that their populations are mixed at random together; there is a tendency for them to separate into different types of microhabitat—a situation of considerable interest epidemiologically, and, as Naumov points out, practically, since control measures during minimum years must be economically applied to each species according to its habits. In just the same way, entomologists are seeking to check incipient locust outbreaks, by finding their 'stations of permanent survival'. Naumov cites evidence from Soviet research that squirrels and hares also retreat to restricted habitats during the depressions in their population.

The steppe lemming (*Lagurus lagurus*) is, like the social vole, confined to the drier regions of the steppes.[29] It ranges from Ukraine eastwards to Yenisei, with southern limits in the North Caucasus, Tien-Shan, and Altai.[26] In many parts of south European Russia it increases formidably in certain years, and it is included in Sviridenko's black list [29(3)] of the six chief mouse-like rodent pests, the others being *Microtus arvalis*, *Chilotus socialis*, *Stenocranius gregalis*, *Mus musculus*, and *Apodemus agrarius*.

It is interesting to find the house-mouse (*Mus musculus*) maintaining permanent populations in open fields and pastures. The habit is developed in the dry, warm climate of southern Russia—though the warmth is only in summer, the winters being well below freezing-point, which suggests that the dryness may be equally important. In the north it is confined to houses. The species living wild on the steppe belong to various subspecies (*hortulanus*, *tartaricus*, *wagneri*, &c.). *Hortulanus*, at any rate, satisfies its domestic instincts in the field by building little hillocks in the autumn, complex underground mansions in which it stores up seeds of weeds and grass to the amount of one to three litres.[16] From this habit it is called 'hillock mouse'. Some of the mice also winter in houses and barns.

This outdoor habit has two aspects. One is historical, since it suggests that the house-mouse built its own houses before it learned to live in ours, thereby greatly extending its range of climatic tolerance. It is probable that we see in south Russia the ancestral habit, and perhaps the ancestral habitat also. The other aspect is economic: house-mice multiply in company with other species, to form plagues[29, 32] in most of the southern steppe region, including southern Ukraine, lower Volga, North Caucasus (east and west); and to a lesser extent in the foot-hills of the Caucasus and in the Ural Region.

We need not give much space to the remaining species. *Apodemus* are mostly wood-mice, but also inhabit open country in certain regions. *Sylvaticus* (the same that is sometimes important in the rest of Europe) takes part in outbreaks in the foot-hills and mountains of the Caucasus, in the Ural Mountains, also in the northern steppe belts of Ukraine, central Chernozem, &c. *Flavicollis* has caused serious damage in Crimea and along the Black Sea shores. *Agrarius*, like *sylvaticus*, multiplies in the damper zones of the U.S.S.R., where it is sometimes a very bad pest in the fields. It has a very wide range in Eurasia, from the Rhine to Korea. In U.S.S.R. outbreaks are recorded in the Central Industrial Region, on the shores of the Black Sea, in parts of the North Caucasus, in the Far Eastern Republic, and elsewhere. But it does not inhabit the dry steppes. In western Siberia it often goes into houses.

Several kinds of hamsters (*Cricetus*, *Cricetulus*, *Mesocricetus*) also add to the troubles of the Russian cultivator, mostly on steppes and salt-steppes. In Kazakhstan (Kirghiz Steppe), central Asia (Turkestan, &c.),

and in the Buriat-Mongol Republic (in Transbaikalia) several species of gerbilles (*Gerbillus*) play a dominant part in the ecology of steppe and desert-steppe pasture-lands (just as other gerbilles do on the South African veld). They also attack cultivation sometimes. The list could be extended a little more by including various rats of house or field (*Rattus*, *Nesokia*), a jerboa (*Alactaga*), one or two other voles and mice and dormice, and the peculiar blind burrowing rodent, *Spalax*. But the emphasis, except in the more desert areas, is on voles and mice.

6

Although the destruction of ordinary planted or sown food-crops is much the most serious practical problem caused by voles and mice in U.S.S.R., there are four other aspects that should be mentioned. Orchards are ravaged (as in the Ural Region in 1927),[32(2)] also forest nurseries (as by *Apodemus sylvaticus* and *flavicollis* in the central Chernozem Region).[32(9)] But the problem is not so acute as in countries which have not got an almost inexhaustible supply of natural timber.

These vast forests (Siberia has over a thousand million acres) have another significance, as the home of a flourishing fur trade which depends to a large extent on rodents and animals that prey upon them. In Transbaikalia a 'squirrel' was a unit of currency, as the 'beaver' used to be in the Canadian forests. The smaller rodents are probably equally important as food of fur-bearers, just as the squirrel itself is eaten by the sable. In the Arctic zone, lemmings support the arctic fox, while farther south there are various species of red-backed voles (*Clethrionomys = Evotomys*), woodmice (*Apodemus*), and other forest forms, which are no doubt eaten by marten and fox. There does not seem to have been very much intensive research done on these forest rodent populations, except on the red squirrel, which does not concern us here. Formozov[4] gives a valuable review of some of these northern forest problems.

The third aspect is the effect of rodents on the natural pasture which covers such a huge part of the southern U.S.S.R. Central Asia alone supports millions of cattle, horses, and sheep, which have to live in some kind of equilibrium with all the burrowing rodents that draw on the same food supply. Research on ground squirrels has already been mentioned. Recently attention has been drawn also to the importance of voles and mice.

Formozov and Voronov[6] have analysed the rodent populations of pastures and meadows in the flat grassy table-lands and *Artemisia*-covered valleys of western Kazakhstan. Here large numbers of *Citellus* lived, also *Microtus arvalis* and the steppe lemming (*Lagurus lagurus*), various hamsters and gerbilles, and other forms. The number of steppe lemmings was about 50 to the acre, and the number of burrows 480 to the acre. This species eats out whole patches of grass completely and then moves away. One hundred and seven different plants were found to be eaten by it, but the better pasture grasses suffer most, so that the relatively unpalatable species and wormwood (*Artemisia*) survive and cause the pasture to deteriorate. The soil is also affected by rodent action, and many other curious interrelationships were discovered.

Formozov and Prosvirnina[5] did similar work in the alpine and subalpine pastures of central Caucasus and Daghestan. They found that a vole, *Pitymys major*, feeds on forty-six species of plants growing in alpine meadows. Voronov,[33] studying *Chilotus socialis* in the pastures of Daghestan, found that it ate 155 species; but experiments on captive voles showed that there was a certain order of preference. Kalabukhov[9] has pointed out that these natural food plants of rodents have a double economic significance, since they are also the food of domestic animals; while their exhaustion may cause rodents to move into areas of cultivated crops.

The fourth aspect is the relation of rodents to disease in man and his domestic animals. This is much too large a subject to summarize here. Tularaemia has already been mentioned in connexion with water-voles. That this problem is a large and subtle one is indicated by the discovery[28] in Kazakhstan of tularaemia not only in water-voles but also in a species of *Microtus*, in *Apodemus sylvaticus*, *Mus musculus severtzovi*, and *Gerbillus tamaricinus*. It was not found in hamsters, jerboas, or musk-shrews.

The bubonic plague district in south-east U.S.S.R. has been known as a centre of infection for a good many years. The first known epidemic was in the province of Astrakhan in 1877–9, and after 1899 the presence of this disease was well established. But it was not until 1913 that research on wild rodents was begun. This has been especially centred on *Citellus*, but also extends to various voles and mice. In all this work much attention has been given to the parasites (especially fleas) that carry plague, and the climatic factors that restrict them to certain regions. Wu Lien-Teh's learned survey[34] of plague problems for the League of Nations in 1926 describes the general background out of which later studies have grown. Much of this later work, so far as rodents are concerned, has been published in the Russian *Revue de Microbiologie, d'Épidémiologie et de Parasitologie* (*Saratov*) (which also contains papers on tularaemia, &c.), and some of it is abstracted in English in the *Tropical Diseases Bulletin*. It comprises a whole chain of investigations upon rodent populations, ectoparasites, the bacillus of plague, their epidemiological relationship, and the incidence of human plague, which I cannot hope to relay adequately and shall therefore pass by with the remark that here, in south-east Russia, is being done one of the most thorough dynamic studies of animal-borne human disease of any in the world.

7

The central ecological problem in all these rodent populations is their fluctuation, which has been the subject of a very large amount of discussion and speculation and not a little excellent research on the part of Soviet workers. These fluctuations are frequent, affect large tracts of country at the same time, usually occur in several species more or less at once, and have a wide amplitude. Nevertheless, they have not yet been scientifically analysed in any final way.

In 1930 Vinogradov and Obolenskii wrote: [32(6)] 'Laws governing mass reproduction of rodents remain unknown. For the solution of these very important problems, it would be desirable to have not only many more biological observations, but also data of a statistical character, sent in fully and at definite intervals of time.' Kalabukhov in 1935 stated: [8(1)] 'The problem of mass increase of mouse-like rodents has for a long time attracted the attention of past and present investigators, workers on plant protection, and epidemiologists. . . . In spite of this, up to now the study of the mode of life, ecology and mass increase of rodents has been limited to occasional observations, which are not sufficient to explain the causes of the fluctuations in numbers.'

It will be understood, therefore, that one is here surveying incompletely a field of research that is still incompletely developed. And yet, in its energy, breadth of view, and clear realization of many of the essential lines to be followed, the Soviet research on rodent populations is far ahead of that in any other country in the Continent of Europe.

The history of fluctuations in various parts of U.S.S.R. has, so far as the records exist to make it possible, been reconstructed by Sviridenko[29] and by Vinogradov[31] in their recent monographs. Vinogradov's citations are particularly exhaustive. Beginning with occasional records in the early part of the nineteenth century, the history becomes increasingly well documented after 1875 and goes up to 1933. To quote examples would only be to repeat a type of description with which the reader will by now have become thoroughly familiar. The Russian outbreaks differ chiefly in their gigantic scale. They did not happen every year, and there is some evidence, as we shall see, that the greatest of them have occurred at intervals of about ten years. But many regions have had outbreaks more frequently than this.

One of the great difficulties about this information is that it seldom tells us what species of vole or mouse was responsible for the outbreak. We cannot assume, as in so many of the European field-mouse plagues, that the chief operator is *Microtus arvalis*, for it has already been seen that any of half a dozen species may take part, and these do not all have a common ecology. Sviridenko clearly recognizes this difficulty, which is rather a serious one, since we have no assurance that any sequence of 'mouse years' for a single region is the history of homogeneous fluctuations in one species. The same difficulty has been met with by people studying historical records of outbreaks of locusts or forest tree pests, or indeed of epidemic fevers in man.

The other difficulty in interpreting the dates is the absence of any objective standard of what an 'outbreak' means. In a scientific sense it means the complete occupation of their environment by field-mice, and the corresponding destruction of crops, with some kind of eventual decrease to follow. But from the Government's point of view, it is the area of devastation, as well as its intensity, that matters, and so most records represent a combination of area and intensity. But there must be many gaps in the early records, which make it dangerous to apply this method of measurement and to say 'this year was the maximum in Russia'.

Sviridenko stresses the irregularity of recurrence, and the great differences between contiguous regions. Vinogradov, while clearly recognizing this irregularity, brings out the strong ten-yearly trend which keeps showing itself, like a long swell emerging through a sea of shorter, choppy waves. He notes that, in Russia, the possibility of some law underlying such recurrent outbreaks was first adumbrated by Turkin and Satunin in 1902, and more definitely discussed by Rossikov [24a] in 1914, who suggested that the existence of a major ten-year periodicity was probable. Combining the records assembled by Rossikov for years up to 1890, with his own collation from original sources for the next forty-three years, Vinogradov defines the dates of major regional outbreaks of Russian voles and mice. These he sets against a theoretical ten-year cycle as follows:

Actual.	Theoretical.
1822	1823
1832	1833
. .	1843
1855	1853
1863.	1863
1872	1873
1880 } 1884	1883
1893–5	1893
1901–3	1903
1910	
1913–14	1913
1922–4	1923
1932	1933

It is rather difficult to judge of the validity of the dates singled out as major outbreaks, since so much is left to the investigator's estimation of what a major outbreak is to mean. A perusal of the records cited in such detail by Vinogradov makes one inclined to take his view. And he wisely qualifies it by this remark: [31(1)]

'It must further be borne in mind that up to now we have been dealing exclusively with large waves of mass increase covering large territories, whereas the real picture of fluctuations in the numbers of mouse-like rodents is far more complex, because, in the intervals between these large waves of increase, there are numerous smaller waves embracing individual territories and individual species. . . . It is not possible to discern any conformity to law in the rise of these "small" waves.'

It would appear that exact empirical forecasting on the basis of rodent periodicity has not yet much application in Russia. It is possible, perhaps, to predict a year or two of safety after a large 'crash' in the population, since there are plain limits to the rate of recovery even of a vole. Beyond this, the danger exists, but there is no way at present of predicting when it will develop, except by constant observation of the numbers every year, and by intensive research on rodent ecology, with the thought in mind that previous experience may be repeated in the form of a ten-year maximum outbreak. The only evidence of a regular cycle is given by Plyater-Plokhot-skii[19, 20, 21] for the far east of Siberia, where he says that the mouse years were in 1914, 1919, 1924, 1929, and 1933. In 1936 he published a warning of new increase in 1936. The voles and mice had begun in 1935 to recover from their previous crash in 1933–4. I have no information about more recent fluctuations.

We have considered the gigantic scale, the frequency and the geographical distribution of these Russian outbreaks, and the various mouse-like agents causing them. There still remain the questions of their causes and of the practical measures possible for their control.

Kalabukhov's remark, already quoted, about our ignorance of the causes of vole fluctuations might equally well have been made about almost any group of animals, whether rodents, fish, insects, or plankton Crustacea. After all, the science of animal populations is very young: it has only about twenty years behind it. The registration of the fluctuations themselves is only just passing from the phase of general recording by means of subjective estimates and impressions ('a big mouse year') to that of objective census ('400 mice to the acre').

8

The methods of taking rodent censuses have been very energetically studied in Russia, especially during the last few years. Trapping, marking with tags and releasing, flooding burrows to drive out the animals, closing holes to see how many are reopened, trace records, and counting the voles and mice in the pellets (castings of indigestible bones and fur) of hawks and owls are all employed. The works of Kalabukhov[8, 9] and Rall'[23, 24] give excellent reviews of this technical progress. Rall''s monograph upon the traces of small mammals in the Volga–Ural sandy steppes is a fascinating achievement in sheer detective work, which suggests the emergence of a new kind of 'scientific woodcraft' applied to small mammals in the field.

Much of the census system was originally worked out on ground squirrels (*Citellus*): trapping samples; digging up samples; marking, releasing, and recapturing. A few examples of its application to mouse-like rodents may be mentioned, though this research is advancing so rapidly in Russia that one's remarks will inevitably fall out of date. Kucheruk, Krotov, Ryumin, and Sokolov[14] estimated the densities of *Microtus arvalis* during an outbreak in the Moscow region in 1934 to be 400–1.600 per hectare, or about 160–640 per acre. These investigators followed the crash in this area in the winter of 1934–5, from 600–680 per acre down to only 6–8. Kalabukhov and Raevskii measured the density of house-mice (*Mus musculus*) in hay-stacks in the North Caucasus in 1932–3. They used marking methods, and estimated 50–70 mice per cubic metre. But when the crash took place there was only a density of less than 1 per cubic metre.

Such methods hold great promise and are evidently being employed with vigour, partly owing to the need for census figures on which to base costings for operations of control. But until they are fully developed technically and kept going continuously for some years on particular populations, we shall not have the exact background against which the importance of rival theories about population dynamics can properly be assessed.

The further stage still, analysis of the things that control this moving equilibrium of numbers, has only just begun. One difficulty is to judge how far a process operating in the population of one species can safely be assumed to dominate the picture to the same extent in another. So far, no completely intensive study of a single species over a number of years has been done in Russia. This is a not unexpected condition in a country where trained ecologists are still few in comparison to the vast extent of the land and its varied economic problems. The research worker is apt to be moved from point to point according to the exigencies of each year. If the Soviet research on rodents is to achieve its highest level it must set aside certain stations for prolonged and uninterrupted study of a limited number of species, in some such manner as is described in Chapters VIII and IX. An atmosphere of quiet, continuous investigation would make it possible to test and modify the various hypotheses that have been put forward to account for fluctuations.

Population densities, it is now evident, are the product of the operation during some past period of three things, all variable within certain limits characteristic of the species. These are movements, reproduction, and mortality.

Suppose a large area of steppe is occupied at a period of minimum numbers by scattered families of voles. When they begin to increase, the density on the occupied areas is obviously influenced to a high degree by the extent to which voles wander away and settle down on to unoccupied places. Whether these small patches increase or not also depends on the balance between upsurging reproductive powers and destruction by various factors of mortality. Even in an optimum environment (that means much food of the right kind, no mechanical or climatic accidents, no enemies or disease, every resource for home, and no family quarrels) there would still be the normal physiological dying off, in its later stage called 'senescence', whose causes we do not know, to be balanced against reproduction and emigration.

Soviet research has thrown useful light on some of these questions. In the following notes I have relied chiefly on the two excellent summaries by Kalabukhov, published in 1935 and 1937, supplementing them by reference to some of the works of Vinogradov and Obolenskii, Naumov, Sviridenko, Rall', Fenyuk, and others.

9

One belief that has always flowered freely during outbreaks of field-mice, and which one meets repeatedly in the older accounts, is that the mice have invaded suddenly, coming in a swarm from another district. French agricultural and biological research workers still use for outbreaks the term 'invasions', even though they now believe that the sudden increase is chiefly due to multiplication on the spot. To the growing realization that outbreaks of field-mice (unlike those of the Norwegian lemming) are not usually caused by mass migration over great distances, Soviet research has contributed some experimental evidence, which falls into line with recent work of the kind in America and England.

Although ornithologists have since 1890 studied movements by placing numbered rings on the legs of birds, it is only within the last fifteen years that the ringing and tagging of mammals has been undertaken. It is now a widely used technique that is already forming the core of many new population studies: a tremendously powerful instrument for obtaining precise quantitative measurements of population change and movement in the field. With it, new methods of catching and handling animals alive are being invented every year, and these are introducing a radical change in field-work upon mammals which we may compare with another important movement in natural history: the use of the camera instead of the gun.

These Soviet experiments with marked mice and voles, like the independent pioneer ones done by the Johnsons in 1926 and 1927 on American wood-mice (*Peromyscus*), and by Zverev[9] in 1926 onwards on Siberian ground squirrels; and the recent ones by Chitty[1a] on British wood-mice (*Apodemus*) and voles (*Clethrionomys* and *Microtus*[35]), have not been pushed far enough to give a full range of statistical material for any one species. They illustrate the use to which the method can be put, they suggest certain new ideas about population dynamics, and foreshadow a very large development in future.

In 1931 Isotov,[7] an ecologist working at a biological institute near Kiev, in Ukraine, ringed voles and mice with numbered aluminium rings on the hind legs, in order to find out how many might be eaten by owls, from whose cast food pellets the rings could be recovered. His animals were chiefly voles (*Microtus arvalis*); but he also ringed some *Apodemus*, a musk-shrew (*Crocidura*), and even frogs (*Pelobates*). This experiment was rudely interrupted by the flooding of the River Dnieper that drowned some of the rodents and drove others up on to higher ground, where they were attacked by owls. The statistical results were therefore of less general application than they might have been.

In 1932–3 Kalabukhov and Raevskii[10] ringed 928 house-mice (*Mus musculus*) inhabiting grain stacks in the Petrovsk District of North Caucasus. The mice ringed at four different points, 500–1,000 metres apart, and within a month to six weeks 189 were recaptured. None of them had moved to the other stacks at which the ringing was originally done, and some were caught several times at the same point.

Two other field experiments have been done more recently. Varshavskii[30] marked a number of voles (*Microtus arvalis*) and mice (*Mus musculus* and *Apodemus sylvaticus*) in 1933–4 on the Zymliansk area of Azov–Black

Sea region, and stated, from his recaptures, that the animals seldom reached more than 200–1,000 metres from the point of release. For *arvalis* he gives these figures for 71 animals moving to various distances:

0–100 m.	.	.	.	51 per cent.
100–500 m.	.	.	.	34	,,
600–1,000 m.	.	.	.	10	,,
1,000–2,000 m.	.	.	.	4	,,
2,000–5,000 m.	.	.	.	1	,,

He also followed the tracks of these voles in the snow, and found a good deal of evidence that many were killed by predators such as polecats and weasels. Four voles that travelled more than 1,000 m. were all killed in this way.

Similar results are reported by Fenyuk and Demyashev;[3] who studied two kinds of gerbilles, *Pallasiomys meridianus* and *Meriones tamaracinus*, on the steppe. The distances moved by different individuals of *Pallasiomys* (111 animals altogether) were as follows:

0–50 m.	.	.	.	67 per cent.
50–100 m.	.	.	.	12	,,
100–200 m.	.	.	.	7	,,
200–400 m.	.	.	.	7	,,
400–500 m.	.	.	.	5	,,
500–1,000 m.	.	.	.	2	,,
1,000–5,000 m.	.	.	.	0	,,

Again it seemed that the majority of animals moved less than a hundred yards, though a few wandered farther. Much the same behaviour has been recorded for ground squirrels (*Citellus pygmaeus*) in Russia.[9]

Fenyuk and Sheikina[3a] marked a number of *Microtus arvalis* with aluminium rings in their ears and released them again at various points. When they were released in old straw-stacks they showed very little inclination to wander far; in fact, 126 out of 131 were subsequently retaken in the same stacks. When, however, voles were released on open pasture, they wandered far, sometimes as much as $2\frac{1}{2}$ kilometres, and they showed a remarkable capacity for finding the stacks in which they lived before. The authors sum up these vole movements as follows: 'Voles have a high attachment during the spring–summer period to their habitat (of the stack type), at least so long as the living conditions necessary to the voles are maintained in them.'

These preliminary observations form the prima-facie case for moderate rather than long-distance movements in populations of small rodents. Kalabukhov puts it thus:[9(2)] 'Evidently increase in the area of distribution is a gradual process and is due to "molecular" movements, in all directions, of animals at the "borders" of occupied patches.' He points out that this study may throw light on the way in which density on the occupied patches is controlled, on mortality, on epidemiological contacts, and on policies of control. For one practical conclusion is that an area on which rodents have been destroyed, whether by man or by natural causes, may not immediately be recolonized on a large scale.

10

There are a good many technical criticisms that could be made of these marking and recapturing operations. Perhaps the most important is that ordinary trapping sets up cordons round the points of release of the marked animals, so that the chances are high that these will be caught before they have moved very far. Nevertheless, we may accept as a provisional working hypothesis the idea that voles and mice move fairly short distances normally, but in certain circumstances undertake longer journeys. From this simple idea Kalabukhov has developed[8] the following ingenious theory about population dynamics.

He points out that as a population of voles or mice or ground squirrels increases, the food supply on the occupied areas will tend to diminish. When food is scarce the animals move about over larger distances. This greater movement exposes them more to their enemies and so mortality through these predators will be greater. Also, the deaths from accidents may be more frequent. 'The more food there is in a given territory, the smaller is the radius of movement of rodents, and the less the possibility of their death from predators.' [8(4)] So, if these processes were operating, an unusually good food supply would, through its influence on movements, reduce mortality and encourage mass-increase towards outbreak scale. When high density had again reduced the food supply, the wider range of movement would automatically tend to remove a larger number of animals through predation. We might add to this (though he does not) the analogous and parallel action of disease: favourable food supply encouraging resistance, reduction of food supply, increased movement promoting the spread of disease organisms with a resulting higher (sometimes catastrophic) mortality.

Kalabukhov's theory has in it a flavour of the American idea of the 'carrying capacity of cover', widely current now in game-bird population studies. This was crystallized in American research upon the bobwhite quail, which claims that there is a sudden rise in destruction by predators among quail populations that have begun to overflow the normal protective cover. Kalabukhov does not seem to have considered the fact that the food supply of many mouse-like rodents, and especially voles, *is* their cover, and that eating down the available food, besides causing increased movements, may often automatically expose the animals more to their enemies. This further concept reinforces his own theory.

In assessing the value of Kalabukhov's theory, we naturally wish to know whether outbreaks do coincide with years of abnormal food supply, whether the range of movement of rodents varies according to the supply of food, and whether (this being so) the animals suffer more severely from their predatory enemies by ranging further or being more active. As regards the first point, the evidence is very vague, or at any rate inaccessible to me. Kalabukhov and Raevskii cite[10] chiefly the effect of a bumper crop of wheat on the numbers of *Mus musculus* and *Microtus arvalis* in the North Caucasus in 1932. Here it was shown that the mice and voles multiplied strongly under cover of the standing stacks of cut wheat, and the conclusion was drawn that the heavier crop would provide heavier cover and therefore a greater increase. Another example was noticed in the same region that year, an increase of the steppe lemming, *Lagurus lagurus*.

'In this case the increase in numbers was connected with abundance of wild grasses and weeds in the open steppe. The abundance of precipitation in 1932 created conditions in which the usually bare summer steppes of Turkmensk, Blagodarnensk and Petrovsk districts of the North Caucasus region were covered by a dense carpet of wild grasses and weeds. As a result, there was abundant food for *Lagurus*, the intensity of movements diminished, and there was a striking decrease in mortality from predators.'[8(3)]

In both these examples cover may have been of equal importance with food, perhaps it may have been the dominant influence in reducing exposure to enemies. This type of evidence requires, however, a very solid backing of field experiment which has not yet been given; or it may be that I have not yet seen it in the Russian literature. Kalabukhov has reviewed[9] some rather extensive evidence about *Citellus*, which certainly supports the theory of varying food supply causing outbreaks. But for mouse-like rodents we are still in a stage of unproved hypothesis.

The evidence that movements vary with food supply—necessarily hard to obtain—is non-existent still, except for *Citellus*. And the evidence that far-moving individuals are more often killed by predators seems to consist so far only in the statistically negligible records of Varshavskii already mentioned. It does not follow that a theory is wrong because it has not yet been substantiated. These ideas are obviously of great importance, and we should seek to test them in future field investigations.

11

Kalabukhov's theory rests also upon the important assumption that destruction of mouse-like rodents by predators takes place on a significant scale. It is well known that most owls and some hawks, also foxes, weasels, and small carnivores generally, depend largely for their food on voles and mice: there have been enough solid studies of the food of predators in Europe to leave no doubt of this. What we need to know in addition, however, is whether the actual number of rodents destroyed is sufficiently large to affect the control of numbers. To settle this we require figures for the density of predators, the amounts of rodents that each species eats in a certain time (and in different seasons), and the densities of the various rodents concerned.

It has been a commonplace of economic biology during recent years to label various predators as 'beneficial' or otherwise, on the strength of what has been ascertained about the nature of their food. An owl is 'beneficial' if it eats mainly rodents, but '10 per cent. harmful' if 10 per cent. of what it eats is insect enemies of an insect pest. So the crude reasoning runs. But whether the existence of this species of owl has more than a negligible influence on the rodent populations within its hunting area depends on the other considerations just mentioned. If a public health official vaccinated only one in every ten thousand people for small-pox, we should not be justified in describing him as 'beneficial' or even as having any appreciable influence at all on the small-pox outbreaks. He is only *potentially* effective, and his potentialities would have to be increased by a higher rate of vaccination, or by adding to his department. So with predators taking prey.

This tendency to pave the temple of economic biology with the good intentions (or potentialities) of predatory animals and birds is frequently to be noticed. Soviet ecologists have appreciated the difficulty and have already done some field experiments, using the new marking method. Isotov's Ukraine experiment, already mentioned, we may probably discount because there were abnormal conditions of rodent movement and concentration associated with river floods. Kalabukhov and Raevskii,[10] during their Caucasus house-mouse investigation, recovered rings from the pellets of predatory birds, and calculated that about 1·5 per cent. of the mice were eaten by these birds every day. This is apparently the only investigation so far in Russia which fulfils a good many of the criteria we need. It suggests an enormous destruction of mice by birds.

A rather different method is to work out how many rodents are eaten by owls in a certain time. This has been done both by observation in the field and by experimenting on captive birds (as earlier on by the Germans Rörig and Knoche). The most considerable Soviet research has been done by Pidoplichka.[18] He worked out, for instance, that the barn owl (*Tyto alba guttata*) in nature consumed 85–128 small mammals in a month. Combining these figures with the estimated hunting territory, he concluded that (for one particular area) an owl would kill five small animals on an acre in a year. But to finish this story we need to know the densities of owls and small mammals.

Klimov[12] describes a heavy destruction of voles (*Stenocranius gregalis*) and hamsters (*Cricetulus zongarus*) by hawks and owls on a field in Siberia. By setting up regular 'pellet posts' and collecting the pellets at intervals, some idea of the number of animals eaten could be obtained. He states that an initial population of 58 rodents per acre was reduced to about 9 per acre in a month—a destruction of 85 per cent. I have not been able to study the details of technique in this investigation.

We shall not, perhaps, attach too much importance to the actual findings of these and other field experiments, which are still too limited to allow any generalizations to be made. But they show that in many parts of Russia and Siberia predators are still an important factor to be studied and that they have locally, and perhaps over wide areas, an effect that is not negligible, and may be important. It is possible that they are indeed a master factor in rodent oscillations, as Kalabukhov believes.

It is the fruitfulness of the methods that should be marked. The older and still very valuable statistical studies of the food of predators (from stomachs and crops and pellets) lead to these further stages: laboratory studies of the amount and rate of feeding; field observations at roosts and nests and 'pellet posts', to check the laboratory conclusions; recovery of marked animal remains from the food; and the execution of these studies on areas where the densities of eater and eaten are also known.

A good deal of space has been given to the discussion of Kalabukhov's idea, as it is one of the special Soviet contributions towards the theory of the subject. Also, it has been put forward in Soviet literature in such a way as rather to displace the theory that epidemic diseases dominate the dynamics of rodent populations. It is, in fact, the application of epidemiological ideas, usually thought of in connexion with host-parasite interrelations, to the interaction of preys with their predators—a group of concepts that has already been widely canvassed in the theoretical speculations of Lotka and Volterra, and more recently, of Nicholson and Gause.

12

We naturally ask what evidence has been obtained about the frequency of epidemic diseases among mouse-like rodents in Russia. It appears that this aspect of the subject has, with the very large exception of research on bubonic plague and tularaemia, received comparatively little attention yet from Soviet workers. Still less has been done upon any possible mortality factors of an even more obscure nature, such as food deficiency or competition among members of the same species. It is certain that mouse-like rodents are subject to epidemics of sylvatic plague (caused by *Pasteurella* (*Bacillus*) *pestis*, and of tularaemia (caused by *Brucella* (*Bacterium*) *tularense*), the former mainly in definite regions in southern Russia. Although much splendid research has been done on the epidemiology of these plague rodents, most of the population studies have been on ground squirrels (*Citellus*). In these it has been shown that plague is epidemic when the rodents reach high density and rare in proportion when the animals are scarce. That it is a limiting factor to high density seems to be absolutely certain. In some areas it is a master factor, both in ground squirrels and in mouse-like rodents.

But this research hardly touches the main problem: what makes the upper limit to natural increase in mouse-like rodents on the steppe generally? Kalabukhov has rather left this question open, and we may infer that the kind of continuous investigation in fixed localities for many years, which has been carried out on rodents that create public health problems, has not yet been adopted to elucidate their epidemiology in other places. Yet the brilliant scientific success of this long-range research on plague rodents, exemplified by various *Citellus* studies, should encourage the development of such organizations.

There is a third theory about mortality in mouse-like rodents that has been put forward rather persuasively by Sviridenko.[29] He points out that these animals, although they have temperature regulation in their bodies, are really very easily upset by abnormal heat or cold, and that recent experiments show the body temperatures of voles and mice to vary several degrees according to the temperature of their surroundings. Nikolaevskii,[17] in Transcaucasia in 1916, exposed *Microtus arvalis* to sunlight at an air temperature of 27·5° C. They died in less than half an hour. At 31·2° C. some other voles died in less than thirteen minutes. Some voles kept in strong sun on the Kalmyk Steppe died in five minutes and their body temperature went up to 44° C.

Similarly damp or wet fur soon causes voles to die of cold. We may sum up Sviridenko's theory in his own words: [29(6)] 'As has been shown by experiments and observations, the organism of voles and mice is very unstable, and is affected by the varying factors in external conditions. Any great deviation from optimum conditions rapidly upsets the balance of its biological functions, and often leads to death.' From this premise, which seems supported by a good deal of evidence, he goes on to explain the sudden disappearance of rodents after abundance by abnormal weather conditions. Of this phenomenon he gives a number of supposed instances, but it is pretty hard to know what value to attach to the evidence, since search by pathologists for alternative causes of death was very seldom done. We may take it that weather does at times destroy voles and mice outright, but that we still do not know how important this influence is. Heavy rains or sudden melting snow cause floods that can undoubtedly drown the rodents, as Belskii noted in one place in the Ukraine in 1923.[29(7)]

One difficulty in applying the theory generally is that this type of mortality has no relation at all to density of the animals: it is an Act of God that smites the sparse and crowded populations alike. In this respect it is antithetic to the theories of control by predators or parasites. Kalabukhov has pointed out[8(2)] that physiological sensitivity does not necessarily cause ecological instability of a rodent population. For the habits of voles and mice are adjusted to meet such difficulties and dangers. The animals live underground, or under dense vegetation cover, or beneath warm snow cover in winter, or they are nocturnal. Or else they store food in their burrows, and come out only when the weather is suitable. According to Rall', *Microtus arvalis* and the steppe lemming, *Lagurus lagurus*, and a hamster, *Cricetulus migratorius*, stayed in their burrows when the air-temperature was less than −15° or −20° C., blocking the entrances with earth,[22] just as we should keep the outer door of the house shut in bitter weather, and stay at home.

These, then, are the three theories most commonly considered by Soviet workers to account for varying mortality in rodents: predators (combining with abnormal food and greater movements), parasites, or abnormal weather. Little or nothing has been done on accidents, on competition and fighting within the species, or on nutritional disturbances. In all these phases there is still a vast open field for investigation.

There is another side to the fluctuation problem that has received some attention in Russia. It is known that all these small rodents have something of a pause in reproduction during the winter. The breeding season varies, however, not only between different species, but in the same species in different years. It is therefore natural to look for the cause of outbreaks in unusually long breeding seasons, or in greater reproductive rates. Going deeper, we need to know the reasons for these variations in the breeding season: whether light or temperature or food or something else. This subject will be referred to in Chapter VIII. Here we note that there is not yet enough field evidence to enable us to judge whether varying reproduction or varying mortality plays the dominant part in causing fluctuations, or if both are interlocked. Naumov[15a] has studied this question, with *Microtus arvalis*.

13

I shall not describe at any length the methods of control that have been used in Soviet Russia, since they follow in many respects the practice of other European countries. We may note the enormous use of poisons, aided locally by other devices such as flooding, trapping, and gassing. Biological control by means of bacterial cultures has not much support. Vinogradov and Obolenskii in 1930[32(10)] gave this as their opinion. 'Unfortunately, one cannot yet speak of bacterial control as useful for field work, or even in peasant property (i.e. buildings).' Kalabukhov, appreciating the enormous scale and cost of such operations (and shall we add, their frequently doubtful usefulness), has advocated a more subtle, ecological, approach to the problem.[9(3)] He believes that much can be done to deprive rodents of food and cover on cultivated areas: to adjust the operations of agriculture so that the conditions for mass increase are removed. One example of this is the quick clearing and clean threshing of wheat stacks, which may prevent the multiplication of mice and voles. Fenyuk[2] has contributed a penetrating study of this aspect of control.

With such suggestions we may strongly agree, and yet the creation of such a policy presupposes much more research on the dynamics of these populations, and for this the vital need is for long continuous research on a single species, using every idea and technique that is available. One would say that the deepest need for this Soviet research, with its vital enthusiasm, its huge staff and endless resources, and its modern and original concepts, is to focus research. Hitherto the research on rodents (except perhaps for the *Citellus* work for plague) has been done in patches, here and there, now on one species, now on another. These different lines need to be combined and concentrated for the elucidation of principles in population dynamics.

REFERENCES

* means that a full translation in English is available in the Bureau of Animal Population, Oxford. (Copies of these are obtainable.)
† means that the reference has not been seen in the original. The others have been read either in full or through the summaries in non-Russian.

1. CARPENTER, J. R. (1939). 'Recent Russian work on community ecology.' J. Anim. Ecol. 8: 354–86.

1 a. CHITTY, D. H. (1937). 'A ringing technique for small mammals.' J. Anim. Ecol. 6: 36–53.

*2. FENYUK, B. K. (1937). ['The influence of agriculture on the numbers of mouse-like rodents, and the biological foundations of rodent control.'] Rev. Microbiol., Saratov, 16: 478–92. (In Russian.)

*3. FENYUK, B. K., & DEMYASHEV, M. P. (1936). ['Duration of life in nature of the gerbille Pallasiomys meridianus Pall. (Mammalia).'] Rev. Microbiol., Saratov, 15: 407–12.

*3 a. FENYUK, B. K., & SHEIKINA, M. V. (1938). ['A study of vole—Microtus arvalis Pall. (Mammalia)—migrations by the ringing method.'] Sci. Rep. Saratov St. Univ. 1, No. 14 (Biol. Ser. No. 2): 85–102. (In Russian; summary in English.)

*4. FORMOZOV, A. N. (1937). ['A brief summary of works on the ecology of birds and mammals during twenty years (1917–1937).'] Zool. Zhurnal, 16: 916–49. (In Russian.)

5. FORMOZOV, A. N., & PROSVIRNINA, J. B. (1935). ['L'activité des rongeurs au Caucase et leur influence sur les phytocenoses des pâturages et des prairies.'] Bull. Soc. Nat. Moscou (Sect. Biol.), 44: 82–9. (In Russian; summary in French.)

6. FORMOZOV, A. N., & VORONOV, A. G. (1935). 'Principal features of the activity of rodents on pastures and meadow land.' C. R. Acad. Sci. U.R.S.S. (New Ser.), 3: 370–2. (In English.)

7. IZOTOV, I. P. (1931). ['Investigations on inter-relations between Tyto alba guttata Brhm. and small rodents.'] Ukrainian Academy of Sciences, Dept. of Natural Science and Technique, Materials of the Regional Research on small mammals, and birds feeding on them, pt. 1: 93–100. (In Ukrainian.)

*8. KALABUKHOV, N. I. (1935). ['On the causes of fluctuations in numbers of mouse-like rodents.'] Zool. Zhurnal, 14: 209–42. (1) p. 209. (2) p. 225. (3) p. 235. (4) p. 234. (In Russian; summary in English.)

*9. KALABUKHOV, N. I. (1937). ['Results of twenty years (1917–1937) investigations of the ecology of injurious rodents of U.S.S.R.'] Zool. Zhurnal, 16: 950–71. (In Russian. Large bibliography in Russian.) (1) p. 951. (2) p. 963. (3) p. 967. (4) p. 952.

*9 a. KALABUKHOV, N. I. (1937). ['Principal laws of the dynamics of mammal and bird populations.'] Advances in Modern Biology, 7: 505–31. (In Russian.)

*10. KALABUKHOV, N. I., & RAEVSKII, V. V. (1933). ['Methods for the study of certain problems in the ecology of mouse-like rodents.'] Rev. Microbiol., Saratov, 12: 47–62. (In Russian; summary in German.)

*11. KASHKAROV, D. N. (1934). Preface to his translation of Elton, C. (1933). 'The ecology of animals.' Moscow and Leningrad. (In Russian.)

†12. KLIMOV, I. N. (1931). ['On the biology of Microtus (Stenocranius) gregalis and the method of its control.'] Bull. Plant Prot. Siberia, 1: 100–25. (Cited by Kalabukhov, Ref. 8.)

13. KOLESNIKOV, I. I. (1932). ['Materials for the study of the significance of some rodents for new rubber yielding cultures.'] Bull. Plant Protection, Ser. 4, No. 2: 9–22. (In Russian; summary in English.)

94 PLAGUES OF

14. KUCHERUK, V., KROTOV, A., RYUMIN, A., & SOKOLOV, M. (1935). ['Quelques données sur la multiplication en masse des rongeurs (campagnols et souris) dans la région de Moscou en 1934.'] Bull. Soc. Nat. Moscou (Sect. Biol.), 44: 414–27. (In Russian; summary in French.)

*15. NAUMOV, N. P. (1936). ['On some pecularities of ecological distribution of mouse-like rodents in Southern Ukraine.'] Zool. Zhurnal, 15: 674–96. (In Russian; summary in English.)

*15 a. NAUMOV, N. P. (1936). ['Reproduction and mortality in the common vole (*Microtus arvalis* Pall.)'.] Miscellany of the Works of the Zoological Inst. of Moscow State Univ., No. 3: 144–70. (In Russian; summary in English.)

16. NAUMOV, N. P. (1937). ['On the distribution of muriform rodents (*Microtus arvalis* Pall., *Microtus socialis* Pall., *Lagurus lagurus* Pall., *Mus musculus hortulanus* Nordm.) in different habitats.'] Sci. Rep. Moscow St. Univ. 13: 3–38. (In Russian; summary in English.)

†17. NIKOLAEVSKII, L. A. (1916). ['The Caucasian vole (*Microtus arvalis caucasicus*).'] Vestnik Un-ta Shaniavski, No. 1. (Cited by Sviridenko, 1934.)

18. PIDOPLICHKA, I. G. (1930). ['Harmful rodents on the right side of the wooded steppe and the importance of particular groups in agriculture.'] Kiev Agric. Sta. 63: 1–106. (In Ukrainian; summaries in Russian and German.)

19. PLYATER-PLOKHOTSKII, K. (1935). ['On the study of the biology, ecology and economic significance of the Eastern vole (*Microtus michnoi pellicus* Thom.) in the Far Eastern region.'] Bull. Far E. Branch, Acad. Sci. U.S.S.R., No. 11: 57–75. (In Russian.)

20. PLYATER-PLOKHOTSKII, K. (1935). ['Sur la question de l'étude de la loi de la multiplication des rongeurs de la race des souris dans les conditions de la région de l'Extrême Orient.'] Bull. Far E. Branch, Acad. Sci. U.S.S.R., No. 13: 71–87. (In Russian; summary in French.)

21. PLYATER-PLOKHOTSKII, K. (1936). ['Harmful rodents in the Southern Districts of the Far Eastern Region in 1935.'] Bull. Far E. Branch, Acad. Sci. U.S.S.R., No. 18: 35–47. (In Russian; summary in English.)

22. RALL', YU. M. (1931). ['On the winter biology of *Gerbillus tamaracinus* Pall. and other rodents in the neighbourhood of Urda.'] Rev. Microbiol., Saratov, 10: 189. (Cited by Kalabukhov, 1935.)

23. RALL', YU. M. (1935). ['Identification of rodents and other animals of the Volga-Ural sandy steppe by their traces.'] Problems of Ecology and Biocenology, 2: 37–73. (In Russian; summary in English.)

*24. RALL', YU. M. (1936). ['Some methods of ecological census of rodents.'] Problems of Ecology and Biocenology, 3: 140–57. (In Russian; summary in English.)

†24 a. ROSSIKOV, K. N. (1914). 'Field mice.' Publ. Dept. Agric. (In Russian; cited by Vinogradov, 1934.)

25. ROUBAKINE, A. (1930). 'Tularaemia.' League of Nations Monthly Epid. Rep., R.E. 134: 11–19.

26. SACHTLEBEN, H. (1932). 'Rodentia, Nagetiere.' In Reh, L. 'Handbuch der Pflanzenkrankheiten,' 5, pt. 2: 858–926.

27. SCHMIDT, P. Y. (1899). ['The Moscow Industrial Region of the Upper Volga.'] In ['Russia. Full geographical description.'] Ed. by V. P. Semenov-Tian-Shanskii. St. Petersburg. Vol. 1, p. 60. (In Russian.)

28. SINAI, G., & RAPPOPORT, I. (1935). ['Reservoirs of tularaemia.'] Med. Parasitol. and Parasit. Dis., Moscow, 4: 213–17. (In Russian.)

*29. SVIRIDENKO, P. A. (1934). ['Increase and decrease of mouse-like rodents.'] Bull. Plant Protection, Ser. 4, No. 3: 1–59. (1) p. 17. (2) p. 18. (3) p. 21. (4) p. 22. (5) p. 20, &c. (6) p. 38. (7) p. 41. (In Russian; summary in English.)

*30. VARSHAVSKII, S. N. (1937). ['Seasonal migrations of mouse-like rodents.'] Zool. Zhurnal, 16, No. 2: 362–92. (Cited by Kalabukhov, 1937.)

*31. VINOGRADOV, B. S. (1934). 'Materials for the study of the dynamics of the fauna of mouse-like rodents in U.S.S.R. (Historial review of mass increases.)' Peoples' Commissariat of Agriculture, Association for Controlling Pests and Diseases in Agriculture and Forestry, Record Service Dept. Leningrad. 62 pp. (1) p. 49. (In Russian.)

*32. VINOGRADOV, B. S., & OBOLENSKII, S. I. (1930). ['Injurious insects and other animals in U.S.S.R., No. 5.'] Lenin Acad. Agric. Sci. U.S.S.R., Bur. Appl. Entomology, works of Appl. Ent. 13, No. 5: 257– . (1) p. 300. (2) p. 308. (3) p. 299. (4) p. 271. (5) p. 272. (6) p. 315. (7) p. 305. (8) p. 274. (9) p. 298. (10) p. 291. (In Russian.)

33. VORONOV, A. (1935). ['Quelques observations sur l'action du campagnol vivant en sociétés (*Microtus socialis* Pall.) sur les pâturages situés au pied des montagnes du Daghestan.'] Bull. Soc. Nat. Moscou (Sect. Biol.), 24: 314–23 and 391–406. (In Russian; summary in French.)

34. WU LIEN-TEH (1926). 'A treatise on pneumonic plague.' Publ. League of Nations, III. Health, 1926. III. 13. Geneva.

35. Bureau of Animal Population, Oxford University, Annual Report, 1936–7, p. 12.

CHAPTER VI

ROUND THE WORLD: PALESTINE, AUSTRALIA,
UNITED STATES, AND CANADA

'These hints we note in passing. They may serve to put our minds in a state of
preparedness for the more formal and decisive attack of the problem, to which
we shall be led in the last division of our enquiry, dealing with the dynamics of
life-bearing systems.' A. J. LOTKA, *Elements of Physical Biology.*

Palestine

1

IN this survey we have been moving gradually eastward, following several
threads of thought. There were the outbreaks of *Microtus arvalis*, traced
from the Atlantic coast of France into the interior of Asia, where their
farthest limits are still undefined. There were the fluctuations of a number
of other species, overlapping and mixing with one another, but each with
its own main zone of activity. At the same time it was possible to distinguish certain places where the analysis of population changes and controls had been seriously undertaken and had begun to supplement and test
traditional and largely uncritical measures of repression: small beacons
of research, signalling across wide spaces to one another, but scarcely able
yet to warm the hopes of the farmer, forester, or health official struggling
to apply control. And we saw that the light of research in Soviet Russia
(by far the most powerful agent of the new ecology on Continental Europe)
has largely been hidden from the rest of the world by the barriers of
political and linguistic isolation.

Something was noted in Chapter IV of the Mediterranean centres of vole
and mouse outbreaks (Italy and the Balkans). Palestine is another place
which commands attention, for several reasons. This country lies on the
border-line between two great biogeographical regions,[4] the Mediterranean
(with alternate dry summer and wet winter, and yet a moderate fluctuation
of temperature between the two), and the Irano-Turanian (also with
seasonal, but much lower, rainfall, and with those very violent fluctuations
in seasonal heat and cold that form a continental climate). Both are
ecologically dry, and very warm in summer, but the Irano-Turanian represents the extremes of climate that fall on the margins of continental
deserts. To the east and south are deserts, and to the north massive
mountain ranges. We therefore find in Palestine a fauna of rodents very
similar to that which inhabits the steppes and desert margins of the
U.S.S.R., but differing in the actual species, and mixed with additional
elements from Mediterranean Africa and Europe. Genera common to
Palestine and U.S.S.R. are *Citellus, Cricetulus, Mesocricetus, Mus, Apodemus, Nesokia, Gerbillus, Arvicola, Microtus, Spalax,* and possibly *Alactaga.*
The steppe lemming, *Lagurus,* is missing from Palestine, which has, however, several additional gerbilles, also the desert spiny-mice (*Acomys*).[4]

There are a good many other differences, but it is seen that Palestine concentrates in a small area a rich assemblage of rodent types that are distributed over much broader zones in U.S.S.R. Still another element is represented by the alpine vole, *Chionomys*, a genus characteristic of high mountains in Europe (Pyrenees, Alps, Balkans) found in Caucasus, and reaching its southern limit in the Syrian mountains.

The fluctuations of *Microtus* in Palestine are specially interesting because they occur in populations living at the southern limits of the range of this genus in this part of the world. There are no voles in the Sinai Peninsula, in Egypt, or in other parts of Africa, except one species in Cyrenaica[47a] (in north-eastern Libya). Two species of vole divide the country between them. In the south, *Microtus philestinus* inhabits the coastal plain as far up as Messina. The other, *Microtus guentheri*, ranges from the mountains north of Jerusalem, through northern Palestine and Asia Minor as far as the mountains of Armenia. It is related closely to the species that lives in Thessaly (Chapter IV).

2

All the important work on vole populations in Palestine has been done by Bodenheimer and his associates in the Hebrew University at Jerusalem.[4, 5] They have studied the distribution of the outbreaks, something of their recurrence and means for their control, and further than this have undertaken a number of quantitive investigations upon the number, reproductive powers, and length of life. The publication of this population study will be awaited with interest.

The smaller, northern *philestinus* has agriculturally serious outbreaks chiefly in a limited region in the Plain of Philistia, between Ekron and Ben Shemen. The other one, *guentheri*, multiplies primarily in the mountains but spreads into the neighbouring plains—apparently an example of genuine, though not necessarily very abrupt, invasion on an important scale. These invasions have been especially noted in the Plain of Esdraelon. The Biblical references to Palestine outbreaks have already been noticed in Chapter I.

Bodenheimer and Klein say that the habits of the two species are not very different; but *guentheri* is the one which has been the subject of intensive study. Conditions are very different to those of less arid climates, since there is not a permanent dense cover of vegetation in the habitats that the voles frequent, and the animals have their runways mostly underground. In certain years great increase is observed, and the voles, especially in the winter and spring, attack and partly destroy crops of grain and alfalfa, also clover. Of the grain they devour both sown seed and sprouting blade.

The following years of outbreak in Palestine are recorded: 1904–6, 1914, 1921–3, 1925, and 1929–31. The first and last of these were very big, and in 1930–1 a parallel increase occurred also in wild 'house'-mice, *Mus musculus gentilis*, and in gerbilles, *Meriones tristrami*. This *Mus* is the common, all-greyish variety that is found over much of the Mediterranean. It lives in cultivated lands as well as in houses. The gerbille is also an inhabitant of cultivated fields, but is widely distributed, and goes as far as the deserts south of the Dead Sea. These *Microtus-Mus* outbreaks remind us again of the southern Russian scene.

The period of recurrence of these outbreaks was about 9, 8, 4, 5 years. These dates alone scarcely justify Bodenheimer's deduction that 'smaller waves of mass increase apparently occur every 3–5 years . . .'. Nevertheless the recurrence is sufficiently frequent to afford a valuable field for population analysis, which, as remarked above, is still in progress.

There is still quite a considerable and interesting fauna of predatory birds and animals in Palestine, many of which attack voles and mice. Great concentration of these (perhaps increase too) is observed during vole abundance: mongoose, foxes, jackal, cats, falcons, buzzards, kites, harriers, various owls, and snakes.

Australia

3

This is as far as the present survey of vole and mouse plagues in Europe and Asia goes, except for the western fringe (Great Britain and Scandinavia) where *Microtus agrestis* is chief vole. Before coming to this region (see Part II) we shall take note of some other parts of the world where mice or voles or both are important.

This order of treatment is part of a design which the reader may have already begun to detect in this book. The first thing has been to bring out, as vividly as possible, the scale of the field-mouse problem in human affairs in Europe. The problem is resolved into an ecological one, of population increase and decrease. The research hitherto done in Europe, as we saw, has found out little about the causes of increase, while the nature of the decrease has been often hidden by a cloud of repressive measures of which the most interesting biologically is the use of mouse-typhoid cultures. It will have become clear how the first feature—the destructive powers and immediate menace of the vole plague—by leading to the second feature— the intensity of organized repression, has obscured the natural phenomena which form the cycle of increase and decrease.

Out of this confusion, a third feature arises: the existence of natural fluctuations, with a natural termination to each period of extreme abundance—what one might call the *vis muricida*, corresponding to the *vis medicatrix* which helps the sick patient to recover in due course, whether he be treated or not. We have seen the signs of this tendency for vole populations to oscillate naturally: in France, Germany (e.g. Bavaria), Holland, Italy, Russia, and Palestine.

The rapid survey of other regions of the world serves to point out further examples of natural outbreaks in which human efforts at control have been either absent or ecologically negligible and in which, accordingly, the natural course of events is less obscured. This part of the survey is concentrated on Australia, the United States, and Canada. We then return to Great Britain for the analysis of two historic vole plagues in grass-land and for the description of how research on fluctuations has been organized there in the hope of discovering their nature. From this point we shall go on first to Scandinavia, then to Labrador and the Canadian Arctic, to give the story of some long-continued oscillations in wild populations which closely resemble in many ways the British ones, and which may yield to organized research the meaning of their regular periodicity. These population cycles, with their important relation to the fur trade and wild-life conservation, provide at the same time a model which, if it is properly analysed by research, may contribute towards the amelioration of vole- and mouse-plague problems elsewhere.

We skip straight to Australia, leaving aside a great many interesting subjects—such as the three-year cycle in north Siberian foxes that the natives described to Von Wrangell over a hundred years ago, and which probably depended on field-mice ; the position of Japanese river valley or tsutsugamushi fever (really a form of typhus), carried by harvest mites to man, from a reservoir of the virus in voles (*Microtus montobelloi*) ; the complex network of rodent life on the South African veld, with gerbilles, wild rats, and mice carrying bubonic plague and other diseases, and fluctuating with a short cycle which attracts the interest of the League of Nations in Geneva ; similar fluctuations of mouse-like rodents, associated with plague in India, and with Rift Valley fever of man and sheep in East Africa ; the sudden increases of wild rats and other species that occur in India, Burma, Brazil, and elsewhere, as a result of the periodic flowering and seed-production of bamboos ; almost innumerable kinds of rodent damage, interlocked with population balance and change, described in the works of Sachtleben and others. The field is huge, and this book only suggests a method of approach to understanding of it.

And now for Australia, in which, as most people know, the chief mammals are pouched marsupials. It is not so generally realized that Australia has also more than forty endemic species of true rodents, including a water-rat, a jerboa rat, a number of other wild rat-like forms, and a good many species of so-called field-mice (*Pseudomys*), but no members of the vole family. Information about them is given in Longman's monograph.[32]

There are also several species of rodents introduced in historical times by man, including ordinary rats; and the house-mouse (*Mus musculus*), living wild, that is mainly (though not entirely) responsible for mouse plagues in Australia. These outbreaks happen chiefly in the wheat-growing districts of South Australia, Victoria, and New South Wales, and although there seems to be no very complete published investigation of the subject, some very interesting observations have been recorded.

4

I have found information about three serious outbreaks within the last thirty years. The first was in 1911, according to an eyewitness from whom

Dr. John R. Baker got the record for me in 1928. It affected at any rate northern Victoria, and consisted of local outbreaks in the wheat country during winter. Since this witness described correctly the next outbreak, in 1916–17, for which there is ample published confirmation, we may accept the earlier one as being also probably reliable.

In 1916 there was a terrific multiplication of mice in South Australia, Victoria, and New South Wales, which severely damaged the wheat belt and was also experienced in bush country. The following account is given by Hinton,[28] presumably based on records accessible to him in England. One of these is by Darnell-Smith:[12]

'Recently South Australia and Victoria have been visited by a very severe mouse plague, the worst ever experienced in Australia. The principal species involved was the House Mouse, but it was assisted not only by various native species but by battalions of rats as well. The plague developed in the bush as well as in the wheatland in 1916 and 1917, after two abnormally heavy harvests. The wheat grown was sold to the British Government, and the grain was stacked in bags ready for shipment. Shipping was cut off and the stacks remained unprotected from a possible attack by the rodents. As cold weather approached the mice invaded the stacks; an eye-witness of the result says: "The wheat stacks instead of being as orderly as a brick wall are now evil-smelling heaps of wheat, mice alive, mice dead, and rotten bags." The damage done to the wheat is estimated to be well over £1,000,000; . . . One farmer put down poisoned meat in the house, and next morning he picked up 28,000 dead on his verandah, and he added that he only stopped then "because he was tired". At one wheat-yard 70,000 were killed in an afternoon; . . . Myriads died from a disease in appearance somewhat resembling ulcerative syphilis; and the men trying to cleanse the stack contracted a kind of ringworm. Large quantities of hay were also ruined, and horses fed upon the dirty residue were killed. . . . At Port Lorne, South Australia . . . the seaweed on the beach was swarming with mice.'

According to Osborne[36] the outbreak was first noticed in February and March of 1917, and was at its maximum between April and August. At Lascelles 3 tons, reckoned to be approximately 200,000 mice, were taken in one night. Up to the end of June 1917 the recorded total weight caught came to 544 tons, thought to represent at least 32 million mice! Dr. Baker's informant said that the mouse plague began after the harvest of 1916, chiefly in the wheat-lands of Victoria and New South Wales, that the mice got a skin disease and their hair fell out, and that the men handling wheat developed skin disease on their necks, shoulders, and arms, and had to be paid extra to do the work. Towards the end of 1917 every mouse had the skin disease. In some places a plague of fleas was noticed after the mice had disappeared, and these were said to have attacked people.

No doubt a fuller story could be built up from agricultural archives in Australia, but the main facts seem undeniable. In 1932 another outbreak of house-mice developed in the same wheat-growing regions. Osborne gives the following note on the outbreak in Victoria, which attests the formidable biomass of these mice: 'After all wheat had been trucked from the Lah railway station, near Warracknabeal, a raid was made upon the mice. The site was fenced, and two 40-gallon drums were sunk in the ground. The dunnage was then cleared and the mice driven into the drums. On the first night the catch, placed on the weigh-bridge, weighed one ton, and on two successive nights 8 cwt. and 10 cwt. were caught, the weight for three nights being nearly two tons.'

5

Dr. D. Murnane[35] of the Veterinary Research Laboratory of the Division of Animal Health, Council for Scientific and Industrial Research, published a careful study of the mouse epidemics that arose from this outbreak, and has also kindly given me some further information about the distribution of it:

'The mouse plague in question occurred (as have all previous plagues) in the North-western area of the State, which is the wheat belt. Rarely do we experience a serious plague in the southern areas. The area affected by the recent plague extended beyond the South Australian border on the West, beyond the New South Wales border on the North, to Echuca and Bendigo on the East, and approximately to a line connecting Bendigo, Horsham, and Servicetown on the South. In all, an area of approximately 2400 square miles was involved.'

The species concerned was the house-mouse (*Mus musculus*). The original object of Dr. Murnane's study was to find out whether epidemics artificially introduced among the mice were likely to be effective. This is what he discovered.

The epidemic was not a simple affair, but contained at least three different elements. The first was a kind of mange, of which no details are given. Presumably this may have been caused by mites. The second was also a skin disease—favus, a variety of ringworm, caused in this case by the microscopic fungus, *Achorion quinckeanum*. It affected the heads of the mice badly, and was easily transmitted from one mouse to another. Here we have the same feature that was noticed in the 1916–17 outbreak, but there is no mention of human infection in 1932. However, Jaffé[30] in his text-book of the diseases of small laboratory animals mentions that this particular fungus can infect man. It seems probable, therefore, that it was the very one that caused trouble to the men in 1917.

There are, however, other kinds of ringworm that can pass from mice to men. An epidemic caused by *Trichophyton gypseum asteroides* (another fungus) attacked about half the animals in a laboratory stock of tame mice in an institute in Kent. Parish and Craddock[37] studied the outbreak in some detail. The disease made patches on the skin of the necks, heads, and rumps of the mice, but the death-rate was low and experimental transmission was not very successful. The ringworm spread, however, to four laboratory assistants, three of whom had slight lesions of the neck or hand or arm, while the fourth suffered more extensively. The same kind of ringworm was also found on two horses in the stables of the institute.

Dr. G. M. Findlay informs me that ringworm is a disease well known to all who handle white mice, that people fairly often catch it, and that it is most prevalent in the spring.

The third disease organism in the Australian outbreak was 'Gaertner's bacillus'—*Bacterium* (or *Salmonella*) *enteritidis*, which Murnane isolated from the spleen and liver lesions in some of the mice, and subjected to careful cultural and serological tests. Here we have, in a natural epidemic of wild house-mice in Australia, the same type of bacillus that we have seen to cause food poisoning in man, and to be used so liberally (in one of its varieties) in France.

Murnane remarks:[35] 'From the point of view of human health, the finding is of significance, showing, as it does, how mice readily act as carriers of this food poisoning (so-called "ptomaine poisoning") organism. This is of particular importance to residents in mouse plague areas, and to those handling infected mice and contaminated grain.'

6

These Australian hordes of house-mice, living in the fields, give an almost diagrammatic illustration of the issues that may arise from a large-scale rodent outbreak. We have the crop destruction, and belated efforts at control of the mice; the natural end to the outbreak; the flaring up of not one but several diseases, indicating that the whole parasite fauna and flora tends to increase in concentration with the growing numbers of the host, and suggesting also that a lowered resistance of the host due to the pressure of overcrowding opens the way to a mass invasion from several different parasites; the passage or possible passage of some of these diseases to man; the sigh of relief among politicians when the crisis has passed before any permanent organized study of the problem need be set up; and the recrudescence of the trouble in much the same form a few years afterwards.

Whether the house-mouse is often a carrier of diseases harmful to man is not known; but there have been a fair number of instances in which it was strongly suspected. One was mentioned in Chapter III, the case of a child in an English town who may have contracted food poisoning from mouse contamination. Perhaps when people give up using food-poisoning bacteria for domestic mouse and rat control, the situation will appear more clearly. Perhaps it may be found that the cat's milk is really a small fee to pay for health insurance. The whole question of house-mice in warehouses where food is stored on a large scale also needs more attention than it has received.

We do not quite know why house-mice take to the fields so much more in some regions than in others. On the mainland of Great Britain, wild house-mice (outside the immediate neighbourhood of house and garden) are seldom found. On many islands around the British coast (as in the Outer and Inner Hebrides, the Isle of May, also on some Irish islands) house-mice usually live out in summer, returning in winter to the houses of the crofts. The same is probably true of the Faroes. In parts of the

United States they are often found in the fields, just as in Australia.[56] In the warm region round the Mediterranean, and parts of the East, there are various species of house-mice living quite wild, and this we may take as having been the ancestral habit of our own species, which pushed its way north by hugging the warmth of man's habitations and stealing his food. These occasional excursions out again are worth speculation and further research, especially when they lead to serious outbreaks in the fields, as in Australia, in the Russian districts where it is also a problem, and in the American incident shortly to be described.

Although the authorities in Australia recommend a good many poisoning and trapping methods for the control of outbreaks, opinion there is definitely against the use of disease for biological control. In recent years there has been a strong movement towards the adoption of *mouse-proofing* for buildings and stacks.[1] This protection is made by building the stack of hay on a raised platform known as a 'staddle', and capping the posts that support it with flat galvanized iron plates overhanging a few inches. For existing buildings there are other means of mouse-proofing, as by surrounding the building or stack with a fence of sheet-iron buried at the base. These systems of protection remind one of the old mushroom-shaped staddle-stones which were commonly used in England to keep out rats and mice from stacks and to allow the corn to dry. They are still used in a few places, but mostly have grown obsolete, though they are often seen as garden ornaments. The Australian system of protection is a frank recognition of the difficulty or impossibility of controlling the field outbreaks themselves once they have developed on a large scale. One writer, at least, recognizes the natural fluctuation that takes place: 'Once a plague reaches its maximum intensity, natural control invariably asserts itself. The subsidence of a plague usually begins to take place during the winter and spring, disease, predaceous animals and birds eventually getting control.'

The United States

7

Since about half the species of voles in the whole world live in the United States, we shall not be surprised to find them pullulating and competing at many points with the human beings who have been making such profound encroachments on their environment in recent times. The oscillations of animal populations in unexploited wild country are remarkable enough, as the last two sections of this book will illustrate. Add to them the deep disturbance of conditions brought about by the clearing of forests, draining of marshes, and ploughing of prairie over hundreds of thousands of square miles, and the result will be a new riot of unforeseen oscillations. Shall we then wonder at the urgent search for rodent control which has produced in the United States powerful organizations both of research and of animal destruction? And is it at all astonishing that rodent-destruction measures, needed for the swiftly recurrent crises of farmer, fruit-grower, or forester, should have far outstripped the necessarily patient operations of research ?

The chief agency for dealing with outbreaks of rodents has been for a good many years the U.S. Bureau of Biological Survey, a Federal organization with a very fine tradition, said to have been set up originally to study the control of the alien English sparrow. The Biological Survey, with its combined strength of museum knowledge, field investigation, and organization for animal destruction, is unique in the world, and has provided much of the material for studying rodents in North America. And rodents are only one part of its field of action, which covers the vertebrate kingdom. Equally, it handles much wild-life restoration as well as pest control.

American naturalists have always shown a very strong interest in their mammal fauna, just as the British naturalists have delighted in butterflies and beetles. The growth of the American Society of Mammalogists, and its scientific *Journal of Mammalogy*, have provided a very strong focus for mammal investigations, and a forum for their discussion. We have, therefore, in the United States, on the one hand powerful Federal and State organizations dedicated officially to the study and necessary management of vertebrate animal problems, and on the other hand a constellation of museums, universities, and naturalists who find much of their expression, so far as mammals are concerned, through a central independent society and journal. There is, in consequence, a prolific output of research, a huge literature, and an astronomically great annual bill for rodent (and other mammal) control.

So far as general types of rodents are concerned, there is little broad difference between the United States and the U.S.S.R.—at any rate in the rodents responsible for economic damage and the carrying of disease. There are different species, and sometimes different genera; but there is a very similar range of ecological types. Just as in Russia, two of the chief rodent groups that cause trouble are the ground squirrels and the mice and voles. This is only what we should expect on faunistic grounds, since North America and Eurasia possess a largely common stock of mammals— *Microtus, Pitymys, Clethrionomys, Lagurus, Citellus*, and other important genera being spread around the whole of the northern hemisphere. Where, as with the deer-mouse, *Peromyscus*, the genus differs, the ecological status may be the same (for this is the analogue of the Eurasian wood-mouse, *Apodemus*).

The phenomenon of two great countries facing identical problems with similar weapons of research, yet almost completely out of touch with one another's results and theories, is a very remarkable one, which cannot indefinitely persist. The following brief survey can only give an introduction to the ecological history of American vole and mouse plagues, but it may have value for comparison with the notes already given about the Russian situation.

8

The main taxonomic relations of the genus *Microtus* were settled by Vernon Bailey in 1900.[2] The series of monographs, known as *North American Fauna*, in which his study was published, contains also revisions of other important groups of voles and mice. In 1907, 1908 and 1909 there appeared three surveys of the economic relations of voles, one (the most comprehensive) by Lantz,[31] and the other two by Piper,[39, 40] who had been engaged on a field study of the great Nevada outbreak about that time. These four reports, all coming from the U.S. Bureau of Biological Survey, laid the main foundations for further work of the same sort.

This later work developed along several lines. There is the small army of collectors and taxonomists who have added a great deal to our knowledge of the structure and exact distribution and habits of voles. At the same time there has been a quite spectacular onslaught upon the rodents by Federal and State agencies. To this end has been trained and harnessed a technically formidable force of experts, using especially poisoning methods in their campaigns. These campaigns have at times conflicted with the desire of naturalists that all species should be in some degree preserved. In recent years they have been criticized by some of the ecologists who are making a deeper study of population control, and whose work forms a third line of development which we shall examine.

There is no doubt that in face of rodent outbreaks man felt his supremacy threatened by very formidable competitors, and has taken for granted that his self-appointed god-like status can be completely vindicated only by ruthless war on voles and mice and ground squirrels. We see him thundering, in the spirit of Jeremiah's wrathful God: 'Therefore thus saith the Lord; Behold, I will cast thee off from the face of the earth: this year thou shalt die,.because thou hast taught rebellion against the Lord.' And the rebels are destroyed, and many harmless creatures with them.

We must take note of poisoning and control campaigns generally, as a powerful new biological disturbance. While it is recognized that every body politic has to have some means of resisting invasion, whether it be the reticulo-endothelial system, the police, the army, or the insect and rodent control sections of the agricultural department, yet it were most desirable that this gigantic crow-bar flung into the delicate and complex works of the animal community should receive the serious study which is beginning to be made possible by the technique of modern population research.

9

Several factors converge to make vole and mouse plagues a serious problem in the United States. There are the general disturbances I have mentioned, of human occupation coming into a wild landscape, and of the control measures that inevitably follow. The variety of species is also large, and this means a variety of different habits and aptitudes for taking advantage of the new habitats produced by human settlement. Voles of one kind or another occur in almost every zone of terrestrial life in the country, from the desert edge to forest and almost swamp, and from sea-level to a great height in the mountains: a continent-wide team of specialists, of which one or more is always found ready to adapt itself to the glorious new vistas of food and protection that agriculture and forestry offer. It was the Land of Opportunity for all.

The continental climate that covers much of the country with thick snow in winter is also a vital protective element, just as it is in Europe. Much tree damage happens during the winter period and is only revealed when the snow melts in spring. Some of the American *Microtus* seem to have a much longer breeding season than European ones, and certainly than the British and Scandinavian species; on the other hand, they are eaten by an impressive host of enemies such as Europe no longer preserves. It is not intended that these preliminary remarks should supply any theory about the dynamics of American vole and mouse populations. I am only stating several obvious differences between Europe and America: in the United States there are more species, more different habitats, more recent human interference in these habitats, a richer fauna of predators (because man's occupation is recent), and apparently a higher potential of reproduction in some of the voles.

These broad differences have influenced in several ways the attitude of American workers towards the problem. The multiplicity of species and their ecological reactions has scattered research instead of concentrating it, a diffuseness obviously accentuated by the great distances between research centres. It has also underlined the importance of precise taxonomic studies (subspecies, geographical races) at the expense of field observation. The wide range of species and habitats also accounts partly for the unpleasantly long list of damaged products. The mouse-like rodents attack all kinds of cereals and forage crops, as wheat, oats, barley, rye, buckwheat, maize—the seed in the ground, the struggling blade, the ripe standing crop, and the harvest in shock or barn. They ravage hay meadows and range pasture; garden produce such as carrots and celery and melons; fruit-bushes—by girdling the stems—such as currants, vines, raspberries; and shrubs in field and park and arboretum. They damage thousands of young trees in nurseries and plantations, both hardwoods and conifers of many species. But above all they girdle fruit-trees, especially small new-planted ones, though they also bark completely the lower trunks of fruit-trees over 6 inches in diameter. This orchard damage is perhaps the most conspicuous feature of American vole depredations, because it is not anything like so widespread in Europe, and because the damage is such as to hit the farmers in the eye.

But the aggregate destruction of other crops is also very great, and was well described by Bailey some time ago. He wrote:[2]

'If they would confine themselves to meadows, their chief mischief would be limited to the destruction of a comparatively small amount of grass; but they prefer growing grain to grass, and by running long tunnels under ground, or making little paths under cover of the vegetation, gain easy and safe access to the fields. With a stroke of their chisel-like teeth they fell the stalks of wheat and oats and eat the tender parts, together with some of the grain. It is so easy to cut down the stalks that they destroy many times as much as they need for food. The work of a few animals is insignificant, but the work of millions makes heavy inroads on growing crops. Later in the season, when the grain is cut and left standing in the shocks or stacks, the field mice take possession, building their nests and establishing their homes under its cover. In shocks of corn and wheat left for a long time the grain is often completely devoured, and that remaining all winter in stacks suffers in proportion to the number of the little animals that make their homes in it. Even stacks of hay are often found in spring with the lower parts cut to chaff and filled with the nests of meadow mice . . . in spring, when the snow disappears, trees and shrubs are found stripped of their bark for a wide space near the ground. The marks of tiny teeth remain in the hard wood, and little piles of dry outer bark, mixed with characteristic pellets of excreta, show what animal has been at work. . . . Shrubs and small trees are often stripped of their bark and killed, and sometimes even well-grown apple trees, 10 inches or a foot in diameter, are completely girdled. Usually, however, large trees are only gnawed on one side. In this case, although they are not killed at once, the wood thus exposed usually decays in a few years, the trees become hollow at the base, their productiveness is impaired, and they die prematurely.'

10

There is not much point in tabulating numerous examples of actual outbreaks and the years of their occurrence, since much has been written already in America, and may easily be found in the monographs of Lantz[31] and Hatt.[25] The former gives some information gained from two special inquiries sent out by the U.S. Bureau of Biological Survey, as well as other records. The first inquiry, in 1886, was concerned with damage by mammals to crops, and went to farmers generally. A similar inquiry, but dealing with field-mice, and sent to orchard owners and nurserymen, was made in 1906. From 1,003 questionnaires sent out in this year, there were 520 replies, of which 172 reported serious damage, 175 'some damage', and 175 no serious damage. These answers mostly concerned the year 1906, but they illustrate the practical importance of the problem.

The greatest outbreak among American forage crops that is on record took place in Humboldt Valley, Nevada, in 1907, and we owe to Piper[40] an excellent account of it. The increase began really in the spring of 1906, and bad damage in the winter of 1906–7. By the autumn of 1907 four-fifths of the fields were desolate: alfalfa (lucerne), hay, root crops, and potatoes were all devoured. The direct loss was thought to have reached £60,000. Besides eating up the crops, the voles (*Microtus montanus*) killed shade-trees and even large Lombardy poplars were completely girdled. By the New Year of 1908, the plague had passed: not a surprising end to anyone who has seen the photographs in Piper's reports, which are of ravaged fields scored with the runways of voles: no plants alive, no food, no cover. Some biological features of this outbreak we shall notice later.

Humboldt Valley was the worst patch of a general outbreak that was noted in other parts of Nevada, also in Utah and north-eastern California. There seem to have been similar outbreaks in Humboldt Valley in 1889–92 and 1899–1901, while smaller periods of local abundance were noted in between. Piper[39] recorded his opinion that

'while the Nevada plague is the most serious recorded in the United States, frequent milder outbreaks in many parts of the country indicate that practically all our species of short-tailed field mice periodically tend toward enormous multiplication. . . . Agricultural development, however, distinctly increases the danger of plagues by furthering the destruction of their natural enemies, by furnishing a great abundance of food, and by increasing the area in which they find favorable homes. The reclamation of arid lands affords most suitable conditions in large areas which were formerly uninhabitable.'

The other American 'mouse plague' that has been most written about (by Hall,[18] Piper,[41] and others) took place in Kern County, California, in 1926. Here is a dried-up lake, known as Buena Vista Lake Basin, formerly a reservoir for controlling river floods, but later falling into disuse. In 1925 crops were planted in the centre of the almost dry lake bottom, and by 1926 there were nearly 11,000 acres of kaffir maize and barley, as well as some unplanted ground. The rest was desert or alkali. The lake bed was very quickly colonized by house-mice (*Mus musculus*) and voles (*Microtus californicus*), which multiplied enormously and on 24 November 1926, began the first of three astonishing migrations. There is little doubt that the emigration was the result of the crops being eaten up, so that the mice and voles had no more food or surface cover. Sheep-grazing in the late summer and winter may have accentuated this condition. On 8 to 10 December, and finally on 10 to 12 January 1927, there were further waves of emigration.

Most of the country around the lake is desert with scattered oil-field communities and only a few isolated farming tracts. But most of the latter are more than ten miles away. Inhabitants were astonished at the armies of mice (and a few voles) that invaded their houses and land. The house-mice travelled as far as ten miles, and voles up to five. Hall estimated that there was about one dead mouse to every square yard of road for seventeen miles along the highway north of the lake, and this after rain had washed many more away. For the original centre his estimates of density are astronomical—17 mice to a square yard, or over 80,000 to an acre! No wonder they emigrated. There were other peculiarities of the plague which will be noticed later.

One can instance a number of very serious outbreaks in American orchards, as in the Valley of Virginia, with a loss of over £40,000 in one winter (1918); and comparable losses in Massachusetts in 1919–20, in California in 1920, and in Washington State in 1922.[49] The reports of Silver[49, 50] and Burnett[7] have some good descriptions of this damage. much of which (at any rate in the eastern States) is done by the pine-mouse. *Pitymys*, as well as by *Microtus*. We may recall that *Pitymys* also attacks

Italian orchards. For an example of damage to forest trees, reference may be made to Hatt,[26] who describes the inroads of voles in the Harvard Forest during the winter of 1917–18. Here they nibbled especially young pine-trees. But the literature gives more than forty species of American trees and shrubs that are injured at times seriously.

11

Underneath these major waves of population, with their accompanying calamities, can we detect minor fluctuations, and if so of what regularity and dynamic characters? To tackle this question statistically would require a complete ravishing of the government files, especially in the U.S. Bureau of Biological Survey. For most of the rodent control is done without any published record either of the scale and nature of the outbreak or of the action of control operations. Possibly the information has never been regarded as having a scientific value. Indeed, if we may judge its ecological significance by the monographs that Soviet ecologists have written on similar records of early outbreaks, there are possibly too many difficulties of identification and estimation to make the story good enough for fluctuation analysis. Still, a great deal more could be done to assemble, codify, and map the information that comes to hand each year.

We are left, then, with a few studies made by ecologists, and with the bare dates of some earlier outbreaks, recorded by Lantz and others. It would seem that Lantz[31] understood quite well that many rodent outbreaks are normal fluctuations in the population, for he remarks: 'Among the more interesting facts connected with wild animals are the sweeping changes in the relative numbers of certain species to be noticed from year to year in almost every locality.' And he gives the fluctuation in Norwegian lemmings and in Siberian field-mice in illustration of the point.

It is really interesting, however, to notice the *naïveté* with which such fluctuations were regarded at that time (1906), in contrast to the profound subtlety that modern research upon them is revealing.

'The careful observer, however, sees little mystery in the phenomena mentioned. He has studied the general habits of animals—their food, their powers of reproduction, their migrations, the checks on their increase due to natural enemies, disease and varying climate—and consequently he attributes sudden changes in their numbers to known causes. In such changes he recognizes, especially, the influence of man, both direct and indirect, and his responsibility for interferences that greatly modify the operations of nature.'[31]

Nevertheless, we may accord to Lantz a broad ecological view and insight denied to most of his contemporaries. Piper appears to have shared the same general views, and certainly attributed part of the decline after an outbreak's peak to natural causes, including enemies and disease.

In 1923 A. Brazier Howell[29] further developed the fluctuation theme, with a fine range of examples from his own experience as a collector in the field. He remarks: 'Extensive trapping in many states has convinced me that there is a pronounced fluctuation in the numbers of most, if not all, small mammals.' These are two of his examples. In the region of Yellowstone Park small mammals were unusually abundant in May 1919. In June 1920, although he saw many traces of voles from the previous summer, nearly a thousand trap-nights yielded only a single vole. On Mount Rainier (New York State) the big water-vole (*Microtus richardsoni arvicoloides*) was numerous in 1919; but in 1920, although old traces were abundant enough, Howell caught only 7 voles in over 700 trap-sets. Similar observations were made by Mailliard[33a] in north-eastern California. Here, in the hills at several thousand feet, voles had great abundance in 1922, followed by decrease and scarcity in 1923. An area south of this had, however, abundance in 1923.

Plenty of other information of this kind has now been collected, and it shows the general occurrence of oscillations in North American rodent populations. Some of these would pass unnoticed by the practical farmer or forester, while others rise into the zone of density that causes obvious damage and justifies the name of 'mouse plague'. We may agree with Howell's comment (1923): 'It is astonishing that the question of periodic fluctuations in the numbers of small mammals has been so neglected by mammalogists, when it merits much study.' Let us consider now, how this study has progressed in the United States in the following fifteen years.

By far the most important American contributions to population dynamics of animals have come from Alfred Lotka, working in New York, and Raymond Pearl and his team of associates in Baltimore. But, since the dazzling intellectual empire conquered by Lotka has mostly lain unexplored by rodent ecologists, and Pearl's ideas are also considered by them as speculative, we may leave them with this very inadequate reference.

12

Hamilton did, almost single-handed, a comprehensive study[19-22] of *Microtus pennsylvanicus* populations near Ithaca, in New York State. This work took nearly four years, with, behind it, an earlier field experience of voles since 1924. For about two and a half years he did monthly trapping censuses, and during the whole period examined 4,000 voles. This well-planned assault on the vole-cycle problem was comprehensive and included most of the elements necessary for a general statement of the population dynamics of voles—numbers, movements, reproductive rates, length of life in the field, and causes of mortality. It was not to be expected that all these mysteries would be laid bare by one man in four years. The notable thing was that someone had gone into the matter armed with a clear realization of its nature and with methods of elucidating it. It is all the more unfortunate that many of the essential statistics have been published only in a tabloid form that may satisfy the agricultural administrator's hunger for the knowledge that gives control, but not that of the inquisitive ecologist.

The voles that Hamilton studied lived in orchards, lucerne, and hayfields, and on waste patches overgrown with weeds and grass. Eleven areas were used for census work; they ranged from $\frac{1}{2}$ to 12 acres. The censuses were done with baited break-back traps, and later with live traps, either by trapping out whole blocks in the central part of a patch, or by lines placed in a standard way. The densities calculated from these operations varied from 15 to 250 voles to an acre, and there was a general cycle of population in the whole district, starting with increase through 1932, 1933, 1934, and 1935, and then a strong decrease amounting to a 'crash' in the spring and summer of 1936. We may accept the general evidence for this cycle, and the proof that the range of densities was quite low compared with the huge pullulations of historic outbreaks. But one needs the full statistics for a finer interpretation of the density changes given.

Hamilton caught over 600 voles alive, gave them anaesthetic, cut off one or more toes as a system of identification, and released them to find how far they moved. About a hundred of these voles were recaptured repeatedly, and it was concluded that they wandered little, seldom inhabiting a territory larger than about 150 square yards. Again, we need more detailed figures of trap-spacing and distances of recapture, for there are a good many pitfalls in the interpretation of this kind of experiment, one of the chief being that there is a high chance of recapture before a vole can reach the more distant traps in a network, and so the movements calculated by such a means always tend to be smaller than they might be in natural conditions. If voles lead a life of restricted local movement, the trap censuses are all the more reliable. There is evidence from America, U.S.S.R. and Britain that the vole does not move far.

In Hamilton's census figures the seasonal increase and decrease, superimposed on the general cycle, and the peak followed by decrease are clearly seen. He believes that there is a regular four-year cycle in the vole populations of New York State, and gives the earlier peak years from his field observations as 1919–20, 1923–4, 1927–8, 1931–2. The next came in 1935–6. Another observer gave him similar dates for vole abundance farther west, in Illinois and Indiana: 1923–4, 1927–8, 1931–2, and 1935–6.

The cause of decline in the voles between March and June 1936 was not discovered, though it was proved that some disease was killing them. The theory that the depth of winter snow determines vole abundance was shown to be untrue, since the period of increase in the cycle coincided with several winters in which little snow lay on the ground. The peak winter of 1931–2 had little snow, but that of 1935–6 had plentiful snow. But deep snow may encourage tree damage at times when voles are numerous. Predators were believed to have no essential controlling power over voles; this aspect did not receive much study, although an instance of the *Microtus* diet of short-eared owls is given.

Hamilton also devised a method of trace census, by noting the presence or absence of fresh vole-droppings on small sample areas along a line. Reproductive rates were studied by several indices, and he concluded that the size and frequency of litters and the length of the breeding season all varied from year to year and partly accounted for the cycle of increase and decrease. Here again we are unable to examine the evidence because no detailed figures are published. It seems at any rate established that *Microtus pennsylvanicus* in New York State has a longer breeding season and one which varies much more from year to year than that of the British vole, *agrestis*.

In another respect the two are similar. The weight distribution of these *pennsylvanicus* populations throughout the season suggests that the species has a complete annual turnover of population, few of the large old voles surviving for a second winter. 'The adult mice ostensibly die in the late winter, when less than a year old.'[21] This conclusion seems mainly reliable, although it contains the assumption that old mice do not lose weight to any extent. The same considerations have been shown by Baker and Ranson to apply to the British vole.

13

Some of the practical applications of these discoveries are enumerated by Hamilton[19] in a bulletin for farmers. Among these is forecasting of abundance on the basis of peak cycles—a procedure already recognized in the fur trade, where cycles in wild rodents and their enemies are often very regular and persistent.

'Assuming there will be no deviation from this frequency, we may look for the next high in 1939–40 and every fourth year thereafter. Eternal vigilance and constant warfare should not be relaxed, for local conditions often permit exaggerated populations to appear before the anticipated climax of the cycle. Based on observations outlined in this paper, it was possible to forecast high populations of mice 18 months before their appearance, while the mouse population was far from numerous. Following extensive warnings and suggested field practices $1\frac{1}{2}$ years prior to the outbreak, orchardists were able to safeguard their trees in part from the most severe mouse infestation New York has ever experienced.'

The 'pine-mouse', *Pitymys*, also has cycles. It is really neither a mouse, nor confined to conifer woods, but a vole, closely related to *Microtus*, and most commonly found in deciduous woods, and in orchards. It is greatly attached to an underground life, and this difference in habit is correlated, as Hamilton has pointed out, with a lesser susceptibility to the attacks of predators, and a lower fecundity. He has brought together[23] the evidence about pine-mouse fluctuations, which is scanty but suggests that they are well defined, at any rate in some habitats.

'Like other cyclic rodents, the pine mouse population varies from year to year. In suitable areas, where they find agreeable living conditions, their numbers approach optimum densities with regularity, and apparently coincide, at least in New York, with the *Microtus* [*pennsylvanicus*] cycle. In the winter of 1931–32, both species, but notably *Pitymys* [*pinetorum*], did considerable damage in the lower Hudson Valley, and were reported by orchardists as unusually abundant. I visited the area during the summer of 1932, and while old signs were everywhere, dying trees most evident, and other signs of recent abundance pronounced, there was little evidence of their actual presence.'

By 1935 they were having another peak, with a density in one orchard of 200–300 per acre (mainly *Pitymys*). By 1936 they had crashed once more. But in some of the maple-beech woods in central New York State the numbers fluctuate little. In 1936 there was epidemic mortality among some of the orchard pine-mice.

14

With the rest of the lavish literature on American voles and mice I do not propose to come to very close quarters, since little of it has the coherent planning that characterized Hamilton's approach to the population problem, and since it tells us little about the extent and nature of natural fluctuations. The reproductive potential of *Microtus pennsylvanicus*, and the technique of keeping it as a laboratory animal, have been worked out by Vernon Bailey.[3] Townsend[54] did an elaborate study of the reaction of this and other small mammals to being trapped, a study that provides abundant observations and a huge bibliography, but suffers from a fallacy contained in the estimations of density from sample trapping. Hatfield[24] and Selle[48] have each added to our knowledge of Californian voles, without, however, relating these biological facts to fluctuations. Dice[13] measured some of the habitat limits of prairie voles.

Deer-mice (*Peromyscus*) have been the subject of an enormous amount of research, especially as regards their species and races and their general ecology. Some of this work has covered whole communities of small mammals, including *Microtus* and other genera. Perhaps the studies of Dice, Burt, and their associates at Michigan University are the most sustained and comprehensive. I shall not attempt to relay the abundant literature about *Peromyscus* or on small mammal surveys, and will only draw attention to two interesting essays by Dice[14, 15] on census methods; and to two particularly important recent studies, by Burt[7a] and by Bole.[4a]

Burt made elaborate observations upon the small mammal community in an area of deciduous woodland in Michigan, from 1935 to 1937. By live-trapping, marking and releasing and subsequent recapture, on a large scale, he set out to estimate the movements and territorial limits of individual rodents, and was also able to arrive at some estimates for the actual density. These densities varied, of course, with the species, time, place, and habitat. In the course of the work 1,722 small mammals were marked, of which 1,499 were mouse-like rodents—the rest being flying squirrels, ground squirrels, moles, and shrews. Of the 1,499, 1,382 were one species of deer-mouse, *Peromyscus leucopus noveboracensis*; the rest being another *Peromyscus*, a *Microtus*, a *Pitymys*, a *Synaptomys* (lemming vole), and a *Zapus* (jumping mouse). For the common *Peromyscus*, densities were estimated and these were mostly less than eleven per acre—the higher apparent abundance suggested by previous workers being due to the large range of movement of deer-mice relative to ordinary trapping grids. This study contains a wealth of good technical ideas and is dynamic in its outlook.

The report by Bole reflects the development of modern technical ideas on the problem of taking small mammal censuses. He also chiefly worked in deciduous forest, the beech-maple forest of Ohio, and the field work (including some pioneer studies by other workers) lasted from 1932 to 1939. By completely trapping out areas that were large in relation to the normal movements of mouse-like rodents, he was able to get some substantially accurate measurements of density. He remarks: 'Only once during seven years quadrat work have we found populations greater than 100 per acre for any one species. At Aurora Pond, Ohio, in 1938 *Microtus pennsylvanicus* registered a total of 118 per acre in a rich, wet meadow. This density the writer believes to have been artificial, caused by a flooding of part of the normal habitat through the raising of the pond's water-level.' Of course, we must remember that the piece of land here studied was not such as would be expected to develop a serious vole plague. The following figures give an idea of the *highest* densities per acre ascertained by Bole, for this region:

Shrews	*Sorex fumeus*: 15, in upland forests (once 58).
	Sorex cinereus: 1–11, in old fields and fallows, meadows, swamp forests, &c.
Moles	*Parascalops breweri*: 24; average 7·6 for climax deciduous forest, much lower elsewhere.
	Condylura cristata: 6, in a sedge meadow. (Also abundant in swamp forests.)
Deer-mice	*Peromyscus leucopus*: 46, in beech-maple forest. (Average for all upland forest habitats, 29.)
	Peromyscus maniculatus: 22, on sand beaches and dunes; 4 in other open habitats, average for fallow fields 0 to 1·5.
Voles	*Microtus pennsylvanicus*: 118, in rich meadow. This was exceptionally high. Other peaks for different habitats were: bog forests, 24; bog meadows, 36; fallow fields, 29; wood margin, 12; thorn scrub, 16; flood-plain forest, 16; coastal sand-dunes, 4.
	Pitymys pinetorum: 18, in forest, exceptionally high.
	Synaptomys cooperi: 6, in forest.
Jumping mice	*Zapus hudsonius*: 18, in rich meadow.
	Neozapus insignis: 10, in bog forest.
House-mouse	*Mus musculus*: 4, in sedge meadow.

Bole also noted great fluctuations, though he did not study their causes deeply. He remarks of *Peromyscus*: 'Great cyclical disturbances occur in the deer mouse populations of any Ohio woodland.' *Microtus* had peaks in 1929, 1932, 1935, and 1938. The maximum densities given above therefore represent peak conditions.

15

There are three more subjects that are closely connected with the American mouse-like rodent problem: disease, especially sylvatic plague; predators and their status in agriculturally occupied country; and the large-scale destruction of rodents by poison.

It is well known to epidemiologists that the world is still under the scourge of a great pandemic of plague, bubonic or pneumonic according to the conditions that cause it to break out. The Black Death is one of the most certain and unpleasant ways of dying. After wiping out a large part of the population of Europe in the fourteenth century, it gradually retreated to a few isolated endemic centres, of which one was in inner China. From here, in the eighties of the last century, plague began to creep down to the seaboard, whence it spread by ship rats and their fleas to other parts of the world.

Although international precautions now make many seaports fairly safe from plague, the disease moved inland in a number of places before it could be stopped. In some countries it established itself in wild rodents in an endemic form known as sylvatic plague—a form characterized by a low rate of occurrence in human beings, perhaps chiefly due to a lack of epidemiological contact rather than simply to lower virulence. The chief regions infected with sylvatic plague were thought, until recently, to be Mongolia, Southern Russia, India, South Africa, California, and Argentine. The last four of these centres, at any rate, seem to have been produced by the spread of the pandemic.

In California sylvatic plague was known before 1914. Within the last five years new plague surveys have disclosed its presence in nine other western States (Oregon, Washington, Montana, Idaho, Colorado, Wyoming, Nevada, Utah, and New Mexico); the human cases have, fortunately, been very few. Although the chief reservoirs hitherto disclosed are ground squirrels and their fleas (just as in Russia *Citellus* is the chief carrier), plague has also been found in mouse-like rodents, including the deer-mouse *Peromyscus* and the wood-rat *Neotoma*, or in their fleas. It is not yet actually established, though generally believed, that the sylvatic plague line is spreading eastwards in the United States. But even the present situation requires some knowledge of the part that disease in general, and plague in particular, may play in populations of wild rodents. Research in this direction is being undertaken by the Sylvatic Plague Committee that Dr. Karl Meyer[34] has organized.

The native diseases of American mice and voles have been little studied. Piper[39] reported of the Humboldt valley vole outbreak in the winter of 1907–8: 'At intervals from January to March dead and dying mice were noticed in locations where poisoning could not have been the cause, but efforts to prove this mortality due to some specific bacterial disease failed.' Wayson[55] of the U.S. Public Health Service examined house-mice and voles dying after the Buena Vista emigration in 1926, and found conclusive evidence of an epidemic caused by *Bacillus murisepticus*, which is identical in many ways with *B. rhusiopathiae*—the organism of a disease in pigs known as swine erysipelas. Hamilton's New York voles died of an unknown disease, whose symptoms were described but the cause not ascertained.[22] And now there is plague in wild mice.

The definite entry of voles and mice into the lists of public health control is going to have a vital influence on the methods of control. Hitherto poisoning campaigns have attained local and temporary success by concentrating on valuable agricultural land. What happened on waste lands was of less importance, and owing to their still huge extent, control was often impossible except at a ruinous cost. Even at that it would probably be impossible over enormous areas. But these are some of the areas in which plague rodents flourish. This new situation is likely to make the professional rodent controller stop and scratch his head. It raises in a very challenging way the whole question of rodent population limits and fluctuations, and in particular the part that natural checks such as predatory enemies play.

16

The United States had, and still miraculously has, a majestic fauna of predatory animals and birds. One says 'still has', because there has been for many years a steady pressure on their populations, from farmers and game-preservers (as we are here considering chiefly the enemies of mouse-like rodents, we may ignore the directly dangerous enemies of man). This pressure has long been resisted both by naturalists and by the more far-seeing economic biologists, who contend that predators form an important element in keeping down rodents that otherwise would become a pest. (A parallel argument has been developed by professional game managers: that predators preserve the quality of the stock, by weeding out the weaklings. And there are other subtleties too.) The naturalists and conservationists want species preserved, for science and for our pleasure and because utter destruction is sinful. In this way predators become in turn the prey of politicians.

The chief animals that eat voles and mice form an imposing gallery, a fauna that the Briton, even in Neolithic times, would find astonishingly rich. Wolves, lynxes, foxes, badgers, raccoons, opossums, skunks, weasels, mink, and shrews; dogs and domestic cats; hawks, buzzards, owls, shrikes, cuckoos, crows, herons, bitterns, storks, ibises, gulls; and snakes.

Within most of these names are a number of species. Some are more murivorous than others. The skunk counts voles and mice its second most important food. For weasels they may be the first. Ecologists are beginning to measure the populations of some of these species, and relate them to rodent fluctuations. Until that is thoroughly done, the political future of the skunk and buzzard and rattlesnake will hang undesirably upon opinion, and often on heated opinion. There is another important issue connected with predators that one can only touch on. That is the fur trade. The skunk, for instance, is one of the chief fur-bearing animals of California,[17] as are the fox and mink in more northern States. In the five years 1920–4 42,460 striped skunks' skins, with a value of over £22,000, were traded for fur in California. So the mouse carries quite a big responsibility, if it carries plague, supports a fur-bearing animal (that both robs the poultry-roost, partly prevents catastrophic mouse increase, and is beautiful to watch), and also damages orchards and grain-fields.

The predator problem leads on to the general question of controlling rodents. Such control includes not only large and small outbreaks, but any rodent population that threatens damage to crops or trees, and which can be destroyed at a reasonable cost. As Thoreau[53] has said, the farmer 'knows Nature only as a robber'. The logical aim of these operations, happily prevented by practical difficulties, is the complete extermination of nearly all rodent species. One reason why even very efficiently organized destruction of rodents does not extinguish them is really the same reason that a predatory animal does not usually wipe out its prey: when rodents become very scarce, pursuit is no longer worth the expenditure of energy needed to make a kill. Another reason is that there are an infinite number of reserve areas from which repopulation can take place. So one effect of human control of rodents is to create something of a cycle in numbers. We suggested this phenomenon also in German vole control.

Rodent control in the ecological community has some resemblance to the control of disease in the human community. You may attempt prevention of the outbreak in various ways: burn or cut down protective cover, encourage predators, place protective or repellent barriers between the rodents and your crops or trees, or in other ways make multiplication difficult. Secondly, you may destroy the pest itself, by administering to the diseased body a poison (as quinine) that kills the invader without killing the community—in the case of rodents mainly by the use of poisons, of which strychnine mixed with maize or wheat is the most effective; or in other ways destroy the pest by trapping, hunting, or flooding. Then there are, thirdly, certain cures for the damage done, of which bridge-grafting for large fruit-trees is one of the most striking American practices. This method consists in placing twigs as bridges between the two cut ends of bark on the trunk, to make new temporary channels for the flow of sap.

The scale of poisoning campaigns against rodents nowadays in the United States will be gathered from the fact that the U.S. Biological Survey's poison-bait station at Pocatello in Idaho, in the year 1935–6 distributed nearly 900 tons of poison bait, which went to every State in the country except three.[46] In the year 1937–8[47] the Survey supervised rodent destruction on over 29 million acres of land. It is not surprising that there have been violent controversies about the effects of all this poisoning upon wild animals other than injurious rodents. Through this relationship the influence of vole and mouse fluctuations, already vastly complex, is still further felt by other members of the animal community they live among. We can discern, in this constant warfare of man on mouse, a disturbance of many thousand already delicate relationships. The point is not so much that the disturbance can be avoided, as that we should do our best to find out the effects of it. The more steady and unfluctuating the disturbance, the more easy it would be to study the results.

9

Canada

17

In the majestic zones of life that divide up the several million square miles of Canada there is much resemblance to the broad ecology of Russia and Siberia, except that semi-desert and desert are lacking. There is the same sequence of high Arctic, desolate barren lands merging into forests of larch and spruce and pine, the southern hardwood forests, the wooded steppe (here called grove belt), and the bare steppe (here called prairie). On the Rocky Mountains these zones again follow one another, but with many special peculiarities, from the arid plains and foot-hills of southern British Columbia and Alberta, up to alpine peaks and snowfields.

We see, as in U.S.S.R., voles and mice in two opposite rôles: pests of cultivation and one of the chief supports of fur-trade. In the grain-fields of the prairie and grove belt and on the cultivated land that now stands on the cleared sites of former forest, they are chiefly pests, though supporting at the same time a crop of fur in fox and coyote and skunk and weasel, which forms at times an important supplement to the farmer's resources. Farther north they support a large part of the fur-trade, but nevertheless commit quite serious ravages in the gardens and stores of remote fur posts.

In both main economic regions of Canada small mammals fluctuate remarkably, causing on the one hand a periodic intensification of agricultural and orchard damage, and on the other hand a cycle in the supply of fur. Since Parts III and IV of this book are concerned with these fur cycles in north-eastern Canada, I shall chiefly mention here the influence of voles and mice as pests in the settled part of the country. As a bridge between these two aspects of a single ecological phenomenon, we may take the experiences of some of the early settlers in the Maritime Provinces of eastern Canada.

Patterson[38] tells us that Nova Scotia and Prince Edward Island were periodically ravaged by field-mice in these early days of settlement. Dièreville, a Frenchman who wrote in 1699, made this record: 'The Island of St. John [Prince Edward Island] is stated to be visited every seven years by swarms of locusts or field mice alternately—never together. After they ravage the land, they precipitate themselves into the sea.' Later writers (with less spirited imagination) mention other plagues of mice on the island. A serious one in 1775 nearly caused some new Scottish settlers at Georgetown to starve because all the crops were eaten up by mice. They were only saved by the help of a French colony some distance away.

One of the greatest outbreaks came in 1815 in Nova Scotia, where it was long remembered as 'the year of the mice'. The following description of it was collected later on in the nineteenth century by the Rev. Hugh Graham from old inhabitants, and handed on by him to Patterson. On a coastal strip some eighty miles in length and forty miles in depth (upwards of 3,000 square miles) meadow-mice began to increase greatly. The whole of Antigonish, Pictou, and Colchester counties, and part of Cumberland

County to the north-west, as well as parts of Guysborough and Halifax to
the south, were affected by the outbreak. This was in the summer of 1814.
All along here was primeval forest country with settlements only along the
coast and up some of the rivers. At the end of the winter of 1814–15 the
mice seem to have invaded the clearings. At any rate they became very
numerous and by midsummer 1815 had destroyed great quantities of hay
and grain. Cats and dogs, martens and foxes gorged themselves on mice,
and some cats became feral and multiplied in the woods and fields.

The plague passed quite suddenly. Towards autumn the mice became
languid and were noticed crawling slowly about. They died in hundreds.
There was some evidence that they swam out to sea and into lakes. By
1816 there was hardly a mouse to be seen in the whole region, except just
in one spot which had been first cleared and settled in the 'year of mice'.
Here the voles continued to be a scourge for several years.

Many parts of Nova Scotia and New Brunswick are still not unequally
balanced between wild country and settlement, and mouse abundance
shows very clearly here its double rôle. Rand[44] gives an excellent ecological
impression of the interior of western Nova Scotia at the present time and
remarks:

'Mammals play an important role in the lives of the settlers in the region.
Fur is an important source of income, and moose and deer are used for food.
Their depredations are few. Bears sometimes kill sheep, and mink and fox raid
chicken yards. Woodchucks, porcupines, rabbits and deer appear in the gardens,
but when all this is balanced against the value of the fur catch, the mammalian
fauna well repays its debt from an economic standpoint. . . . Some mammals
are moving in. Skunks and raccoons are probably recent additions to the fauna.'

Rand also experienced the fluctuations of voles (*Microtus pennsylvanicus*).

'The meadow mouse must be very common in certain years. In damp
pastures, in sphagnum-sedge bogs, and bluejoint-maple-alder associations, old
runs and droppings and grass stalks cut into short lengths were very common
[1928] but a line of several dozen traps would bring in perhaps one or two
individuals. In examining the runs for places to set the traps, fresh signs were
rarely found. This decrease in the number of meadow mice must have an
important effect on the carnivores that prey upon them and must undoubtedly
influence their abundance. In one grassy swamp they were fairly common if not
abundant. . . .'

This was in 1928. 'In 1931 these mice were fairly common along the edges
of the bogs but few were found in the grassy swamps where they had been
common in 1928.' Certain other voles and mice that were previously
scarce had also increased by 1931.

That such fluctuations in wild voles and mice are a normal feature of
the southern parts of the Canadian forest zone could be proved by a great
many examples, of which it is sufficient to give only one. In the years
1921–4 Dymond, Snyder, and Logier[16] did a faunal survey in the region of
Lake Nipigon, Ontario. They observed that the deer-mouse (*Peromyscus
maniculatus*) was extremely numerous in the summer of 1921, then very

scarce in 1922, and again more common in 1923 and 1924. They wrote:
'It is believed that other species of small rodents suffered a reduction in
numbers at the same time, for meadow mice, red-backed voles and mole
shrews were also noticeably scarce during the early part of the summer of
1922. . . . May it not be that the white-footed mouse plays a similar rôle
in the northern coniferous forests of Canada, to that played in the more
northerly regions of Europe and America by the lemmings and voles ?'

18

Canada has no such highly organized system for dealing with voles and
mice as the United States and Russia, though the magnitude of the economic problems raised by them is considerable, even apart from the
fur-trade. So we have to depend for our view of the situation upon the
occasional surveys of naturalists and upon one or two inquiries organized
in recent years. Much of the literature on small rodents is contained in the
Canadian Field-Naturalist, the contributions of the Royal Ontario Museum
of Zoology, and in the *Journal of Mammalogy*. In 1928 the National Parks
Branch of the Canadian Government organized, at my request, a questionnaire inquiry about wild mice, which went to many observers in all parts
of Canada. The launching of this inquiry was made possible by the co-
operation of Mr. J. B. Harkin (then Commissioner of the National Parks)
and of Mr. Hoyes Lloyd, who supervised it. This material, which exists in
duplicate at Ottawa and Oxford, they have generously allowed me to draw
upon for the present book.

Also at Oxford there is a very large body of information obtained from
Hudson's Bay Company posts since 1925. This material has not yet been
analysed completely, and since it comes chiefly from the northern forest
and Arctic posts, and is used in the last part of this book, I shall not touch
it here.

Preble,[42] the American naturalist whose biological surveys of Canada still
outshine anything that has been attempted since, collected notes about the
fluctuations of *Microtus drummondi*, the commonest vole in the Middle West.
In 1894 it was very numerous in the oat-fields near Edmonton, Alberta.
'During the autumn of 1900 great numbers of mice, probably mainly of this
species, overran central Saskatchewan and central Alberta.' They also multiplied in some parts of Manitoba, and all over the Middle West a great deal
of grain was devoured by them, both in fields and storehouses. 'Immense
numbers, many of which were floating down the river, were found dead.'

The National Parks inquiry adds a note, from Henderson[27] of Belvidere,
Alberta. In the summer and autumn of 1900 'the country was simply alive
with them. Most of them died during the winter. . . . They were lying dead
in heaps in their nests in the spring of 1901.' During this spring Preble
made a collecting trip in the country north of Edmonton, and found many
signs of previous abundance, but hardly any fresh traces or living voles.
These and other more recent records prove that voles are a serious pest on
the cultivated land of central Canada, especially in grain-fields.

Todd,[52] an Inspector of Fisheries, wrote from Edmonton in 1928:

'During summers of 1926 and 1927 when driving through the country at night I used to notice a great number of mice running across the roads: these would show up in the head-lights of the car. Since the first of October this season I drove some four thousand miles through the country, and I don't think I have seen more than a half dozen mice in all that time.'

'As you are no doubt aware, there was a great lot of grain in Alberta that was not thrashed during the fall of 1927 and was thrashed in the spring of 1928. This grain, some 12,000,000 bushels, stood in the stook all winter. I made a trip through the southern part of the province early in the spring when this grain was being thrashed and in conversation with many farmers, in the Pincher Creek and High River Districts, regarding the condition and quality of the grain as compared with that thrashed in the fall of 1927, at least 90 per cent. of the farmers stated that the mice were very numerous and were very destructive. The estimate of loss of grain through mice getting into the stooks ranged from eight to ten bushels per acre. This would indicate the mice were most abundant during the fall and winter of 1927–28, and my personal observations when driving at night would indicate that the mice were plentiful during the summers of 1926 and 1927 but for some reason either died off during the spring or summer of 1928.'

Proctor[43] of Woodlands, Manitoba, also records fluctuations:

'Meadow mice apparently, had reached their maximum numbers, in the autumn of 1927: since that time fully ninety per cent. have disappeared. These creatures appear to wax and wane in numbers, very much as do the rabbits. . . . In the harvesting in the autumn of 1927, it was common to see from one to six mice at a stook of grain, while in the autumn of 1928 the average would be from one to two mice per half dozen stooks.'

Voles also attack trees in Canada, both orchard trees and young nursery stock. Much of this is done by *Microtus*; but Stuart Criddle[11] found at Aweme in Manitoba that red-backed voles (*Clethrionomys*) were injuring trees in 1922–3 and 1929. Extensive girdling of orchard trees by 'mice' is also reported from Quebec, Ontario, the Maritime Provinces, and British Columbia.

With the vole increase there is a noticeable local increase of predators, part influx and part reproductive. Stuart Criddle[10] saw an increase of the least weasel (*Mustela rixosa*) at Aweme in 1922, which was the result of abundance of *Microtus drummondi*. One curious result was that the weasels wiped out completely some colonies of a much rarer vole, *Microtus minor*, during the winter following the peak in the other voles. One wonders whether subsidized exploitation of this type may not be an important element in animal communities. It resembles somewhat that of domestic cats, well provided for by man, and often suppressing by their powerful battalions wild rodent populations that would otherwise live in a more simple moving equilibrium with them.

In the same country Norman and Stuart Criddle[9] noticed a big increase in Bonaparte's weasel (*Mustela cicognanii*) during a severe outbreak of voles in 1916–17. When the voles decreased, the weasels also became rare. The same sort of thing takes place among birds of prey. Randall[45] saw a great increase in short-eared owls (*Asio flammeus*) at Castor, in southern Alberta in 1925. This was a big year of voles. In previous years the owls had laid clutches of not more than six eggs, but this year Randall found seven nests with nine eggs each. This high rate of reproduction in the short-eared owl has often been noticed in other countries during years of vole and mouse abundance. It is one of the best authenticated examples of the direct effect of food upon reproductive rates, a phenomenon which is by no means as common as would be supposed.

In British Columbia voles also fluctuate and cause much damage to cultivation. The statement of Allan Brooks,[6] in answer to the National Parks inquiry, gives an excellent view of the situation there:

'Voles or meadow mice of several species were at the peak of their abundance this year [1928] and last. These cycles of abundance and scarcity are of fairly regular rotation, as I have noted since 1881, and are not caused or influenced by any killing off of predators. . . . 1927 was a year of heavy rainfall and luxuriant growth in the Interior of British Columbia. The following winter was one with deep snow. Conditions were exactly right and the time ripe for the peak of the cycle which ensued. . . . I can remember, and have records of exactly the same conditions of food supply and snowfall in 1896–97–98 at Vernon, B.C. The voles in 1896 were so abundant that I could collect all the Drummond's voles or dwarf voles that I wanted with my hands in broad daylight. Disease followed and there was a long period of extreme scarcity of voles. . . .'

Of the period of crash generally he adds: 'The mammals could be picked up dead in their nests below logs, underground and beneath snowbanks in the following spring.'

19

We get a general impression that voles fluctuate naturally in many parts of Canada, sharing a part of their periodically swelling biomass with various enemies that prey on them. I suppose their economic relation to man could ultimately be expressed in the gain or loss of heat from human and animal bodies. For when voles damage crops they remove some of the food that keeps up the body heat of men or domestic animals. When they become the origin of fur, they help men to keep in the heat that is being lost (here we ignore cattle, which do not commonly wear fur coats). Looked at from this point of view the small rodents of northern Canada are busy remedying the heat losses caused by those in the cultivated south!

We know very little about the periodicity and nature of vole fluctuations in Canada, and little census work has yet been undertaken, even less pathological or reproduction research. There are some important investigations going on in Toronto University, which promise a future understanding of mouse population dynamics. There are a few hints about mortalities in voles and mice. From Victoria on Vancouver Island there is an interesting observation[8] upon the ticks that sometimes infest voles—for instance, an individual dying with eighty ticks upon it. There are a good many affidavits of large mortality with voles seen lying dead. These all speak for an important rôle of disease.

The rather recent spread of the house-mouse (*Mus musculus*) into the interior of Canada possibly constitutes an additional danger to cultivation. Stirling,[51] of Bright Bank, Alberta, wrote in 1928:

'The whole of the Edmonton district is now badly infested with the common house mouse (imported). They are as far West as the Pembina River at Entwhistle and were even seen 11 miles up the river on a wilderness farm. I have not done farm work further west so cannot tell how far west to the Rockies they are. They first appeared in the Stony Plain district about 1911. . . . Presumably the railways, which built into the Stony Plain just previous to that date, brought them in. I have observed them under grain stooks half a mile from any building.'

Stuart Criddle[10a] also states that the house-mouse is abundant in the fields in summer at Aweme in Manitoba.

After what is no more than a sketch of Canadian vole and mouse affairs, we take the first boat to Glasgow and thence proceed to the sheep hills of the Scottish Border, whose two historic vole plagues serve as an approach to vole fluctuations in western Europe.

REFERENCES

C.N.P.B. refers to the questionnaire inquiry about mice sent out by the Canadian National Parks Branch in 1928. The letter-numbers indicate the particular reply filed with the National Parks Branch (now Bureau) in Ottawa, and the Bureau of Animal Population in Oxford.

1. ANON. (1932). 'Damage by field mice and measures to prevent it.' Agric. Gazette of New South Wales, 1 June 1932. (Other notes by various writers in the same journal, 1 Sept. 1927, 1 Aug. 1932, 1 Oct. 1932, 1 Dec. 1933.)
2. BAILEY, V. (1900). 'Revision of American voles of the genus *Microtus*.' N. Amer. Fauna, No. 17: 1–79.
3. BAILEY, V. (1924). 'Breeding, feeding, and other life habits of meadow mice (*Microtus*).' J. Agric. Res. 27: 523–35.
4. BODENHEIMER, F. S. (1935). 'Animal life in Palestine. . . .' Jerusalem. (1) Ch. 2. (2) pp. 95–105.
4 a. BOLE, B. P. (1939). 'The quadrat method of studying small mammal populations.' Sci. Publ. Cleveland Mus. Nat. Hist. 5, No. 4: 15–77.
5. BODENHEIMER, F. S., & KLEIN, H. Z. (1928). 'Field mice control in Palestine.' Zionist Executive Agric. Exp. Sta. and Colonis. Dept. Extension Divn. Circular, 17:1–12. Tel-Aviv. (In Hebrew, summary in English.)
6. BROOKS, A. (1928). C.N.P.B. (B.C. 5).
7. BURNETT, W. L. (1916). 'Meadow mice (*Microtus*).' Colorado State Entomologist, Circular 18: 1–11.
7 a. BURT, W. H. (1940). 'Territorial behaviour and populations of some small mammals in southern Michigan.' Misc. Publ. Mus. Zool. Univ. Michigan, No. 45: 1–58.
8. BURTON, W. F. (1928). C.N.P.B. (B.C. 53).
9. CRIDDLE, N., & CRIDDLE, S. (1925). 'The weasels of southern Manitoba.' Canad. Field-Nat. 39: 142–8.
10. CRIDDLE, S. (1926). 'The habits of *Microtus minor* in Manitoba.' J. Mammal. 7: 193–200. (And personal information.)

10 a. CRIDDLE, S. (1929). 'An annotated list of the mammals of Aweme, Manitoba.' Canad. Field-Nat. 43: 155–9.

11. CRIDDLE, S. (1932). 'The red-backed vole (*Clethrionomys gapperi loringi* Bailey) in Southern Manitoba.' Canad. Field-Nat. 46: 178–81.

12. DARNELL-SMITH, G. P. (1918). 'A fungus disease of mice.' Agric. Gaz. N. S. Wales, 29: 131–2. (Cited by Hinton, Ref. 28.)

13. DICE, L. R. (1922). 'Some factors affecting the distribution of the prairie vole, forest deer mouse, and prairie deer mouse.' Ecology, 3: 29–47.

14. DICE, L. R. (1931). 'Methods of indicating the abundance of mammals.' J. Mammal. 12: 376–81.

15. DICE, L. R. (1938). 'Some census methods for mammals.' J. Wildlife Management, 2: 119–30.

16. DYMOND, J. R., SNYDER, L. L., & LOGIER, E. B. S. (1928). 'A faunal investigation of the Lake Nipigon region, Ontario.' Contr. R. Ontario Mus. Zool. No. 1, in Trans. Roy. Canad. Inst. 16: 233–91.

17. GRINNELL, J., DIXON, J. S., & LINSDALE, J. M. (1937). 'Fur-bearing animals of California. . . .' Berkeley, vol. 1, pp. 11–13.

18. HALL, E. RAYMOND (1927). 'An outbreak of house mice in Kern County, California.' Univ. California Publ. Zool. 30: 189–203.

19. HAMILTON, W. J. (1935). 'Field-mouse and rabbit control in New York orchards.' Cornell Extension Bull. 338: 1–24.

20. HAMILTON, W. J. (1937). 'Activity and home range of the field mouse, *Microtus pennsylvanicus pennsylvanicus* (Ord.).' Ecology, 18: 255–63.

21. HAMILTON, W. J. (1937). 'Growth and life span of the field mouse.' Amer. Nat. 71: 500–7.

22. HAMILTON, W. J. (1937). 'The biology of Microtine cycles.' J. Agric. Res. 54: 779–90.

23. HAMILTON, W. J. (1938). 'Life history notes on the Northern pine mouse.' J. Mammal. 19: 163–70.

24. HATFIELD, D. M. (1935). 'A natural history study of *Microtus californicus*.' J. Mammal. 16: 261–71.

25. HATT, R. T. (1930). 'The biology of the voles of New York.' Roosevelt Wild Life Bull. 5, No. 4: 513–623.

26. HATT, R. T. (1930). 'The relation of mammals to the Harvard Forest.' Roosevelt Wild Life Bull. 5, No. 4: 625–71.

27. HENDERSON, A. D. (1928). C.N.P.B. (A. 185).

28. HINTON, M. A. C. (1931). 'Rats and mice as enemies of mankind.' British Museum (Nat. Hist.), Econ. Ser. No. 8: 46.

29. HOWELL, A. BRAZIER (1923). 'Periodic fluctuations in the numbers of small mammals.' J. Mammal. 4: 149–55.

30. JAFFÉ, R. (1931). 'Anatomie und Pathologie der Spontanerkrankungen der kleinen Laboratoriumstiere.' Berlin. p. 627.

31. LANTZ, D. E. (1907). 'An economic study of field mice (genus *Microtus*).' U.S. Dep. Agric. Biol. Surv. Bull. 31: 1–64.

32. LONGMAN, H. A. (1916). 'Notes on classification of common rodents.' Australian Quarantine Service, Service Publ. No. 8. Melbourne.

33. MCCARTHY, T. (1922). 'A note on mouse plagues.' Agric. Gazette of New South Wales, 1 Sept. 1922.

33 a. MAILLIARD, J. (1925). 'Notes upon the numerical status of rodent populations in parts of California.' J. Mammal. 6: 102–5.

34. MEYER, K. F. (1938). 'Sylvatic plague.' Amer. J. Publ. Health, 28: 1153–64.

35. MURNANE, D. (1934). 'Mouse plague investigations.' J. Council Sci. Industr. Res. 7: 45–9. (And personal information.)

36. OSBORNE, W. A. in ANON. (1932). 'Mice plague in Australia.' Nature, Lond. 129: 755.

37. PARISH, H. J., & CRADDOCK, S. (1931). 'A ringworm epizootic in mice.' Brit. J. Exp. Path. 12: 209–12.
38. PATTERSON, G. (1886). '"The plague of mice" in Nova Scotia and Prince Edward Island.' Canadian Record of Science, 2: 472–80.
39. PIPER, S. E. (1908). 'Mouse plagues, their control and prevention.' Yearbook U.S. Dep. Agric. for 1908: 301–10.
40. PIPER, S. E. (1909). 'The Nevada mouse plague of 1907–8.' U.S. Dep. Agric. Farmers' Bull. 352: 1–23.
41. PIPER, S. E. (1928). 'The mouse infestation of Buena Vista Lake Basin, Kern County, California, September, 1926, to February, 1927.' Mon. Bull. Dep. Agric. State of California, 17, No. 10: 538–60.
42. PREBLE, E. A. (1908). 'A biological investigation of the Athabaska-Mackenzie region.' N. Amer. Fauna, No. 27: 186–8.
43. PROCTOR, J. (1928). C.N.P.B. (M. 254).
44. RAND, A. L. (1933). 'Notes on the mammals of the interior of Western Nova Scotia.' Canad. Field-Nat. 47: 41–50.
45. RANDALL, T. E. (1925). 'Abnormally large clutches of eggs of short-eared owl (Asio flammeus).' Canad. Field-Nat. 39: 194 (and personal information).
46. Report of the Chief of the U.S. Bureau of Biological Survey, 1937. p. 67. Washington.
47. Report of the Chief of the U.S. Bureau of Biological Survey, 1938. p. 62. Washington.
47 a. ST. LEGER, J. (1931). 'A key to the families and genera of African Rodentia.' Proc. Zool. Soc. Lond.: 957–97. (pp. 975, 991.)
48. SELLE, R. M. (1928). 'Microtus californicus in captivity.' J. Mammal. 9: 93–8.
49. SILVER, J. (1924). 'Mouse control in field and orchard.' U.S. Dep. Agric. Farmers' Bull. 1397: 1–14.
50. SILVER, J. (1924). 'Rodent enemies of fruit and shade trees.' J. Mammal. 5: 165–73.
51. STIRLING, H. L. (1928). C.N.P.B. (A. 188).
52. TODD, T. R. (1928). C.N.P.B. (A. 199).
53. THOREAU, H. D. (1854). 'Walden or life in the woods.' Everyman ed. London, 1927, p. 145.
54. TOWNSEND, M. T. (1935). 'Studies on some of the small mammals of central New York.' Roosevelt Wild Life Annals, 4, No. 1: 1–120.
55. WAYSON, N. E. (1927). 'An epizootic among meadow mice in California, caused by the bacillus of mouse septicemia or of swine erysipelas.' U.S. Public Health Rep. 42, No. 22: 1489–93.
56. WOOD, F. E. (1910). 'A study of the mammals of Champaign County, Illinois.' State Lab. Nat. Hist. 8, Art. 5: 501–613.

PART II

FLUCTUATIONS IN NORTH-WEST EUROPE

CHAPTER VII

THE SCOTTISH HILLS: VOLES AND SHEEP

'The outlook is darker than it has ever been in the history of sheep farming in Scotland, at least as regards the wide area over which the plague extends. It is not too much to say that unless a remedy is found, ruin is staring in the face not a few of the pastoral farmers in the Southern Highlands of Scotland.' (Leading article in *The Scotsman*, 11 April 1892.)

'The President of the Board of Agriculture replied that . . . he was afraid the plague was mainly due to climatic and natural causes, and that it was only to natural causes that they could look for its disappearance.' (Speech in House of Commons, 7 April 1892; reported in *The Hawick Advertiser*, 8 April 1892.)

1

THE hills of which Scotland is formed mostly look wild and bare, but are nearly all exploited for one or other of four human occupations: raising sheep, stalking deer, shooting grouse, or growing trees. All these occupations have interesting ecological distributions and there are often strong tensions between them. On the grassy moors there can be deer or sheep, but not both. The heather moors provide the best grouse land. The forests can grow on various kinds of land, but not above a certain height (conventionally about 1,200 feet) and not if sheep are allowed to graze. New plantations become the refuge of deer, especially roe-deer, and these may themselves menace the young trees.

The interplay of these forces is important for vole populations, especially where sheep or forestry are the dominant element. For sheep, by grazing, create conditions of vegetation that are unfavourable for vole increase. They prevent the growth of thick grass cover, and they also trample the ground with their delicate sharp hoofs. This condition is reinforced by the burning that hill farmers do to clear away old grass. Forest planting brings about exactly the opposite conditions: the grass, no longer grazed or burned, springs up luxuriantly and encourages the increase of voles, by giving them shelter and food. It is all the more remarkable that there have been, within the last seventy years, two enormous outbreaks of voles on the sheep hills of Scotland. These outbreaks are so well documented that I am devoting the present chapter to them, leaving to the following two chapters the consideration of vole fluctuations on forest-planted land.

The biggest sheep populations are kept on what geographers call the Southern Uplands of Scotland, that is, the massive rolling hills that raise their barrier between the valleys of Forth and Clyde in the north and the Border of Scotland and England (with the Cheviots) in the south. The southern third or half of these hills (the definition is a little vague) forms the Scottish Border of history and romance.

The part of these uplands with which we shall be particularly engrossed lies in the centre, in the counties of Dumfries-shire, Roxburghshire, Selkirk-shire, and a little in Kirkcudbrightshire, Peebles-shire, and Lanarkshire. This central region has the Galloway Hills to the west, the Pentland Hills and Lammermuir to the north, and the Cheviots (in England) to the south-east. A fan of smaller rivers (Teviot, Ettrick, and Yarrow) runs into the Tweed, the whole system draining the north-eastern slopes. The Clyde flows to the north-west, and a series of separate rivers (Liddel, Esk, Annan, and Nith) southwards into Solway Firth. It was chiefly upon the central watersheds of these rivers that the vole outbreaks happened. Here the hills run up to between two and three thousand feet: the voles abounded up to the highest tops.

It is a country of smooth contours, though often with steep-sided hills, a core of old rocks rising out of the surrounding cover of glacial drift. Although the lower country and valleys have a varied and rich agriculture and woodland, and some industrial towns, the higher land is almost entirely dedicated to sheep. Much of the hill land is peat-covered, often to a depth of several feet, and grown with grass and rush and heather. The traveller who crosses this range of hills on his way from Carlisle to Glasgow or Edinburgh sees mostly green hill land in the early summer, turning with the withering of the grass and rushes to a silvery brown from late summer to spring. Everywhere he sees sheep, mostly of the white-faced Cheviot breed. Each sheep needs from 2 to 4 acres of land to support it through the winter—a great deal less than a red deer requires.

2

In medieval times these hills were mostly covered with forest, in which the Scottish kings and nobles hunted the red deer and the roe-deer. The forest gradually disappeared, it is supposed through cutting for timber and clearing for sheep-raising and other purposes. But in the sixteenth century remnants of great forests still survived on Ettrick (in Selkirkshire) and on the Pentland Hills. Of Ettrick Forest the chronicles record[31] that in the sixteenth century James V 'showed a disposition to change the forest into what it now is (1833),—a sheep-walk, by stocking a part of it with exten-sive flocks'. James V is said[27] to have had ' 10,000 sheep going in the forest under the keeping of Andrew Bell, who made the king as good an account of them as if they had gone in the bounds of Fife'. At the same time the king still hunted often in the forest. The chronicler of the adjoining parish of Yarrow wrote[27] in the same year: 'The woodlands of this district were formerly inhabited by various animals that have disappeared; as the urus, the stag, and another species of deer. The wolf, the mountain-boar, and the wild cat, were common in early times. We learn from the old song that Ettrick abounded with "the hart, the hynd, the doe, the roe, and of a' beasts great plentie;" and hence it was long reserved for the royal chace.' Of the parish of Moffat (containing some of the high hills of Dumfries-shire), there is a record[17] for 1834: 'In former times, the *hart* and *hind* were

found in this parish; the last hart was killed in 1754, having been long
single. The *roebuck* and the *doe* were also natives, but have long since disappeared. . . . The sheep stocks are large and excellent. . . .' The highest
hill near Moffat is still called Hart Fell. The same chronicler[17] says elsewhere: 'Of *natural woods* in a parish that was, at one period, richly wooded,
there are now very scanty remains at Craigieburn, and in a few other
places.'

In these early days the Cheviots also had not yet been turned into the
great sheep-walks that they are now. In the reign of Henry VIII they still
kept some of the character familiar in the old ballad of 'Chevy Chace', as
Leyland recorded:[24] 'In Northumberland, as I heare say, be no forests,
except Chivet Hills; where is much brushe-wood, and some okke; grownde
ovargrowne with linge, and some with mosse. . . . There is greate plenté of
redde-dere, and roo bukkes.'

By the end of the seventeenth century these uplands had been almost
completely transformed into sheep-walks. The forests had dwindled away,
and the red deer and roe-deer disappeared soon after.[26] Towards the latter
half of the eighteenth century there was a strong revival of forest planting
by the great landowners, as a result of which the lower land became much
better wooded. By the middle of the nineteenth century the roe-deer had
begun to drift back into these woods, but the red deer is still absent. In
the last twenty years the State has begun to cover parts of the higher hills
as well, and in doing so, to drive out sheep-farming again. But there has
not yet been enough planting to alter appreciably the general appearance
of the hills. The greater impact of forestry has been along the English side
of the Border, and in the north and west Highlands. The cycle is not yet
complete.

These remarks are made in order to set in a broad historical frame the
events that will be described in the rest of the chapter. Here was a range
of wooded hills devoted to hunting deer, or else wilderness, converted
within the last four hundred years into a huge sheep-ranch. Two hundred
years ago a slight recovery of the woodland had begun, and it is now proceeding with much greater speed, owing to the intervention of the State.
But the higher hills are still predominantly grazed by sheep, to form an
industry that also greatly influences the agricultural mosaic at lower levels.

3

Most of the green carpet of vegetation that sheep-ranching has brought
to these hills is potentially a habitat for voles, which eat much the same
species of plants that the sheep graze upon. James Smith, minister of the
parish of Ettrick, whose notes on the parish in 1833 have already been
referred to, wrote[31] an excellent description of this vegetation carpet,
which I have only edited by adding, where necessary, the modern names
of the species. It gives a vivid idea of the ground on which the balance
between sheep and vole is decided.

'The grasses found here, as connected with the soil, and with the feeding of the flocks, are more interesting, as they are more useful. Deer-hair (*Scirpus caespitosus*), is generally found on a thin mossy soil, mixed with heath; it is only of service for summer pasture. Stool bent (*Juncus squarrosus*) rises where there is a considerable mixture of sand with the soil; this is an evergreen, and is preferable to the deer-hair. It has been called "an excellent bait", being a hardy perennial. White bent (*Nardus stricta* [with also *Deschampsia flexuosa*]), and flying bent (*Aira* [= *Molinia*] *coerulea*) are also less valuable, being less durable, living and dying in autumn with the deer-hair, and leaving a whiteness on the hills like the decay of winter, and straw-like rustling leaves ever borne and wafted by the wind in gusts among the hills. But of the three following, we believe, the shepherd would say, we could scarcely speak too highly. 1. *Eriophorum vaginatum* [cotton-grass], which in its youngest state is called moss-crops, is greedily pulled up by the sheep; in a farther advanced state it is called *ling* or *laing*. This, to speak in the words of one who has long observed its advantages, is a very valuable spring pasture; it is a hardy perennial, and affords a grateful and nourishing food. 2. *Sesleria coerulea* [? a *Carex*] blue moor-grass, or *pry*, is also a hardy perennial. It resists the severity of the winter. It remains green through the spring months, and is one of the most valuable of all our mountain grasses. 3. *Juncus acutiflorus* [*conglomeratus* etc]., sprett, is very abundant among the hills. It grows most luxuriantly on a wettish soil. While it serves for pasture, it is chiefly cut for hay, during the autumnal months; and, while it is very serviceable for the black cattle during the winter, a portion of it is usually kept for the sheep, in case of a "lying storm".'

Within the term 'pry' are probably contained various grasses such as *Poa* and *Holcus*, as well as sedges (*Carex*).

Although this account has an ecological insight that is to be noted in other natural history descriptions a hundred years ago, it is quoted here chiefly to illustrate the seasonal rhythm of sheep-feeding on the hills, and the way in which prosperity there depends upon a particular combination of pasture plants, each with a special value that varies with the time of year. It will be understood how such a delicate adjustment with the environment will be upset by any great increase of voles. Elliott[11] in 1878 gave a description of this seasonal rhythm, which amplifies that of Smith:

'The hardy flocks bred on the higher Border hills retain much of their wild nature, and depend almost wholly on natural instinct in seeking their daily food. The flock or *hirsel* on a large farm forms itself into three, four, or more divisions called *cuts*, each keeping to its own range of pasture, and feeding gradually upwards to its resting place for the night near the top. . . . During the summer months they range over the whole hill-side within their limits, cropping the tender shoots of the heather, and browsing on the *moss, ling, deers-hair*, and other favourite grasses, on which they thrive and become fat. As winter approaches, and vegetation slackens, the *bents*, and stronger hill grasses become dry and sapless, and the sheep betake themselves to the *lay* or *lea* grasses, which under the general name of *spret*, flourish on the land lower down. This lea land, perhaps once cultivated, or at any rate more sheltered, lies along the lower part of the valley, and borders the moist *bog* land, of which the more luxuriant growth has already been cut, and stacked for winter hay. These spots continue fresh and verdant till the frost and snow of winter render them also no longer available for winter feeding.'

'The sheep are now reduced to considerable straits, and fall off in condition. . . . The shepherd now comes to their assistance and doles out the bog hay, which had been stored for such a contingency, and this enables them to struggle on till herbage revives with returning spring. The earliest plants that appear, which are known by the vernacular names of *moss, ling, spret*, etc. then afford them welcome relief, until the luxuriant growth of summer restores them to plenty. The importance of these early grasses to flocks emaciated by previous scanty fare, at a time when the ewes, gravid with young, require more than ordinary nourishment to enable them to rear their lambs, explains how disastrous any diminution of their still scanty food might prove, whether from severity of weather or other unusual cause, such as the swarming of the voles.'

It may be added that the grassy vegetation which these writers are describing falls into the modern ecological categories of *Eriophorum* and *Scirpus* moors, grass-moor, and siliceous grass-land. With other adjoining plant communities, such as pure heather and bracken, we are not here concerned, since these do not support high vole populations, and in any case form a minor constituent of the vole plague region. Wyllie Fenton[13] has evidence that sheep have greatly reduced the heather on the southern uplands: at any rate it has diminished there in the last half century. There is a possibility that some more general climatic factor has assisted the sheep, for a parallel decrease has been noticed in juniper and pine in many parts of Scotland. At any rate sheep chiefly control the balance by which grass-land is maintained on the hills. They may, however, also have helped the establishment of bracken, in which voles do not live.

4

The two great vole plagues in 1875–6 and 1891–2 stand out monumentally and alone in the annals of the Border country. I think it is reasonably certain that there have been no other outbreaks there on anything like that scale in the last hundred and fifty years. The two outbreaks themselves were, by fortunate chances, exceptionally well documented by energetic and well-informed scholars and naturalists, who drew upon the memories and hill-lore of an unusually clear-eyed and intelligent population of farmers and shepherds.

Farther back still we have the remarkable New Statistical Account of Scotland, a carefully planned survey of sample parishes throughout Scotland, consisting of articles written by the resident ministers, from which I have already given some quotations. This survey came out in the 'forties of last century, though the material had mostly been written in the early 'thirties. This was a time when scientific knowledge was still a natural part of the Scottish clergy's view of life: the evolution controversy had not yet thrown down its thunderbolt on to this pleasant and well-integrated philosophy. So we find these men closely familiar with weather, the structure of rocks, the Latin names of plants (including grasses), the animal life, and the natural structure and rhythm of agricultural practice. In addition, the two men who wrote of Yarrow and Ettrick seem to have been exceptionally good observers of natural history.

Robert Russell,[27] of the former parish, describes several severe outbreaks of insects in the hill grass-land and bogs: a moth in 1762, 1802, and 1824–6; and a Tipulid fly in 1829 (also a plague of beetles or saw-flies on turnips in 1805). It therefore seems pretty certain that any large plague of field-mice would have been included with the others. This man lived among people who had long memories, a fund of oral tradition, and often great age—one old woman alive in 1833 remembered helping to hide household chattels from the Highland rebels of 1745! It was here, as with the Eskimos and fur-traders whose reports fill the later part of this book: the people's lives were closely bound to animal life and the things that helped or afflicted it. They were sheep ecologists, and, for country folk, well-educated ones. (In 1833 Ettrick parish had 26,000 sheep on less than 43,000 acres.)[27]

The reports on the two vole plagues are so well upholstered with subsidiary inquiries, and research on chronicles, that it is also safe to assume that any great vole plagues between 1833 and 1892 would inevitably have been noticed. Since 1892 there has been nothing of the sort on open pasture, though certain minor fluctuations have occurred, as doubtless also in earlier times. Recent inquiries by A. D. Middleton gave a substantial confirmation of this broad immunity. The late Sir Herbert Maxwell was chairman of the Vole Committee in 1892, and had a deep and continuous knowledge of this region (though more particularly the western, Galloway, part) until his death a year or two ago. He also authoritatively expressed, in correspondence, the same opinion.

5

The outbreak in 1875–6 was not so thoroughly studied as the later and larger one; yet the accounts of it are very much better than might have been expected in such a remote hill district. These good records we owe to the industry of Sir Walter Elliott, a local Scottish landowner, retired colonial administrator, oriental scholar, and keen naturalist, who wrote a general description of the plague for the Berwickshire Naturalists' Club; and to the Teviotdale Farmers' Club, an active and intelligent group of sheep-farmers who made inquiries and drew up a report on their conclusions, and also discussed the matter at some of their meetings of which a record exists. Elliott took the matter up in a very thorough style, and wrote to a number of people and published a questionnaire about voles (as in *The Field*,[1] and elsewhere). His paper[11] is a model in its time, and not only embraces the vole situation on the Border hills, but ranges farther afield in a most erudite and pleasant way: to treat of the shepherds' names for different grasses, Fatio's sympathetic observations of the habits of voles in Switzerland, the detailed annals of other British field-mouse outbreaks, mice in the Old Testament, the cult of Apollo, later plagues in Europe, and the climatic variations that might have caused the Scottish outbreak.

The report of the Teviotdale Farmers' Club on voles originally appeared in a small local newspaper, but Elliott reprinted it as an appendix to his paper; while both these were in turn reprinted in Appendix 3 of the great Blue-book of 1893.[22] The record of the Club's discussions[5] was brought to my notice by Mr. Charles W. Grieve, whose father and grandfather had full experience of the voles on both occasions. I am grateful to him for very valuable help, of which further acknowledgement is given in the account of the later plague.

It will be remembered that the Teviot and its tributaries drain the eastern slopes of the central Border hills. It was around the head waters of some of these streams that the outbreak first began to be felt. The Farmers' Club, being apprised of this catastrophe, selected a group of its members to visit four of the infested farms, Howpasley, Craik, Craikhope, and Wolfcleughhead, which lie in a cluster at the top of Borthwick Water, a small tributary that joins the Teviot a few miles below at the town of Hawick. The slopes of the pleasant valley in which Borthwick Water runs are cultivated along the lower part, but turn towards the head into green permanent hill pastures which continue inland into quite wild rolling hills, all grazed by flocks of sheep.

The farmers' committee[5] found this land in a sorry state:

'the scourge had not come suddenly, but the mice had been steadily increasing in numbers, and in the extent of their devastation during the past five years. They had so thoroughly consumed the pasture which should be ready for the sheep in the spring months on the lower and more sheltered grounds, that these were now abandoned by them for higher regions, where the work of destruction was still in active progress. This was quite borne out by the inspection of the lower slopes on Howpasley Hill. There the pasture was known by the name of "true bog", and the grass destroyed by the mice was, in the shepherds' vocabulary, called "spret". It was much relished by the sheep in April and May, and at the time of the committee's visit should have been two or three inches long and of fresh green colour, affording a full bite until the later grasses came to maturity. In many places, however, there were no traces of its existence as a living plant. Instead of green herbage, there were large tracks covered with dead grass, the tops of the plants cast aside by vermin. Where it could be seen, the young shoots were just beginning to appear above the ground, the tops bearing unmistakable signs of having been nibbled. The mice ate it at the white part just above the root and though they did not in every case entirely destroy its vitality, they so retarded the progress of the grass that it was not forthcoming at the season when it was most in request by, and indeed indispensable to, the healthy condition of the sheep. But perhaps the most striking evidence of the mischief was found in the thick grass bushes known as "bull snouts". An application of the hand and foot to those showed that their weight only kept them in their places, the vegetation connecting them with the soil being completely severed by the mice. On removing them, the bare earth and withered stalks and roots were alone visible, varied here and there by the reviving nibbled shoots already alluded to. All around, too, were traces of the retreats where the depredators retired in the hour of danger, the surface of the ground being literally riddled with holes, and presenting much the appearance of ground in the neighbourhood of targets for rifle practice. On repairing to the higher lands and among the "bents" where the mice were now at work, similar evidences of their presence were to be seen, though the havoc made there was not yet quite so considerable. It was conjectured that they might not so much relish the food they got at the greater altitude, but it was quite sufficient to sustain them till, if unchecked, the more favoured pastures were again in readiness for them. The mischief was pretty equally distributed over the four farms mentioned. It was not too much to say that the vermin had destroyed 30 per cent. of the grass which should at the time of the committee's visit have been available for the sustenance of the sheep. At any time such a condition of things would be a serious matter, but in the lambing season it was peculiarly unfortunate, especially in a year when, "lingering winter chilled the lap of May". The committee saw a few of the vermin on the uplands, but, quick of sight and hearing, they made for their holes so rapidly that it was with difficulty one or two were captured.'

6

Elliott gives us a wider view of the plague's extent. It only harassed severely the higher sheep-farms, especially those lying on the watershed between Teviot (east), Esk (south-west), and Liddel (south)—that is, on the borders of Roxburghshire, Selkirkshire, and Dumfries-shire. The Teviot side included the heads of Borthwick and Ettrick and Tema Waters, of which Borthwick suffered most. Farther west there was damage also on some of the Upper Nithsdale hills and in western Dumfries, in the parishes of Tynron, Penpont, and Durisdeer. But here it was less severe, though serious enough to harm the sheep. This bad damage happened in the winter and spring of 1875–6, but on some farms at any rate (as at Craik) the voles had been more numerous than usual for several years before the climax, though they had not at first been doing noticeable damage.

Elliott learned that some other hill pastures had experienced abnormal numbers of voles in the same year, though in few cases so great as to harm the sheep. 'No complaints were heard from Northumberland, or the sheep-walks to the eastward along the Cheviot range, but in many places they were observed to be more numerous than usual. The same may be said of the Cumberland and Westmorland sheep-farms, and of those in North Wales, but in parts of the West Riding [of Yorkshire], as in Wensleydale and Bedale, they were found to be troublesome.'

The Border hill plague seems to have ended rather suddenly, though we know little enough about the circumstances. Elliott notes: 'By the middle of April the herbage was so much impaired that the voles themselves began to feel the want of food, and the occurrence of severe frost, with a sprinkling of snow, about the middle of the month, completed their discomfiture. Many died of starvation, and by the end of May they had mostly disappeared.' We may accept the date of decrease without giving very much weight to the explanations of it.

The special value of these records is that they relate all the typical features of a vole plague in which the gradual increase culminated in great density, damage to agriculture and was then followed by abrupt decrease, but without any serious measures of vole destruction being undertaken. It is certain, therefore, that the outbreak ended through natural causes. Had some huge campaign been undertaken, much of the credit would no doubt have been given to it, as frequently happens on the continents of Europe and North America. Here, on the contrary, we find sincere attempts to describe the phenomenon and to probe its causes, with the result that several interesting facts were brought to light.

7

Several kinds of predators were unusually numerous upon the scene of the outbreak: hawks (presumably kestrels), owls (including short-eared and long-eared), foxes, and weasels. These may partly have multiplied within the area, during the upward trend in voles. But there was at least one unusual visitor as well: the rough-legged buzzard (*Buteo lagopus*). This species does not normally live in the British Isles at all, but arrives periodically, often during or just after a vole, mouse, and lemming year in Scandinavia. 1875–6 was a peak year of the small rodent cycle in Norway (see Chapter IX), and the buzzards that appeared on the Scottish Border may have been bred from it. A shepherd in Eskdalemuir reported as many as seven on the wing at one time. They were also noted in other parts of the country.

We have no means of knowing to what extent the other birds of prey also were immigrants: probably some of the short-eared owls, for these also were more abundant than usual over the country generally. In January 1877 from Cwm, near Aberystwyth, in central Wales, there was this note:[8] 'I have noticed the unusually large numbers of the short-eared owl (*Otus brachyotus* [= *Asio flammeus*]) which have arrived in this country this year. I saw the first on the 19th of November [1876], and since then I have seen no less than fourteen; eleven of them . . . were dead.' These were shot by keepers. There were other ornithological notes of this kind.

Several theories about the vole plague were canvassed at the time. Some of the farmers believed that it was caused by the destruction of the enemies of voles by game-preservers, and also by the farmers themselves. It seems certain that there had been no specially active destruction of predators such as would account for the outbreak coming when it did. But it is equally certain that predators had been gradually becoming scarcer in this region during the nineteenth century. Elliott remarks: 'So successfully has the war against birds and beasts of prey been waged for a long period, that as naturalists well know, several of the most useful indigenous species have been wholly or well-nigh extirpated.' The marsh harrier, hen harrier, and common buzzard had entirely disappeared from the Border country; the kestrel was becoming rare; the badger was practically extinct, leaving only some place-names like Brockielaw and Brockcleugh; the polecat, marten, and wild cat had quite gone; the stoat was rarer than formerly. Only the weasel and fox still held their own.

This picture of vanishing predators is confirmed at every point and strengthened by information from other sources: the Old and the New Statistical Accounts of Scotland, the natural history notes in old journals, and various faunal studies. To assemble and discuss all these in detail would make another book, and I shall have to give only a few general conclusions here. Fortunately there are studies that cover between them the faunal history of much of the southern uplands of Scotland and northern England. I have drawn particularly upon Bolam,[4] for Northumberland and Berwickshire and neighbouring districts; Abel Chapman,[6] for the Cheviots and many other parts of the Border; MacPherson,[20] for the English Lake District; Evans,[12] for a good deal of the same country that Bolam covered, also Roxburghshire, Selkirkshire, and Peebleshire; Gladstone,[14] for Dumfries-shire; Bell,[3] for Eskdale, in the same county; Mac-William,[21] for the Clyde area and Ayrshire, for which Gray[15] also has some notes. To these works can be added William MacGillivray's[19] delightful book on birds of prey, which, with the historical accounts already mentioned, gives a picture of the eighteen-thirties.

The last hundred and fifty years have seen a continuous decrease of most birds of prey in this country, owing to persecution by man. Much of this persecution came about through the development of small-arms and steel traps and the increasing efficiency of game preservation, involving the indiscriminate destruction of 'vermin'. But farmers and shepherds have also been responsible for a good deal, and in some cases (as with the peregrine falcon) egg-collectors. In the early seventeenth century churchwardens in the Lake District were offering rewards for the destruction of buzzards and hen harriers, in order to protect the poultry. In 1836 MacGillivray[19] wrote: 'These birds [hawks generally] would doubtless be much more numerous, were it not for the care bestowed on the preservation of game, which causes great destruction among them. Indeed, it is somewhat wonderful that so many remain in the land, seeing the perpetual war that is waged against them by shepherds, farmers, gamekeepers, and others.' Elsewhere[19] he says: 'Should we, on a fine summer day, betake us to the outfields bordering an extensive moor, on the sides of the Pentland, the Ochill, or the Peebles Hills, we might chance to see the harrier, although hawks have been so much persecuted that one may sometimes travel a whole day without meeting so much as a kestrel.'

8

The species that come into question are chiefly these. The asterisks show the ones that are known to feed to any great extent on mice and voles. Of mammals: fox* (*Vulpes vulpes*), badger* (*Meles meles*), stoat* (*Mustela erminea*), weasel* (*Mustela nivalis*), polecat* (*Mustela putorius*), pine marten* (*Martes martes*), and wild cat* (*Felis silvestris*). Of owls: tawny owl* (*Strix aluco*), long-eared owl* (*Asio otus*), short-eared owl* (*Asio flammeus*), barn owl* (*Tyto alba*). Of hawks: peregrine falcon (*Falco peregrinus*), hobby (*Falco subbuteo*), merlin (*Falco columbarius*), kestrel* (*Falco tinnunculus*), golden eagle (*Aquila chrysaëtus*), common buzzard* (*Buteo*

buteo), marsh harrier (*Circus aeruginosus*), hen harrier* (*Circus cyaneus*), kite* (*Milvus milvus*).

To these must be added quite a large battalion of foreign migrants (hawks and owls) arriving especially in the winter months, and often most commonly on our eastern coasts and inland from them. These numbers fluctuate greatly, with the state of raptorial affairs on the continent of Europe.

The Tweed area had in the eighteenth century fox, badger, stoat, weasel, polecat, pine marten, and wild cat. By the nineteenth century the cats had gone, within another fifty years most of the badgers, polecats, and martens. The same thing happened elsewhere in southern Scotland. The records of the Candlemas hare fair at Dumfries, which annually sold many thousand skins of fur to buyers who came from afar, show the dying out of the polecat.[32, 28]

This fair was a very ancient institution which still flourished in the early part of the nineteenth century. The chief furs were hare and rabbit, and the sales of these ran into many thousands. But there was also a lesser number of polecat (called 'foumart' or 'fitch') and otter skins, which were put up for sale with the rest. These furs represented the sifting and concentration from a great many keepers and farmers and domestic servants, who sold them to storekeepers, from whom they were in turn collected by travellers acting for the large fur-sellers. In this early period furs came in from practically the whole of Scotland south of the Forth and Clyde, also from Cumberland, and even Northumberland. Dealers brought their wagons to the fair from as far away as London, Sheffield, Sunderland, and Greenock. The Dumfries fair gives us a good index of the changes in polecat numbers over a very wide area which entirely includes the vole outbreak region.

'In 1828 foumart skins were unusually scarce . . . proof that these vermin are falling off in numbers.' But as late as 1840 'a considerable number of foumart skins were shown . . . the general price was 2s. to 2s. 4d. per skin'. By 1856 we read that: 'The polecat or foumart has become rather uncommon, except on lands where agricultural improvement has not made much progress, or where turf dykes or high banks and baulks afford ample space for burrowing.' But even in 1856 about twenty dozen skins were offered at the fair, which gives some idea of how numerous polecats must have been in older times. The actual figures are only available for certain years:

1829	.	.	. 400	1860	.	.	. 168
1831	.	.	. 600	1866	.	.	. 12
1845	.	.	. 120	1869	.	.	. 0
1856	.	.	. 240	1870	.	.	. 0

By 1866 polecat skins were becoming every year more rare. In the Tweed area Evans estimates that there were very few left by 1850. The general history of polecat decrease in Scotland has been reviewed by Harvie-Brown.[16]

We know rather little about the natural habits of the polecat in Britain, where it is usually supposed to have preyed chiefly on rabbits,[16, 23] but a recent Soviet investigation[18] of their food habits in European Russia has proved that, in that country at any rate, they are very largely dependent there upon mouse-like rodents, especially during the winter months. Here then is possibly one important actual or potential vole-hunter that had been almost eliminated by gamekeepers before either of the great vole outbreaks happened on the Border.

The badger and pine marten, which were scarce in that area by the middle nineteenth century, are two other species that prey partly on small rodents; and in northern Britain pine martens (as in the English Lake District and in Sutherland) are by no means confined to wooded places, but live on moors and rocky places. The history of the fox, with hunting holding a balance in its favour, is less clear. But undoubtedly it has always been regarded by sheep-farmers as an enemy to lambs, and in many places on the Border has been consistently destroyed. It eats a great many mice and voles.

9

Turning to raptorial birds, we find there is only one hawk which has completely held its own—the kestrel, perhaps because even keepers have usually realized its comparative innocuousness to game and its useful- ness as a killer of voles and mice and rats. The disappearance of the golden eagle and the progressive decrease of the peregrine falcon and, less markedly, of the sparrow-hawk are also a result of persecution by farmers and gamekeepers, though these species do not directly affect the vole situation since they are not eaters of small rodents. The decrease of kites, common buzzards, and hen harriers may have been more important. Kites, now represented by a few pairs in Wales, struggling along under the direct protection of bird guardians, were formerly abundant in Britain. In the eighteenth century they bred, among other places, in the Border country and the Clyde area, where they were known under the name of glead or gled (a name confusingly used also for the hen harrier, and some- times for the buzzard). The kite is a slow-flying bird of buzzard habits, and it seems probable that its omnivorous tastes included small rodents. Most of the kites disappeared in the early nineteenth century, and practi- cally none survived after 1850.

The common buzzard certainly eats voles and feeds its young on them, as well as catching other small animals and picking up carrion. It used to be fairly common in the counties on both sides of the Border, but gradually became scarce as a breeding bird during the nineteenth century. For Northumberland, Bolam[4] wrote in 1912:

'Now only a casual visitant, chiefly during the winter months, but it was formerly a not uncommon resident, breeding in all the Border counties, where many people of the last generation were quite familiar with it, and could point out nesting sites which they recollected to have seen occupied. The ease with which it could be trapped, however, and its conspicuous habit of soaring over its eyrie in spring . . . soon brought about the extirpation of the buzzard when game preserving began to be taken seriously in hand.'

We may contrast this with Selby's picture[4] in 1831: 'In the hilly districts of Selkirk, Dumfries, and Peebles, it is very numerous during the breeding season, and almost every precipitous dell or rock contains an eyry.' Here also they hardly breed at all nowadays. In the twentieth century there has been a good recovery in buzzard populations, notably in the Lake District, but it is still unusual to see them on the hills of the vole outbreak area.

The hen harrier's downfall has been even more spectacular, for it was at one time one of the commonest moorland hawks in the south of Scotland, Northumberland, and the English Lake District. In the Clyde area, where it was numerous, few remained after 1850. In four years 310 were killed on one estate in Ayrshire. The same cycle occurred in the Tweed area, in Dumfries-shire, in the Lake District, and in the eastern Border country and Northumberland.

'Until well into the last century, it bred regularly on many of the Northumberland moors, where I have talked with many people who had once been familiar with its nests, and had taken and reared the young; but with the advent of the gamekeeper, with his traps and guns, it was swept away almost as effectually as has been the last species [the marsh harrier]. That it has not so entirely disappeared is due to its more migratory habits, most, if not all, of the specimens taken, or seen, during recent years, being, without doubt, immigrants from other countries, seeking winter quarters in what, to them, must be one of the most dangerous spots on the face of the globe, albeit the plentiful supply of food may not be without its counter attractions.'[4]

The hen harrier preys to a great extent on birds, but it also eats mice and voles, and in Gaelic its name is *Luch shealgair*, which means 'mouse hawk'.

This brief review of a large and complicated subject will at any rate be enough to show the reality of predator decrease in the south of Scotland. Abel Chapman[6] has well expressed this change in his description of the eastern Borders: 'As showing the changes that have taken place within the lifetime of one man, my venerable friend, Canon Tristram of Durham, told me that he himself, during the 'thirties, found nests of the following, all in the parish of Eglingham, Northumberland, to wit: Buzzard, very common; kite; marsh- and hen-harriers; peregrine and raven. Of the six birds the four first named have now absolutely vanished as breeding species.' This was written in 1893, though published in 1907.

It should be added that in quite recent years there has been a local recovery in the numbers of, at any rate, common buzzards; but this would still be unimportant in the Border country, though more marked in the English Lake District and in Wales and the south of England.

10

Here then is a suggestion of one factor in the Scottish vole plagues. We have seen that there is no record (in a region where memories and records are good) of any major vole plague in the hundred years before 1870, while there have been two serious ones in the seventy years since. And there was a marked decrease of many kinds of vole enemies from the early nineteenth century on. This decrease may have made possible the large outbreaks caused by other factors operating in particular years. We can make a rough analogy with outbreaks of forest fires. A decrease in the fire-fighting service does not necessarily cause more fires to break out; but it may result in more serious and extensive outbreaks that previously would have been automatically checked. One must not throw too much weight either on the analogy or on the original suggestion. The facts may be true and important, yet unconnected. And yet one would expect that the extraordinarily ruthless and efficient control of predators which has been carried out during the last hundred years by game-preservers must have had a good many profound effects upon the dynamic equilibrium of other species. The subject certainly deserves a thorough historical and ecological research.

The Teviotdale Farmers' Club made the very interesting suggestion that predators could be encouraged deliberately:[11] 'Round the farmhouses of Howpasley and Craik there are dense fir plantations, which would prove most desirable day retreats for the owl, and the abundance of food awaiting it would make the region quite a paradise for the solemn bird of night. Then the erection of a few stone cairns here and there on the farms would afford accommodation for weasels, which would undoubtedly enjoy an abode in such plentifully stocked hunting grounds.' Of the house cat they had slenderer hopes: 'It could not be induced even by the presence of great spoil to domesticate itself on the breezy hillsides of Upper Teviotdale.' This is the earliest example I know of the idea of planned predator management for rodent control in this country. However, it is doubtful if anything was done, except by chance, for the plague was over so soon after this report was made. The idea was used, however, still earlier, for the destruction of moles. In 1824 the Duke of Buccleuch's gamekeeper is said to have checked a plague of moles on sheep pasture at Glenquhargen, by tethering a young hawk on the ground.[32] [(1)] The parent hawks continued to feed the young one. 'During the first week no fewer than 80 moles were killed, and their skins and carcases placed within reach of the youthful bird of prey.' As a result of this arrangement the place was practically cleared of moles!

11

A second theory put down the increase of voles in 1875 to a succession of abnormal seasons, with weather favourable to increase. We know from modern investigations on the Border (Chapter VIII) that voles usually stop breeding during the winter months, starting afresh towards the end of March or in April. But several shepherds and farmers attested to Elliott that in certain abnormal years they would find young voles as early as February and as late as November. We have modern evidence (from keepers and foresters) that winter breeding of this sort occurs in the west of Scotland, where it may be less unusual, and where the recovery rate of vole populations is very high. There is no reason to doubt that varying lengths of breeding season occur, and that they *could* cause severe outbreaks. But we simply do not know whether they did so either in 1875 or 1891–2. Furthermore, although we can partly control the breeding of voles experimentally by means of the artificially manipulated climatic factors of light and temperature, we do not know, except by rather general reasoning, what kind of seasonal abnormality would cause a longer breeding season. There is here a complex physiological and meteorological puzzle that is still unsolved. We are left with the bare question: were the seasons preceding the 1875 outbreak in any way abnormal? The evidence given by Elliott[11] can be summed up as follows:

TABLE 4

Temperatures in S. and E. Scotland

	Difference from mean ° F.	Remarks
December 1870	−3·9	Much frost
January 1871	+2·6	Much frost
February 1871	+4·4	V. little frost
December 1871	+0·7	Little frost. Some snow
January 1872	+3·2	Little frost. Some snow, partly lying
February 1872	+3·9	V. little frost. Some snow
December 1872	+0·3	Little frost
January 1873	+3·9	V. little frost
February 1873	−1·8	Some hard frosts and snow
December 1873	+2·9	Little frost. Some snow
January 1874	+5·9	Little frost or snow
February 1874	+0·7	Little severe frost. Some snow
December 1874	−8·3	Much hard frost and heavy snow
January 1875	+5·4	Little frost. Some snow
February 1875	−1·3	Little hard frost or snow
December 1875	+1·1	Little frost. No snow
January 1876	+3·9	Little frost
February 1876	−0·3	Some frost, and much snow, not lying
March 1876	−2·3	Much snow
April 1876	−1·1	Some frost and snow

The December-January-February air temperatures were, on the average, higher than usual in 1870–1, 1871–2, 1872–3, 1873–4, and 1875–6, but not in 1874–5. The last had, however, heavy snows in the coldest month, which would have insulated rodents to a large extent. So far as they go the figures certainly support Elliott's suggestion, but there are a great many difficulties which prevent us from carrying the proof any farther. For one thing, these meteorological observations give only a very crude idea of the micro-climate that the voles actually experienced. For another, there are some large differences between the months. And we still lack the proof that a high temperature causes early breeding in wild voles in nature, or that early breeding occurred in these years.

A third theory about vole increase, held by some farmers at the time, was that mole destruction had encouraged the voles. There is so little to support this suggestion, and so much against it that it can be dismissed. The other two theories were biologically sound. One looked to greater reproductive increase (mild winters), the other to lesser mortality (fewer predators). We find these theories turning up in different guises in most countries where vole outbreaks occur, and they were again canvassed during the inquiries about the next one, in 1890–2, which we have now to consider.

12

The great vole plague in 1890–2 is rather fully documented and I shall go into it in a good deal of detail. The cycle followed this general course. The voles were first noticeable in the summer and autumn of 1890, though only in some parts of the area they were to overrun a year or two later. The plague swelled into importance in 1891. By the following winter the pastures of many hill farms began to have a ravaged and desolate look. A crisis was reached in the spring of 1892, when many sheep and lambs had to be fed with special consignments of fodder, lambs died, the flocks were lean, and the prospects of a crop of bog hay in the summer seemed remote.

Some mild amusement is to be derived from the fact that, although the plague really began in the autumn of 1890, the Intelligence Department of the Scottish Board of Agriculture only became aware of it about eighteen months later, in the winter of 1891–2. At about the same time the Highland and Agricultural Society had also begun to take notice. Once the Intelligence Department had been told about the outbreak, it acted energetically, sending to the stricken area two of its inspectors, R. F. Dudgeon and J. I. Davidson, whose reports[9] give a good survey of the extent of the damage. Meanwhile independent committees of farmers, meetings of protest, letters to the national and local press, and questions in the House of Commons began to make their pressure felt. The voles continued also to get worse. During the winter the matter was eagerly debated at meetings of the Highland and Agricultural Society and of the Teviotdale Farmers' Club. The Abington Agricultural Society set up a committee. The Scotsman published leading articles (also a letter from a correspondent who advocated the use of phosphorus poison baits flavoured with oil of rhodium, oil of carraway, oil of lavender, oil of aniseed, and tincture of musk—a mixture which he wisely advocated 'should be kept in a well-stoppered bottle'!).

An army officer wrote to The Times[25] to say that he had seen the same sort of thing in the Karen Hills of Burmah, and that it had ended through natural causes. 'I believe', he said, 'that farmers may await with confidence the early cessation of this plague from natural causes. I understand that the voles disappeared in Burmah almost as mysteriously as they appeared, and that in the following year the crops were good.' From the scientific point of view this letter was probably one of the best contributions to the discussion which raged at that time.

A dispassionate reader of the literature that accumulated round this vole plague cannot help being struck by the resemblance of the excitement caused by the voles to the process of resistance in the body when it is invaded by bacterial disease—an analogy I have hinted at in previous chapters. The damage to some of the cells, let us say gland cells, causes intense activity in some of the other body cells; white blood corpuscles visit the scene of attack; groups of special corpuscles form defence organizations; the invasion contracts in extent, abates, retires; the tissues mend. The phagocytes disperse, the lymph glands and bone-marrow are quiet again. Typhoid bacteria are the voles, the gland cells are the grass, connective tissue and muscles the sheep, the minor lymph glands the farmers' committees, the spleen (major lymph gland) is the Board of Agriculture. And the House of Commons? Perhaps the lungs—to ventilate grievances.

13

At the end of both events there is plenty of scientific doubt as to what really checked the invasion. It is at any rate doubtful whether any of the measures adopted in 1890–2 influenced appreciably the majestic sequence of the outbreak. These committees and protests and reports were emotional and political manifestations, mostly quite honest, that had to appear. Their great virtue is that they left some fine records for our perusal now. The chief of these archives are given in a list below.

1. The Board of Agriculture printed a report[9] of their Scottish inspectors' surveys in the vole plague area. In this there are also some very good letters from local farmers and landowners, supplied by the Highland and Agricultural Society and also published independently in their *Transactions* for 1892. The whole of this report of the Board was reprinted as an appendix to the main Government Blue-book. It gives a good condensed account of the areal limits of the outbreak and some of the effects of it.

2. Although the President of the Board of Agriculture had announced, in his speech in April 1892, an attitude of fatalism about the vole plague (see the headpiece to the present chapter), he was later on led to appoint a committee of investigation. Sir Herbert Maxwell, a well-known Scottish landowner and naturalist, was the chairman, and J. E. Harting, a very good mammalogist, the secretary. There were four other members: the Earl of Minto; the Rev. John Gillespie (a clergyman living in the infested area); Prof. D'Arcy W. Thomson, a zoologist; and a Mr. Walter Elliott (not, however, the man who wrote about the 1875 outbreak). The Committee went to the Border country in June 1892 and interviewed a great number of witnesses. The 2,015 answers of these people were recorded in a large Government Blue-book,[22] which houses in addition a number of appendices mostly reprinting information from other sources. The

98 small-print foolscap pages of this great report convey a fascinating impression of the people and practical problems involved in a grass-land vole plague, and of the blankness of scientific knowledge about the subject. The report also has a map on which some of the ravaged farms are indicated, and several illustrations, including a spirited sketch of two voles wearing appropriately sinister and active expressions.

3. A file of cuttings from newspapers and journals (chiefly *The Scotsman* and *The Hawick Advertiser*) was kept during the outbreak by Mr. W. Eliott Lockhart. After his death Mrs. Lockhart handed them on to Mr. C. W. Grieve, who recently presented them to the Bureau of Animal Population for its archives. This file contains some unique records and it must be counted as very fortunate that its possessors took such care of it, and that through their generosity it has become permanently available to ecologists.

4. A vivid first-hand description and commentary on the outbreak is to be found, a little unexpectedly, in a book called *My Strange Pets*, by Richard Bell,[3] who lived for some years at Castle O'er, up in the hills of Eskdalemuir, and whose notes gain a special value owing to his intimate knowledge of the wild animal life of that region.

5. Several naturalists made notes and surveys at the time. Harting's notes in *The Zoologist* mostly extract or incorporate parts of the official reports which he helped to compile. Adair made[1, 2] a remarkable survey of the distribution of short-eared owls during the plague and left some notes also on the period of decrease. Robert Service, a well-known naturalist who lived as a nurseryman in Maxwelltown, Dumfries, also published some notes.[29, 30] There are a few others as well.

6. Mr. A. D. Middleton has helped me on several matters, from his experience of field surveys in this region, and in particular with some of the notes he obtained from older residents who still remembered the outbreak; while Mr. J. F. MacIntyre supplied some useful records collected by him in Liddesdale.

14

The area of the outbreak overlapped parts of six counties: Roxburghshire, Dumfries-shire, Kirkcudbrightshire, Selkirkshire, Peebleshire, and Lanarkshire. The two Board of Agriculture inspectors, Dudgeon and Davidson, visited these six counties during their survey.[9] In Roxburghshire 30–40,000 acres suffered, in the upper parts of Teviotdale, and in south-west Liddesdale. On this land it was estimated that over four-fifths of the rougher pasture was destroyed by the end of 1892—that would be about half the whole pasture area on these farms. And some other parts of the ground were also ravaged, though the voles did not multiply much on arable land. In Dumfries-shire nearly 50,000 acres was more or less seriously damaged—three separate sectors in Eskdalemuir, in upper Annandale (near Moffat), and in upper Nithsdale. Here again the rough hilly 'bog' land was affected most. Still farther west, in Kirkcudbrightshire, we come to the limits of the plague, bad infestation being recorded only from the northern tip of the county, on the hill farms of Carsphairn and round

Dalry (i.e. in the Valley of Ken, which is a northern branch of the (Galloway) River Dee).

In Selkirkshire the Ettrick and Yarrow valleys were the main centres; in Peebles-shire the outbreak was apparently restricted to the Tweedsmuir district; in Lanarkshire it was also limited in extent (though quite severe) to the hills round the upper waters of the Clyde.

Dudgeon's figures for the three southern counties add up to between 68 and 80,000 acres. These were, indeed, mentioned with some caution in the Blue-book,[22] which remarks: 'Your Committee received no estimate of the area affected in the counties of Selkirk, Peebles, and Lanark, nor had they the means of verifying Mr. Dudgeon's calculations in respect to the other counties affected, but a reference to the map accompanying this report will show that an area not less than 60 miles in length and from 12 to 20 miles in breadth has been overrun.' This is an area of between 720 and 1,200 square miles. A planimeter measurement of the area marked on my own map gives a gross acreage of 696,000 or 1,088 square miles. It seems likely that the area really badly infested must have been well over 100,000 acres, probably a great deal more than this.

15

The lavish record, mentioned above, enabled me to build up a fairly detailed map of the outbreak (Fig. 3). No previous map has been made, if we except the few places marked on the one that accompanies the Blue-book. But this gives only a few even of the places mentioned in the report itself. The present map was constructed in the following way. The position of every farm known to be affected in 1890–2 was marked with a large spot on a map of sixteen miles to the inch. The area of the spot is a little larger than the average size of the farms, most of which, however, run to several thousand acres. Some were over 7,000. It will be noticed that as a result of making the spots larger than the average farm, there is some overlapping between neighbouring spots. The idea here was that the farms represented known samples of a widely affected area, and therefore the country just outside the limits of each farm was likely also to have high vole populations. This is mostly confirmed by the distribution of the small-sized stippling, which gives the approximate general distribution of the infested area, described in various reports.

There is bound to be a certain amount of doubt about the exact limits of the whole area, as these were not always specified, especially in the west and the south-east. But the main distribution is compact and clear and serves as a basis for correlations.

It we compare this distribution with a physical map, it is seen to be almost exclusively on the hills, that is, on the sheep-walks and not very much in the more cultivated valleys and lowlands. The area of the 1875 outbreak is contained within the same limits, and has the same double grouping on the hill blocks to east and west of the central pass that is formed by the Annan valley on the south and the upper Clyde valley on the north. (It is over this col that the London–Glasgow train is hauled.) The earlier outbreak was, however, much more limited, and since it seems to have fallen entirely within the area of the later one (though the records are admittedly rather more vaguely given), we may consider the two together. What circumstances favour the development of vole plagues on these particular hills at such long intervals ?

This question cannot be answered at present; but I have been able to establish one very clear correlation which may eventually help towards a solution, and which to some extent defines the area of potential danger in the event of another outbreak. Fig. 4 shows the average distribution of annual rainfall contours in the south of Scotland. The map was made chiefly from the standard atlases of meteorology. But it received some extra grooming from more detailed (unpublished) maps which Dr. A. H. Goldie, superintendent of the Scottish Meteorological Office, kindly lent me. It should be explained that rainfall maps are not made in quite the same way as topographical maps. Rainfall stations are comparatively few, and the contour lines are therefore very much rougher indicators than are the height contours of an ordinary map. Also, to get his detailed contours, the rainfall mapper acts on certain established principles about the way that the lines behave in relation to features of the hills and valleys, and that they depend on the prevailing winds and other things. The map of rainfall therefore represents the meteorologists' idea of the probable (and long-term average) distribution of rainfall, in relation to sample stations where it is actually known. This situation is well known to the meteorologists, but not perhaps so much to other people. It is necessary to keep it in mind when comparing rainfall contours with the distribution of the voles.

It can be seen at once that the outbreak falls almost entirely within (that is above) the 50-inch rainfall contour. The high hills, with rainfall over 60 inches, had some very bad outbreaks. The only parts (apart from isolated farms that may or may not have been connected with the main outbreak) that extended beyond the 50-inch line are on the eastern margin, and they are not considerable. The outbreak was, in fact, concentrated in the high rainfall region of southern Scotland. The Pentlands, Lammermuir, and Cheviots, where similar pasture conditions might have been expected to encourage voles, were practically immune from severe infestation. On the other hand, parts of the Galloway Hills in the west, coming inside the high rainfall contour, seem also to have escaped.

16

Although there were a few records of vole increase in the year or two before 1890 (as at Closeburn, where they plagued the lower ground in 1889, and a farm on Eskdalemuir in 1888) the plague did not become perceptible on most of the farms until 1890. And on a great many it was not bad until 1891. There seems to have been this variation of a year or two in all parts of the general area of the outbreak. The Committee began its meetings

just when the plague was reaching its zenith, so that we cannot glean from
their evidence much information about the period of decline. Fortunately
Adair, who had made the owl survey, visited and corresponded with
farmers in many parts of the area in 1892 and 1893, and published some
very useful notes in the *Annals of Scottish Natural History*.[1,2] Out of 21
farms mentioned in his list, 9 reported that the plague had begun in 1890,
9 in 1891, and 2 in 1892. These statements can hardly be given a standard

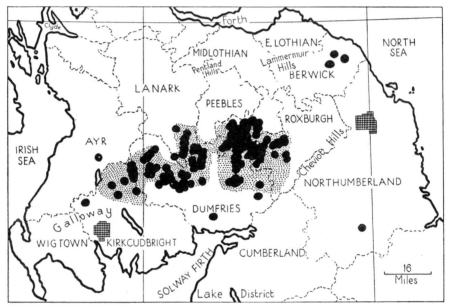

FIG. 3. Distribution of vole infestation on the lowland hills of Scotland during 1891–2.
(For explanation of symbols see text.)

valuation as measures of population increase: they represent a variable
opinion of a combination of vole density and damage to pasture. Most
farms had their worst time in the winter and spring of 1891–2 or during
1892. One or two were still troubled with voles in the early part of 1893.
But practically all reported decrease at some period during 1892 (from
spring onwards) and complete clearance of the ground by the spring of
1893. The difference in vole population between 1891 and 1893 must have
been colossal. But the accounts mostly speak of a gradual, rather than a
sudden, increase. Adair's notes are confirmed by a few notes from other
sources. In any case he covered an excellent sample of the ground, including farms in Teviot, Ettrick, Eskdalemuir, Liddesdale, Yarrow, Moffat,
and Galloway.

As there is not space to quote all the curious features and effects of this
outbreak, many of which only repeated on a larger scale those of 1875–6,
I shall have to restrict the description to a few quotations, which, strung
together in a not too logical way, may give some impression of this extraordinary outburst. We may begin with its impact upon the commission,

when it first visited the farm of Howpasley in the early summer of 1892.[22] 'In walking across the hill your Committee saw numbers of voles darting about in every direction, and caught several for examination. The grass, which, at the end of June, should have been in full flush of verdure, was lying in withered wisps over a large extent of the farm. . . .' One gets here, I think, quite a vivid feeling of the unheeding multiplication of the busy

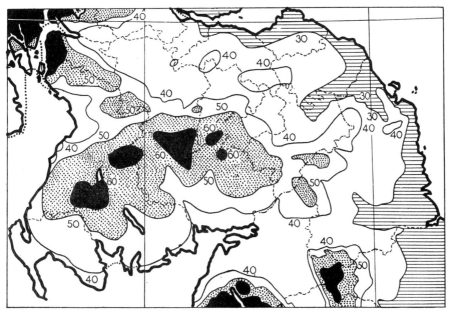

FIG. 4. Distribution of annual rainfall on the lowlands of Scotland.

mice, surprised by a dignified parliamentary committee come to attend this death-bed scene of grass and lambs and (soon afterwards) voles.

Dudgeon wrote of Roxburghshire farms:[9]

'As the bog or rough pasture becomes foul or exhausted, the voles spread to the barer lea land, and even to the heather, which they bark, at the same time biting off the young shoots. The grasses are first attacked close to the surface of the ground, and the stalk consumed as far as it continues white or succulent; young shoots are also nipped off; grass tufts are to be seen completely eaten through, what is left by the voles being absolutely valueless. Sheep are suffering severely . . . large portions of many flocks have been removed to winterage, wherever that can be found, artificial food and purchased hay is given to the stock on many hirsels.'

John Oliver wrote:' 'I had a man killing for a month on Glenkerry, and he would in that time kill upwards of 15,000. He had two collie dogs, and used a common spade himself. . . . Killing, however, is of little avail, and never seems to make them appear any fewer.'

Richard Bell, writing[3] of the voles on his farm on Eskdalemuir:

'It was only on the snow-wreaths dissolving that my shepherd became aware of their presence, and his notice was called to this by seeing the pasture had entirely disappeared in the places previously covered by the wreaths. He told me that during the hay season, when his children were at home for their school holidays, their whole time was taken up destroying the nests of voles containing young ones; and that his dogs, who devoured large numbers, became so emaciated that they were quite unfit for work.'

17

Of the effect on sheep and lambs, the Blue-book[22] notes:

'All witnesses from the infested farms testified to the low condition of the ewes at the time your Committee visited the district, but they varied greatly in their estimate of the increased death rate. One farmer, in the Hawick district, put the deaths at six per cent. above the average, while the tenant of Middlegill, and the shepherd at Medlock, both near Moffat, averred that it had been doubled. The tenant of Ettrick Hall, in the Hawick district, lost 140 ewes out of 1,000, whereas the average death rate for the last five years was 45. The tenant of Nether Cassock, in Eskdalemuir, estimated the deterioration on 3,000 sheep at 2s. a head in 1891, and at 4s. a head in 1892, or £900 in two years. The crop of lambs appears to have been seriously diminished in consequence of the low condition of the ewes. The shepherd on Rushiegreen, near Hawick, stated that 1,400 or 1,500 ewes produced 344 lambs fewer than the average. The tenant of Ettrick Hall and Nether Hall, in Selkirkshire, had only 333 lambs, whereas an average would be from 600 to 700. In Dumfries-shire, the tenant of Barr, near Sanquhar, said he had only 60 lambs per 100 ewes, the average being 90. The deficiency was variously calculated at from 15 to 50 per cent. below the average.'

There can be no question that the farmers suffered altogether a severe loss from deaths in sheep, poor lambing, deaths of lambs, and the expenses of extra feeding and other emergency measures. Although we have no census of the voles, we do have censuses of the sheep population for each county and every year. These figures (supplied from the Agricultural Economics Research Institute, Oxford University, by the kindness of Mr. K. A. H. Murray) are given in a table below. I have taken two ten-year periods, to test the effects of each of the big vole plagues. The censuses were taken in June, so that they included all the lambs of that year. (The chief sales take place in the autumn.) They ought to show any catastrophic effect of the vole plagues. The reader will notice what a large sheep population there was in the three counties of Roxburghshire, Selkirkshire, and Dumfries-shire alone—it never fell below a million in the twenty years shown in the table. It can also be seen that there were marked fluctuations, the lowest figure being 1,061,774 in 1886 and the highest 1,227,788 in 1874. Most of the fluctuations obviously had no connexion with the two vole plagues, being due to innumerable other influences, biological and economic. It cannot be said that, on the whole, the voles caused any abnormally catastrophic fall in the total sheep population of these three counties, or in any one of them taken separately. The following analysis brings out the fact that, although some drop occurred in the bad vole years, it was not as great as we might have expected from the descriptions of the plague.

TABLE 5

Year	Roxburghshire	Selkirkshire	Dumfries-shire	Total (3 counties)
1870	468,681	152,418	484,255	1,105,354
1871	474,434	164,809	512,670	1,151,913
1872	496,880	172,995	515,130	1,185,005
1873	508,924	172,384	513,849	1,195,157
1874	516,903	176,610	534,275	1,227,788
1875	**498,004**	**165,031**	**480,968**	**1,144,003**
1876	**489,357**	**162,719**	**493,020**	**1,145,096**
1877	504,440	161,128	503,086	1,168,654
1878	512,541	167,556	502,520	1,182,617
1879	497,692	157,198	485,880	1,140,770
1885	494,152	164,314	490,641	1,149,107
1886	452,482	148,538	460,754	1,061,774
1887	483,255	158,518	486,349	1,128,122
1888	476,321	155,936	473,911	1,106,168
1889	488,751	161,621	497,227	1,147,599
1890	517,629	163,724	527,319	1,208,672
1891	**512,794**	**163,946**	**530,254**	**1,206,994**
1892	**504,642**	**172,448**	**516,106**	**1,193,196**
1893	507,569	177,075	507,734	1,192,378
1894	511,909	183,421	524,304	1,219,634

TABLE 6

Percentage differences

	Roxburghshire	Selkirkshire	Dumfries-shire	Total (3 counties)
1875/4	−3·7	−9·1	−9·9	−6·9
1876/5	−1·7	−1·4	+2·5	+0·01
1891/0	−0·9	+0·1	+0·5	−0·01
1892/1	−1·6	+4·9	−2·7	−1·1

Of these three counties, taken for illustration, the first was not very badly infested, while the other two were the worst ravaged. There is a corresponding effect shown in the total sheep: a drop in 1875 and little change in 1876; and a drop in 1892, after little change in 1891. The variations are all less than 10 per cent. and mostly less than 5. The aggregate drop over the three counties was 6·9 per cent. in 1875 and 1·1 per cent. in 1892. These figures do not in themselves prove that the drop was caused by voles, or indeed that the effect of the voles was not in itself more or less than this. They simply prove that in the presence of two major vole plagues the sheep population did not fall more than 10 per cent., and during the biggest plague, less than 3 per cent. The figures of course include lambs, which are influenced by many other factors and especially by spring weather. But the Committee in 1892 at any rate believed that the drop was caused by voles.[22] 'On the whole, therefore, it may be

11

assumed that the lambing season of 1892 in the south of Scotland was fully of an average character, and the extraordinary death rate among ewes and deterioration in the number and quality of lambs is to be attributed to the scarcity of grass caused by the ravages of the voles.'

In assessing these figures we have to remember that they are for whole counties, and not just for the badly-ravaged parts. But the comparatively small effect of the voles in most instances is probably explained by the emergency measures adopted by farmers. In the absence of supplementary feeding the death-rate would have been extremely high. Even as it was, the deaths were serious, and the temporary deterioration in quality even more so, and it cost a great deal to save the rest.

18

The flocking of predatory birds to the scene of the outbreak was similar to that in 1875, but on a far grander scale. The two commonest species were the short-eared owl and the kestrel. There is plenty of testimony on the subject in the Blue-book and other sources that have been cited; but the best evidence comes from the enterprising private survey done by Peter Adair,[1] who visited many parts of the area in 1892 and made inquiries from farms whose aggregate area was over 70,000 acres. Adair got reliable records of at least 301 nests of short-eared owls, distributed over Teviot, Ettrick, Yarrow, Eskdalemuir, and Moffat. This was only a minimum figure representing what had actually been observed: there must have been many hundreds more that escaped observation or were on farms not included in his survey. He believed that even the figure of 301 represented at least twice as many broods, since the owls were having more than one brood in the season. His average estimate of 8–10 eggs in a clutch and 7 young in each family gives an output of over 4,000 young in a single season. Without attaching too much weight to this particular calculation, we may at any rate assume that the short-eared owl population on the vole outbreak area in 1892 reached many thousands.

In normal years owls were not at all common on the hills. When the invasion began many farmers spoke of them as 'the new owls'. Nevertheless, Adair got evidence that short-eared owls had been breeding in past years, though in small numbers, on some parts of the district, e.g. in Eskdalemuir and in the upper parts of Teviot and Borthwick. But the numbers during the vole plague suddenly became enormous, and can only be accounted for by immigration supplementing the increase of the local owl population. An acquaintance of Bell's saw 14 owls sitting in a row under the bank of a river, and another time counted 42 on the wing at once.[3] On Craik farm, in Borthwick dale, there were in 1892 about 40 nests spread over 3,500 acres.[9]

These owls preyed chiefly on voles. One man found 29 dead voles at a nest, and removed them. Next day there were 27 more. This was before the eggs had hatched. Another man counted 37 voles at a nest.[9] Kestrels also were very numerous during the outbreak, and it was a common thing for a farm to have half a dozen or more pairs nesting. At Craik 30 kestrels were seen hunting at once.

There is less information about other birds of prey. Buzzards, perhaps rough-legged ones from abroad, turned up on some places. And nocturnal owls also seem to have preyed on the voles where woodlands grew next to the pastures. Rooks (*Corvus frugilegus*) were active in digging up vole nests:[1, 22] but this was only a local phenomenon. Black-headed gulls (*Larus ridibundus*) were also seen to prey on voles.

The following note[34] suggests the part played by foxes: 'A number of foxes which have recently been killed while hunting in the Border districts, particularly in Dumfries-shire and Roxburghshire, have been opened, and without exception have been found to have been feeding apparently entirely on voles.' Weasels and stoats were the only other important vole-eaters left by this date.

An echo of the main vole plague comes from Abel Chapman:[6]

'In 1893 the last expiring ripples of the vole-plague lapped over the Border into Northumberland. We had, that year, the shooting of Ilderton, near Cheviot; and on that one moor, at least a dozen pairs of [short-eared] owls nested on the open heather. . . . Each nest contained families of ten or a dozen, and even more; these were, moreover, in all stages—from fresh eggs and downy owlets, up to full-feathered fledglings, side by side in the same nest. The old owls might often be seen hunting by day, sometimes half-a-dozen being in sight at once. . . . After the vole-plague ceased, the invading owls vanished.'

There is no record of these voles being bad enough to cause damage to the Cheviot pastures.

According to Robert Service,[30] the plague was also about a year late in Galloway: 'On the sheep farms of the Galloway hills the voles found their western limits as a plague, and they were a year or two later than elsewhere in reaching predominant abundance. At no time did these lands present the same bare, verdureless, wind-blown aspect as did the Dumfries-shire highlands.' He mentions that short-eared owls were common in 1892–3 but had mostly left by November 1893.

The disappearance of voles drove away most of the predatory birds. But some of them simply died, probably of starvation. According to Adair:[2] 'After the plague ceased, the supply of food having failed, the old birds almost entirely disappeared from the farms, and the greater number of the young died. A number of full-feathered birds were also seen dead on most of the farms; but these may have been birds of an early hatching.' Service[29] found two emaciated short-eared owls in Galloway in November 1893, one of them dead; while Alfred Chapman[7] also found dead owls on Cheviot in March 1894. This owl catastrophe may be the explanation of an extraordinary discovery,[2] apparently authentic, by a shepherd, of 76 dead short-eared owls in a fox's earth on the hills of Teviotdale. Sixty-eight were young of different ages. Besides owls, there were game-birds, curlew, plover, rats, voles, and remains of lambs. The five young foxes must have

eaten well. This earth was opened on 11 May 1893, and the shepherd
believed that most of the owls had been killed that spring.

The kestrels also suffered and many of them died before they could
emigrate.[2] In some cases the death of owls and hawks was helped by
severe weather, but it seems likely that the weather would not have
harmed them if food had been plentiful. At one place in Selkirkshire,[33] in
February 1893: 'The keeper counted over 30 of the short-eared . . . owl,
and eight kestrel hawks—some lying dead, others able to fly a few yards
only, while several sat until lifted with the hands.' The voles had diminished and almost disappeared here during the two previous months.

19

The external features of the outbreak have now been set out, but they
leave unsolved the two central mysteries of this (and most other) vole
plagues: what caused the abnormal increase, and what brought it to an
end. For the increase several explanations were put forward at the time,
and some of these led to more or less violent arguments between the sheep-
raisers and the game-raisers, and (to a much less extent) between the
tenants and the landowners. Some people put the chief blame on God or
the Government. There were four chief theories (if we ignore the inevitable
draggle-tail of idiotic suggestions that flowed in from all quarters). First,
that gamekeepers had killed off the natural enemies of the voles. Secondly,
that the farmers had not been burning the pasture sufficiently, so that
heavy cover was left for voles (protecting them from weather and enemies).
Thirdly, that draining had been neglected on the hills, so that there was a
development of coarse boggy vegetation. Fourthly, that climate had
favoured vole increase and the survival of young, through the influence of
mild winters and dry springs.

I have already shown in this chapter that the predator population of
these hills had become greatly thinned by gamekeepers, and also to some
degree by the farmers and shepherds themselves. There is no doubt that
this part of the first theory was perfectly sound. But there was practically
no evidence that the destruction had been any greater than usual in the
years preceding the outbreak. Furthermore, there were quite large stretches
of sheep country (including some of those most severely ravaged) that had
no game preservation at all. The general scarcity of enemies may have
made the outbreak worse once it had started, but can scarcely have been
responsible alone for its origin. As to burning and draining, there is no
really conclusive evidence on which to base a theory at all. It is left rather
doubtful whether the vegetation was unusually rough and thick over the
area as a whole (a difficult enough thing to assess), and if so whether decreased burning or draining had anything to do with it. All we can say
now is that these are factors in the situation that need watching and
investigation. The same doubt surrounds Robert Service's theory that
good seasons of climate had favoured increase. It is the same as with the
earlier plague. The evidence does not climb on to a scientific plane at all.

We can only say of the outbreak that it was practically confined to hill land in the southern uplands of Scotland; and (with a few exceptions) to those parts with more than 50 inches average rainfall; that the population of natural enemies had for many years been reduced; and that there was a fairly definite opinion among some observers that the vegetation cover had been unusually heavy during the period of increase. And it is important that all except perhaps the last of these conditions were similar in the previous outbreak. There is something in this particular region of the hills which brings about occasional vast increase of voles. The correlation of the outbreak limits with a particular meteorological contour, and the very wide area covered by it strongly suggest that climatic factors had something to do with the increase. There is no possibility of vole migrations having taken place on a scale large enough to produce the outbreak by spreading from a single centre, after the fashion of locusts or lemmings. No movements on this scale were seen—and they would have been noticed. Also the increase developed simultaneously on a number of widely separated farms, and on different hill units. We may provisionally conclude that climatic factors either favoured abnormal reproduction or caused unusually successful survival—or both. These favourable circumstances were only able to express themselves in very high vole increase within the limits of a particular meteorological régime. There are so many factors that could be analysed, and detailed reliable meteorological records for that region are so few, that it has not been thought worth while at present to follow this line any further.

A similar mystery surrounds the eventual decline of the plague. As has been said, it was not very abrupt, often fairly gradual. The enormous number of predators must have played a part in checking increase. Conceivably this was the predominant cause. But there is also some evidence of voles dying in other ways. Several people in different districts found large numbers dead. 'Mr. Thomas Glendinning, farmer, Fingland, however, states, with reference to his farm, that, though dead voles had not been noticed on the surface, during their disappearance he had sometimes kicked out nests with the dead inside: in some instances only one, in others two or three. This points to some epidemic.[2]. . .' Mr. Andrew Moffat[36] remembered seeing a mortality among the voles on his farm at Ettrick at this time: 'From my own observations I have not the least doubt that the voles were stricken by a disease. For a few days before they disappeared they seemed to lose all their alertness and vigour at the approach of danger, and only kept moving listlessly about. Very few dead voles, practically none, were found on the surface. . . .' Similarly, Col. F. J. Carruthers[35] remembered seeing many dead and dying voles in the spring of 1893, in one part of Dumfries-shire.

We still know very little about the causes of mass mortality in voles. These observations merely give us a hint that the factors ending the outbreak may have been partly biotic—the combined cumulative effects of enemies and disease. But we know nothing of factors that may have been equally important: deficiencies in the food, actual starvation, thirst, deaths from exposure, failure to breed at normal rates, strife between individual voles. Only one thing is certain: direct action by man had very little influence, either before, during, or after the outbreak. There was some killing (a negligible effect); a few experiments with *Salmonella* cultures and poison (too small or too late); some extra burning (not thought to be effective, though it may have been so locally); and protection of predatory birds. The last was ordained by most landowners, whose keepers were given definite instructions to hold their trigger-fingers in control. This action must have helped to increase the number of owls especially.

20

In the impressive march of this outbreak we have seen a common but not extremely abundant inhabitant of the south Scottish hills increase suddenly within a year or two up to the absolute limit of subsistence, partially eliminating its chief competitor (the sheep), attracting to the area and maintaining for a short while a cloud of predatory birds, and giving also a feast for ground predators. Then its population subsides and leaves the predators in turn without subsistence. The grass recovers quickly and gives one of the best crops the shepherds have known. One farmer in Selkirkshire wrote in later years: 'One thing it did, it cleared the ground. The year they left, the bent came up like a braird of corn. I had a valuation at Dalgleish that Whitsunday, and when I rode up Tema I thought I never saw anything so fine as the dark green of the abundant fresh young grass. It was a great lamb year, although the numbers were small. Mine of Sundhope were sold to kill for London and a man who saw them hung up said he never saw such perfect carcasses.'

REFERENCES

1. ADAIR, P. (1892). 'The short-eared owl (*Asio accipitrinus*, Pallas) and the kestrel (*Falco tinnunculus*, Linnaeus) in the vole plague districts.' Ann. Scot. Nat. Hist.: 219–31.
2. ADAIR, P. (1893). 'Notes on the disappearance of the short-tailed field vole (*Arvicola agrestis*), and on some of the effects of the visitation.' Ann. Scot. Nat. Hist.: 193–202.
3. BELL, R. (1905). 'My strange pets and other memories of country life.' Edinburgh and London. pp. 248–65.
4. BOLAM, G. (1912). 'Birds of Northumberland and the Eastern Borders.' Alnwick.
5. CATHRAE, T., compiled by (1909). Part from 1859 to 1874, in 'Resumé of the Discussions of the Teviotdale Farmers' Club, 1859–1909.' Publ. by Hawick Express Office, Hawick. (1) pp. 69–73 (1875–6 vole outbreak). (2) pp. 176–9 (1891–2 vole outbreak).
6. CHAPMAN, ABEL (1907). 'Bird-life of the Borders on moorland and sea....' London.
7. CHAPMAN, ALFRED C. (1894). 'Short-eared owls in Northumberland.' Zoologist: 114.
8. COSENS, G. W. (1877). 'Usefulness of the short-eared owl.' The Field, 49: 19 (6 Jan.).
9. [CRAIGIE, P. G., & others] (1892). 'Reports on the plague of field mice or voles in the South of Scotland. 1892.' Board of Agriculture. London. 22 pp. (Reprinted as Appendix I of the 1893 Blue-book.)

10. ELLIOTT, W. (1877). 'Depredations of field mice.' The Field, 49: 77 (20 Jan.).
11. ELLIOTT, W. (1878). 'Some account of the plague of field mice in the Border farms, in 1876–7, with observations on the genus *Arvicola* in general.' History [Proc.] of the Berwickshire Naturalists' Club, 8: 447–72. [Reproduced also in the 1893 Blue-book as Appendix II.]
12. EVANS, A. H. (1911). 'A Fauna of the Tweed Area.' Edinburgh.
13. FENTON, E. WYLLIE (1939). 'Bracken, heather, and mat grass: an ecological triangle.' Scot. Geogr. Mag. 55: 35–40.
14. GLADSTONE, H. S. (1912). 'A catalogue of the Vertebrate fauna of Dumfries-shire.' Dumfries.
15. GRAY, R. (1871). 'The birds of the West of Scotland including the Outer Hebrides. . . .' Glasgow.
16. HARVIE-BROWN, J. A. (1881). 'The past and present distribution of some of the rarer animals of Scotland. III. The polecat.' Zoologist: 161–71.
17. JOHNSTONE, A. (written 1834; published 1841). 'Parish of Moffat.' In 'The Statistical Account of [Scotland.] Dumfries-shire.' Edinburgh and London. pp. 102–23.
18. LAVROV, N. P. (1935). ['On the biology of the common polecat (*Putorius putorius*) L.'] Bull. Soc. Nat. Moscou, Sect. Biol. 24: 362–73. (In Russian; summary in French.)
19. MACGILLIVRAY, W. (1836). 'Descriptions of the rapacious birds of Great Britain.' Edinburgh.
20. MACPHERSON, H. A. (1892). 'A vertebrate Fauna of Lakeland. . . .' Edinburgh.
21. MCWILLIAM, J. M. (1936). 'The birds of the Firth of Clyde. . . .' London.
22. [MAXWELL, H. E., HARTING, J. E., & others] (1893). 'Report of the Departmental Committee appointed by the Board of Agriculture to inquire into a plague of field voles in Scotland, with minutes of evidence and appendices. . . .' London (H.M. Stationery Office, C.—6943). 98 pp.
23. MILLAIS, J. G. (1905). 'The mammals of Great Britain and Ireland.' London. Vol. 2.
24. PERCY, THOMAS (1765). 'Reliques of ancient English poetry.' Everyman ed. (1926), vol. 1, p. 230.
25. RAMSAY, R. G. WARDLAW (1892). 'The mice plague.' The Scotsman, 29 April.
26. RITCHIE, J. (1920). 'The influence of man on animal life in Scotland.' Cambridge.
27. RUSSELL, R. (written 1833; published 1841). 'Parish of Yarrow.' In 'The Statistical Account of [Scotland.] Selkirkshire.' Edinburgh and London. pp. 29–58.
28. SERVICE, R. (1891). 'The old fur market of Dumfries.' Scot. Nat.: 97–102.
29. SERVICE, R. (1894). 'Mortality amongst short-eared owls in Scotland.' Zoologist: 57–8.
30. SERVICE, R. (1894). 'Short-eared owls in Solway.' Zoologist: 264–5.
31. SMITH, J. (written 1833; published 1841). 'Parish of Ettrick.' In 'The Statistical Account of [Scotland.] Selkirkshire.' Edinburgh and London. pp. 59–77.
32. The Dumfries and Galloway Courier. (A file of natural history notes from this newspaper was kept by Robert Service, and subsequently copied for the private library of Mr. Hugh Gladstone, who allowed me to draw upon them. A file of my extracts is in the Bureau of Animal Population. They were partly collated and published by Service. See 28.) (1) 9 Nov. 1824.
33. Hamilton Advertiser, 11 Feb. 1893.
34. Hawick Express, 23 Dec. 1892.
35. Information given by Col. F. J. Carruthers to A. D. Middleton, Sept. 1931.
36. Letters from Andrew Moffat to M. G. Thorburn and A. D. Middleton, Aug. and Sept. 1929.
37. Letter to M. G. Thorburn, Aug. 1929.

CHAPTER VIII

BRITISH RESEARCH ON THE POPULATION DYNAMICS OF
VOLES AND MICE: 1923–31

A good question is like one beating a bell.

Chinese proverb.

Mystical dance, which yonder starry sphere
Of planets, and of fixed, in all her wheels,
Resembles nearest; mazes intricate,
Eccentric, intervolved, yet regular
Then most when most irregular they seem;

MILTON, *Paradise Lost.*

1

THE two great vole plagues described in the last chapter happened at
a period when naturalists were taking a lively interest in such things,
though professional zoologists still saw in them only occasional, almost
freakish, disturbances of the balance of nature. The still earlier annals of
mouse plagues in this country have been so thoroughly reviewed by other
writers that it is not worth while to repeat their history here. Indeed,
though the anecdotes are interesting, they add little to our understanding
of the phenomenon, and certainly no more than can be gained from the
accounts from various other countries that I have already given. The
people who experienced these calamities would probably have agreed with
the sentiments that come in one of Handel's oratorios: 'Be comforted, nor
think these plagues are sent for your destruction, but for chastisement.'
Those who wish to read the stories of these mouse plagues may be referred
to the early masterpiece already quoted in Chapter I, and to the works of
Elliott,[8] Millais,[23] and Barrett-Hamilton and Hinton.[5] Elliott's review is
concise and fascinating, but hard to get hold of; Millais has the fullest
description and bibliography, but as a single volume of his book weighs
$12\frac{1}{2}$ lb., some may prefer the brief summary given by Barrett-Hamilton
and Hinton. The records are of very occasional outbreaks among crops, in
pastures, and in plantations. They generally lasted a year or two, and
sometimes the flocking of predators to the scene was noted, sometimes also
the rather sudden disappearance of the mice.

By the time of the Scottish outbreaks the Divine Purpose had begun to
seem more obscure, although most people still attributed the plagues to
natural causes, without yet knowing exactly what these were. As Powell
had surmised, the god Apollo was being turned into a Government Department; and in 1892 Harting was his priest. Also, the new idea was creeping
in, that man himself might be responsible for the outbreaks, through the
disturbance of natural conditions or the unwise administration of artificial
ones. The further realization that most of these fluctuations are an integral
property of the living cosmos, that the structure and dynamics of animal
communities are such that these have to fluctuate. and that the fluctua-

tions are not merely symptoms of an accidental interference by man with a naturally balanced state of nature, did not establish itself until nearly half a century later. It was the beginning of this realization that gave rise to the series of researches at Oxford during the last seventeen years, described in the present chapter.

2

In the summer of 1923, on the way home from an expedition to Spitsbergen, I spent some of my last shillings in buying at a shop in Tromsø, Robert Collett's book[6] on Norwegian mammals, *Norges Pattedyr*, and later translated from it the passages which describe the lemming and its extraordinary migrations. It seemed that these inundations of lemmings from the mountains into the lowlands were periodic in their recurrence, and were usually accompanied by increase also in other mouse-like rodents, and of predatory animals and birds. One saw in Collett's records the periodic waxing and waning of a whole community of birds and animals, without any suggestion that the oscillation could be caused by human interference.

I had been reading also Gordon Hewitt's book[16] on *The Conservation of Canadian Wild Life*, which contained some of the fur returns of the Hudson's Bay Company. These also showed extraordinary fluctuations in the catch, due apparently to real changes in the rodents upon which the fur-bearing animals live. The Canadian arctic fox had a short fluctuation similar in length to that of the Norwegian lemmings and voles—and arctic foxes live chiefly on lemmings. The snowshoe hare had a 9–11-year periodic cycle, which was reflected in the fur returns of lynx and red fox. It did not need much search of other records to make one realize that fluctuations are characteristic of every species that has been observed from this point of view, although few of them achieve the remarkable regularity shown by some of these northern fur-bearing animals; indeed, if they did, the problems of fishery research and economic entomology would be infinitely simpler than they are.

This impression of the instability of animal populations was not exactly a new idea in biology, although it was still unfamiliar to most zoologists, and quite new to me. Lotka[18] has noted the insight of Herbert Spencer, who discussed the question before anyone else, in his *First Principles*. In 1863 he wrote:[25]

'The other form of rhythm is to be traced in that variation of number which each tribe of animals and plants is ever undergoing. Throughout the unceasing conflict between the tendency of a species to increase and the antagonistic tendencies, there is never an equilibrium: one always predominates. . . . Among the creatures uncared for by man, such oscillations are usually more marked. After a race of organisms has been greatly thinned by enemies or lack of food, its surviving members become more favourably circumstanced than usual. During the decline in their numbers their food has grown relatively more abundant; while their enemies have diminished for want of prey. The conditions thus remain for some time favourable to their increase; and they multiply rapidly. By and by their food is rendered relatively scarce, at the same time that their enemies have become more numerous; and the destroying influences being thus in excess, their number begins to diminish again.'

Here, about sixty years in advance of ecological ideas, is a clear statement of the Lotka-Volterra oscillation. Spencer realized intuitively that a level balance of numbers is *unnatural*, that it is as difficult for such a delicate adjustment to be maintained in a complex environment as for a razor to stand on its edge or an egg on its end.

However, the confirming of these ideas of Spencer's came, not through the labours of zoologists, but from the growing statistical evidence about fisheries and agricultural pests and fur catches and natural epidemics, and from the observations of open-minded naturalists like Collett in Norway, Cabot in Labrador, and Seton in Canada. The work at Oxford was part of a slow world-wide realization of the ecological importance of fluctuations, and a search for new ideas and methods with which to study them.

3

The concept of unstable populations seemed sufficiently far from the current thoughts of zoologists to merit a general essay,[9] which appeared in 1924. In it I tried to bring out the possible importance of fluctuations in the evolutionary process, as well as in ecology. .

The chief object of this paper was to draw attention to the existence of fluctuations as a general phenomenon among animal populations; to show that the numbers of a species have something of the same rhythmical quality as atoms, sound-waves, tides, planetary orbits, and indeed also many of the features in animal and plant physiology; and to suggest how these fluctuations might partly mould the evolution of the animals that experience them. Of the possible causes of the fluctuations, my interest was concentrated particularly upon three: climate, epidemics, and animal food. It is now easy to see that one was trying to give a general validity to three particular causes, and that there are a good many others that matter equally as much. Above all, the question whether animal communities would show fluctuations if environmental features such as ocean and climate remained absolutely constant was never directly considered, although the facts of epidemiology and the effect of rodents upon predators implied the possibility of independent population rhythms.

The general idea that animal communities simply by their structure and organization have the ability to generate fluctuations was not explicitly discussed by anyone at all (except Spencer) until about 1925. In this year Lotka,[18] an American mathematical expert on human population dynamics, published his remarkable analysis of the world as an ecosystem; and about the same time Volterra,[26] a pure mathematician working in Italy, arrived at somewhat similar ideas about fluctuations. The great difference between their theories and those of ecologists like myself was that I had thought of external disturbances such as climate as the primary generating force in causing populations to oscillate, the other factors such as epidemics and predator population changes being a secondary result. But Lotka and Volterra believed that they could prove by rigid mathematical arguments that groups of ecologically linked species must fluctuate, so that climate and other external influences would merely tend to interfere, with the natural rhythms, producing very complex consequences. There is very little doubt that their conclusions are broadly true. It is remarkable that such an important concept should have originated independently in the minds of two mathematicians living four thousand miles apart, one officially studying human vital statistics and the other not directly connected with biology at all. Their discovery is a fundamental one, and it suggests that the technical equipment of every population ecologist should if possible include an arm-chair and some knowledge of mathematics!

However, ecologists have to study a world which does not have constant climatic and oceanic conditions, but which shows, on the contrary, all kinds of fluctuations, some rhythmical, some much more irregular. These fluctuations are on all scales, from the changes brought about by a cloud passing across the face of the sun, through daily and tidal and annual rhythms, up to longish climatic recurrences like the Brückner cycle (30–40 years) and ultimately to mighty rhythms such as those of the Ice Ages. In the sea we know that many of the chief fluctuations in the basic animal communities that support the fisheries are caused by recurrent changes in the extent and quality of ocean waters; and in economic entomology climate plays a dominant part in the origin of insect outbreaks. It seemed reasonable to attribute to climate an important part in causing the fluctuations in mammal numbers. I have already mentioned the three practical human problems that are bound up with this one—epidemics (e.g. of plague), rodents as pests, and rodents as the food of fur-bearers.

4

There were, in 1923, no censuses of rodent populations to provide a real measure of changes from year to year, no systematic studies either of reproductive potentials or of rates and causes of mortality. One had therefore to make use of records which were indicators of the underlying population changes. And the records had to cover a long period of years. The best were of the lemming migrations and associated periodic 'peak years' of Norwegian rodents, and the Canadian fur returns. Also there was a good deal of rather heterogeneous information about 'mouse plagues' in various countries; but this was not much drawn upon until some years afterwards, when the literature about it had been assembled.

The case for climatic control of these fluctuations (then admittedly overstated) rested chiefly upon two correlations, the first of which was concerned with sun-spots. The approximately ten-year cycle in many Canadian forest animals represented in the Hudson's Bay Company's fur returns was thought to be correlated with the approximately eleven-year cycle in sun-spot numbers, and a hypothesis was made that the sun-spot cycle affected the earth's climate, that climate (in some way not understood) caused the snowshoe rabbit to fluctuate, setting up further ecological rhythms of disease, and of cycles in numbers of predators such as the lynx and red fox, these in turn being important sources of fur. Later this theory was qualified by saying that whether the sun-spots caused the cycle or not, there must at any rate be a climatic pulsation operating to cause parallel animal fluctuations across a whole continent.

I do not intend to go very deeply here into this theory about the sun-spots. There can be little doubt that it is wrong: the arguments against it have been reviewed by MacLulich,[19] and they agree with my own unpublished evidence. The chief point is that the biological rhythm is slightly shorter than that of the sun-spots, and long series of fur returns shows that the two cycles pass right out of phase. The place of the climatic factor in the ten-year cycle remains an open and interesting question, but it is one that cannot be followed further here. The sun-spot theory is mentioned chiefly because I also suggested[9] a correlation between the early records of mouse plagues in Great Britain and the sun-spots, which can also no longer be seriously upheld. Incidentally, it is a pity that several text-book writers have quoted as a fact the sun-spot explanation of the Canadian forest cycle, which was explicitly put forward as a hypothesis to be tested by further research.

The second correlation was between the Scandinavian lemming cycle and the Canadian arctic fox fur records. This northern fluctuation, about three or four years in length, is the main subject of the rest of this book. The reason for invoking a climatic rhythm to explain these two ecological cycles was (and is still) their remarkable resemblance, and tendency to run parallel on opposite sides of the Atlantic, also the synchronization of the fluctuations in different Norwegian populations isolated geographically from one another. There was, however, no observed climatic cycle to do the trick, and the argument rested on circumstantial evidence, most of which needed strengthening and extending.

We are now coming to the end of this preliminary history. In describing the further research that arose from these first inquiries, I shall spare the reader any detailed history of the ways and means by which the research was organized and financed, though this would make an instructive story in itself. It is sufficient to say that from 1925 to the present time the maintenance of this series of researches at Oxford has resembled the organization, under severe difficulties, of a succession of expeditions to the Polar Regions or the Andes. Each expedition had slightly different personnel, each tried to improve on the methods of the last, each encountered formidable difficulties in obtaining money for the work, and usually involved a high personal risk to the continued livelihood of some or all of the members. The search for money entailed a fantastic waste of energy and has slowly developed a skill in negotiation which can bear only an accidental relation to the real scientific value of a particular project. The organizer of ecological research in England would do well to bear in mind the Tibetan saying that: 'Speech must be as bold as a lion, soft as a gentle hare, impressive as a serpent, pointed as an arrow, and evenly balanced like a sceptre held in the middle.' Through all this saga of ecological exploration, there has been a single object, just as expeditions (whether balked or not) may still return to study the Polar Regions or the Andes. The chain of ventures at Oxford is now known as the Bureau of Animal Population, and it will soon be ripe for a new reconsideration (and, it is hoped, reincarnation) by the University in which it resides, and which pays for a proportion of its upkeep.

5

Whatever the original cause of rodent fluctuations may be, there can be no doubt that they are often accompanied by periodic crises of epidemic mortality, after the population has reached high density. Darwin showed,[7] in the *Origin of Species*, that he was aware of natural epidemics of this kind: 'When a species, owing to highly favourable circumstances, increases inordinately in numbers in a small tract, epidemics—at least, this seems generally to occur with our game animals—often ensue.' After the frequency of fluctuations had become manifest, it was natural to suggest that, in mammals at any rate, the periodic decrease is usually brought about by the faster spread of parasites with higher density of their hosts and resulting outbreaks of disease: that the numbers of mammals are 'regulated by disease'. Having made this hypothesis, I applied it[10] to the particular case of bubonic plague in rodents, suggesting that plague outbreaks might partly be traced to periodic disease in wild rodents, and that since the disease occurred periodically it should be possible to predict it by keeping watch on the numbers of the rodent that was the reservoir of plague.

There is no doubt about the disease epidemics of wild rodents and other mammals. They happen and they are often big ones. Also they usually break out when density is high. They have been noticed in voles, water-voles, lemmings, mice, rats, muskrats, beavers, gerbilles, squirrels, marmots, ground squirrels, rabbits, hares, capybaras, moles, hedgehogs, foxes, weasels, deer, zebras, hippopotami, kangaroos, opossums, and many other kinds of animals. Some of the records will be found in a later paper of mine.[11] There is also a good deal of evidence that some bubonic plague epidemics happen at high density during cyclical changes in rodent populations. Indeed, plague was one of the few diseases in rodents of which the causal organism was actually known. Tularaemia was another. It was quite natural that knowledge about the diseases of wild animals should be greatest for those which were of immediate interest to human medicine. But what of the others? Here was a vast unknown field for research, research previously not undertaken because wild animals were thought to be naturally healthy, with disease only an occasional accidental feature. It is not very surprising that our growing knowledge puts the simple 'epidemic theory of fluctuations' in a different light from what it was in fifteen years ago. It is still true, but is not by any means the whole truth.

Although we began by using the fluctuations of fur-bearing animals as indicators of the cycles in numbers of the rodents that form their food, there might obviously be great practical possibilities from reversing the method, and using the numbers of rodents as indicators of the coming fur crop, especially as there is generally some lag in the increase of the enemy over that of its prey, because of the former's larger size and lesser breeding capacity.

The climatic theory, the mystery of rodent epidemics, and the key position of rodents in the northern fur trade, all demanded a deeper research into rodent populations. The opportunity for this came in two different ways, in 1925. The Hudson's Bay Company, to whom I had written for fuller information than Hewitt's book contained, engaged me as a biological consultant, a position I kept for five years, working at Oxford. And a team of men in Oxford decided to study the dynamics of a population of wild mice and voles for several years, in order to find out the nature of fluctuations.

The Hudson's Bay Company work really comprised a straightforward analysis of fur fluctuations and a search for their causes, in order if possible to develop forecasting. With the powerful and far-sighted aid of Mr. Charles V. Sale, then the Governor (to whom this book is dedicated), it was possible to set up a system of recording annual changes in the numbers of animals over a large extent of Canada, and at the same time to begin building up from various old records the past history of the different cycles. These investigations have continued ever since, and some of them fill the second half of this book. They have enabled the climatic theory to be tested both backwards and forwards: backwards, by reconstructing long series of past cycles; forwards, by getting full records from year to year on a standard plan. And the general relation between fur-bearers and rodents has been thoroughly established.

6

In September 1925 we began a deeper study of a small mammal population, in order to try and throw some light on the method of fluctuations. The site of the work was Bagley Wood, three miles outside Oxford. This is a private wood belonging to an Oxford college, where we had the advantages of undisturbed surroundings and of not being too far from a laboratory. The chief species we studied was the wood-mouse or long-tailed field-mouse (*Apodemus sylvaticus*)—a form not unlike the American deer-mouse (*Peromyscus*) in its general appearance and habits. With it lived the bank-vole (*Clethrionomys*—formerly called *Evotomys*—*glareolus*); this belongs to a genus known in America as 'red-backed voles or mice'. In open grassy places there were a few common voles (*Microtus agrestis hirtus*), and these were abundant in some of the grass fields round the outside of the wood. *Microtus* is the 'meadow-mouse' in America. Two shrews occurred, the common one (*Sorex araneus*) and the pigmy shrew (*Sorex minutus*). These five species made up the small mammal population that turned up in the traps. (There were also some moles (*Talpa europaea*), but they did not go into our traps.) The ordinary naturalist would seldom see these animals at all, except sometimes one or other of the voles abroad by day, or an occasional dead shrew. Their life has to be deduced from trapping and by the signs of their occurrence: a special brand of ecological work which offers little of the aesthetic appeal that natural history observation often gives, and which yet has a strong fascination and challenge to the imaginative detective impulse. It is really a very technical kind of woodcraft.

The investigation was organized on a principle which has been followed since, with modifications that will be mentioned. Since the numbers of a population are the result of reproductive rates and mortality rates, research has to try and measure all three of these components over a term of years. (It was realized afterwards that movements form an exceedingly important fourth component; but at this time there was no good method of tracing movements in the field.) Census, reproduction records, and measurements of mortality obviously necessitated a team of workers, partly to share overhead routine, and partly to supply special services. The group started with members of the staff of the Department of Zoology and Comparative Anatomy in the University: J. R. Baker, E. B. Ford, and myself.[1, 12] A. D. Middleton joined the team as understudy to the others; while A. D. Gardner undertook pathological examinations at the School of Pathology.

We had no idea at first of the scale on which such work would have to be done. Our ideas of rodent densities were coloured by the earlier descriptions of mouse plagues. After a few weeks trapping it began to be clear that the task of getting adequate samples for analysis would be a heavy one. Trapping was done for 595 nights spread over three years, and more than 2,000 mice and voles were examined, together with several hundred shrews. The total number of *Apodemus* caught was 1876 (though not all of these were examined, and some were caught several times after being released) and the total number of 'trap-nights' was 71,769. This work was laborious, but lightened by the opportunities it afforded of being out in the woods in every possible mood of weather and season.

The census method was a simple one: lines of traps set through the wood at an approximately standard interval. The technical details cannot be given here, but it should be said that the later work of Chitty has shown that the nocturnal movements of *Apodemus* are so comparatively extensive that slight differences in spacing of the traps probably do not seriously affect the index of abundance that a trap-line gives for this species. As the results of this investigation have already been published in full, I shall only describe the main points.

The routine examination of mice after they were caught was organized on the pork-factory principle, so that as much information as possible should be extracted from each specimen. This was the procedure:[12]

'a large index card was kept for each mouse, which was given a serial number irrespective of its species, the latter being distinguished by a different colour of card. On this card was first noted the date, locality, ecological type of habitat, and whether the mouse was alive, comatose, or dead. Towards the end of the time the stick-number of the trap in which the mouse was taken was also entered on the card for future comparison with a map of the trap-lines. The mouse was put (still in its bag) into a jar, and killed with chloroform. It was then taken by Elton and examined carefully for ectoparasites (fleas, lice, ticks, mites, etc.) of which as complete a collection as possible was made, both of the species and individuals. After this the mouse was measured (body- and tail-lengths) and weighed to the nearest gram. It was then handed over to Ford, who carried out a blood examination for trypanosomes, made Leishmann preparations for later study, and took a culture of the blood from the heart. The kidneys (or one of them) were then removed by Middleton and examined for spirochaetes, with dark-ground illumination, by either Gardner or Middleton. The next thing was an examination by Baker or Middleton of the reproductive organs, some of which were weighed. After this the mouse was returned to Elton, who searched for internal worm parasites in the gut, etc. He removed the caecum and some-times part of the duodenum as well, and these were left in salt solution for the study of living Protozoa by Ford, or bacteria by Gardner. By this time there was very little of the mouse left. The remains were preserved, however, with the ultimate object of working out the ages of the mice from their teeth and skulls. . . . In the course of the procedure described above a general look-out was kept for diseased organs or any sign of disease in the body. Any suspiciously abnormal organ was kept and sectioned and usually examined at the time bacteriologically by Gardner.'

7

The fluctuations in the trapping index are shown on the lower graph in Fig. 5, and the rhythm of breeding in the upper histogram. It was realized that the trapping index gave a measure, not of abundance alone, but of abundance and activity combined. A higher rate or greater range of move-ment might send up the numbers in the traps in the same manner as a higher real density. To this difficulty two answers could be made. Since we were studying epidemiology, one of the important things was the rate of contact, or circulation of individuals, which would be related to the trapping index if this measured density and activity combined. The second point was that the reproductive index would be expected to give some measure of changes in actual density. It can be seen in Fig. 5 that the broad seasonal differences in increase and decrease follow the per-centage of adult female mice pregnant each month. There were some notable exceptions, which we attributed to abnormal movements, particu-larly in the early autumn and in January and February 1927.

The diagrams are most easily understood if one looks at the three winter seasons, say November–February. During the first winter the mice were not breeding at all (actually not from October to March). The numbers showed a general falling in trend: the mice were not balancing their budget of population. But when summer breeding began the numbers in the traps went up again. In the second winter breeding practically stopped, but it went on further into the autumn and began sooner in the spring. The

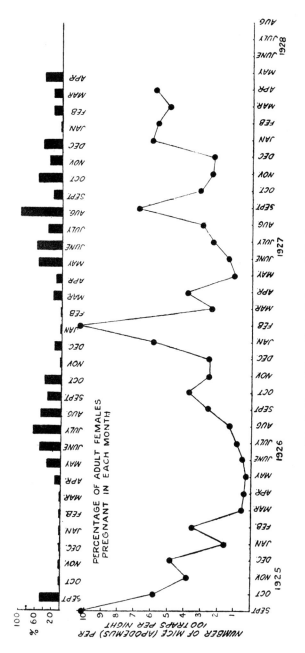

Fig. 5. From Elton, Ford, Baker, and Gardner.

12

numbers began to drop in November, but there was an extraordinary increase in the number caught early in 1927, which we attributed to abnormal
movements. The usual summer increase occurred that year. The following
winter was remarkable, for breeding practically never stopped, and the
population never fell to the low level it had reached in 1926.

One thing clearly dominating these fluctuations was the breeding rhythm,
which not only showed the expected annual cycle but varied very much in
different years. This variation is summarized in Fig. 6, which shows that

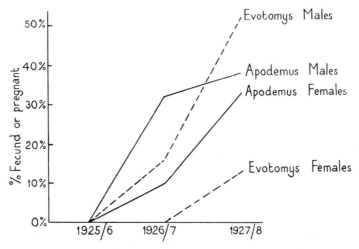

FIG. 6. Graph showing the amount of winter reproduction. The points are joined by
lines to aid the eye. The graph shows that there was no reproduction in the winter of
1925–6, and that the amount of winter reproduction increased in the successive winters
in both sexes of both species. (From Elton, Ford, Baker, and Gardner.[12])

the same thing occurred in the two quite different species, wood-mouse and
bank-vole. Like all 'explanations' in science, and in ecology particularly
(since this is one of the upper stories of biology, underpinned by many
other subjects), this explanation of fluctuations leaves one with a further,
in this case physiological, mystery. As a matter of fact, we still do not
know what factors control the breeding season of *Apodemus* or *Clethrionomys*. Baker was able to show that temperature differences were certainly
not responsible. There this particular chain of connexion still ends.

One could, however, accept the fluctuation associated with varying
breeding rates, and inquire what effects the changes in numbers had on
the parasite fauna, and whether these in turn could account for any decreases that were unexplained by breeding or the hypothesis of seasonal
activity changes. It was surmised, though without direct proof, that the
greater numbers caught in certain autumn months were the result of wider
ranging activities associated with the storage of food for winter. The chief
other anomaly was shown in January and February 1927. Here was a
relatively huge rise in the numbers trapped, followed by a dramatic fall to
low numbers reaching a minimum in May.

8

The chief result of pathological work was to show the very good health that most of the mice maintained. So far as normal examination and testing could show, the *Apodemus* were extremely free from heavy invasions of bacteria or Protozoa or worms, or lesions of disease in the tissues (Table 7).

TABLE 7

Disease in Apodemus sylvaticus

Part of mouse	Number examined	Number diseased	Per cent. diseased
Blood (cultures) . . .	468	0	0
Liver	989	25	2·6
Lungs . · . . .	475	2	0·4
Alimentary canal . . .	719	2	0·3
Spleen	719	1	0·1
Skin of legs (mite-scab) . .	924	102	11·1
Skin (other lesions) . . .	1,156	1	0·1

In January 1927 the mice began to appear in abnormal numbers in the traps, and by February an average of one trap in ten had a mouse in it every night. In December the figure had been only one in forty traps. Many of these mice were surplus to our needs and were kept alive in cages, where they lived quite well, as did those kept in later years. Some lived for more than twenty-eight weeks. But from the end of February until about the end of June the mice brought in died quickly, many after a day or two, and most of them within a week. The cause of death was never established, but Gardner got a little evidence of the transmission of a neurotropic disease that appeared about the same time in wild *Microtus* from another part of the Oxford district. The evidence for Bagley Wood was only sufficient to suggest a sudden disturbance of the population leading to great activity, and followed by mortality reflected both in the times of survival in captivity and decrease of the population within the wood.

The absence of detectable parasitic diseases was certainly not caused by a scarcity of parasites. Quite apart from bacteria and possible viruses, the *Apodemus* population contained on or in it at least forty-one species of parasites. Of these thirteen were numerous enough to be of epidemiological significance; they were distributed, like any natural animal community, in different ecological niches—being here the different organs of the body. The ear had a tick larva and some mites; the fur had at least a dozen sorts of mites, a beetle, eleven kinds of flea, and a louse; the skin had most of these as blood-suckers, and also a more persistently attached adult tick and a kind of mite causing scabs on the limbs; the anus and genital organs had the harvest mite (*Trombicula*); the liver had a tapeworm larva whose adult comes in cats; the stomach a roundworm; the small intestine was the abode of three other roundworms, two tapeworms, three flatworms, and six Protozoa belonging to four different orders; in the blind gut was a Protozoan; in the kidney a spirochaete; and in the blood a trypanosome.

This noble fauna was not all found on the same individual mouse, nor at all seasons of the year. The bacteria and viruses would add further nobility and richness, as can be gauged by the interesting habitat chart made by Gardner[15] elsewhere for the bacterial flora of the human body. Just as the epidemiology of man is complicated by his sharing many parasites with other species (plague with the rat, the *Brucella* of undulant fever with the cow, tapeworm with the pig, and so on), so the parasite community of *Apodemus* was by no means confined entirely to it. This fact emerged from the rather wide survey that we undertook.

Take first the ectoparasites. The flea census (Table 8) illustrates very well the complex host relations that occur. There was one abundant species of flea that came on all three rodents, though not on the shrew.

TABLE 8

Fleas on mice and shrews

Species of flea	*Apodemus sylvaticus*	*Clethrionomys (Evotomys) glareolus*	*Microtus hirtus*	*Sorex araneus*
Nosopsyllus (Ceratophyllus) fasciatus (Bosc.)	1	*	0	0
Malareus penicilliger (Grube) . . .	1	17	2	1
Megabothris walkeri (Roths.) . . .	1	3	17	1
M. turbidus (Roths., 1909) = C. mustelae (Dale)	4	12	2	0
Ctenophthalmus agyrtes (Heller) var. nobilis (= celticus) (Roths., 1922) . . .	38	57	34	0
C. bisoctodentatus (Kolenati) . . .	0	0	0·5	0
Rhadinopsylla pentacanthus (Roths.) . .	1	3	0·5	0
Doratopsylla dasycnemus (Roths.) . .	1	1	1	26
Palaeopsylla sorecis (Dale) . . .	1	2	1	40
P. minor (Dale)	0	0	0	0·5
Leptopsylla spectabilis (Roths.) . . .	0	0	20	0
Hystrichopsylla talpae (Curtis) . . .	1	6	12	12
Total number of each host examined .	788	281	368	292

The figures show the frequency of different species of fleas on mice and shrews from Bagley Wood and neighbourhood between September 1925 and April 1928; they represent the percentage of individuals of each host species carrying each flea. The figures for *Apodemus* and *Clethrionomys* from mice caught alive; those for *Microtus* and *Sorex* from dead animals, and therefore lower. Therefore *Apodemus* and *Clethrionomys* can be compared directly with each other but not with *Microtus* and *Sorex*. The relative number of fleas belonging to different species on the same host are probably comparable in *Microtus* and *Sorex*, and certainly in *Apodemus* and *Clethrionomys*.

Note.—* Indicates one specimen of *N. fasciatus* on a dead *Clethrionomys*.

But the shrew flea came sometimes on the mice and voles, which also had the large mole flea sometimes. Each rodent or shrew had its own peculiarities, yet each had some mutual flea contact with the other hosts. Lice, however, were much more specific in their hosts: *Apodemus* had one species, *Microtus* another, and *Clethrionomys* practically never any lice at all.

The mites, though not all analysed quantitatively owing to difficulties

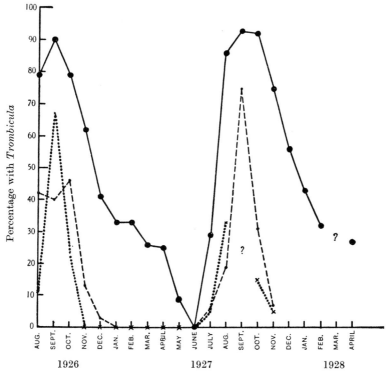

FIG. 7. Percentage of mice and voles with *Trombicula autumnalis*. (From Elton and Keay.[13])
– – – *Apodemus sylvaticus* . . . *Microtis agrestis hirtus* ——— *Clethrionomys (Evotomys) glareolus.*

of determining the species, gave a similar picture of interrelations, two species occurring on all three rodents, four on two of them, and the rest of the mites (at any rate so far as these samples tell us) on one host only.

9

A special study[13] was made of the harvest mite, whose larva it is that madly irritates one's skin in some localities during the late summer months. Here the host relations were particularly interesting. All three rodents had larvae of *Trombicula autumnalis* settle upon them at the end of July or early August. They showed an extraordinary preference for different parts of the body on different hosts: in *Clethrionomys* deep inside the ears, in *Apodemus* and *Microtus* on the hind parts of the belly.

The chart (Fig. 7) illustrates the failure of these larvae to winter upon the last two species, and their success in surviving inside the ears of *Clethrionomys* until the following summer. This instance combines in an elegant way the two phenomena of host sharing and of different habitat preferences on the body of each host. It is likely that bank-voles and rabbits are two of the reservoirs that help to maintain the harvest mite in England, since Keay[17] found the larvae abundantly throughout the winter on the ears of rabbits.

Protozoa (Table 9) and worm parasites (Table 10) show a similar mixture

TABLE 9

Protozoan infections in the three species of mice studied, showing percentages and total numbers examined

	Apodemus sylvaticus	Clethrionomys (Evotomys) glareolus	Microtus agrestis
Trypanosoma	580	192	16
	0·5%	11%	19%
Giardia sp. a (muris ?) . . .	147	36	10
	4%	Not found	Not found
Giardia sp. b (microti ?) . .	147	36	10
	2%	94%	(100%)
Trichomonas muris . . .	443	118	51
	66%	16%	96%
Hexamita muris . . .	443	118	51
	46%	9%	71%
Entamoeba muris . . .	444	116	51
	50%	41%	47%
Eimeria falciformis . . .	380	84	40
	38%	36%	38%

of specificity and catholic range in their hosts, though the worms have a comparatively high restriction to one host. Nothing, I think, could bring out with more diamond clearness the fundamentally interlocked condition of animal populations than this survey of parasites and their hosts. Here we had a wood, itself a very mixed mosaic of habitat types, flanked by fields and hedges with a very different fauna. Yet many parasites are common to several major habitats, though not always on the same host. The difficulty of making a population study of any single parasite can at once be seen. On the other hand, we are able to perceive a very important epidemiological situation, in which the increase of the parasite population in one host must react on that of another; while there is a wide distribution of blood-sucking ectoparasites (fleas, mites, ticks) that might be in turn the vectors of disease.

10

Among other facts, we discovered a rather curious relation between parasite density and mouse density. One had started with the idea that the density of a parasite increases automatically with that of its host; but

TABLE 10

Parasitic worms in Bagley mice

Type of worm	Habitat of worm	Apodemus sylvaticus	Clethrionomys (Evotomys) glareolus	Microtus hirtus
			Species of mouse	
N	Small intestine (usually upper part).	Nematospiroides dubius Baylis, 1926.	Heligmosomoides glareoli Baylis, 1928.	Heligmosomoides polygyrus (Dujardin, 1845), Boulenger, 1922.
N	Small intestine (rarely in caecum).	Syphacia obvelata (Rudolphi, 1802).	Aspiculuris tetraptera (Nitzsch, 1821).	..
N	Upper part of small intestine.	Capillaria ? muris sylvatici (Diesing, 1851).	Capillaria ? muris sylvatici (Diesing, 1851).	..
N	Stomach.	Capillaria or Hepaticola, sp. indet.	..	..
C	Upper part of small intestine.	Catenotaenia lobata Baer, 1925.	Catenotaenia pusilla (Goeze, 1782).	..
C	Lower part of small intestine.	..	? Paranoplocephala blanchardi (Moniez, 1891).	? Paranoplocephala blanchardi (Moniez, 1891).
C	Small intestine.	..	Paranoplocephala sp. indet.	Paranoplocephala sp. indet.
C	Small intestine.	..	? Andrya sp. indet.	
C	Small intestine (chiefly upper part).	Hymenolepis sp. indet.	..	Hymenolepis ? microstoma (Dujardin, 1845).
C	Liver.	Taenia taeniaeformis (Batsch, 1786) = 'Cysticercus fasciolaris' Rudolphi, 1808.	Taenia tenuicollis Rudolphi, 1819 = 'Cysticercus innominatus hypudaei' Leuckart, 1856.	Taenia tenuicollis Rudolphi, 1819 = 'Cysticercus innominatus hypudaei' Leuckart, 1856.
T	Upper part of small intestine.	Lyperosomum vitta (Dujardin, 1845).	..	..
T	Lower part of small intestine.	Harmostomum recurvum (Dujardin, 1845).	..	..
T	Small intestine.	Lepoderma ? muris (Tanabe, 1922).	..	..

N = Nematode (Roundworm).   C = Cestode (Tapeworm).   T = Trematode (Fluke).

this was not always found to be so. The small red tendril-shaped roundworm, *Nematospiroides dubius*, which inhabits the upper part of the small intestine of *Apodemus*, was abundant and could be counted accurately. Fig. 8 shows the average number in any mouse that had worms in it, at different periods.

It is seen that the worms were most abundant when the mice were scarce, and vice versa—there is a progression following inversely the winter changes of population in successive years. The reason for this peculiar relationship can be understood from Figs. 9 and 10, which give the frequency in mice of different weights, here taken as some measure (though not a direct linear one) of the age. The worms grow more numerous as their hosts grow older. If the mice are breeding fast, the large number of young mice in the population reduces the average percentage of infection, while in a winter like 1925–6, when the *Apodemus* are all old mice, the average rate is very high.

Such a parasite will therefore not increase rapidly if its host is increasing. This is only true up to a certain point; but in this particular case, at any rate, the point did not appear to be passed. Presumably a very high mouse density would in the end cause the parasite to increase very much. This interesting equilibrium depends on the parasite being commoner in old than young hosts, which is not always the case. But this was found to be so with another roundworm, with a tapeworm, and with the spirochaete that inhabited the kidneys of *Apodemus*. This spirochaete deserves some mention.

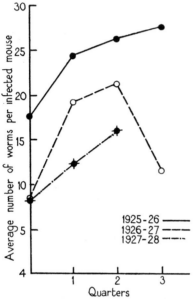

FIG. 8. Average number of worms (*Nematospiroides dubius*) per infected mouse (*Apodemus*, all weights, both sexes) in different quarters between October 1925 and April 1928. (The second quarter of 1928 based on figures for April only.) First quarter January to March, and so on. (From Elton, Ford, Baker, and Gardner.[12])

There is a dangerous form of jaundice, known as Weil's disease, happily not common in this country except occasionally among sewermen, slaughterhouse workers, fisherwomen, and miners, which is derived from rats. The organism, *Leptospira icterohaemorrhagica*, lives in the kidney of the rat, and occasionally contaminates water or in some other way enters the body of man. An organism very similar to it was found by Gardner in the *Apodemus* of Bagley Wood. Eight per cent. of the mice had it at the time of our survey.

This organism was not found in young mice, but showed an increasing rate of infection with age. In a later research at Oxford Middleton[19a] proved that in *Leptospira* infection of wild brown rats (*Rattus norvegicus*) the same phenomenon occurs. In these rats, uninfected during youth, over 50 per cent. had the jaundice spirochaete when they were old. The comparative rarity of this type of jaundice as a human disease in England reminds us that the barriers to infection that exist in an animal community may be just as remarkable as the numerous channels of connexion that have been stressed above.

11

This Bagley Wood investigation had taught us a number of things about the methods of approaching such a problem in the field, and had also brought to light some definite facts about fluctuations. The two woodland species fluctuated, and the fluctuations were primarily due to variation in the breeding rate, but we did not know the cause of the latter. There were also probably fluctuations in activity (suggested also by extraordinary seasonal changes in the sex ratio of trapped mice), but we had no way of

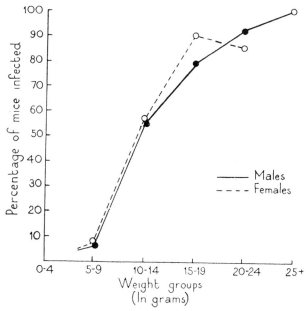

FIG. 9. Age distribution of worms (*Nematospiroides dubius*) in *Apodemus*, showing the increasing percentage of mice infected as age (weight) increases. Sexes are plotted separately. (From Elton, Ford, Baker, and Gardner.[12])

studying movements. There was a very complex parasite fauna, but it had not caused any considerable disease. The host-age relations of some parasites appeared to be one check upon the development of high parasite infestations. The reasons in other cases were not clear. But there apparently had been disease, though the cause of mortality was not ascertained, partly because no supply of control animals was available for experiment. Incidental to the main investigation had come out several discoveries affecting human interests: *Apodemus* as probable alternative host to a tapeworm of the cat; the seasonal cycle and winter bank-vole host of the harvest mite; *Leptospira* in *Apodemus*.

The trapping for mice and voles in and around Bagley Wood brought in as a by-product a small harvest of shrews, mostly *Sorex araneus*, the common shrew. Living with it in the wood, but in much smaller numbers, was a population of *Sorex minutus*, the pigmy shrew—the smallest British mammal, a creature that can pass, with its narrow flexible skull, through quarter-inch wire mesh. These fierce small insectivores and worm-eaters use the runs of rodents and of the mole, and the common species has a wide range of habitats, indiscriminately frequenting the underground tunnels of the woodland mice and voles, the runways of *Microtus* in the fields, and mole-runs wherever they are. Middleton[22] made a separate analysis of the shrew populations, which showed a sharply marked summer breeding season, and some evidence of a complete annual turnover in the population. Both in the mice and voles and in the shrews, the survey of internal para-

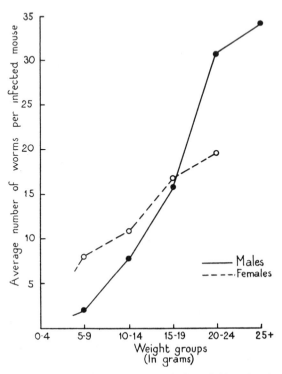

Fig. 10. Age distribution of worms (*Nematospiroides dubius*) in *Apodemus*, showing increased worm-rate (average number per infected mouse) as age (weight) increases. Sexes are plotted separately. (From Elton, Ford, Baker and Gardner.[12])

sites brought to light several new species, or enabled known ones to be properly described.

12

In 1928, after the end of these Bagley Wood investigations, research at Oxford was turned on to the population problems of the common vole, *Microtus agrestis*. This species was to remain the chief object of research during the next eleven years. The development of this work required financial help which the Medical Research Council were no longer willing to provide, since they seemed doubtful at this time how far wild animal diseases were likely to have any bearing on the epidemiology of the British citizen. And they considered, in any case, that technical difficulties might prevent results of any scientific validity being obtained. Their own animal epidemiological work at this period therefore continued to be confined to a series of important pure research experiments on the epidemiology of laboratory mice, initiated by W. C. C. Topley in 1919, and carried on by him, together with Greenwood and others, ever since. I considered that the epidemiology of natural populations would yield corresponding results along different though partly parallel lines, a belief in which I was encouraged at all times by the friendly interest of Professor Topley himself.

The close connexion of rodent fluctuations with agricultural, forestry, and fur-trade problems made it possible to secure support from the Empire Marketing Board, a body which, under the leadership of Stephen Tallents, took an invigoratingly broad view of its responsibilities. So, from 1928 to 1931, we began to study vole fluctuations, having as our basis the information about *Microtus* obtained rather as a side-line (chiefly by Middleton) during the Bagley Wood investigations. Several initial problems of organization and technique had to be tackled. We had to decide the best areas for work; to measure, or at least get reports on, the changes in numbers; to know approximately when to expect the major outbreaks of mortality; to find a pathologist willing to do this work; to have a supply of healthy voles for the pathologist to use in his experiments and as controls; to find how to breed voles in the laboratory for this and other purposes; to learn the factors controlling natural breeding seasons in order to get a line on artificial breeding.

The only indices of vole fluctuations that had hitherto existed were the numbers of fur-bearing carnivores shown in fur-trade returns, and the actual records of extreme abundance or scarcity supplied by field observers. There are no fur-trade records of the sort for Great Britain, and in any case such records are open to a number of errors of interpretation. A. D. Middleton therefore began to organize, by correspondence and field tours, an intelligence system for getting records of abundance of voles (and also of various other animals such as squirrels and hares). The information that came in from this network of voluntary observers brought to light certain important factors in the distribution of vole populations. *Microtus agrestis* lives chiefly in grass-land or at any rate among grassy or rushy vegetation, upon which it depends for food. With a few exceptions, it is primarily an eater of green stems and leaves, not of seeds and fruits. Over much of Great Britain grass-land is temporary, i.e. it forms one stage in the rotation of crops; where it forms permanent pasture this is grazed by domestic animals which remove a great deal of the cover and the food of voles. For these reasons the number of places which can support vole populations permanently without disturbance, even for as long as ten years, is limited. In the cultivated parts of the country most of these spots are rather small, or else considerably disturbed by annual mowing or other human activities.

The conditions for British voles are therefore seen to be very different from those of the Norwegian rodent populations described in Chapter X, or of the Labrador voles described in Part III. For making systematic observations it was necessary to find habitats where vole fluctuations could develop undisturbed for a number of years. Even if these habitats were artificially produced by man, they would perhaps represent the type

of natural environment which existed before grazing and cultivation had
so profoundly shifted the equilibrium of British vegetation. The best
environments of this kind lie on the rough hill pastures of Wales, and
northern England and Scotland, especially on the peaty moors that tend
towards comparatively pure grass-land, and discourage the growth of
bracken and gorse, which voles avoid.

13

Middleton saw the enormous possibilities for vole research in the State
forests which were rapidly beginning to occupy large tracts of these upland
hill-pasture areas, and which, by drainage, the exclusion of grazing stock,
and the control of fire, produced optimum conditions for the multiplication
of voles. When hill pasture is drained and fenced off for planting, the grass
and rushes soon develop a luxuriance that is quite surprising to see, and
which makes one realize the dynamic equilibrium in which this vegetation
had previously been held by sheep and cattle. The observer, wading knee-
deep, sometimes waist-high, through the jungle of grass and rushes that
may be found five years after enclosure, is able to study the new equilibrium established in the face of pressure from voles instead.

The Forestry Commission[14] began its planting programme in 1919, and
by 1938 owned 682,000 plantable acres of Great Britain, of which 324,151
acres had been actually planted up, mostly with young conifers such as
spruce and pine and larch. This huge State project has unintentionally
increased the average vole population of this country by many million
individuals, and provided an ideal setting for the study of vole fluctuations
and epidemiology. These fluctuations have also an important repercussion
on the planting programme, because voles often seriously damage young
trees. The district most subject to damage is Argyll, where nearly a
million young conifers were destroyed by ring-barking in the winter
of 1929–30 alone. Here there was further serious destruction in 1932–3,
1935–6, and 1937–8. But damage of this kind occurs widely on a lesser
scale in many forests. To the actual killing of trees must be added subsequent losses caused by the weakening of roots at the time of the vole plague,
and by the 'moth-eaten' pattern of the surviving trees, both factors which
lower the capacity of the trees for wind resistance.

The occurrence of marked fluctuations inside young forest plantations,
the importance of voles to forestry, the consequent willingness of foresters
to supervise vole fluctuation research, and the immunity of such areas
from disturbance, made possible the planning of regular vole census operations at a number of selected stations. Middleton enlisted the co-operation
of the Forestry Commission, without whose very extensive assistance and
facilities this series of researches could never have been accomplished;
later on he got help from other owners of plantations, including Messrs.
Bryant and Mays (who have plantings in Argyll) and Liverpool Corporation (who have planted the slopes of their Lake Vyrnwy water reservoir).
The census was done by means of a standard line of fifty unbaited traps set

in the vole-runs, and carried out for five days each summer by forestry men.

I cannot go deeply into the technical results of this earlier vole census system, but will refer the reader to two of Middleton's reports,[20, 21] in which he set out not only to record the current changes in numbers, but also to build up from earlier reports from various observers a story of fluctuations in British voles. The records previous to 1922 are too few to give a certain proof of his hypothesis that there has been a general four-year cycle in the numbers of *Microtus* in Scotland and the north of England. It seems certain, however, that there have been pronounced fluctuations, and since 1922 these have tended strongly to recur at intervals of three or four years in any one area, though not necessarily synchronizing with other areas (as was at first supposed) except in certain years.

14

The following extract from one of Middleton's reports will show the obvious reality of the fluctuations, and some of the advantages and drawbacks of an extensive intelligence system of the sort:

'In several areas in the northern half of Scotland 1929 was undoubtedly a maximum year for voles, and heavy reductions in numbers occurred during the spring and early summer of 1930. Voles were exceptionally numerous in the Cowal district of Argyll in the autumn of 1929, especially in the Glenfinart and Benmore district (round Loch Eck). In February 1930 a visit was made to this district by the writer and investigations carried out on the ground. Throughout the period August 1929 to March 1930 the numbers were very high, and by the end of February, on many parts of the forestry areas, the ground vegetation of grass, mosses, and rushes was so eaten down that it appeared unlikely that the heavy vole population would survive until the onset of spring growth in the plants produced a plentiful food supply. A great deal of damage was done throughout the winter to young trees in the plantations by ringing and nipping off branches of many species. Although voles were numerous throughout the whole district, trapping showed that the distribution was by no means uniform, even in identical conditions, and the voles appeared to have vacated many parts of the area where the eaten vegetation and damaged trees indicated their former presence in large numbers. . . .'

'From the trapping operations and observations on the area, it appears that a considerable reduction in numbers occurred from the middle of March to the end of April: by the middle of June not a vole could be seen on the area (J. Fraser; H. MacMillan) and during the trapping census in August at Glenfinart not a single animal of any species was caught. (In the corresponding census in 1929 137 voles, 4 shrews and 27 bank voles were caught.) . . .'

'Certain other areas in northern Scotland also experienced a maximum in 1929, notably western Ross-shire as shown by Ratagan (on the shores of Loch Duich) and the Loch Maree district. At Ratagan the numbers were very high in 1929, and amounted to a plague in the forestry plantations, but a reduction to an absolute minimum occurred in the spring of 1930, and no voles were caught in the census in August 1930 (W. Murray). At Loch Maree a considerable reduction from the abundance of 1929 has occurred, but voles are not so extremely scarce there as in the Argyll and Ratagan districts at the present time. In southern Inverness-shire a similar reduction has occurred at Glenhurich (W. Anderson), Corrour (S. Cameron) and Fort William (W. J. Cuthbert); in the northern part of the county the reduction does not appear to be so pronounced. At Glenurquhart in 1929 voles were very numerous, and are still numerous at the time of writing, although there has been no noticeable increase, and possibly a slight decrease (W. Macintosh; the writer). Similarly Glenmore in the Cairngorm district does not seem to have had any marked variation during the two years, though voles are fairly numerous (J. Kennedy); at Grantown-on-Spey they are reported as normal (G. Browne), and in the Nethybridge district no change from a normal scarcity has been observed for many years (W. Marshall). In east Ross-shire at Ardross an increase is recorded and numbers are fairly high there (G. Anderson). On the island of Mull an increase has occurred, giving fairly high numbers for 1930 (J. Drysdale), but on Bute they are reported to be less in 1930 than 1929 (A. Smart). In Caithness a considerable increase is recorded (A. Sutherland).'

Here for the moment I will leave the census work: by 1930 it had given us a good conception of the frequency and reality of vole fluctuations, and of their geographical complexity. And, although we still knew nothing about movements or absolute density, the comparative census method was a great advance on subjective reports, and opened up the possibility of forecasting epidemics.

15

During the years 1928–30 little progress was made with the question of vole diseases, chiefly because it was technically difficult to deliver material from the field in a condition suitable for examination, and also because few pathologists were willing to face the possibility of large amounts of negative work. As a result of these difficulties, Middleton was unable to elucidate the cause of the mortality that he encountered in Argyll in the spring of 1930.

The distance of these favourable vole localities from Oxford, and the consequent difficulties of doing intensive field work on diseases, led me to undertake a fairly elaborate experiment in epidemiology, which, though it was unsuccessful in achieving its immediate objects, was extremely useful in teaching one much about the nature of the problem. In starting this experiment I was also influenced by the belief that voles might turn out to be the reservoir of the pandemic influenza which at fairly long intervals runs like a pestilence through human and horse populations. I shall not discuss the pros and cons of this theory here. But the possibility at that time of its truth led Mr. Charles V. Sale to give his private support to the experiment. The scheme was to get live *Microtus*, keep them out of doors in pens with a surplus supply of food, and artificially induce epidemic disease by overcrowding. The disease was then to be inoculated into horses to see if influenza would result. So far as possible the pathology was to be investigated: in the event, I had to teach myself elementary bacteriology, and practice it under very primitive field conditions. The results of this experiment have not hitherto been published.

Three wired-in pens were set up in a grass field outside Oxford. Each had an area of 25 square yards. From April to June 1928 179 wild *Microtus agrestis* trapped in North Wales were introduced, the gross totals for the pens being 53, 48, and 78. After many practical difficulties they were established and began to nest and breed. They were fed with large quantities of grass and cabbage and lettuce, and provided with a certain amount of artificial cover. Predators were excluded, and the voles could not possibly escape. Owing to a remarkable migratory restlessness that the voles developed when they were slightly hungry, it was possible to count them at intervals, as they all ran about on the surface in search of food. Two of the pens developed flourishing populations, and in spite of some deaths among the adults, the numbers kept up at this very high density. A good many young were born and reared. The pen that started with 78 had on 9 August still at least 65 voles in it.

About this time two things began to happen that eventually spelled the failure of the experiment as it had been planned. One was that the voles stopped breeding about the end of July and beginning of August. This was a blow to the experiment, which had been planned on the assumption that breeding could be maintained if the voles were given a continuous excess of 'natural' food containing vitamin E (the 'reproductive vitamin'). But the food did not succeed in preventing the normal ending of the breeding season. Thereafter it was inevitable that the populations would drop to lower and lower densities.

The other thing was that many of the adult voles developed a kind of skin disease whose aetiology was never settled. It caused scabby sores and was associated partly with a very high infestation of lice. A good many voles died in September, probably from this disease or its consequences. For these and other reasons the populations fell by November 1928 to about a dozen in each of the two pens. The experiment was then closed down.

What had been learned from this experiment? Perhaps the futility of short cuts in research; but also knowledge that the breeding rhythm probably could not be controlled in a simple way by food; that it had not been possible to maintain and increase a vole population introduced in April to June, kept at a density of two or three to a square yard, and breeding only from early June to early August; that such a population had developed disease, though not of the type hoped for; that disease could not easily be identified without a stock of healthy animals for experiment. The complete significance of this experience with an artificial population will be seen when we come to consider later on the dynamic structure of vole populations.

16

In order to clear up the problem of breeding seasons in the vole, Baker and Ranson[2, 3, 4] undertook an investigation which was made possible by further help from the Empire Marketing Board. The investigation was highly successful, and had a far-reaching influence on later research. It was in two parts. In the first, the object was to find out the normal breeding season of the vole in nature, and to correlate this with environmental factors. In the second, these factors were studied experimentally. The field work was carried out by three State foresters: Clarke at Huntly in Aberdeenshire, MacIntyre at Newcastleton on the Scottish Border, and Lomas at Corris in north Wales. They trapped monthly quotas of voles in forestry plantations for two years. This was no light undertaking, for the work had to be kept going in all weathers except in deep snow. Altogether they sent in 2,500 *Microtus agrestis*, which formed the raw material for analysis.

The routine examination of the reproductive condition of these voles proved that there was a rather definite breeding season from about March to September: no pregnancies were ever found from November to February. It varied somewhat at each end, and there was some evidence that it began later at the southern station and went on longer at the northern one. The breeding season, that is to say, was (in these two years) longer in the north than in the south.

The annual rainfall and temperature cycles recorded at the nearest meteorological stations showed no close correlation with the breeding rhythm. The number of hours of sunshine each month gave, however, a much better agreement. Breeding begins to decline sharply in July and August when the summer is still hot, and has practically ceased by October; although this month has about the same temperature as May, when breeding is at its height. But sunshine reaches its peak in June. Baker and Ranson concluded that 'in general mice were breeding in those months in which there were more than about 100 hours of sunshine, and were not breeding when there were less. There were some exceptions to this rule, but there is far closer correlation with hours of sunshine than with any other climatic factor investigated.'

Another interesting discovery was made in the course of this work. The voles that start each breeding cycle in the spring are adult ones that have over-wintered for at least five months without breeding. During the spring and summer these adults increase in weight and are in due course augmented by young ones of the year which begin to appear from about April onwards. During the summer the large voles gradually become scarcer, until no more are caught. It seems certain, therefore, that the population that starts the breeding cycle each spring does not survive until the following spring, but is replaced by its own grown-up offspring. This means that the vole is an *annual*, and has one of the shortest lives of any mammal— shorter than many insects and worms and fish. It is not certain, however, how many, if any, of the young born early in the year breed the same season. On the whole the evidence makes it improbable that voles often breed during more than one season. This discovery is of enormous significance in the population dynamics of the vole. Let us note, in passing, that it was made as an unexpected by-product of a different research.

17

It took a year to find out how to breed *Microtus* successfully in captivity at all. But by the end of 1930 the vole had become a true laboratory animal. These wild voles came originally from the Welsh and Scottish hills. The same stock has been maintained by Ranson at Oxford ever since. With later experience the technique of keeping them was improved, and described by him[24] in 1934.

The experiments followed the trend of the natural seasonal factors of light and temperature and food. The most interesting results were perhaps those with the light. In all experiments the voles were interchanged between the experiments and their controls, in order to eliminate differences that might be caused by constitutional variations. The light experiment lasted for twelve months, the temperature was kept at a high, 'summer' level (nearly always above 18° C.), and the voles were fed on fresh grass or other green stuff, representing a 'natural' diet. The control populations, living in 15 hours electric light each day, and other summer conditions, bred consistently: 25 out of 28 matings were successful. But the other voles, living in only 9 hours ('winter') light, had only 4 out of 27 successful matings. Here was experimental confirmation of the suggestion from the field evidence, that voles need a certain number of hours of sunshine in order to breed. The female reacts more sharply than the male, and it seems that the seasonal population dynamics of the vole are, at the reproductive end, controlled by the physiology of the female.

The temperature experiments were divided into two sections, both, however, having 15 hours ('summer') light. In each section there were controls. The first experiment showed that when voles are kept on grass or other green food in summer light, but at a low ('winter') temperature they hardly breed at all (4 pregnancies against 15 in the controls). But when under similar conditions the voles are given winter grass and grass seeds for food, they are able to breed quite effectively. The kind of food they have determines whether low temperatures stop them from breeding. Here then are three factors, all of which affect breeding. But light is evidently the limiting one, while temperature and food may have additional influences whose action in natural conditions we have not yet been able to assess.

18

Although there was no intellectual break in the chain of researches described in this chapter, it is convenient to pause here for recapitulation. The work arose from a background of exciting, natural fluctuations, revealed through the distorting media of fur-trade returns and records of economic damage, and also through the more direct but still fallible observations of naturalists. Here was something extraordinary and dynamic going on all over the world, and touching human affairs in violent ways. It was something in the texture of wild animal existence which had received little attention from zoologists. Means of elucidating this mystery had to be developed, although it did not seem at all an easy matter.

The first task was to make the most of methods already at hand: to improve and multiply fur-trade records, economic records, and the observations of naturalists. For the first of these the Hudson's Bay Company, with its magnificent network of posts in the Canadian North and its unrivalled fur-trade archives, became the natural agency. For the second and third little was done at first, but after 1928 an intelligence system was gradually developed, under the impetus given by the Empire Marketing Board. With all this there was a vast and scattered literature to be assembled and condensed: some of it forms the early chapters of this book.

Parallel with these enterprises a start was made at Oxford with the technical description and analysis of wild populations, and with some experiments upon them. The Bagley Wood survey of mice and voles showed how variable breeding seasons may cause changes in numbers, and how these variations react in curious ways upon the fauna of parasites. The latter was seen to be a complete community by no means confined to a single host. It was recorded how wild mice, usually in the height of health in nature and in captivity, may suddenly die in large numbers from quite obscure causes. To bear this out it could be shown that a great many rodents, and other mammals, have been found to suffer from epidemic mortality, sometimes communicable to man.

This first survey convinced us of the necessity for team work—for simultaneous exploration of the mysteries of numbers, breeding, and mortality (especially disease). Bearing in mind epidemiology, the fur trade, and rodent pests, attention was turned next upon the vole, *Microtus*.

Reports on vole numbers gave a general picture, and also revealed voles as important forest pests. This picture was inked in by a new system of sample trap censuses. The distribution of the fluctuating populations began to emerge into view. And the Forestry Commission's young plantations were seen to offer excellent sites for ecological study. Here were field stations ready made. An epidemiological experiment at Oxford failed in its immediate aims, but led on to some basic investigations on the breeding season of the vole, which incidentally revealed its surprisingly short length of life. From these researches we had begun to get our bearings. But there were many technical and organization problems still to be solved.

REFERENCES

1. BAKER, J. R. (1930). 'The breeding-season in British wild mice.' Proc. Zool. Soc. Lond.: 113–26.
2. BAKER, J. R., & RANSON, R. M. (1932). 'Factors affecting the breeding of the field mouse (*Microtus agrestis*). Part 1. Light.' Proc. Roy. Soc. B, 110: 313–22.
3. BAKER, J. R., & RANSON, R. M. (1932). 'Factors affecting the breeding of the field mouse (*Microtus agrestis*). Part 2. Temperature and food.' Proc. Roy. Soc. B, 112: 39–46.
4. BAKER, J. R., & RANSON, R. M. (1933). 'Factors affecting the breeding of the field mouse (*Microtus agrestis*). Part 3. Locality.' Proc. Roy. Soc. B, 113: 486–95.

5. BARRETT-HAMILTON, G. E. H. [& HINTON, M. A. C.] (1910–21). 'A history of British mammals.' London. 2: 450.

6. COLLETT, R. (1911–12). 'Norges pattedyr.' Christiania.

7. DARWIN, C. R. (1859). 'On the origin of species by means of natural selection....' London. Ch. 3, p. 70.

8. ELLIOTT, W. (1878). 'Some account of the plague of field mice in the Border farms, in 1876–7, with observations on the genus *Arvicola* in general.' History [Proc.] of the Berwickshire Naturalists' Club, 8: 447–72. [Reproduced also in the 1893 Dept. Ctee. Rep. as Appendix II.]

9. ELTON, C. S. (1924). 'Periodic fluctuations in the numbers of animals: their causes and effects.' Brit. J. Exp. Biol. 2: 119–63.

10. ELTON, C. S. (1925). 'Plague and the regulation of numbers in wild mammals.' J. Hyg., Camb. 24: 138–63.

11. ELTON, C. (1931). 'The study of epidemic diseases among wild animals.' J. Hyg., Camb. 31: 435–56.

12. ELTON, C., FORD, E. B., BAKER, J. R., & GARDNER, A. D. (1931). 'The health and parasites of a wild mouse population.' Proc. Zool. Soc. Lond. 657–721.

13. ELTON, C., & KEAY, G. (1936). 'The seasonal occurrence of harvest mites (*Trombicula autumnalis* Shaw) on voles and mice near Oxford.' Parasitology, 28: 110–14.

14. Forestry Commissioners, 19th Ann. Rep. (1939).

15. GARDNER, A. D. (1933). 'Bacteriology for medical students and practitioners.' Oxford. p. 266.

16. HEWITT, C. GORDON (1921). 'The conservation of the wild life of Canada.' New York. Ch. 9.

17. KEAY, G. (1927). 'The ecology of the harvest mite (*Trombicula autumnalis*) in the British Isles.' J. Anim. Ecol. 6: 23–35.

18. LOTKA, A. J. (1925). 'Elements of physical biology.' Baltimore. pp. 61–2.

19. MacLULICH, D. A. (1937). 'Fluctuations in the numbers of the varying hare (*Lepus americanus*).' Univ. Toronto Studies, Biol. Ser. No. 43: 1–136.

19 a. MIDDLETON, A. D. (1929). '*Leptospira icterohaemorrhagiae* in Oxford rats.' J. Hyg., Camb. 29: 219–26.

20. MIDDLETON, A. D. (1930). 'Cycles in the numbers of British voles (*Microtus*).' J. Ecol. 18: 156–65.

21. MIDDLETON, A. D. (1931). 'A further contribution to the study of cycles in British voles (*Microtus*).' J. Ecol. 19: 190–9.

22. MIDDLETON, A. D. (1931). 'A contribution to the biology of the common shrew.' Proc. Zool. Soc. London. 134–43.

23. MILLAIS, J. G. (1905). 'The mammals of Great Britain and Ireland.' London. 2: 255–77.

24. RANSON, R. M. (1934). 'The field vole (*Microtus*) as a laboratory animal.' J. Anim. Ecol. 3: 70–6.

25. SPENCER, H. (1863). 'First principles.' London. Sect. 96 (pp. 325–6).

26. VOLTERRA, V. (1931). 'Leçons sur la théorie mathématique de la lutte pour la vie.' Paris. [Contains references to his earlier papers in Italian.]

CHAPTER IX

BRITISH RESEARCH ON THE POPULATION DYNAMICS OF VOLES AND MICE: 1931–9

1

I DO not intend to enter at length into the circumstances which made possible the creation of the Bureau of Animal Population in 1932. Its strategic position and aims came naturally out of the investigations just described, and the history of its tactics is irrelevant to the present story of a particular group of researches. Three things, however, should be recorded. In 1931 there took place, in a remote French-Canadian fishing village on the north shore of the Gulf of St. Lawrence, a small international conference organized by Mr. Copley Amory, an American citizen. It was called the Matamek Conference on Biological Cycles,[10, 22] and the idea of it arose from Mr. Amory's preoccupation with the fluctuations in wild-life resources along the North Shore. Nearly all these fluctuations had hit the bottom of their cycles in 1931, in which year there were virtually no fur, animals, no mice, no game-birds, no lobsters, and no cod or mackerel.

This remarkable conference, buoyed by Mr. Amory's personality and vision, gave powerful support to a number of ecological projects that were staggering through the trough of the Depression in the human trade cycle, in particular the Oxford work, torpedoed by the dying out of the Empire Marketing Board and the desperate economies of the fur trade. Partly as a result of the Matamek discussions and partly through an interest already taken in fluctuations of wild life by the Society's president, Mr. Madison Grant, the New York Zoological Society gave initial support, without which the Bureau of Animal Population would never have been able to start.

The third circumstance was the Royal Society's decision to allocate, from their 'Darwin Fund', a large sum of money for research on vole populations. The Forestry Commission meanwhile continued to give us the use of its land and the help of its men. Later on it gave money also. The Agricultural Research Council and other bodies also helped, and eventually the Council took a considerable share in supporting this work at Oxford. This administrative story is recorded elsewhere, in the Annual Reports of the Bureau of Animal Population,[31, 32, 33] together with the progress of cognate researches.

The continuation of this work is best considered under its four natural categories of numbers, reproduction, mortality, and movements. It should be explained that a good part of the full results still remains to be published, and I do not wish to anticipate here what is a joint enterprise under the names of D. H. S. Davis, D. H. Chitty, R. M. Ranson, P. H. Leslie, V. S. Summerhayes, A. Q. Wells, and myself. To those sections of this team research which have already been published I shall refer in full. Some other aspects of it that have been mentioned in outline in the Annual Reports of the Bureau will also be alluded to.

In order to give the story a definite shape I shall confine it chiefly to the vole (*Microtus agrestis*). Even within this field I shall omit reference to the expeditions that have been made from Oxford to study mouse populations and their parasites in the smaller islands around Great Britain, also in the Faeroes and Iceland. These expeditions have been more concerned to record the facts of distribution and to reconstruct the history of island masses, than to analyse the current equilibria of populations. Equally I have to omit a fairly large corpus of research on other rodents, such as squirrels and rabbits.

It was realized from the start that the species *Microtus agrestis* (already split tentatively by taxonomists into two subspecies: *neglectus* and *hirtus*[21]) contains a range of different structural forms. Field trapping has provided abundant material for comparison of the skins and skulls, a material which gains greater significance from being tied up to other biological observations. Davis measured a great many vole skulls and had also the sizes of the animals themselves. One of the objects of this study was to find a good index to age, in the structure of the skull—this proved a difficult matter. But it also brought out the geographical trend in the size of British *Microtus agrestis*, which are small in the south of England, medium-sized on the Welsh and the Scottish Border hills, and very large in the west and north of Scotland. Most, if not all, of the characters that show a difference are dependent themselves on this general factor of size. In the course of these studies a convenient new method was invented,[9] of mounting skins in a flat state, so that they can be stored like index cards, with all the facts about them safely attached. We do not yet know all the effects of such size differences upon local population dynamics. The laboratory stocks at Oxford came from the intermediate category, a mixture of Welsh hill and Scottish Border voles, acclimatized to captivity in 1930.

2

The population work had two layers: first the measurement of fluctuations and of density, secondly the deeper discovery of the controlling causes in different environments. The first meant various census operations, the second a series of attempts to assess breeding, mortality, and movements in their framework of landscape, vegetation, climate, and animal associates.

For census work we started in 1930–1 with ten sample stations, widely scattered over England, Wales, and Scotland. They were all, except one, inside Forestry Commission land enclosed for planting, or already planted with young trees. Several proved unworkable because the soil or climate gave insufficient harbourage for voles. Very soon the scheme had shaken down to seven stations, all on hill country with thick grassy or rushy vegetation: one in Wales, one in the English Lake District, two on the

Scottish Border, two in western Scotland, and one in north-east Scotland. These stations were not random samples of British vole habitats, rather they were random samples of the *best* vole habitats the country could produce. In them we hoped to find most strikingly displayed the periodic results of over-abundance. We intended to give the general observations already made by Middleton and his network of recorders a greater precision, by extending and improving the methods of comparative census, and by learning the behaviour of populations on ground frequently visited by ourselves. This census work meant over 15,000 miles travelling by car each year, the farthest station being more than 500 miles from Oxford. Regular visits were made in April and September, since Baker and Ranson's research on the breeding season made it probable that most populations of voles would be at their lowest seasonal ebb in the spring, and their highest point in the autumn. This work was done by Davis and myself up to 1935, when Chitty took over Davis's part. The results have not yet been fully put together, owing to the axe of war. Since statements without supporting figures are the curse of natural history, I shall only condense here some of the general features of the work.

To the existing methods of recording vole fluctuations (by observers' reports and the trap censuses) we added a new one—the trace census.[11] This gives, by means of a series of small sample observations strung out along standard lines over several miles of country, a measure of the percentage of the whole area that is occupied by voles on a particular day. The method was invented in 1931 by Middleton and myself (also, independently, by W. J. Hamilton for *Microtus pennsylvanicus* in New York about the same time—see Chapter VI). It is very laborious to carry out, but it usually enables one man to define after a day's work the general state of vole occupation on a forest plantation of several thousand acres. In this way the development of a vole cycle and the incidence of the periodic 'crash' can be watched. The observer, moreover, crawling through deep vegetation on his hands and knees, in search of the fresh droppings and other traces left by voles in their runways, is brought into intimate contact with the ecology of the vole.

We had to consider what time of day to do the censuses. This depended partly upon the activity rhythm of the vole: for it would be useless to compare the numbers during an active period with those apparently shown during comparative inactivity. Davis[6] therefore designed some experiments in which captive voles were kept in cages with floors on springs. A pointer attached to the floor recorded activity on a drum which rotated by clockwork. The voles were found to have a persistent rhythm of alternate activity and rest, whose period was quite short—about two or three hours. A normal vole would sleep and be active (and eat) about ten times in twenty-four hours. Since there can be no synchronization between short individual rhythms of this sort, the activity of the population is spread out over the day and night—unlike that of *Apodemus*, which is active only at night. There were some signs of such a major rhythm in the vole, but not sufficient to affect the validity of trace and trap censuses at different times of day. One of Davis's charts is shown in Fig. 11.

3

A trap-line census was also done in April and August, by the foresters, and the voles sent in for examination. The two methods, trace and trap, are really different ways of measuring the same thing: that is, the number of small patches or points on the ground crossed by voles in twenty-four hours. One gives the advantage that animals are not killed and removed from the population, the other kills them, but thereby provides actual bodies for examination. The statistical results have shown that the two methods, with certain exceptions, give the same picture of fluctuations in numbers.

These fluctuations are usually of tremendous amplitude. One year 150 sample points may show no traces or catch no voles at all; three years later nearly all have traces and the trap catch on the first night may be very high. But, although fluctuations in any one district (e.g. the Cowal District of Argyll) may go strongly together in rhythm, there is not, as we had originally supposed, the same exact correlation between distant points. But a single forest will act as a unit in the cycle. The west of Argyll has been most regular, with main peaks in 1922, 1926, 1929, 1932, 1935, and 1938, peaks often separated by troughs when the area seemed to be deserted by the voles.

When one full cycle of 3–4 years had run its course, field work was concentrated more intensively on three areas only: one census station in north Wales, one on the Scottish Border, and two in Argyll. Newcastleton, on the Border, has the longest record of observations, because it was here that the most consistent and active help was received from the forester in charge, Mr. J. F. MacIntyre, to whose co-operation the Bureau is deeply indebted. Trap censuses have been done from 1929 to 1939, and trace censuses from 1931 to 1939. To these stations another has been added more recently, in north Wales.

The ideal population study would be able to preserve a complete mathematical picture or expression of the interplay between increase (by breeding or immigration) and decrease (through death or emigration), with the resultant moving equilibrium of numbers. In such an early era of the subject, with methods themselves only just emerging for their first trials, it is not to be expected that all these elusive and quickly changing phenomena can be grasped and put in relation to one another. Rather, we have to be content with the gradual appearance, in a rather general form, of some of the processes at work, and with a number of reasonable hypotheses that need much further substantiation.

It was not possible to maintain the examination of voles for breeding rates begun by Baker and Ranson, except with material from the trap censuses in spring and autumn. The labour on the forest and in the laboratory could not be found. There is also a fundamental difficulty arising

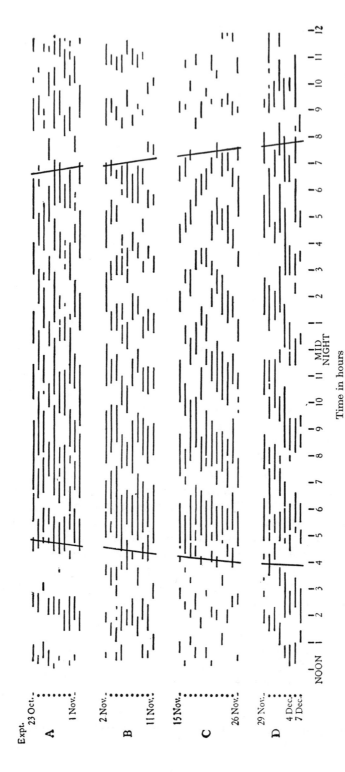

Time in hours

Fig. 11. Records of activity of a vole (*Microtus agrestis*) in four different experiments under different conditions of feeding and gradually lengthening nights. Horizontal lines show periods of activity, sloping lines mark sunset and sunrise. The records show both the short 2- to 4-hour rhythm and the long 24-hour rhythm. (From Davis, 1933.)

from the great scarcity of voles in the low years of the cycle, which makes
the collection of a statistical sample almost impossible. Therefore we have
no direct means of knowing whether variations in breeding rate partly
control the cycle. Such variations might operate either through the length
or the intensity of the breeding season. We can only say, from the two
years of Baker and Ranson's work, that the breeding season is strongly
developed, and probably varies a little from year to year—how much or
how regularly we do not yet know.

4

Although most of the work has been done inside the peculiar conditions
of forest plantations, one has the strong impression that the vole fluctuations are not often developed on open pasture. This we should expect from
the obvious need of voles for food and cover and freedom from trampling
and burning. Therefore, these violent oscillations are seen as an effect
produced by the creation of optimum conditions for vole life, in which they
multiply for a short time up to new limits of environmental pressure
resulting in a crash. Now, these special conditions only exist for a short
period, between enclosure and the ultimate growing up to closed canopy
of the trees, which kill out the grass and rushes upon which the voles
depend. This period is about fifteen years or less. It may be less because
the luxuriant growth of grass protected from grazing and burning, and
often helped also by deep draining of the ground, may not always develop
quickly; and because some trees, such as larch and Sitka spruce, grow up
more rapidly than others. Within this period of fifteen years or less there
is time for three, perhaps four, cycles of population to occur. State planting of forests began in 1919, so that the area of possible vole-cycle ground
was increasing up to 1934. In 1936–7 there were still 284,400 planted acres
less than fifteen years old. With a steady new planting programme this
area would stay approximately constant for a good many years. Equally,
the problem of vole damage will continue to recur on many forests as they
pass through this ecological phase.

There are occasional conditions in which voles multiply on open pasture,
as was seen in Chapter VII; and other smaller examples could be cited.
But the cycle examined in the present chapter arises chiefly from a special
alteration by man of a delicate environmental equilibrium, an alteration
which itself brings into action forces (vole damage) inimical to the object
of the change (the growing of trees). And the scale of new forest planting
is so great that it must have increased the average vole population of Great
Britain by many millions. (To get some fuller information about damage
by voles to trees, the Forestry Commission began in 1936 to get questionnaire information annually from all its forests, for analysis at Oxford.)

Voles at the peak of their abundance exert a terrific pressure on the
vegetation they live in. The eye is struck by the shattered, 'moth-eaten'
appearance of the grass and rushes. Tussocks come away in the hand
where voles have gnawed the roots. There is a sieve-like look about the

moss-clumps. Little piles of grass or rushes, cut into short lengths, are frequent in the runways or under the arching grass tussocks. The seeds of tormentil (*Potentilla erecta*) are harvested by the voles. Masses of greenish dung are evidence of the great ecological transaction that is in full swing. Any young shoot of rush or grass that appears in a runway is soon sheared off. The soil is more than usually drained by holes and deep burrows in the peat.

In order to get an objective record of this pressure on vegetation, experiments were started by V. S. Summerhayes,[26] a botanist at Kew Herbarium, in collaboration with the vole census team. Fine-mesh wire cages were erected on two forests several hundred miles apart. Each cage effectively excluded voles from a patch of vegetation about the size of an ordinary room. There were other patches open to vole destruction, kept as controls. An ingenious method of sampling gave a measure of the plant life present and of the changes in it from year to year. The observations were repeated for eight years. The results were quite conclusive: voles act so powerfully on the vegetation that they keep down dominant grasses sufficiently to permit some species (for instance mosses), that would otherwise be crowded out, to exist, and others to be more abundant. So the vole partly determines the floristic composition on hills (now numerous) used for forestry. With the recent granting to the public of access to some of these forested areas, the vole becomes a notable agent of the 'flower management' for public pleasure and scientific preservation, so eloquently advocated by Leopold.[23]

5

The thick grassy or mossy vegetation gives cover against weather and enemies, which is increased when the young trees start to grow up. Food, except possibly in the critical winter months of a peak abundance, is almost unlimited. Nest material and nest sites are numerous. The runway systems above and underground become well defined and are reoccupied at each recurrent increase. Of the action of climate on vole populations we know still very little, and a strenuous search of meteorological records has only revealed one definite suggestion.

A. H. Goldie, of the Scottish Meteorological Office, noticed a curious anomaly in some magnetic instrumental records, which led him to study recurrences in weather conditions.[20] He found that pressure-gradients, calculated in a certain way, showed a very well-marked recurrent change since 1903, with a periodicity of three or four years. This came out clearly in the pressure differences between Eskdalemuir (not far from Newcastleton, on the Scottish Border) and Lerwick, in Orkney. The rhythm appears also consistently in wind strength and direction. The cycle is therefore essentially a measurement of the average flow of certain air components over Scotland. There are strong correlations also with sunshine, temperature, and rainfall, and Goldie has adumbrated a wide hypothesis of recurrent meteorological changes over quite a large area, to account for all these aspects of the cycle. Here is a rhythm in weather, of the same length as that in voles. Our earlier records of vole fluctuations in Scotland are too thin to use in correlation, and so we can at present only note the two parallel recurrences, and hope that Goldie's discovery may lead to the elucidation of the climatic factors involved in the northern cycle as a whole (see Chapters X–XXII).

We have seen how vegetation, created by human disturbance, brings about the possibility of higher densities (in turn rebounding on vegetation and on human profits) and of conspicuous cyclical change; and how there is a suggestion that climate may also influence the periodicity and its regional distribution. We have now to consider the other biological features of the fluctuation: predators, parasites, disease, length of life and fertility, and movements.

6

It was shown in Chapter VII how scarce the predators of voles have become in the last hundred years. So any conclusion we may draw about them applies only to these shamefully attenuated modern populations. The main conclusion so far has been that voles may strongly control the local abundance of some predators, but the latter do not control the numbers of their prey, cause the fluctuations, or (this is less certain) keep them regionally in step.

Three separate investigations may be selected from a mass of less co-ordinated field observations. Russell Goddard[18, 19] made an annual spring census of short-eared owls (*Asio flammeus*) on the forest at Newcastleton, for comparison with the vole changes. He began in 1934 when voles were reaching their peak of numbers. That spring there were certainly three pairs of owls nesting, possibly four. Their potential foraging area was over 2,300 acres, nearly all good ground for voles. Here they could be watched quartering the ground with slow wing-beats, occasionally pouncing on a prey. Cast pellets of the owls contained *Microtus* and the common shrew (*Sorex araneus*).[11] Vole decrease happened in the spring of the following year, 1935, when only one pair of owls was found. The later censuses have not yet been published, but these two years of counting suggested two definite conclusions: a correlation of owl numbers with vole population changes, and the comparatively small number of owls on ground containing certainly hundreds of thousands of voles.

In 1936 Chitty[3] carried this kind of work to a further stage by measuring the food requirements of a captive short-eared owl. The idea was to calculate how many voles an owl was likely to eat in the course of a year, and so, by combination with Russell Goddard's field censuses, assess the importance of 'owl pressure' in affecting or controlling the numbers of voles. The investigation involved experiments upon the amounts of food eaten and also of the food remains rejected in the form of castings or pellets. The rhythm of feeding was recorded ingeniously in apparatus which timed the feeding and the subsequent vomiting up of the indigestible fur and bones. 'Food was so placed that its removal caused an electric circuit to be completed. . . . Pellets were caught beneath the owl's perch . . . and directed on to a lever that dipped momentarily into a mercury contact. Both operations caused a bell to ring (thereby attracting attention in the laboratory), and separate marks were made on a disc of paper rotating once in twelve hours on the face of an alarm clock.' After making a number of reservations, some of which will occur to the reader, he concluded that eight short-eared owls were unlikely to eat between them more than fifty voles a day, although there would be more than this brought to their young, and perhaps some wasted. 'Nevertheless, even if voles constituted the entire diet, the daily predation [of these eight owls for their own use] cannot have been much in excess of 0·02 to 0·05 per cent. of the vole population, which would not seriously have affected its density.'

The figures suggested that this captive owl at any rate would have eaten something like 2,000 ($\pm$50 per cent.) small mammals in a year, or 47–142 lb. of vole. (About 7 per cent. of this is rejected in the pellets.) The large variation included here is caused by several known factors, for which Chitty was able to define some mathematical relations.

A third predator measurement was started by Chitty and myself in Argyll in 1936, on a hill called Ben Lagan, which forms a massive natural unit some five miles round at the base, and about 1,600 feet high. Here a whole cycle of voles was measured in the standard way, up to the peak in 1938 and crash in the following year. Besides direct observations on raptorial birds, a series of permanent numbered posts was set up, and the pellets collected periodically below them. These figures probably reflect the increase and decrease of predatory birds with the voles, and the method is one that should be tested more widely and over long periods.

Among these Argyll hills one can still get some feeling of the natural community of vole predators: short-eared and long-eared owls, common buzzard, kestrel, fox, and weasel, and there is no doubt at all from our observations hitherto that the vole fluctuation dominates the local abundance of many of them from year to year. Presumably afforestation by the State, in multiplying voles, has also encouraged a renaissance of hawks and owls, wherever the keeper is kept in check. This renaissance may eventually have quite a considerable influence on the course of the vole cycle, taking us back to the conditions of the eighteenth century when, as I suggest in Chapter VII, predators were abundant enough to prevent any very big outbreak of voles on the hills.

7

The most natural theory to account for the decline in numbers of voles after they have reached their peak is that overcrowding leads to an increase in parasites and of contacts between the voles, to further spread of parasites, and the flaring up of disease. I have already described, in the last chapter, the fine collection of fleas, mites, ticks, lice, and worms that mice and voles support. Davis has, similarly, analysed[7] the parasites and 'guests' that live in the nests of voles. And the earlier chapters contain circumstantial stories of disease during vole outbreaks in various countries.

Here, in theory, are the components of a cycle in host-parasite relationships, which suggest a reasonable direction for research. Yet one has to be very careful about relying on any *a priori* reasoning of this kind. In India there are fluctuations in numbers of wild rats, increase in numbers of the fleas, spread of the flea-borne bacteria of plague, epidemic in rats, cross-infection, and epidemic in man. But in this sequence of events other factors like climate may either encourage or completely blanket the ecological trends. Again, take spirochaetal jaundice. An English town may have an abundant population of brown rats, half of which carry the dangerous spirochaete of jaundice in their kidneys. Yet there is no pandemic in man, only occasional effective contacts with people who follow special occupations that bring them into danger. In the United States some factors that are not yet properly known at present screen the human community rather effectively from the menace of sylvatic plague in wild rodents (see Chapter VI). It does not follow therefore that because high density is reached and parasites (including many blood-drinkers) are numerous, that the crash that comes is necessarily caused by epidemic disease. This truth was partly hidden from us in the early years of the work on voles.

There is another situation that may also exist and is liable to lead the ecologist astray. Even if, in a particular instance, disease does break out and kill voles at their peak, this does not prove that disease always controls the rhythm of the cycle. It may be an occasional symptom, not a recurrent dominant cause. To this idea I shall return later in the chapter. Meanwhile we have to examine several pieces of research which have been done on vole diseases.

When Gardner tried to find disease among *Microtus* in the Oxford district in 1927 (see Chapter VIII) he was hampered by having no disease-free laboratory voles to use in transmission experiments. This had always been a difficulty in studying wild animal diseases, if these were specific and the animals had never been kept long or bred in captivity. The difficulty is intensified if the pathologist encounters virus infections, or disease from other organisms which cannot be grown outside the body of an experimental animal. These considerations gave a double value to the success of Baker and Ranson in breeding voles in captivity and so 'breaking in' this species to the use both of the physiologist and the pathologist. Fortunately this stock of voles has remained practically free from disease since it was inaugurated ten years ago.

So by 1932 we had three of the tools needed for investigating vole disease: an intelligence system for following the vole cycle in the field; a staff of ecologists to organize the collection of material at the crucial time; and a stock of laboratory voles for experiments. We were fortunate in getting the fourth element: a versatile pathologist well used to the study of new infections of man and animals, and willing to take a chance with this evidently difficult and unconventional problem. Dr. G. M. Findlay and some of his associates in the Wellcome Bureau of Scientific Research (part of a great privately endowed research foundation in London) have done much to carry this side of the work along.

In the Cowal District of Argyll, and especially on the mountains around the twelve-mile long inland water of Loch Eck, we already knew, through Middleton's inquiries, something of the vole cycle. This had reached peaks in 1922, 1926, and 1929. Before each of these bad damage was done to trees. Renewed increase led to serious damage during the winter of 1931–2, and in the following spring and autumn of 1932 the voles increased still more. Anticipating the periodic crash in the spring of 1933, Middleton began to organize the collection of live voles, only to find that even by the end of January voles had already diminished. During March and April it proved difficult to catch ten a week. The live voles were sent by train to London, and none died during journeys of up to twenty-four hours. They were kept and examined at the Wellcome Bureau, whither other, healthy, voles were sent from Oxford.[17]

A similar situation had developed at Lake Vyrnwy in North Wales, where the slopes round Liverpool's big reservoir have been planted with young trees by the Corporation Waterworks organization. Not much was known about earlier vole history here, but the high numbers and damage to trees in the winter of 1932–3 were thought to foreshadow a crash in the spring. Although there was some mortality among these voles, they recovered during 1933, and did not finally crash to low level until the winter of 1933–4. But in Argyll great scarcity was reached in 1933.

A new disease appeared among the voles that came to London from both places. The symptoms were of a nervous affliction—lethargy followed by convulsions and often paralysis of the hind limbs, leading to death. Gardner had noticed similar symptoms in wild Oxford voles in 1927, though for technical reasons he could not follow the matter through (see Chapter VIII). Findlay, after a thorough search, could find no pathogenic organism except a Protozoan, called *Toxoplasma*, which formed cysts inside the voles' brains. Toxoplasms are rather vaguely placed in the classification of Protozoa. They had, before this, been detected in the brains of various laboratory or captive animals of other species. But this was the first evidence that they might cause an epidemic in nature. Infected brain material reproduced the disease symptoms and the *Toxoplasma*, by passage in laboratory-bred voles, in the stocks of which the parasite was not otherwise detected. Efforts to find out how it might spread naturally failed; but it is known that, in guinea-pigs at any rate, the parasite can enter with the food.

If the brain emulsions were put through fine filters, no disease was produced by inoculation into voles. This made it unlikely that an invisible virus was present. In *Toxoplasma* we therefore had a possible cause of the cyclical crash in voles—the first definite fact about an epidemic disease organism in them. Its occurrence, both in Argyll and north Wales, suggested a wide distribution and a general importance.

8

While these events were taking place in Argyll and North Wales a similar cycle in numbers was developing at Newcastleton, on the western part of the Scottish Border. (Close to the north of this forestry estate lies the great vole-plague region described in Chapter VII. The southern boundary is a stream marking the frontier between Scotland and England. Extending from here south-east and east are large tracts of English plantation where voles also multiply.) The Newcastleton voles reached their peak a year later than those at the other two places, and so it was possible to use the experience gained at them for improvement of methods: in ecological survey, census measurements, trapping and transport methods, and recording mortality rates in the laboratory. Also the work could be started in time to record conditions before, during, and after the crash. The results are fully recorded in a paper by Davis, Findlay, and myself.[11]

From ecological surveys and previous trapping it was known that *Microtus agrestis* was the only important mouse-like rodent living on the 2,020 acres of this forest. Trap censuses over six years had given 546 *Microtus agrestis*, 32 *Clethrionomys* (*Evotomys*) *glareolus*, also 130 shrews, *Sorex araneus*. The live-trapping during the epidemic time gave 270 *Microtus*, 1 *Clethrionomys*, 1 *Apodemus sylvaticus*, and 20 *Sorex*. Here, then, was almost a 'pure culture' of one kind of mouse-like rodent.

Previous trace and trap-line censuses had measured a peak in 1930, followed by a decrease in 1931, and recovery again through 1932 to large numbers in the autumn of 1933. At this time all parts of the younger plantations were closely invested by voles, though in the conditions obtaining here, with very solid grassy vegetation, little tree damage occurred. Intensive work was started in January 1934 and went on until July. A forestry apprentice, James Murray, trapped live voles which were sent by rail to the Wellcome Bureau of Scientific Research in London, moving on each month to a fresh section of similar ground. He also kept full field notes. On each section Davis and I did a trace census before live-trapping began. In this way any sudden drop in numbers could be observed. The occupation index kept quite high from January to March (varying between 80 and 94 per cent.). In the early days of March a sample block of ground was trapped very thoroughly in order to measure the actual density of voles. The figures suggested that these high trace censuses represented vole densities between 100 and 200 to an acre. (The actual block, with a trace census of 72 per cent., had 76 per acre on the central part.) If such figures were roughly applicable to the forest as a whole (and there was evidence of this from our long standard lines, covering a mile or two of country), Newcastleton Forest had at this time hundreds of thousands of voles living in it—anything up to half a million.

In April and May the trace census was still fairly high, though down to 70 per cent. and 65 per cent. But by June there was a catastrophic crash, to 8 per cent., and in July it was still only 9 per cent. This crash took place just when breeding would normally have taken up the slack of the winter pause. Breeding had certainly been going fairly normally in April. Census had shown a definite cycle. What was the evidence about disease?

It is difficult to get a reliable picture of natural epidemics unless the pathologist, with all his armoury of elaborate equipment, is close to the spot. Usually, the dying or potentially sick animals have to be brought some distance before they can be examined. Two errors arise from this. The actual shock and trials of trapping and transport may in themselves reduce vitality and render voles more liable to disease. And those already most susceptible may die selectively before they reach the laboratory, and will usually be too decomposed for reliable testing. In 1934 the trap deaths varied from 35 to 55 per cent., mainly from overnight exposure. A small number died before dispatch and on the way to London. Others died at various intervals after arrival. The figures for deaths after leaving the traps suggest a great increase in mortality just before and during the crash recorded by the censuses:

	Jan.	*Feb.*	*Mar.*	*Apr.*	*May*	*June*
% deaths between leaving traps and reaching laboratory .	6	7	26	**36**	**41**	25
% deaths during first 14 days in laboratory	10	23	**54**	**69**	28	16

The symptoms of disease were studied on a few voles which died under careful observation. In every respect the pathological picture resembled that seen in Argyll and Welsh voles in 1933. *Toxoplasma* was found in many of the brains. Filtered material did not reproduce the disease in healthy voles. But inoculation of unfiltered brain emulsion carried on the disease through four consecutive passages in voles. There was, indeed, one serious gap in the chain of evidence caused by the distance between the area and the laboratory: we could not prove that *Toxoplasma* was present actually on the area or in voles living on it. The evidence, however, pointed very strongly towards this conclusion.

9

Before going on to the later development of this epidemiological research we may turn aside to another aspect of disease in voles. It had always seemed to me that the number of laboratory-bred animals commonly used for the study of human and domestic animal diseases was phenomenally small: a tiny community of domesticated rodents, mostly albino forms. We have house-mouse, Norway rat, guinea-pig, and rabbit; besides these rodents, the cat and dog, though they are too expensive for prodigal use. Yet we live in a world tenanted by many hundreds of species of rodents, to mention only one order of mammals. And it is very well known that success in research on a disease of man or any of the larger domestic animals often depends upon finding a small, cheap, easily handled animal that can be bred in captivity, and which also happens (in the lucky-bag of bacteriological susceptibility) to take the disease in question. For instance, in tuberculosis and in foot-and-mouth disease research, the guinea-pig has been the key animal for experiments. It would be completely impossible to work on the same scale or in the same way with men or cattle. There are, however, still a number of diseases that have no effective small laboratory animal: measles and small-pox are two examples.

In 1928 I suggested to the Medical Research Council that human diseases should be tested systematically upon the small wild mammals that might be suitable for experimental work, at the same time that the natural diseases of these creatures were being explored. Something of the sort has begun to happen in the slow, undirected, and rather solidly organic manner of British research; but there is still need for a more concerted investigation, such as the Government might organize. At any rate the main point continually proves itself in individual pieces of research. The ferret has tremendously advanced our knowledge of dog distemper and of human influenza. The hedgehog opens up new channels of work on foot-and-mouth disease. The Chinese striped hamster (*Cricetulus griseus*) is used for the study of kala-azar, a tropical disease. The vole, as will be shown, enables the pathologist to distinguish relatively quickly between human and bovine strains of the tuberculosis organism. Monkeys and hedgehogs have given an impetus to yellow-fever research. This subject merges into the larger one of wild animals as natural reservoirs for disease of man and his stock; but this cannot be explored here.

Once the vole had become an established animal of the laboratory, efforts were made to encourage its use in other institutions. Already *Microtus agrestis* has been found by laboratory tests to be favourable to the virus of Rift Valley fever[13] (an East African disease of man and sheep); the virus of louping ill[15] (a tick-borne nervous disease of British sheep); the virus of climatic bubo[12] (a rather rare venereal disease of man); the neurotropic strain of yellow-fever virus[14] (mosquito-borne disease of man and wild monkeys, tropical 'Yellow Jack'); human and bovine strains of *Mycobacterium*[28] (the organism of tuberculosis); the virus of foot-and-mouth disease[30] (calamitous contagious disease of cattle and pigs); *Toxoplasma*; rolling disease of mice[16] (caused by a pleuropneumonia-like organism); as well as other agents. Here is a fertile field of discovery, even with the vole alone. An extension of this work at Oxford recently has been the successful breeding of hedgehogs (*Erinaceus europeus*) in captivity, also by R. M. Ranson,[33] primarily for the needs of foot-and-mouth disease research. But every time a new wild mammal is introduced to laboratory life, we have not only a new tool for research upon disease, but the possibility of studying the vital population statistics of a wild species, which aid in the interpretation of population questions in the field.

10

For a year or two after 1934 the pathological side of research on voles

14

proved difficult to organize, partly because Dr. Findlay had necessarily to concentrate elsewhere on a very important advance in the prevention of yellow fever. But from 1936 to 1939 the Bureau was able at last to arrange for the full-time co-operation of a pathologist working in Oxford on the vole disease problem. This research by Dr. A. Q. Wells (with a grant from the Medical Research Council) has produced a remarkable discovery, of which the details have not yet all been fully published, and the working out of which has now been interrupted (like most of the other vole work) by war. Wells was later assisted by an American student, W. S. Brooke.

Given a pathologist, it was necessary to keep him steadily supplied with wild voles, and these had to be, so far as possible, from areas on which something was known about the changes in the population. And the trapping of voles had to be planned in such a way that it would not deplete the population so far as to destroy the object of the work. This meant that the populations, and therefore the areas, had to be large ones. Chitty and I did surveys to find good places that would fulfil these requirements; all these were more than 100 miles away. The extreme amplitude of vole fluctuations made it necessary to keep several sources of supply going in case one dried up for a while. These difficulties were eventually overcome by Chitty's organizing and technical improvements.[4] The areas were, as before, young forest plantations on the Scottish and Welsh hills. The catching was done by the local men of the Forestry Commission and Liverpool Corporation. Trap baiting was improved. A new tunnel-trap set in runways impounded the vole by closing doors at both ends. The vole then climbed into a minute tin hay-loft stocked with food, where it could sleep and eat. This arrangement cut down overnight deaths from 57 per cent. to less than 13 per cent. With good management there are now hardly any deaths. This trapping itself provided an index of numbers, which was so far as possible amplified by other field censuses. Voles now travelled individually in tins, as privileged passengers whose health was a matter of great concern. Sometimes they were as much as thirty-two hours in transit without taking harm. The tins were sterilized and used again. Through all these operations a careful tally was kept for analysis.

With a flow of wild voles coming in from natural populations, and a parallel stream of control ones bred in the laboratory, the first study of vole pathology on a large scale could begin. Hitherto ideas had dwelt mostly on the periodic outburst of disease. The mice and voles in Bagley Wood had predisposed us to expect a long run of health punctuated by epidemics. At first it seemed that this new investigation was going to go the same way, and that the pathologist's job would be to sign an indefinite number of health certificates for voles that had been brought with expense and trouble from their deep grassy runways on the hills to captivity in Oxford. But in January 1937 a wild vole died with symptoms of a tubercular disease.[27]

'The post-mortem examination showed caseous areas throughout the subcutaneous tissues of the body, involving the glands of the neck, axillae, inguinal region, and back, with ulceration of the skin round the right pinna; both lungs contained caseous areas with sharply defined edges; the mediastinal and mesenteric glands were much enlarged and caseous; the spleen was enlarged. The caseous material in the subcutaneous tissues contained a very large number of acid-fast bacilli, which have the morphology of *Mycobacterium tuberculosis*. The caseous areas in the lungs similarly contained a great number of acid-fast bacilli. . . . Cultures made from the caseous material yielded no growth on nutrient agar, but growth was visible after six weeks on Dorset's agar and Petroff's medium. The nature of the growth and the morphology of the organism were similar to that of *Mycobacterium tuberculosis*.'

This organism was then transmitted to other voles and to guinea-pigs, in which the disease could be reproduced.

Although the vole described here had been more than a month in the laboratory, it soon became clear that the new disease certainly existed in wild individuals, and that it was very widespread in Great Britain. It has already been found in 3 places in England, 4 in Wales, and 9 in Scotland: from at least Perthshire to near London, and, incidentally, around Oxford. It is not confined to *Microtus*, for Wells has also observed it in *Clethrionomys glareolus* and *Apodemus sylvaticus*, and even in the shrew (*Sorex araneus*).[33] We have here again that sharing of parasites among different species in the community, that was discussed in Chapter VIII. The disease has never been found in the Oxford laboratory voles.

11

This discovery was extraordinary in several ways. Hitherto it had been generally believed in the medical world that tuberculosis was almost entirely a disease of man, and of domesticated or captive animals and birds. Furthermore there were known to be three well-marked types of *Mycobacterium tuberculosis*: the human, bovine, and avian. The last of these does not come into the present story. The vole organism is quite certainly different from those of human and bovine tuberculosis, yet resembles them sufficiently to be a candidate for the genus and possibly for the same species. In 1937 and 1938 the position could be defined as follows: 'It seems clear from the work already done that it is an undescribed *Mycobacterium* and possibly a new type of *M. tuberculosis*. . . .'[32] 'The exact position of the organism in the genus *Mycobacterium* (to which it belongs) is being systematically studied.'[33]

The failure of previous workers to notice the disease may have been due to the comparatively small numbers of voles that they looked at. What is more extraordinary (and, from the research point of view, fortunate) is that the laboratory stocks at Oxford have been free from the infection, although it has recently been found in voles from both the places of origin of the original wild stock. The extent of infection varies, of course, from place to place and at different times. An epidemiological story for one area in Wales has been rather fully worked out by Chitty and Wells, but the results are not yet published. It can be said, however, that this tubercular disease does not seem to provide a key to the general problem of the vole cycle. It does not act in any simple manner as a general cause of decline at high density. On the other hand, the existence of a partly chronic infection that can, with practice, be easily identified by the pathologist opens up an entirely new vista of epidemiological work on wild populations.

There is another aspect to this discovery that concerns voles, though not the vole cycle. It had long been known, though rather forgotten, that Robert Koch infected voles with tuberculosis. He used the Continental *Microtus arvalis*. More recently Griffith[20a] had infected wild *Microtus agrestis* with both the bovine and the human types, and noticed that the human one did not infect so easily. Wells[28] repeated this work with laboratory voles, which showed an enormously greater susceptibility to bovine than to human tubercle bacilli. From his experiments he suggested that 'a dose of 0·001 mg. moist weight of culture of tubercle bacilli injected intraperitoneally into voles should distinguish unfailingly between human and bovine tubercle bacilli in one month'. The point of this is that tubercle bacilli are very slow to grow in culture media, so that the vole may offer a quicker decision in doubtful cases of the disease in man (which actually may come from either the 'human' or 'bovine' types).

The vole disease has another valuable property. One of the greatest blanks in tuberculosis work has been the general failure to produce immunity to tuberculosis in animals. The chief exception is that human tubercle bacilli arouse immunity in cattle. Wells and Brooke found,[29] in some preliminary experiments that were curtailed by the outbreak of war, that they could greatly increase the immunity of guinea-pigs to both human and bovine tubercle bacilli, by vaccinating them first with live cultures of the vole acid-fast bacillus, to which the guinea-pig is only rather mildly susceptible. These discoveries have altered the bias of medical thought about the group of acid-fast bacilli concerned with tubercular lesions, and they open up plenty of lines for more epidemiological work, both on voles and upon the disease tuberculosis.[1] They still leave that stubborn rock of a problem, the vole-crash, to which we turn now once more.

While Wells was working on the new acid-fast bacillus in voles, he also watched for signs of other kinds of disease. So far, no evidence of *Toxoplasma* or symptoms of nervous disease have been recorded again, even in populations that were passing through their periodic decline in numbers. The elusiveness of *Toxoplasma* seemed surprising after its wide presence in 1933 and 1934. Additional information on this subject was obtained by Professor Edward Hindle in 1938–9. At this time the cycle in Argyll was at its peak. It was much simpler to send live voles across the Clyde to Glasgow than on a 450-mile journey to Oxford. The Forestry School at Benmore mobilized some of its students to trap voles on hills near those on which regular censuses were being made. These were kept in the Department of Zoology of Glasgow University and examined for *Toxoplasma* or kept to see if they died of disease.[33] The results are still unpublished, but Professor Hindle informs me that no signs at all of the parasite were found during the whole period of vole peak and crash.

From all these conflicting, yet evidently real lines of evidence, we may conclude that neither of the two diseases so far encountered throws any light on the *regular recurrence* of vole-crash periods. We cannot say that they never cause severe epidemics in particular cases, but at present they are seen either as local and incidental consequences of high density, or else as phenomena not primarily linked with density. To sum up, there is one disease (from *Toxoplasma*) which is reported in three different cycle crashes and is not seen again; and another (from an acid-fast bacillus) that occurs both as a chronic and epidemic disease, yet does not fit at all clearly into the cyclical picture. If we exclude, for the present, the possibility of some other organism which has entirely escaped the keen notice of pathologists, we are forced to look in other directions for an explanation.

12

The bits of research just described are little more than reconnaissance, preliminary probings into a matter which is still mysterious in a great many ways. It would not be right to decide now that enemies and parasites exert no control over the numbers of voles. But it certainly seems less likely than it did ten years ago that they are a dominant influence. The picture at present is of predators too scarce and disease too erratic to explain the persistent cycles that generate. There are, however, a great many other causes of death in a population, each of which needs a special technique for its study—comparable with the owl census and pellet analysis, or pathological testing and parasite survey. I have suggested elsewhere that there are, in any mammal population, nine main classes of mortality: pre-natal; physiological 'wear and tear' throughout life; food deficiency (including lack of accessory food factors); water deficiency; physical accident; chemical accident (such as poisoning); disease from parasites; death from predators (including man); and deaths in competition (as among rival males and other members of the species). There is some information about the first two and the last of these which may have a close bearing on the vole cycle.

We saw in the last chapter that Baker and Ranson believed the vole to be mainly or entirely an 'annual'. By this was meant that all or most wild voles only have one breeding season in their lives. 'During the winter the species is represented, so far as males are concerned, entirely by small, immature specimens less than a year old. These become fecund next spring and die in the autumn or early winter. The majority of the mature females also die in autumn or early winter.' This would mean that few voles lived to be more than twelve months old. In Baker and Ranson's breeding chart (built on records from three places over two years) one can see the older breeding animals getting heavier and fewer as the summer advances and breeding begins to stop, and below them arriving a mass of smaller voles many of which may not breed until the following spring.

However, this is circumstantial evidence in which we have to use weight to measure age, and there are therefore possible loop-holes in it. In order to find out by experiment how long voles live, a few of the laboratory stock were set aside soon after being weaned, and kept until they died, some in solitary confinement, some with mates. The figures for 144 such pensioners have been collected by Ranson and analysed by Leslie,[25] who found the average length of life (taking both male and female voles together) to be only about eight and a half months. These animals were weaned before the experiment began, and some allowance had to be made for deaths between the times of birth and weaning, which are much heavier than in later life. This factor was also worked out, and the average expectation of life at birth now came out at about seven and a half months. Of 100,000 voles born alive 45,382 would be alive at 32 weeks old, and only 2,357 at 64 weeks, none after 100 weeks. In other words, only 2·3 per cent. of the original population would be alive after 15 months. But these figures only apply to healthy voles in the optimum conditions of a warm laboratory, where there is ample food and water, freedom from most accidents and from the attacks of enemies and rivals. In nature these other agents of death would undoubtedly pull down the average length of life—unless, indeed, what we believe to be optimum conditions in the laboratory actually lack some factor that promotes greater longevity in the field.

This study of the 'life-table' of the vole has several further aspects. We may note that it extends the rather restricted number of cases in which actuarial methods have been successfully applied to the vital statistics of a wild animal. The others that have been done include a wheel animalcule or rotifer, a fly, a moth, and the white rat. A second feature is the shape of the life-curve: Although this varies in different species, and in the same species under different conditions, all the curves have one remarkable property: mortality starts in very early life and rolls on until all are dead. A curve for voles (based in this instance on 119 individuals) is shown in Fig. 12. Looking at such a curve, we cannot say positively when 'old age' begins. Voles drop off at all times of life, though not at the same rates. And these are not 'ecological' deaths; few of them probably are 'parasitological' deaths. We hardly know what process is at work, and for want of a better term we may call it 'wear and tear'. This has the suggestion of internal break-down in the physiological organization. We might almost say that the process of senescence begins at birth. This basic mortality presumably goes on in all vole populations and therefore might be expected to play some part in the cycle.

The marking methods developed by Chitty now provide a third, clinching line of evidence about the length of life in voles, since the fate of a natural population can be followed in the field. The ecologist by this means gives each vole an official individuality and compiles its dossier and records its death with all the care that an insurance company official devotes to his clients. These marking methods are referred to later on.

13

If we accept, provisionally, the idea that wild *Microtus agrestis* ordinarily live for less than a year, with a maximum span of life probably less than eighteen months, certain consequences follow. Given this comparatively short life (with a particular shape of life-curve) and an intermittent breeding season, any vole population in Great Britain runs near the edge of biological safety in the spring of the year: for the continuation of it depends

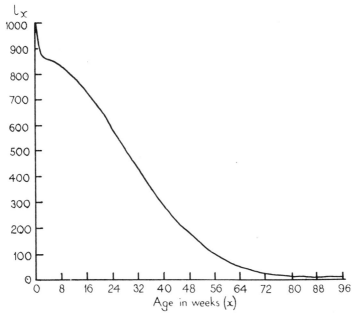

FIG. 12. The smoothed l_x curve, giving the number of survivors out of 1,000 individuals born alive, where from the age of 3 weeks onwards $l_x = 870 \cdot 6295 e^{-0 \cdot 000681126 x^2}$. Based on 119 *Microtus agrestis*. (From Leslie and Ranson, 1940.)

on the success of the over-wintering population in propagating itself before dying from ecological causes, or simply from 'wear and tear'. If mortality from any cause becomes greater in the spring months, these survivors may die before bringing their families through pregnancy and weaning stages, to provide a succeeding generation. Alternatively, any unusual mortality among the young voles of the year will have a similar effect. That a catastrophe of this sort can occur at the peak was suggested in the Newcastleton vole-crash of 1934.

Leslie and Ranson give some exact calculations on this matter, adapting the refined methods of human actuarial science. They try to arrive at a theoretical estimate of the real natural rate of increase in voles, and then, by introducing the extra feature of an intermittent breeding season, to work out the probable maximum rate in otherwise optimum conditions. To do this it was first necessary to have the life-table, which I have already mentioned, and then to construct a fertility table. These combined give a natural rate of increase. Nearly all previous calculations about rates at which animals can increase have ignored the existence of the basic wear and tear, a mortality which no ingenuity has yet eliminated. Any estimate which leaves this out is merely imaginary, while one which includes it can be realized in the laboratory and is a biological fact. The natural rate of increase, if laboratory conditions have been correctly interpreted, gives the theoretical maximum that could be reached in nature by a population that bred continuously and suffered no mortality except from wear and tear. All actual rates of increase must be lower than this, because mortality will in practice be higher, though sometimes not so much as we might expect: for we have to remember that a vole that is, say, killed by a kestrel, might have died *in any case* next day or next week, in its ordained place in the life-curve.

To get a fertility table Ranson allowed female laboratory voles to breed throughout their lives, quickly supplying them with new mates when any of the original ones died. The average size of family was not the same at all ages of the mother: 3·08 in the first month of breeding, 3·72 at its height in the twenty-eighth week, and down below 3 after a year (though few females survived that long to give statistics). The sex ratio (which is equal) and some other breeding 'constants' supplied the remaining raw material. (The work of Brambell and Hall[2] on voles at Bangor has also given some supplementary information on breeding rates.)

A good many assumptions have to be made in a calculation of this sort, and we suspect that the particular 'marriage laws' imposed on these captive female voles are not quite the same as those that occur in the field. Any population with a fixed life-table (i.e. pattern of death-rates at different ages) and allowed to multiply, would soon fall into a stable distribution of ages. At this stage the vole would have an increase rate of nearly 90 per week per thousand head of population. This means (with the basic life-curve) an increase of about six times the population in six months. But during the non-breeding time of winter there is a steady mortality acting on the population with no replacements. The expected fall in numbers is rather steep (and has been confirmed by trace censuses in the field). Leslie and Ranson concluded that there was a very delicate equilibrium here, and that quite a small variation either in the length and intensity of breeding, or in the survival power of old or young, would cause surprisingly large changes in the equilibrium. 'The crucial section of the yearly cycle, if one section can be called more crucial than any other, appears to be . . . the months of March to May or June.' Ranson has been able to get some measurement of pre-natal mortality in the laboratory vole, by diagnosing the numbers of embryos in the pregnant female without killing it. This is achieved by feeling very delicately with the fingers and counting the embryos in the uterus, through the skin and body wall of the vole. A report on these results is being published.[25b]

Another factor in mortality is the temperament of the vole, which is not adapted to the complete occupation of all habitable ground, with heavy pressure of contact from neighbours. Ranson[25a] has noted in his captive voles that 'in the presence of females, males will not live together, but invariably fight to the death, so that the stock of breeding males has to be kept in separate small cages, and mated to two females at a time. . . . If breeding is attempted in large cages, putting four to six females with one male, the same procedure applies except that when females become pregnant and are removed, new females must not be put in to take their place or they will very often be bullied and bitten to death by the other members of the "harem".' This social antagonism among voles probably exists in nature, and may be very important at different levels of population, and may prove to explain some of the mortality at higher numbers.

Without at present putting the matter any higher than this, we can see that there are inherent properties of the population dynamics of voles that may eventually explain their cycle as a self-contained system that is not so much dependent on other animals like predators and parasites as we at first supposed. And that this system is complex and delicate, and not by any means fully understood. We have moved a long way from simple epidemiological or climatic theories into a new region of population research. Some of the tools of study are forged, and the need is for more facts, collected by team work in field and laboratory, and treated by the most refined statistical means.

14

In this analysis I have not said much about the movements of mice and voles. From the beginning we realized that movements are the means by which different densities of numbers become translated into epidemiology. The comparative census index that one gets by trace or trapping is only a measure of numbers and activity, not of numbers alone. But the subject was not followed further, for lack of reliable means of doing so, until 1935–6, when Chitty[5] invented a way of marking mice and voles with numbered nickel rings on their hind legs. For success with this method, live-trapping had also to be improved so that the animals did not suffer from exposure. The first experiments were done in Bagley Wood, site of the original enterprise near Oxford. The species were the wood-mouse (*Apodemus sylvaticus*) and the bank-vole (*Clethrionomys glareolus*). The first idea was to trap them on particular sections of the wood and calculate the density of numbers. But almost at once a curious fact came out: the same wood-mice kept visiting traps even when these were moved over quite large distances. In other words, these mice range widely during the night, moves of several hundred yards in a night or two being not uncommon. The bank-voles were not nearly so wide-ranging. These observations showed how misleading a simple attempt at trapping census might be, unless the movements are also known. For a small block trapped for several nights would 'drain off' the wood-mice from a large area outside the block itself, and the bank-voles from a smaller one. The marking method also proved that there is a seasonal cycle in the activity of wood-mice and a difference between the sexes. More recently F. C. Evans has used this technique for a two-years' investigation of wood-mouse and bank-vole numbers in different habitats of Bagley Wood, the results of which are not yet printed.

The theoretical implications of movements within a network of traps have been considered by Leslie and Davis.[24] The field information came from a population study of wild rats in Freetown, Sierra Leone, in West Africa, done by Davis in 1937. Leslie devised a formula to fit the results, taking as his starting-point the kinetic theory of gases, with its plunging and bouncing molecules and system of random contacts. He was able, incidentally, from this, to suggest some improvements in the design of trapping censuses.

In 1937–8 Chitty began an important piece of work on *Microtus agrestis* populations in north Wales, some of the results of which have been announced in outline.[32, 33] Marking voles was done in the same way, with nickel rings, and with the live-trapping methods devised for pathological work. Several hundred altogether were ringed and trapped every five or six weeks, so that the changes in position could be recorded. The interesting thing was that voles were extremely attached to their own piece of ground, and changes were not often more than 10 or 15 yards, even after many months. All this work was linked with censuses and study of disease and predators and reproduction.

This story of vole research has necessarily been rather bare and stripped of details and statistics which the original papers hold; and so a considerable amount of field data still awaits analysis and publication. In a book that covers many countries of the world, the British part may not carry full sail. I would put as much emphasis on the methods of approach to the subject as on the facts already learned. Throughout the last eighteen years I have tried to develop an organization that could fasten on certain populations of mice and voles, and wring from them the answers that might be of general application to the extraordinary phenomena that are going on in rodent populations over the world. The picture we have so far, which may partly change with the complete analysis of unpublished materials and with the results of further field work, is this. A violent oscillation in numbers of voles wherever man creates the conditions of cover and food they flourish in. A great increase, with forestry planting, of suitable areas of this kind. A corresponding oscillation in predatory birds, perhaps also of animals. A periodic heavy pressure on vegetation that influences its floristic composition. Periodic damage to planted trees in certain localities. The occurrence of peculiar diseases that do not explain the regular fluctuations. (The especial importance of voles in relation to tuberculosis research.) The short life of the vole. Its fertility rates ascertained. The radiating usefulness of the vole as a laboratory animal, for researches on its own vital statistics, and for testing of human and animal disease. The development of census work, marking, and trapping methods. From all this we begin to see vole populations in dynamic terms: with numbers, rates of increase, life-curves, and movements interwoven into a pattern that ten or twenty years' further work may enable us to understand completely. When we have understood this pattern, we shall have learned new principles that will apply to many other populations of animals.

The outbreak of war in 1939 interrupted the progress of this research on voles, although the organization and ideas have been turned to the immediate needs of protecting food from rabbits and rats and house-mice—as a part of national defence. Leaving the subject of British voles at this point, we next turn to cycles in Scandinavia, where voles and mice and lemmings are the central agents in an impressive natural fluctuation. This fluctuation helps to prepare the mind for the North American cycles that follow and fill the rest of this book.

REFERENCES

1. ANON. (1940). 'Vaccination against tuberculosis with the vole bacillus.' Brit. Med. J. 23 Aug., pp. 261–2.
2. BRAMBELL, F. W. ROGERS, & HALL, K. (1939). 'Reproduction of the field vole, *Microtus agrestis hirtus* Bellamy.' Proc. Zool. Soc. Lond. A, 109: 133–8.
3. CHITTY, D. (1938). 'A laboratory study of pellet formation in the short-eared owl (*Asio flammeus*).' Proc. Zool. Soc. Lond. 267–87.
4. CHITTY, D. (1938)., 'Live trapping and transport of voles in Great Britain.' J. Mammal. 19: 65–70.
5. CHITTY, D. (1937). 'A ringing technique for small mammals.' J. Anim. Ecol. 6: 36–53.
6. DAVIS, D. H. S. (1933). 'Rhythmic activity in the short-tailed vole, *Microtus*.' J. Anim. Ecol. 2: 232–8.
7. DAVIS, D. H. S. (1934). 'A preliminary survey of the nest fauna of short-tailed voles (*Microtus agrestis* and *M. hirtus*).' Ent. Mon. Mag. 70: 96–101.
8. ELTON, C. (1937). 'Report on faunal surveys of foot-and-mouth disease areas, in 1934–5.' 5th Progress Rep. Foot-and-Mouth Disease Research Committee (Ministry of Agriculture and Fisheries). Appendix 5: 379–85.
9. ELTON, C. (1938). 'A convenient method of mounting and storing the skins of small mammals.' J. Mammal. 19: 244–5.
10. ELTON, C., & others (1933). 'Matamek Conference on Biological Cycles: Abstract of Papers and Discussions.' Matamek Factory, Canadian Labrador. (Transcriptions of the full Proceedings are deposited in the Bureau of Animal Population, Oxford; and with the New York Zoological Society and several other American centres.)
11. ELTON, C., DAVIS, D. H. S., & FINDLAY, G. M. (1935). 'An epidemic among voles (*Microtus agrestis*) on the Scottish Border in the spring of 1934.' J. Anim. Ecol. 4: 277–88.
12. FINDLAY, G. M. (1933). 'Experiments on the transmission of the virus of climatic bubo (lymphogranuloma inguinale) to animals.' Trans. R. Soc. Trop. Med. Hyg. 27: 35–66.
13. FINDLAY, G. M. (1932). 'Rift Valley fever or enzootic hepatitis.' Trans. Soc. Trop. Med. Hyg. 25: 229–62.
14. FINDLAY, G. M. (1934). 'The infectivity of neurotropic yellow fever virus for animals.' J. Path. Bact. 38: 1–6.
15. FINDLAY, G. M., & ELTON, C. (1933). 'The transmission of louping ill to field voles.' J. Comp. Path. 46: 126–8.
16. FINDLAY, G. M., KLIENEBERGER, E., MacCALLUM, F. O., & MACKENZIE, R. D. (1938). 'Rolling disease: new syndrome in mice associated with a pleuro-pneumonia-like organism.' Lancet, 31 December, pp. 1511–13.

17. FINDLAY, G. M., & MIDDLETON, A. D. (1934). 'Epidemic disease among voles (*Microtus*) with special reference to *Toxoplasma*.' J. Anim. Ecol. 3: 150–60.

18. GODDARD, T. RUSSELL (1935). 'A census of short-eared owls (*Asio f. flammeus*) at Newcastleton, Roxburghshire, 1934.' J. Anim. Ecol. 4: 113–18.

19. GODDARD, T. RUSSEL (1935). 'A census of short-eard owls (*Asio f, flammeus*) at Newcastleton Roxburghshire, 1935.' J. Anim Ecol. 4: 289–90.

20. GOLDIE, A. H. (1936). 'Some characteristics of the mean animal circulation over the British Isles.' Quart. J. R. Meteorological Soc. 62: 81–102.

20 a. GRIFFITH, A. STANLEY (1937). 'Experimental tuberculosis in field-voles and mice.' Vet. Rec. 49: 982–4.

21. HINTON, M. A. C. (1935). 'List of British Vertebrates. Mammals.' Brit. Mus. (Nat. Hist.) London, p. 4.

22. HUNTINGTON, E., & others (1932). 'Matamek Conference on Biological Cycles.' Matamek Factory, Canadian Labrador. 32 pp.

23. LEOPOLD, A. (1940). 'The state of the profession.' J. Wildlife Management, 4: 343–6.

24. LESLIE, P. H., & DAVIS, D. H. S. (1939). 'An attempt to determine the absolute number of rats on a given area.' J. Anim. Ecol. 8: 94–113.

25. LESLIE, P. H., & RANSON, R. M. (1940). 'The mortality, fertility and rate of natural increase of the vole (*Microtus agrestis*) as observed in the laboratory.' J. Anim. Ecol. 9: 27–52.

25 a. RANSON, R. M. (1934). 'The field vole (*Microtus*) as a laboratory animal.' J. Anim. Ecol. 3: 70–6.

25 b. RANSON, R. M. (*in press*). 'Prenatal and infant mortality in a laboratory population of voles (*Microtus agrestis*).' Proc. Zool. Soc. Lond.

26. SUMMERHAYES, V. S. (1941). 'The effect of voles (*Microtus agrestis*) on vegetation.' J. Ecol. 29: 14–48.

27. WELLS, A. Q. (1937). 'Tuberculosis in wild voles.' Lancet, 22 May, p. 1221.

28. WELLS, A. Q. (1938). 'The susceptibility of voles to human and bovine strains of tubercle bacilli.' Brit. J. Exp. Path. 19: 324–8.

29. WELLS, A. Q., & BROOKE, W. S. (1940). 'The effect of vaccination of guinea-pigs with the vole acid-fast bacillus on subsequent tuberculous infection.' Brit. J. Exp. Path. 21: 104–10.

30. 5th Progress Rep. Foot-and-Mouth Disease Research Committee (Ministry of Agriculture and Fisheries), p. 28.

31. Bureau of Animal Population, Oxford University, Annual Report, 1935–6.

32. Bureau of Animal Population, Oxford University, Annual Report, 1936–7.

33. Bureau of Animal Population, Oxford University, Annual Report, 1937–8.

CHAPTER X

WILD-LIFE CYCLES IN SCANDINAVIA: THE LEMMING

'Ther is no tradition among the lemmings of Norway
how their progenitors, when their offspring increased,
bravely forsook their crowded nestes in the snow,
swarming upon the plains to ravage field and farm,
and in unswerving course ate their way to the coast,
where plunging down the rocks they swam in the salt sea
to drowning death; nor hav they in acting thus today
any plan for their journey or prospect in the event.
But clerks and chroniclers wer many in Christendom,
when France and Germany pour'd out the rabblement
of the second Crusade, and its record is writ;'

ROBERT BRIDGES, *The Testament of Beauty.*

1

THE story of the wanderings of the lemming fills a famous niche in natural history. It has always been especially interesting to people in the British Isles because of our many holiday visitors to Scandinavia who have brought home tales about the lemming, and also because of the indestructible theory, still tenaciously held by many, that the lemmings leave their Norwegian mountains and swim out to sea in order to find a sunken Atlantis continent, of which Britain might be a surviving fragment. The mystery of these mighty treks has attracted more attention than the periodicity in their onset, which is the main subject of this chapter. Actually, we know far more about the periodicity of this population change than about its causes, which remain still partly mysterious. I shall first describe a little of the ecological background; then the history of the migrations; their periodicity and how they are an index of fluctuating populations; the similar periodicity in other small mammals and in the willow-grouse; the consequences to dependent predators; and some of the causes of the cycles in all these animals and birds and in particular the part played by disease, which may even reach the human population. These oscillations in wild life in Scandinavia have a majestic rhythm, and their history is about as well documented as any of its kind.

Across the extreme northern part of Asia and Europe runs a broad belt of Arctic tundra, a treeless region of low shrubs, or more often only of herbaceous plants, growing sparser towards the Polar Sea. This Arctic zone, interrupted by the White Sea, reaches its most westerly extension in northern Lapland. Lapland, like much of the tundra farther east, is inhabited by semi-nomad tribes who graze their reindeer herds on the abundant lichens and other pasture. It is quite a natural ecological unit that happens to be divided up politically between four countries: Norway, Sweden, Finland, and U.S.S.R. Because of these political divisions the scientific information about the Lapland fauna is recorded in four different languages to begin with, not to mention the literature of expeditions which have gone there from other countries.

This Arctic region has the same basic fauna of mammals and birds that we shall later be studying in Canada. It is one small section of an ecological zone that practically circumscribes the northern hemisphere. The lemming, the arctic fox, the snowy owl, and the skua are four forms that occur all the way round. The special peculiarity of Scandinavia is the continuation of this northern community of plants and animals far to the southward down the complex and broken mountain range that forms the watershed between Norway and Sweden. Here the Arctic zone becomes the Alpine and Subalpine. It is chiefly from the Subalpine zone that the lemmings pour down at intervals on their long wanderings. The dominance of Arctic and mountain country in Norway gives the lemming possible habitats in something like a third of the country's area.[5] The topography of Sweden makes the proportion of lemming ground there much less than this. Whereas the lemming lives at sea-level in the north of Scandinavia, it is at 3–4,000 feet on the southern Norwegian mountains, its southern limit (outside migration years) being reached in the Langfjeld, in lat. 58°30′ N.

2

The lemming of Lapland and the Scandinavian mountains is *Lemmus lemmus*, a comfortably shaped rodent resembling a very large vole, but brightly coloured in black and yellow and brown. There is oddity in the very short stumpy tail, the bustling gait, and the dark back-stripe running from head to tail. Collett remarks:[5] 'Man does not reap any appreciable benefit from them. Their coats, notwithstanding their beautiful markings, prove to be of hardly any service.' However, the coats are serviceable enough to their stout owners, who in winter partly supplement the outer beauty with a layer of subcutaneous fat. East of the White Sea and in Novaya Zemlya another species, *Lemmus obensis*, is found: this extends to Behring Strait, while from Alaska to Hudson Bay there is a third species, *Lemmus trimucronatus*, that very closely resembles the Siberian one. In former times the growth of the great Scandinavian ice-cap (now restricted to the mountain ice and glaciers of the Svartisen) pushed the whole Arctic zone far southward, and with it lemmings, whose fossil remains have been found right down in Portugal, and those of *L. lemmus* itself in Britain. The northward retreat of the tundra zone past the southern part of the White Sea split the lemming populations into two parts, at the same time pushing them higher and higher up the mountain sides. The mountain lemmings do not, however, form one continuous connected population, but live in normal years in a good many mountain blocks, separated by cross valleys that dip into the woodland zones.

The Subalpine zone where the lemmings ordinarily live lies between the upper limits of the silver-birch forest and the true alpine country (a barren region running up past the permanent snow-line). A typical kind of place for lemmings has low willow and dwarf birch (*Betula nana*) or juniper, grasses, sedges, mosses, and lichens, and often cloudberry (*Rubus chamae-morus*). On the Norwegian Lapland hills one learned to associate this zone also with the two birds, golden plover (*Pluvialis apricarius*) and whimbrel (*Numenius phaeopus*). The lemmings inhabit the drier parts, lurking by day in holes among the peat or stones or tussocks or scrub, and coming out at night-time to run about in a swift elusive way, to feed on grass and moss and other plants.[5, 6, 33, 12]

The Norwegian mountain ranges have rather clear vertical vegetation zones that also appear in a broader pattern from south to north, the zones lying much higher in the Dovre and Jotunheim plateaux than in north-central Norway, and becoming finally reduced to pure tundra at sea-level on the north coast. Different small mammals occupy these zones[6] and a short note is necessary here for understanding of their periodicity years. In the Subalpine the lemming is the only rodent. Below this are, first, birch and then conifer woods (pine or spruce). In these woods are three kinds of red-backed voles, *Clethrionomys rutilus*, *rufocanus*, and *glareolus* (the last, our British bank-vole, a southern species, the first two northern). The wood-lemming (*Myopus schisticolor*) is confined to the forests of spruce. In the same series of woodland zones, but in the open parts, usually with grass, are two voles: *Microtus ratticeps*, confined to the higher regions of the mountains and to Lapland; and *M. agrestis* (our common British species) ranging throughout, though commoner lower down. *Ratticeps* often inhabits the low willow scrub by streams and tarns. *Apodemus sylvaticus* (our wood-mouse) or its varieties is confined to the woods and fields of southern Norway, and does not live north of lat. 62° 40' N. There are a few other kinds of mice and voles, but little is known of their fluctuations. Finally, among insectivores, there is the common shrew (*Sorex araneus*) which ranges through all zones up to the snow-line and into the Arctic.

3

The prime source of our knowledge about lemming and other wild-life cycles in Norway is Robert Collett, whose work is a deep fountain of living natural history. In 1876 he published[3] in a Norwegian journal the first authoritative account of the lemming migrations and biology. This was followed by two later papers in English in 1878[4] and 1895.[5] In the last of these he traces the historical allusions to lemmings. In an early manu-script, probably of the late thirteenth century, the lemming is identified with the locust as a pest. In 1532 a German, Jacob Ziegler, described how lemmings were believed to fall from the clouds—'per tempestates et repentinos imbres decidunt'; and how they crowd together and die of epidemic, and then cause disease among human beings—'ex quarum corruptione aer fit pestilens et adficit Norduegos uertigine, et icterici'; or else are eaten up by wild animals. Ziegler got this information from two archbishops from Trondhjem (then Nidaros), who were staying in Rome in 1522. The story was relayed in 1555 by a better-known writer, Olaus Magnus, who added a spirited woodcut of the lemmings actually falling down from the clouds with spouts of rain. Also in the picture are two ermines each with a lemming in its mouth, transposed from a map that Olaus Magnus had issued sixteen years before. The first dated migration is given in an anonymous treatise, published in Hamburg in 1579: a mass of lemmings seen near Bergen. A little later Peder Claussön Friis described what may have been a continuation of the same movement in 1580. He gilded the story of lemmings falling from the sky, with the new evidence of some 'trustworthy gentlemen'. As Collett remarks here, many Norwegian peasants still believed the theory up to recent times. In 1930 I met a man in Lapland (actually a Finn immigrant) who was among those who took the Norwegian reindeer herd to Alaska for the United States Government. He had seen lemmings (they were white ones, the Alaskan *Dicrostonyx*) suddenly running on a frozen lake as the snow was falling. And he said: 'I think that they came from another planet. . . .'

Collett's great monograph[6] on the mammals of Norway (written in Norwegian) brings the records up to 1910 and adds a great deal more ecology, especially for the mice and voles. It tabulates the lemming years of Norway and, from 1860 to 1910, gives an almost complete list of them. Nordgaard's paper[30] on the lemming years in Trøndelag (the province of which Trondhjem is the chief town) adds some missing records and brings the local story up to 1923. In 1929 Johnsen published his impressive report[22] upon the fluctuations in predatory animals and birds that the Norwegian State bounty figures show. This paper extends the facts and improves the interpretations given by Rasch in the 1860's and 1870's, and Dahl in 1924 and 1927. Since several of the predators depend on lemmings and mice for food, Johnsen tabulated the information he could find and showed a correlation between the cycles in rodents and their enemies. Here, although he relies chiefly upon Collett and Nordgaard, he also usefully extracts some records contained in the *Innberetning fra Skogdirektøren* (Report of the Forest Director) for various years.

For the years since 1929, and also for a few of the earlier ones, I have used records given in the works of some English travellers in Norway; information collected while I was on the Oxford University Lapland Expedition in 1930; and much valuable information in letters from Norwegian naturalists: in particular Dr. O. Olstad of the Zoological Museum, Oslo, and Dr. T. L. Schaaning of Stavanger Museum. Some records from other people are acknowledged later on; I am particularly indebted to Dr. Hugh M. Blair for full notes of his observations during visits to Varanger Fjord in northern Norway. For Sweden, I was fortunately able to get some help from Dr. Sven Ekman of Upsala University; while the work of Pleske[33] is an authority for the eastern parts of Lapland. For Norwegian willow-grouse fluctuations one chiefly depends on Kloster.[25, 26]

In 1924[9] and 1925[10] I summarized much of the lemming cycle up to that date, chiefly by compilation from Collett. The present chapter represents a delayed revision of that work, whose chief contribution was to point out the existence of a short 3–4 year periodicity in Norwegian lemmings, voles,

and mice, the substantiation of which Johnsen's statistics have satisfactorily provided.

4

Collett assumed, no doubt correctly, that the periodic migrations of the
lemming are connected with unusual increase in numbers up to a level at
which the normal habitat no longer provides enough room for the species.
He went further than this in perceiving that such a phenomenon might
occur very widely in the animal kingdom.[5] 'Amongst numerous species of
animals, a more or less increased productiveness occurs at irregular intervals, and species which, as a rule, appear in limited and inconspicuous
numbers may, at such times, make their appearance in multitudes, or, at
any rate, in greater numbers than usual. . . . These temporary augmenta-
tions may be traced, amongst many species of small mammals and various
kinds of birds especially, but are, above all, conspicuous in many kinds of
insects.' Here, clearly stated in 1895, was the idea which was to engross
the minds of ecologists increasingly during the next forty years. It was
Collett who first fully realized that the lemming migration is not a primary
phenomenon, but an index of population changes that have been developing for several years before. Perhaps the first hint of the same idea is contained in an amusing remark by the great naturalist Ray, who refused to
believe in lemmings falling from the clouds and said that anatomical
investigation had convinced him that 'nature had not been such a niggard
of her gifts as to render such a method of gestation necessary'![7]

It is not necessary to spend much space in describing the migrations, as
so many travellers and naturalists have done so before. But it is as well to
understand the really great magnitude of these movements, which attract
much public attention and powerfully disturb the equilibrium of plant and
animal communities below the Subalpine zone. In the big years lemmings
begin to travel down the mountain sides and valleys through the tree belt.
The movement is not always sudden and continuous. You may find pairs
that have stopped to breed a little way below the higher zones. They may
even spend a whole winter before moving farther down. But when the
numbers are great, the lemmings go out over the lowlands, crossing fields
and lakes and rivers and passing through busy towns, until those that
survive reach the coast. Here they swim out and often reach islands
several miles away. Though many drown, even these stay afloat and are
cast ashore in drifts. There is usually a crescendo of migration pressure
through the summer and autumn, and some very strong obsessive impulse
seems to drive these fat but delicate little creatures onwards and downwards
across powerful physical obstacles and without fear of man. For, although
lemmings are rather large as mouse-like rodents go, they die easily from
injury or shock, and the wash of a boat is enough to drown them at sea.
They travel often at night, and that is probably why they seem to have
arrived with such meteorological suddenness. But I have also met them
travelling through the Lapland woods by day, when their clumsy dashes
were very different from the quiet elusive nocturnal movements in their

15

mountain home. When a lemming cannot avoid meeting a man he will often sit on his hind legs and hop up and down as if in excited anger and charge the intruder, who may get his hand bitten deeply if he tries to pick the animal up.

It is not quite clear what social relation exists among the lemmings while they are on the move. But there appears to be more individuality than is commonly supposed. The movement is probably only a massive one because of the huge numbers that leave the mountains, not because all the lemmings flock together closely. They nearly always seem to go downhill, very seldom returning upwards, and this downward drift eventually concentrates them in the valleys and sends them towards the coast. A downward flow of this kind, as of water particles that coalesce into larger streams, is especially effective in a country shaped as Norway is, with steep-sided valleys debouching suddenly into sea fjords. But besides this passive convergence of the lemmings into swarms there may be a measure of social cohesion, shown in the sudden departure of whole bands together from an invaded district. Collett, however, said:[5] 'They are not sociable in the sense of several individuals deliberately joining company for long distances, and, on the whole, keeping together during the march. Therefore they seldom, if ever, advance in close ranks as generally depicted in drawings, as each individual appears to take its own road, even if proceeding substantially in the same direction as the others. . . . Generally they go their several ways, meet, bark at each other, and part again.' This behaviour is confirmed by Pleske.

We begin to see this great biological spectacle that has aroused such wonder and curiosity among naturalists and has been given a tinge of epic romance by two English poets laureate,[1, 28] as a rather tragic procession of refugees, with all the obsessed behaviour of the unwanted stranger in a populous land, going blindly on to various deaths. For, among a great many still obscure features of the phenomenon, one is thoroughly established by observation: practically none of the emigrants or their families return to the mountains. After a year or two, and mostly much sooner, all of them are dead. There remain a number of thin depleted populations on the high hills, as nuclei of further waves of lemmings that will also die out in the lower zones.

These great swarms have long been feared by farmers in Norway. Collett[6] saw eighty lemmings foraging in a grass and clover plot not larger than the floor of a room. They are so numerous sometimes around the towns that dogs and cats get exhausted with killing them and will eat no more. In early times the clergy used to read a Latin prayer of exorcizement against lemmings, of which Clark Kennedy[24] gives the following translation:

'I exorcise you, pestiferous worms, mice, birds, or locusts, or other animals, by God the Father, . . . that you depart immediately from these fields, or vineyards, or waters, and dwell in them no longer, but go away to those places in which you can harm no person; and on the part of the Almighty God, and the whole Heavenly Choir, and the Holy Church of God, cursing you whithersoever you shall go, daily wasting away and decreasing, till no remains of you are found in any place; which may He vouchsafe to do, who shall come to judge the living and the dead, and the world by fire. Amen.'

When we consider that, in addition to such well-aimed curses, the lemmings are at every point being heavily depleted by accidents and the attacks of many enemies, it is astonishing that so many reach the coast alive. Yet in 1868 so many swam out into the inner parts of Trondhjem Fjord that a steamer took a quarter of an hour to pass through them. In 1910 a few reached Oslo itself.

5

In Lapland the lemming partly inhabits open tundra reaching to the Arctic coast, partly lives in Subalpine hills that rise above the birch-clad inland and more southern tracts of the country. In August 1930 I met with small numbers of lemmings migrating in various parts of the provinces of Finmark and Troms, though these seemed to have only local directions of movement. They were the forerunners of much stronger movements later in the year. Two records will illustrate how, even in this northern zone, mass movements of lemmings may reach the sea. Mr. E. A. Cockayne, while serving with a British force at Yukanski on the Russian Murmansk coast, informed me that he saw no lemmings in 1915. But in 1916 great numbers arrived at the coast and climbed up the ships' hawsers and many also swam out to sea. In 1917 he only saw a single lemming, and a special mammal collector working in the region found no small rodents at all, except one in a skua's stomach.

Dr. S. S. Folitarek, a Soviet worker, made some similar observations, for which I am indebted to Dr. A. N. Formozov of Moscow. In 1930 there was a mass migration of lemmings in the western region of Murmansk, first reported by the captains of steamers who observed them swimming eastwards in the open sea near Kildin Island bank about 20 June. On Ruibachii Peninsula (west of the Kola Fjord and some miles from Kildin Island) other lemmings were seen swimming in great numbers across a bay on 17 September. Eastwards from here the town of Alexandrovsk was invaded from 10 September onwards, and about 20 October the lemmings had moved southwards and were swimming south-eastwards over the Tuloma River. Other movements were reported from eastern Murmansk. These records show that there are in certain years strong migrations among the tundra lemmings, though without the well-defined common direction that is so often found in the more mountainous parts of Norway.

It can now be seen that the apparent mystery of where the lemmings are *going to* on their migrations is cleared up when we assume that they are *going away from* the mountains on account of some unfavourable conditions caused by increased density of population. As with all emigrations of the sort, there are several layers or stages in the process: what increases the environmental pressure periodically, what physiological or psychological changes occur in the lemmings, why such stimuli and changes make most of them emigrate yet leave a few behind, why (if at all) the emigrants follow a particular direction, what their behaviour is during migration, why they stop or do not stop, whether there is a return migration and if so under what stimulus. And behind all these components of the present-day phenomenon, how evolution by natural selection could have maintained the migratory stimulus when all those that respond to it perish, and those that do not are the survivors.[11]

In answer to the first two questions we can only adduce the evidence that the emigration is associated with periodic increase to great numbers. As we shall see, this increase may take place without migration setting in, at any rate without a large-scale movement. As to the causes of the cycle in numbers, we are brought back to all problems discussed in previous chapters, and must keep judgement suspended until a complete and continuous research on the population dynamics of Norwegian lemmings has been done. When the emigration is seen as a result of high numbers, it is easier to understand how a few animals are likely to remain behind after the earlier masses have left the mountains and made living conditions presumably more tolerable. In just the same way a diminished population of Norwegian people remained behind in the valleys after emigration to America had partly emptied them and so relieved the scarcity of means to live.

The fourth question—direction—is partly answered by the downward trend of the lemmings and by the topographical shape of Norway. The theory that they seek a sunken continent is sufficiently knocked on the head by the southward movement of many lemming bands (as into Oslo), by the variety of directions followed in Lapland, and by the more or less eastward movement of Swedish lemmings down the valleys there. Unless we are prepared to invent also an Arctis and a Baltis, the lost Atlantis can hardly be maintained as the lemmings' goal. This conclusion does not at all imply that the lemming has no 'sense of direction' beyond the usual perception of landmarks and weather. There is more than a suggestion of sustained movements along certain lines that cannot be explained with our existing knowledge; and this goes not only for the lemming but for other mammals, and for birds and fish. But the drift of movement is downhill and therefore towards the sea, and the apparent obsessiveness of the lemming's behaviour while he is migrating gives this movement great force and distance. No doubt the continued reinforcement from behind adds somewhat to the impetus and the general direction of the treks.

Leaving the obvious drama of these recurrent outpourings from the hills, we now turn to an analysis of their periodicity, which, though less full of popular interest, affords a fascinating mosaic of ecological facts.

6

This table (11) of lemming years summarizes everything that I am aware of about the subject: except that minor records have been omitted where they are covered by the larger general statement of some Norwegian authority; and also that there must be records since 1929 in Norwegian periodicals which I have not examined. However, the table gives an

TABLE 11

Lemming migration years in Norway, 1862–1938

Unless otherwise indicated the records come from Collett (1911–12). 'South Norway' includes South Trøndelag as its northern limit. 'Central Norway' is here used to cover North Trøndelag and Nordland. 'North Norway' covers Troms and Finmark and includes Norwegian Lapland. Although records are not complete, the occurrence of a migration in one part of any region by no means implies its unrecorded occurrence in the other parts.

1	2	3	
South	Central	North	Details and references
1862–3	..	..	1. One of the biggest years of the century in nearly all S. Norway, from Dovrefjeld and Lomsfjeld down to Lindesnaes (the south cape of Norway). Full details in Collett.[5] Main peak in west was in 1862; east of Gudbrandsdal main peak was in 1863. Many reached Oslo and south coast towns
1866	..	..	1. Christiansand district (Aaseral) and Søndfjord (probably all the western mountains). Collett[5] noted that these were possibly local migrations
1868–9	..	..	1. S. Trøndelag. Some details in Collett.[5] Crotch[7] mentions great abundance, apparently at Vaage, at 4,000 ft. in the Dovrefjeld, and migration at Heimdal (near Trondhjem) in 1867–8. The last date conflicts with the general statements of Collett, who (1895) notes it as probably a minor migration. Nordgaard[30] gives great numbers swimming in Trondhjemsfjord in Nov. 1868. We may probably accept 1868 as the chief year of migration
1871–2	..	..	1. All mountain districts in S. Norway, south to Mjøsen and Telemark, and north to S. Trøndelag. (Crotch[7] gives 1870–1 for Heimdal)
1875–6	..	1876	1. All southern mountains. Details in Collett:[5] in 1875 autumn in Telemark and S. Langfjeld, swarms in valleys of Christiansand district and S. Oslo district. Some reached Oslofjord and Lindesnaes (Oslo being about 90 kilometres from nearest normally inhabited lemming mountains); in 1876 northern Langfjeld, Romsdal, and Dovrefjeld and valleys, and north to Trondhjemsfjord, also in south. Somerville[35] mentions coast from Oslofjord to Christiansand swarming in Apr. 1876 with lemmings from previous autumn migration
..	..	..	3. East Finmark (Collett[5])
..	1878	1878	2. Northern Nordland (Saltdal)
..	..	..	3. Troms
1879–80	1881	1880–1	1. Gudbrandsdal and Østerdal mountains. A minor migration (Collett[5])
			2. Local migration in Namdal (N. Trøndelag)
			3. Troms and Finmark (Johnsen[22])
1883–4	1883–4	1883–4	1. Trondhjemsfjord, Romsdal, Søndmør, down to Fillefjeld and Vass, i.e. the north-west part of this southern area
			2. Trondhjemsfjord (presumably covering parts of N. Trøndelag also). Northern Nordland (Saltdal)
			3. Troms, north to Tromsø district
1887–8	..	..	1. Lomsfjeld and Dovre and north to region of Trondhjemsfjord. Nordgaard makes it clear that this fjord was reached by migrations from the southern mountains. Noted by Somerville[35] on mountain plateau near Rjuken Foss in Telemark

1	2	3	
South	Central	North	Details and references
1890–1	..	..	1. In 1890 on Dovre, Gudbrandsdal, and Østerdal mountains, to a lesser extent on the Langfjeld. 'Not considerable, however, but formed the advance guard of the abnormal production in the following year', Collett.[5] In 1890 great emigration to lowlands, to Oslofjord, Telemark, S. Trøndelag, &c.
1894–5	1895	..	1. All mountains of S. Norway. In 1894 peak especially in the western mountains down to Numedal and Lyngdal; in 1895 peak in the eastern mountains (Gudbrandsdal and Østerdal), also S. Trøndelag 1894–5 was one of the greatest years 2. N. Trøndelag and Nordland
1897	..	..	1. Lemmings seen on Hitteren Island, outside Trondhjemsfjord (information from Lord Walsingham to A. D. Middleton). No indications in literature
1902–3	1902–3	1902–4	1 and 2. Trondhjem mountains (presumably N. and S.) and some districts of Nordland. (No reports of migration in the main southern mountains of Norway) 3. Tromsø region, 1902–3, East Finmark in 1903–4 (Schaaning[34])
1906	1906	1906	1. Sporadic in southern mountains (Gudbrandsdal, Valders, Østerdal) 2. N. Nordland. Also Namdal, Meraaker, and Steinkjer in N. Trøndelag (Nordgaard[30]) 3. Troms and Finmark. A great lemming year over the whole of north Norway
1909–10	..	..	1. Big year in 1909 in southern high mountains, from Jotunheim over Valders and all the western mountains down to Christiansand region. (For notes on Hardanger region see Grieg.[17]) Smaller increase this year in Østerdal Mountains. Great emigration over lowlands. In 1910 there were still great numbers in Østerdal, but recession set in elsewhere; though Nordgaard[30] mentions lemmings this year in various parts of S. Trøndelag
..	..	1911–12	3. Finmark. Great migrations (T. L. Schaaning, letter, 19 Feb. 1925). Confirmed by L. Munsterhjelm (letter, 18 Jan. 1925), who worked in NE. Lapland in 1911
1918	..	1918–19	1. 'Prof. K. Dahl also informs me that not inconsiderable numbers of *L. lemmus* were observed in certain localities in the Hardangervidde during the summer 1918' (O. Olstad, letter, 11 Mar. 1924). No other information about the period 1913–19, during which time, it is certain, from private reports received from Norwegian naturalists, that no large migrations occurred, and possibly no migrations at all 3. Abundant on mountains near Punta, N. Troms, but no migration here, though they came down to the valley at Ancemokka, farther up Reisendal (information from E. Gjetmundsen, Aug. 1930)
1920	..	..	1. 'During spring 1920 not inconsiderable quantities of lemming were observed in various localities in the Gudbrandsdal. Until July they appeared to increase in numbers. Later in the summer they appeared to be decreasing, until they seemed to have disappeared in September' (O. Olstad, letter, 11 Mar. 1924)
1922–3	1922–3	..	1. Great abundance and migrations over nearly all S. Norway (Nordgaard[30]; Johnsen[22]; T. L. Schaaning, letter, 19 Feb. 1925)

1	2	3	
South	Central	North	Details and references
1926–7	..	1926	2. Namdal, N. Trøndelag (Johnsen[22]) 1. Great lemming years, especially 1926, in many parts of S. Norway, e.g. Gudbrandsdal, Hallingdal, Rogaland, Hardangervidde, Dovrefjeld, &c. (Johnsen;[22] Grieg;[17] letters from O. Olstad, 17 Jan. and 6 Sept. 1927; from T. L. Schaaning, 15 Jan. 1927 ('1926 has been the greatest lemming year we have had in Norway in the last 20 years, I think'); information from Miss Frances Pitt) 3. Finmark (Polmak: T. L. Schaaning, letter, 15 Jan. 1927; Laxelv: information from A. Bye, July 1930)
1930	1930	1930–1	1. Incomplete records of lemming abundance at several points and some migration. Near Molde and at Hardanger (information from H. W. Freeman); Lillehammer (information from traveller) 2. Stjordal, in Trondhjemsfjord, N. Trøndelag (Thompson[38]) 3. Troms and Finmark. (Various records obtained during Oxford University Lapland Expedition, 1930. Varanger Fjord (1931) from H. M. Blair, letter, 2 Jan. 1932)
1933–4	1933–4	1933–4	1. A very good review, with maps, was supplied by O. Olstad (letters, 9 Mar. 1934 and 16 May 1935). A broad distinction was shown between the southern mountains, with main peak in 1933, and N. Norway, with main peak in 1934. In 1933 lemmings were numerous in parts of Hedmark, Telemark, and Hordalund districts. In 1934 abundance in Østerdal and mountains east of it. General abundance in 1933 confirmed by T. L. Schaaning (letter, 3 Feb. 1934) 2. Abundant in parts of Nordland in 1933, also in 1934— Bodö northwards (O. Olstad, letters above) 3. Abundant in Lyngen (Troms) in 1933, and in many parts of Troms and Finmark (up to Porsangerfjord) in 1934 (O. Olstad, letters above). 'In 1933 there were only local migrations, but in 1934 lemmings were very abundant in Northern Norway' (T. Soot-Ryen, letter, 3 May 1935)
1938	..	1938	1. No complete story available, but scattered notes suggest a peak in places: part of Dovrefjeld (information from J. Buxton); scarcity in same place 1939 (information from H. N. Southern); Lake Faemund, on the mountains between Osterdal and the Norwegian-Swedish frontier (Grimaldi[18]) 3. 'Norwegian Lapland' (Nattrass[29])

otherwise complete and unselected list of records on the subject. One can see, without fine analysis, an obvious tendency towards recurrence of lemming migrations every third or fourth year; but, before this cycle is discussed, it is necessary to consider some other components of it.

7

These fluctuations are observed not only in the Subalpine zone (with its cycle in lemmings, and as we shall see, also of willow-grouse and of predators associated with both of them), but also among other mouse-like rodents in the lower zone of woods and fields. Information about them is much less complete than about the lemming migrations: what is available is summarized in Table 12.

TABLE 12

Years of great abundance of voles and wood-lemmings in the 'forest zone' (including all habitats) of Norway

The following abbreviations are used: *Ms* = *Myopus schisticolor*; *Ma* = *Microtus agrestis*; *Mr* = *Microtus ratticeps*; *Cg* = *Clethrionomys (Evotomys) glareolus*; *Crut* = *C. rutilus*; *Cruf* = *C. rufocanus*. Records from Collett (1911–12) unless otherwise stated. Regions of Norway as in Table 11.

1	2	3	
South	*Central*	*North*	*Details and references*
1863	..	..	1. *Mr* in southern mountains
1872	..	1872	1. *Mr* in southern mountains
			3. *Cruf* in Finmark
1876	..	1876	1. *Ma* in Trondhjem region. *Mr* in southern mountains
			3. *Mr* and *Cruf* in Finmark. *Crut* in E. Finmark
..	1880	1880	2. *Ma* in Nordland
			3. *Ma* in inner Tromsø districts. *Crut* in Troms. *Cruf* in Finmark
1882–4	1882–3	1883	1. *Ms* in 1883 in Oslo region (Urskog, Hurdal, Eidsvold) and up into Hedemark. Also lasted into part of 1884. *Ma* in 1882–3 in Oslofjord region, up to Mjøsen
			2. *Ma* in Saltdal (Nordland). *Cg* in 1883 over whole of S. Nordland, up to Saltdal and Beieren
			3. *Mr* in Finmark. *Crut* in Troms
1888	1887	1887–8	1. *Ms* in 1888 near Mjøsen
			2. *Ma* in Saltdal and other parts of Nordland. *Cg* in same region as in 1883
			3. *Ma* in inner parts of Finmark (e.g. Porsanger), in 1888. *Cruf* in Finmark in 1887
1891–2	1891	1890	1. *Ms* in 1891–2 in Oslo region, from Ringerike up to Valders, and round Randsfjord. *Ma* in Trondhjemsfjord in 1891. *Mr* in southern mountains in 1891
			2. *Ma* in Nordland
			3. *Mr* in Finmark
1894–5	1894–5	..	1. *Ms* in Trysil (Hedemark). *Ma* over a great part of S. Norway (especially Bergen area). *Mr* on southern mountains in 1895
			2. *Ma* over whole of Nordland
1897	1897	..	1. *Ma* in part of Gudbrandsdal
			2. *Ma* in Namdal (N. Trøndelag)
1902	1903	1902–4	1. *Ms* in Oslo region and around Randsfjord
			2. *Cg* in same region as in 1883
			3. *Ma* and *Mr* in 1902 in Finmark. *Crut* in 1903 over a great part of Finmark (S. Varanger and Alten) and around Tromsøfjord. *Cruf* in Finmark in 1904. Schaaning[34] mentions rich *Microtus* year in E. Finmark in 1903
1906	1906	1906–7	1. *Ma* in upper Østerdal
			2. *Ma* over a great part of Nordland. *Cg* in Hatfjelddal, Vefsen, and Ranen (Nordland)
			3. *Crut* same region as in 1903. *Cruf* in Finmark in 1907
1909	..	1910–12	1. *Mr* on the southern mountains
			3. *Mr* in 1910 in Finmark. *Crut* in 1910 over whole of W. Finmark down to Maaselvdalen and Malangen (inland from Tromsø). T. L. Schaaning (letter, 19 Feb. 1925) notes *Mr* and *Cruf* abundance in 1911–12 in Finmark
..	1914	..	2. *Ma* in Hatfjelddal (Nordland): identification presumed by Johnsen[22]

South	Central	North	Details and references
1	2	3	
1920	..	..	1. *Mr* abundant in spring in Gudbrandsdal (O. Olstad, letter, 11 Mar. 1924)
1926–7	..	1926–7	1. *Mr* in 1926 in parts of Hedemark (e.g. Gudbrandsdal), (T. L. Schaaning, letter, 15 Jan. 1927; O. Olstad, letter, 6 Sept. 1927). '*Microtus*' on Dovrefjeld: abundant 1926 and 1927, scarce 1928 (information from Miss Frances Pitt to A. D. Middleton)
			3. *Ma* in 1926 in Finmark (Johnsen[22]). '*Microtus*' and *Cruf* in 1926 at Karasjok, Finmark (information from T. Frette, forestry superintendent, 1930). *Clethrionomys* at Kautokeino, Finmark, in 1926 (information from doctor in Reisendal, 1930). H. M. Blair has supplied complete notes about Varanger Fjord from 1923 to 1927 (district between Komagvaer in the N. and Gaukfjeldet on Upper Pasvik R. in S.). Gradual increase in *Mr* and *Cruf* from 1923 to 1926. This abundance lasted over 1927, but there was scarcity in 1928. Epidemic among *Cruf* at one place in 1926 (see Elton,[13] where date is incorrectly given as 1927)
		1930–1	3. 'Voles' (probably *Mr* and *Cruf*) abundant in Varanger Fjord in 1930 and 1931, scarce 1932 (H. M. Blair, see above). *Ma, Mr, Cruf, Crut* abundant in several places in Finmark and Troms visited by me during Oxford University Lapland Expedition in 1930
1934	..	1934	1. *Microtus* peak followed by scarcity in 1935–6 at Østre Slidre in Valdres district (J. Baashuus-Jessen, letter, 19 Mar. 1938)
			3. *Clethrionomys* in Varanger Fjord (H. M. Blair, see above)

8

These records of 'mouse years' were certainly not selected by anyone in order to prove the existence of a regular fluctuation, nor, indeed, to prove a connexion with lemming years, from which they often differ slightly, by a year or so. They are the field observations of trained naturalists, often supported by the experience of other residents in the country, that in certain years these species conspicuously swarmed in numbers over a wide area, and (often, though this is less fully substantiated in every case) that they disappeared or became scarce in the year following. So, although the records are not based upon trap censuses or other precise measurements of the sort, I shall treat them as being reliable sample observations of fluctuations which have not been studied so completely as those of the lemmings: this, of course, because the wood-lemmings and the voles do not usually perform any large migrations, and do not cause the same popular excitement.

There is an obvious similarity in the general rhythm in Table 12 to that of the lemmings in Table 11, and a strong tendency towards a recurrent cycle of three or four years. It does not need elaborate analysis to prove that we are dealing here with a cycle in the mouse-like rodents of Norway as a whole: on mountain, forest, heath, and grass-land. There are, in

Collett's book,[6] a few records for *Apodemus* and for the water-vole (*Arvicola amphibius*) which also fit into this general cycle. But I have omitted them, from a desire to present a homogeneous picture of the cycle in land voles and lemmings, which have all a somewhat similar way of life, though in different zones and habitats.

Although Collett was the first to grasp the existence and ecological complexity of the Norwegian cycle, its recurrence and wide distribution and far-reaching effects in the community, and has left us by far the richest store of records about it, he does not seem to have noticed its predominant 3–4-year periodicity. This was (so far as I am aware) first formulated in a scientific way by me in 1924, when it was compared with the similar cycle in the fur returns of the Canadian arctic fox. My analysis was quite independently done from the facts in Collett's book; but there can be little doubt that the general idea must have been current or taking shape also in the minds of Norwegian workers, amongst whom Johnsen has made such a notable contribution to the subject in his monograph in 1929 (which in turn seems to have been built up without reference to my work). As early as 1878, Clark Kennedy,[24] a British traveller, remarked of the lemmings that 'they appear in vast quantities every three or four years'. The reason why this periodicity did not strike Collett and other earlier workers was probably this. Although we can now bring together evidence that the migrations arise from cyclical overabundance, these migrations do not happen at every cycle peak in every area. They are very widespread in some lemming years, regional in other, quite local in others, and occasionally (as between 1913 and 1917) fail to develop at all. The intervals between migration years at any one place have therefore usually been irregular. It is only when we look at Norway as a whole, or at any rate in large divisions, that the cycle can be appreciated. Of the migrations we can say, from Table 11, that *somewhere in Norway* there has practically always been a migration about every third or fourth year. The local irregularity, which distracted attention from the underlying population rhythm, is immediately comprehensible when we grasp that the migrations are overflows that are not always produced, just as a river periodically in flood will not always burst its banks, or if it does, will not break them every time at the same points.

The proof of a cycle in numbers in the lower zones among rodents that do not migrate is solid support for this explanation. Strictly speaking, the records in Table 12 only prove a *tendency* for abundance to happen at regular intervals. They do not prove that the abundance is always universal in the country, any more than the cycles among voles on British forest plantations prove that fluctuations are going on outside them. We may reasonably assume, however, that the vole fluctuations in Norway are at any rate a good deal more widespread than the few observers have actually been able to record. We come now to another piece of evidence which confirms in a rather dramatic manner the nature of the cycle that has been suggested above.

9

Norwegians have for many years adopted a material and ruthless policy towards their wild predators—perhaps because the country is not very rich in resources, and there is little room for the toleration of natural robbers and competitors, however handsome they may be. Our own record in this respect (as I have indicated in Chapter VII) is not much better, and the difference is perhaps chiefly that we carried out our extermination a longer time ago and have partly forgotten it, whereas in Norway the process is fairly recent and still going on. We have begun to try and get some of our predators back; that rival predator, the game preserver, though powerful and numerous, is kept in partial check; the State is, on the whole, in favour of protecting vanishing forms. In Norway there is a State system of rewards for the killing (in all or practically all parts of the country) of the following animals and birds: brown bear (*Ursus arctos*), wolf (*Canis lupus*), lynx (*Lynx lynx*), wolverine (*Gulo gulo*), pine marten (*Martes martes*), arctic fox (*Alopex lagopus*), red fox (*Vulpes vulpes*), otter (*Lutra lutra*), golden eagle (*Aquila chrysaëtus*), white-tailed eagle (*Haliaeëtus albicilla*), osprey (*Pandion haliaetus*), goshawk (*Astur gentilis*), gyrfalcon (*Falco rusticolus*), peregrine falcon (*Falco peregrinus*), sparrow-hawk (*Accipiter nisus*), and eagle owl (*Bubo bubo*).

From 1845 successive laws have gradually swept all these species into the net, and a good many of them have by now become catastrophically scarce, though it is not unlikely that the rooted tendency of bounty systems to perpetuate the populations they seek to destroy, by converting them into a permanent source of petty cash, may assert itself in certain instances. These aspects of the system are mentioned in passing, but our chief concern with it here is that it supplies a wonderful series of figures that reflect the Norwegian wild-life cycle.

Since the full figures have been published by Johnsen, who has analysed them and pointed out successfully the correlation between certain predators and cycles in their rodent food supply, I will not reproduce them fully here. Table 13, with a re-analysis of the fox bounty records, contains the most striking instance. The fox figures are divided into the same three regions of Norway as the lemming and vole records in Tables 11 and 12. (Johnsen gives the full subdivision into political districts.) Since the State makes its bounty records, in the case of mammals, for the second half of winter onwards, it is correct to attribute the fox 'crop' to the previous year. There are a good many snags in the interpretation of this kind of statistics, which Johnsen has carefully weighed. The correct identification is sometimes difficult (thus many early records of 'eagles' were probably rough-legged buzzards (*Buteo lagopus*)). The local official is not always above accepting the wrong bird in return for votes. The numbers are an index of what is taken, not of what remains, and therefore not a direct index of population. However, the mammal records are evidently pretty good, and the fox figures show a remarkably persistent cycle, closely following the lemming and vole years, with often a lag of one year. The catastrophic decrease in Troms and Finmark foxes after about 1907 is a clear warning against overtrapping in Canadian and Labrador fur trade (see Chapter XIV).

TABLE 13

Numbers of foxes brought in for bounty in Norway, 1880–1931

The figures are put back one year. They include both red fox (*Vulpes vulpes*) and arctic fox (*Alopex lagopus*). The regions are the same as in Tables 11 and 12. (1880–1926 from Johnsen,[22] reanalysed; 1927–31 from *Norsk Jaeger- og Fisker-Forenings Tidsskrift.*[39])

Year	All Norway	South	Central	North	Year	All Norway	South	Central	North
1879	10,584	6,566	1,760	2,558	1905	8,300	6,845	740	715
1880	13,383	7,671	2,329	3,383	6	10,587	8,085	1,115	1,387
1	7,933	3,965	804	3,164	7	15,281	8,614	3,612	3,055
2	5,509	4,227	667	615	8	11,943	8,536	1,580	1,827
3	7,851	5,471	1,021	1,359	9	10,986	9,785	979	222
4	11,718	7,472	2,201	2,045	1910	11,922	10,185	1,429	308
5	5,618	4,205	730	683	11	10,325	6,850	2,806	669
6	6,512	4,760	817	935	12	8,566	7,427	749	390
7	9,116	6,208	1,375	1,533	13	9,636	8,680	828	128
8	8,529	3,320	1,587	1,733	14	10,997	9,438	1,413	146
9	6,016	4,297	894	915	15	12,661	10,758	1,673	230
1890	8,461	6,401	1,077	983	16	10,825	9,365	1,297	163
1	10,758	7,453	1,661	1,644	17	8,503	8,084	359	60
2	11,400	7,593	1,567	2,240	18	10,570	9,673	778	119
3	8,646	6,178	1,044	1,424	19	8,411	7,141	1,126	144
4	10,362	8,297	1,071	994	1920	9,912	8,337	1,317	258
5	13,605	9,512	1,726	2,367	1	9,436	8,469	692	275
6	13,642	8,208	1,895	3,539	2	8,385	7,584	606	195
7	9,163	6,699	881	1,583	3	8,271	7,066	1,114	91
8	10,206	7,595	1,126	1,485	4	8,259	6,850	1,305	104
9	10,312	7,807	1,380	1,125	5	6,983	6,256	595	132
1900	9,872	7,451	1,152	1,269	6	9,177	7,521	1,466	190
1	8,949	7,375	773	801	7	8,279	7,001	1,176	102
2	8,745	6,735	922	1,088	8	5,365	4,802	502	61
3	13,503	7,770	2,226	3,507	9	6,046	5,221	825	60
4	11,514	7,098	2,015	2,401	1930	9,174	7,586	1,395	193

10

This cycle in the foxes and mouse-like rodents of Norway is extraordinarily like the one in Labrador and Ungava described in the rest of this book: the same genera or species, the same grandeur of geographical range and seismic amplitude of fluctuation, the same period of recurrence (but with the same minor flexibility and very occasional breakdown of periodicity), a similar influence on human profit from the foxes, the same baffling questions of population control and dynamic equilibrium. The Norwegian story fills a specially useful niche in this scientific survey, because, with its undeniable evidence about rodent fluctuations, it strengthens the structure of argument for the Canadian cycle, where the rodent evidence, though weighty, has not nearly so complete a history.

These lemming and vole years (often coming simultaneously over big tracts of country) are magnets that draw in together many kinds of predators and fortify (temporarily) their numbers. There are the species that normally live or range up in the Subalpine zone or the tundra, preying partly on lemmings: the stoat or ermine (*Mustela erminea*); the weasel (*Mustela nivalis*); the rough-legged buzzard (*Buteo lagopus*); in the north the Lapp owl (*Strix lapponica*); and several of the crow tribe. Many predators feed partly on voles and mice in the lower zones. Though fairly omnivorous, in years of great rodent abundance they probably eat them to a much greater extent. Such may be the pine marten, whose fluctuations in some districts (as Nordland) are not unlike those of the foxes.

Some predators appear to visit Norway chiefly or only in lemming and vole years.[6] The snowy owl (*Nyctea nyctea*) normally breeds in a few places from the southern mountains up to Finmark. But in lemming years it is often much more numerous in Finmark and may overflow (but chiefly in winter) to the southern regions of Norway. Its arrivals in Finmark are probably too heavy to be explained by a purely local increase, and may be attributed to a piling up of migrant individuals from other Arctic countries. In the same way the arctic skua (*Stercorarius parasiticus*), a northern bird that partly gets its living by robbery at sea, nests during lemming years on Norwegian tundras and on mountain moors far south of its usual range. (The snowy owl and skuas are famous for this capacity to appear and breed at the places where lemmings are temporarily abundant.) Another example is the hen-harrier (*Circus cyaneus*), which is an immigrant from Central Europe to the high moors of Norway, but only known to breed during lemming and vole years (though not very often, even then).

Some mountain predators (as the arctic fox) may follow the lemmings right down into the lowlands. Conversely, sea-gulls go far inland. Domestic animals eat lemmings: pigs, goats, reindeer. Also snakes (as the adder), and fish in the rivers and lakes (as pike and trout). And a cod caught at sea off Nordland had sixteen lemmings in its stomach. Nature in these years opens a sort of sixpenny bazaar to which everyone in the community flocks in a natural greedy way.

The parallel cycle in willow-grouse or rype, shortly to be described, complicates the detailed interpretation of cycles in some of the predators, since these may eat both small rodents and willow-grouse, as well as other species whose population trends are unknown. Such is the case with the eagle-owl (*Bubo bubo*). At any rate, a good many of the bountiable species whose records Johnsen studied, show the short 3–4-year cycle strongly developed, though usually in a less regular manner than in the fox and marten. According to him, the curve for 'eagles' in Opland (a district of south Norway) from 1871 to 1926 really registers chiefly rough-legged buzzards, owing to misidentification by the people concerned. . . . This curve shows beautifully clear main peaks in 1875–6, 1880, 1884, 1888, 1891, 1894–5, 1898–9, 1902, 1906, 1909–10, 1913–14, 1919–20, 1922–3 (I omit a very small rise in 1878). These peaks, from the method of collecting the bounty on birds of prey, are the real 'years of production' and can be directly compared with the fox peaks shifted a year back (as in Table 13).

Other birds that show the cycle strongly are eagle-owl, goshawk, and sparrow-hawk. For a fuller enjoyment of these intricacies the reader must consult Johnsen's masterly monograph, which includes several excellent diagrams of the relation between predator bounties and lemming and mouse years; also the cycle in rype, about which a little must now be said. To go deeply into this subject would, however, take us too far into problems of game control and disease.

11

The willow-grouse or lirype—usually called the rype in Norway—is *Lagopus lagopus*, a very close relative of our native red grouse, *Lagopus scoticus*. One of the striking differences between these two is that, whereas the red grouse keeps its autumn plumage through the winter, the willow-grouse has a special winter dress with a great deal of white in it. But the two species hybridize, as abortive introductions have shown. The rype is the mainstay of Norwegian shooting men, and is the object of so much interest that there are records about its numbers from the eighteenth century onwards. It lives not only in the southern mountains, but also right up in Finmark, where one may share the cloudberries with it on lemming ground above the birch-trees. It also comes commonly in birch woodland. From the work of the Norsk Jaeger- og Fisker-Forening. and of Bergen and Oslo Museums, and especially from the researches of Kloster, Olstad, and Johnsen, a great deal has been found out about its ecology, which cannot be discussed here.

There are vivid fluctuations in rype populations that have been studied by Robert Kloster.[25] His historical notes cover many places in different years, but the clearest story is for what Norwegians call 'Central Norway', that is, East Telemark, Hallingdal, Valdres, Gudbrandsdal, and Østerdal. These districts occupy the eastern part of what I have called in this chapter 'Southern Norway', in the sense that anyone looking at an atlas would choose it. Kloster got most of his evidence from other historical monographs of game, especially Krefting's and Barth's, as well as from various ephemeral journals and sporting magazines. One may accept his diagrammatized summary as a real picture of the rype cycle, to be compared with that among rodents and predators in the southern mountains.

The peak years and years of scarcity (these in brackets) were as follows: (1869), 1872, (1873), 1876, (1877), 1880, (1881–2), 1883, (1884), 1887, (1888), 1891, (1892), 1895, (1896), 1897, (1900), 1903, (small drop in 1904), 1906, (1907), 1908–9, (1910), 1911–12, (then catastrophic drop, with slight upward check in 1914, to 1916–17), rising again in 1919–21. A further paper by Kloster[26] carries this record up to 1927. There were poor or poorish years in 1922–4, but 1926 had strong increase, with a drop again in 1927. I have not followed the later story. The peak years here are close enough to those of the rodents to warrant fully Johnsen's statement that: 'The lemming and the rype [fluctuations] are parallel phenomena, they have the same production years.'

It may be mentioned here that the red grouse in Scotland does *not* fluctuate in harmony with the voles there, having a longer period (not very constant, however) averaging about six and a half years.[27] But it resembles the willow-grouse in the way that epidemics decimate both bird populations at their peaks. In Norway, coccidiosis is believed to be the chief agent (especially attacking young birds); in Scotland, coccidiosis in the young and worm infestation from *Trichostrongylus* in the old birds. But behind these parasite outbreaks there is a background of epidemiological influences that has not been explored very far. The coincidence of the cycle in several ecological zones of Norway, on so many different parts of the country (also in Sweden, as will be shown), in at least seven species of voles and lemmings, one game-bird, and half a dozen or more predators (both mammal and bird), suggests some very profound influence, making the environment alternately favourable and unfavourable for life.

The rype cycle became less regular after 1905, and a considerable literature has grown up in discussion of this change. There is evidence of more frequent disease in the populations, and Brinkmann[2] has sought to explain this by the disappearance of predators, which might be expected to maintain the standard of grouse fitness by weeding out diseased and more vulnerable birds. This theory is not generally accepted, however. Nordhagen[31] has suggested a connexion between the berry crop and winter survival of the birds. The chief berries eaten are crowberry (*Empetrum nigrum*), bilberry (*Vaccinium myrtillus*), another large bilberry (*Vaccinium uliginosum*), the bearberry (*Arctostaphylos alpina*), and the cloudberry (*Rubus chamaemorus*). These berries fluctuate in abundance very much from year to year. Unfortunately the only gauge of the berry crop in past years is the export of this commodity from Norway. Nordhagen uses the curve of export from Oslo and Kristiansand as the best index of the crop. There are certain agreements between this curve and Kloster's for the southern rype years, but not enough to clinch the connexion, as Johnsen also points out. Since commercial figures may be a fairly poor guide to the real crop, this does not at all rule out the theory.

We have really got only five indications of the factors at work in the lemming and vole cycle. None of these gives a conclusive explanation of the widespread synchronization of its rhythm, although they tell us a little about why there is a cycle at all. In the first place, the oscillation might be caused and maintained by the predator-prey relationship alone. The enemies are varied and some of them still fairly numerous. Lotka and Volterra believe that an ecological system of this sort will always tend to oscillate. The far-flung movements of the predators, especially of birds of prey, would tend to keep the system swinging along in step in distantly separated regions. Against this as a single master factor are two facts: the pressure of the bounty laws has greatly depleted predators, yet the leming-vole fluctuations retain their rhythm and extent right up to the present

day (though the rype has kept going less consistently, as explained above);
and there are other factors actually operating which must be given a
place. The most important of these is disease.

12

Collett[5] wrote in 1895:

'It is obvious that the great masses of individuals which perish incessantly
during a migratory year, must have an influence on sanitary conditions, especially
during the warm season of the year. Everyone who has visited the mountain
plateaux during a great prolific year, will have noticed that their oblong pellets
of dung are to be found strewed about everywhere, and in such great quantities
that it is often difficult to place one's foot on a spot that is entirely clear of
them. It follows of itself that all running water will be contaminated by this
decaying excrement. To this may be added the dead animals, which will be
found lying scattered about in great numbers, and which, during hot summers,
become quickly decomposed. The rain carries the putrid matter on to the nearest
watercourse, whence it makes its way to wells, and becomes mixed with the
drinking water of the inhabitants. During some great prolific years, definite
forms of sickness have appeared in certain of the over-run districts, and the
people have given these the name of "Lemming Fever," as they presumed that
they were connected with the appearance of these animals. Many of the doctors
practising in the country have turned their attention to the disease, and diagnosed
it in their reports.'

We have already seen that this connexion was noted as early as 1532, by
Jacob Ziegler.

The symptoms of this lemming fever were known to include, besides the
fever, digestive upset, ulcers in the mouth, swelling of the maxillary glands,
and often abscesses in the glands of the throat, arm-pit, &c. The acute
illness usually lasted about eight days, and was followed by great weakness
and prostration. Note especially the swelled glands and the ulcers and
abscesses. Little progress was made on the subject until 1912, when Horne,
a veterinarian in Oslo, published[19] a full description of disease in the lemmings themselves. His material came from epidemics in several separate
lemming years, 1896, 1903, and 1909–10. The 1896 lemmings were dead
ones found at Hjerkin in the Dovre region (presumably migrants from
1895). Horne cultured bacteria from all these epidemics, and successfully
reproduced the disease in guinea-pigs and white mice. The organisms were
very small bacteria that invaded the blood and organs in practically pure
culture.

In 1933 I asked the opinion of Dr. A. D. Gardner about Horne's description, and he replied: 'It is very suggestive indeed of tularaemia. His use
of the name *Streptococcus* is confusing. . . . Most of the data agree very
well with the known characteristics and pathological effects of *B. tularense*.
And the cases of lemming fever quoted from Olaus Wormius, 1653, look
exactly like tularaemia.'

Meanwhile another line of research was leading towards the same point.

In 1926 and 1929 Thiøtta, another Norwegian veterinarian, studied[36] three cases of a peculiar new disease, which turned out to be tularaemia, with somewhat the same symptoms as 'lemming fever'. But three of these people had apparently caught the disease by handling hares, one in Telemark, the other two in Hallingdal; Thiøtta clinched the proof by testing the blood of these patients against the highly specific agglutinin of *Bacterium tularense*, supplied from America, where the disease was first discovered. In that country it is caught chiefly from hares and rabbits, though by no means only found in them; in U.S.S.R. it is caught from water-voles (see Chapter V).

Later on, Thiøtta was able to show,[37] by serological tests, that over fifty people in Norway had had tularaemia, many cases being of men who had handled large numbers of the hares used as food for foxes on fur ranches. There were also several cases with no history of contact with hares, but a strong suggestion that they might have received contamination from voles or lemmings. Tularaemia, like leptospiral jaundice, is usually transmitted through abrasions in the skin. Francis states that 'a water-borne epidemic of 43 cases was reported in 1935 from Russia in peasants who drank water from a brook which was thought to have been contaminated by water rats' [= voles]. The infection may also enter by insect or tick bites or through eating badly cooked meat containing the bacterium.[14]

The final link in this story comes from Swedish Lapland, where Olin,[32] in 1930–1, studied an epidemic of tularaemia in over 200 people. He was able to prove that lemmings (though not in the same locality) were carrying the disease, which he transmitted to laboratory animals. There was here some difficulty in establishing any connexion by polluted water, and Olin suggests a possible carriage of the disease by mosquitoes. It is well proved that biting flies can transmit it in America, where it was known as 'deerfly' long before the bacterium was discovered. So, if lemmings, as seems certain, die of tularaemia after the peak of their cycle, the disease may reach human beings in several different ways. According to Collett and other observers, the lemmings most often die while they are under the winter snow, and their bodies are found after the snow disappears in spring. But they also die quite frequently during migration itself.

13

We have considered two factors in the cycle, predators and disease. These happen to be known about; but there must be many more that we have still to discover. At present, our chief knowledge is about what happens to the lemmings that leave their homes, that is, to the overflow populations. This does not necessarily apply to the ones that stay behind. If we explain the onset of migration by overcrowding, we are still thrown back on the mountain populations themselves and their population rhythm. Of this we know very little, except that it goes on. Two more clues may be mentioned, however, as possibly important. Collett[5, 6] states categorically that, although the first waves of migration contain adults from the previous year, the later ones in the autumn are almost entirely young of the same year. If this picture were true of the populations that remain behind, it would suggest that the lemming has an annual turnover in population, similar to that which we predicate for the British vole. And with this would go the same sensitivity to loss of young ones in the peak year, whether by migration or any other cause.

The other suggestion comes from Johnsen,[22] who has found some connexion between the temperatures recorded at Røros and lemming years in S. Trøndelag. His full evidence has not yet been published, so that the connexion cannot be regarded as proved. He states, however, that a lemming year seems to have an early spring following a late autumn in the previous year; while the autumn of the migration often has winter setting in early. Here are, then, five factors that may cause or control the cycle: predators, parasitic disease (possibly spread by other parasites or blood-sucking flies), emigration, short life and removal of the replacing generation, and a climatic factor. There must be other elements of which we are still ignorant.

So we are left, as with the British cycle, with a good many hints of some great cosmic oscillation, expressing itself in periodic upheavals in the biotic community, but we still lack the full key to the problem. Probably we shall have to make new sorts of observations over a good many years, before the nature of the cycle will become quite exposed. The kind of organization needed for this work has been described in Chapters VIII and IX. There will have to be permanent ecological outfits or stations in all places where this extraordinary cycle challenges our curiosity. We have such stations now in Great Britain and Palestine and some parts of the United States. The basis for another already exists in Norway. When some group of scientific workers has devoted ten years' steady field and laboratory work to the population dynamics of lemmings and voles in the southern mountains of Norway, exchanging ideas and methods with similar groups in Great Britain and Labrador and Arctic Canada, we may begin to understand this extraordinary oscillation, which, I cannot help believing, will lead us back to very curious meteorological and perhaps astronomical processes, as well as to new relations between climate, physiology, and disease. In this connexion the theories of Baashus-Jessen[20, 21] may be noticed, although he has not been able to produce much direct evidence for their application to the Norwegian cycle. He believes that climatic changes are capable, through alteration of the vegetation or directly by lowering the immunity of the body, of causing high mortality in small animals and birds—a mortality, which may be expressed in the symptoms of food deficiency or by successful invasion of tissues by micro-organisms. More will be said about this theory in Chapter XXII, and it is here mentioned to offset the simpler ideas of epidemic through crowding alone. It has some affinity with Sviridenko's theory (Chapter V).

14

Finally, we may inquire how far this cycle exists outside Norway itself. As would be expected, the Swedish mountain lemmings generally fluctuate together with those in Norway, though the records have been less thoroughly searched by me. I owe to Professor Sven Ekman a valuable summary of the dates of abundance and migration in Sweden, abstracted chiefly from

TABLE 14

Comparison of known peak years in Scandinavian cycle

Dates combined from Tables 11, 12, 13, and text. (They do not apply to all species of the vole group each time, or to all localities.)

South Norway				Sweden	Central or N. Norway or both			N. Finland
Lemming	Voles, &c.	Foxes	Willow-grouse	Lemming	Lemming	Voles, &c.	Foxes	Lemming
1862–3	1863	..	..	1862–3	..	..	..	1862–3
1866	..	..	..	..	..	..	..	..
1868–9	..	..	..	1868	..	..	..	..
1871–2	1872	..	1872	1872	..	1872	..	1871–2
1875–6	1876	..	1876	1876–7	1876	1876	..	1875–6
..	..	..	..	..	1878	..	..	..
1879–80	..	1880	1880	..	1880–1	1880	1880	..
1883–4	1882–4	1884	1883	1883–4	1883–4	1882–3	1884	..
1887–8	1888	1887	1887	..	..	1887–8	1888	..
1890–1	1891–2	1892	1891	1890–1	..	1890–1	1891–2	1891
1894–5	1894–5	1895	1895	..	1895	1894–5	1896	1893–5
1897	1897	1899	1897	..	..	1897	1899–1900	1897
1902–3	1902	1903	1903	1902–4	1902–4	1902–4	1903	1902–3
1906	1906	1907	1906	1906–7	1906	1906–7	1907	..
1909–10	1909	1910	1908–9, 1911–12	1911	1911–12	1910–12	1911	..
..	..	1915	1914	..	..	1914	1915	..
1918	..	1918	..	..	1918–19	..	..	..
1920	1920	1921	1919–21	..	..	..	1920–1	..
1922–3	..	..	..	1922–3	1922–3	..	1924	..
1926–7	1926–7	1926	1926	..	1926	1926–7	1926	..
1930	..	? 1930	..	1930	1930–1	1930–1	? 1930	..
1933–4	1934	..	..	1934	1933–4	1934	..	..
1938	..	..	..	..	1938	..	..	..

the Swedish literature. (These, and the Finnish ones mentioned below, have already been published by me.[9]) The lemming years since 1850 he gave as follows (I give only a rough geographical analysis of the records): 1868 (S), 1872 (S), 1876–7 (S), 1884 (S), 1890–1 (S), 1902–4 (N), 1906–7 (S, N), 1911 (N). The letters S and N stand for the south half of Sweden (up to and including Jämtland) and the region north of this (including Lapland). It is not easy to compare these regions exactly with those of Norway, because Swedish Lapland lies to the south of Norwegian Lapland. To these may be added from other sources 1862–3 (N)[6]; 1891 (N)[8]; 1922–3 (N)[23]; 1930 (N)[15]; 1934 (N).[16]

Dr. Ekman also gave me the lemming years recorded for north Finland (i.e. Finnish Lapland). These are as follows: 1862–4, 1871–2, 1875–6, 1891, 1893, 1894–5 (especially the latter), 1897, 1902–3. These ~ears, though incomplete, fit in mostly with the Norwegian cycle, and suggest that the phenomenon is one of Scandinavia as a whole. There are a few observations from Russian Lapland, but not enough to be worth fine analysis. It is, however, from his expedition there that Pleske[33] has left the vivid account of lemming biology and migration that everyone interested in the subject should read. There is also a beautiful coloured plate of two lemmings set against a background of rolling wooded hills and moors.

To sum up the whole story, the dates of abundance or migration that we know of in different species are set out in Table 14.

REFERENCES

Some references to personal communications, given in Tables 11 and 12, are not repeated here.

1. BRIDGES, ROBERT. See heading to chapter.
2. BRINKMANN, A. (1926). 'Coccidiosen hos lirypen.' Bergen Mus. Årbok: 3–71.
3. COLLETT, R. (1876). 'Bemærkninger til Norges pattedyrfauna.' Nyt Mag. Naturv. 22: 1818.
4. COLLETT, R. (1878). 'On *Myodes lemmus* in Norway.' J. Linn. Soc. (Zool.) 13: 327–34.
5. COLLETT, R. (1895). '*Myodes lemmus*: its habits and migration in Norway.' Forh. VidenskSelsk. Krist. 3: 1–62.
6. COLLETT, R. (1911–12). 'Norges pattedyr.' Oslo.
7. CROTCH, W. DUPPA (1878). 'On the migrations and habits of the Norwegian lemming.' J. Linn. Soc. (Zool.) 13: 27–34.
8. DAVIES, S. A. (1892). 'A naturalist's ramble in Swedish Lapland.' Zoologist, 16: 81–7.
9. ELTON, C. S. (1924). 'Periodic fluctuations in the numbers of animals: their causes and effects.' Brit. J. Exp. Biol. 2: 119–63.
10. ELTON, C. S. (1925). 'Plague and the regulation of numbers in wild animals.' J. Hyg., Camb. 24: 138–63.
11. ELTON, C. (1930). 'Animal ecology and evolution.' Oxford.
12. ELTON, C. Unpublished observations and information obtained during the Oxford University Expedition to Lapland, 1930.
13. ELTON, C. (1931). 'The study of epidemic diseases among wild animals.' J. Hyg., Camb. 31: 435–56.
14. FRANCIS, E. (1937). 'Sources of infection and seasonal incidence of tularaemia in man.' Publ. Hlth. Rep., Wash. 52 (Reprint No. 1799): 103–13.
15. FREEMAN, H. W. Information.
16. GLEN, A. R. Information.
17. GRIEG, J. A. (1911). 'Dyrelevninger fra de gamle bopladser paa Hardanger-vidden.' Bergens Mus. Årbok: 1–23.
18. GRIMALDI, C. B. 1938). The Times, 4 November.
19. HORNE, H. (1912). 'Eine Lemmingpest und eine Meerschweinchenepizootie. Ein Beitrag zur Beleuchtung der Ursachen der Lemmingsterbe in den sogenannten Lemmingjahren.' Zbl. Bakt. (Orig.) 66: 169–93.
20. JESSEN, J. BAASHUUS- (1937). 'Periodiske vekslinger i småviltbestanden.' Norges Svalbard- og Ishavs-Undersøkelser, Medd. No. 36: 1–15.

21. JESSEN, J. BAASHUUS- (1937). 'Periodiske vekslinger i småviltbestanden. II.' Norsk Jaeger- og Fisker-Forenings Tidsskrift, 66: 149–53.
22. JOHNSEN, S. (1929). 'Rovdyr- og Rovfuglstatistikken i Norge.' Bergens Mus. Årbok, 118 pp. & appendix of tables. (Includes topographical, vegetation, and settlement maps of Norway.)
23. JOURDAIN, F. C. R. Information.
24. KENNEDY, A. W. M. CLARK (1878). 'To the Arctic regions and back in six weeks.' London. p. 107.
25. KLOSTER, R. (1921). 'Veksling i rypebestanden.' Norsk Jaeger- og Fisker-Forenings Tidsskrift, 50, No. 5: 317–32.
26. KLOSTER, R. (1928). See Johnsen (1929), p. 110.
27. LEOPOLD, A., & BALL, J. N. (1931). 'British and American grouse cycles.' Canad. Field-Nat. 45: 162–7.
28. MASEFIELD, JOHN (1923). 'The Lemmings' in 'Collected Poems', p. 670.
29. NATTRASS, T. M. (1938). The Times, 17 October.
30. NORDGAARD, O. (1923). 'Lemenår i Trøndelag.' K. Norske Vidensk. Selsk. Skr. 1922, No. 3: 1–11.
31. NORDHAGEN, R. (1928). 'Rypeår og baerår. . . .' Bergens Mus. Årbok: 1–52.
32. OLIN, G. (1938). 'Études sur l'origine et la mode de propagation de la tularémie en Suède.' Bull. Off. Int. Hyg. Publ. 30, No. 12: 2804–7.
33. PLESKE, T. (1884). 'Übersicht der Säugethiere und Vögel der Kola-Halbinsel. Theil 1. Säugethiere.' In 'Beiträge zur Kenntniss des Russischen Reiches und der angrenzenden Länder Asiens.' Ser. 2, vol. 7. St. Petersburg. 212 pp. (Contains beautiful coloured plate of *Lemmus lemmus*.)
34. SCHAANNING, H. T. L. (1907). 'Østfinmarkens fuglefauna.' Bergens Mus. Årbok: 1–98.
35. SOMERVILLE, T. T. (1891). 'Notes on the lemming (*Myodes lemmus*).' Proc. Zool. Soc. Lond.: 655–8.
36. THIØTTA, T. (1930). 'Three cases of tularaemia, a disease hitherto not diagnosed in Norway.' Avh. Norske VidenskAkad. No. 1: 1–16.
37. THIØTTA, T. (1931). 'Fortsatte iakttagelser over tularemiens forekomst i Norge. . . .' Norsk Mag. Laegevidensk.: 32–40.
38. THOMPSON, H. C. MEYSEY (1938). The Times, 4 November.
39. Norsk Jaeger- og Fisker-Forenings Tidsskrift (1930) 59: 446–7; (1931) 60: 191; (1932) 61: 446, 482.

PART III

WILD-LIFE CYCLES IN NORTHERN LABRADOR

CHAPTER XI

THE BACKGROUND

1

MOST connoisseurs of the more startling literature about mice know of the essay that William Cabot added as an appendix, a sort of brilliant afterthought, to his book *In Northern Labrador*.[1a] This essay has been quoted in several scientific books, and even swam once on to the middle page of the London *Times* in a letter[5] which, after first passing skilfully from Cabot to Aristotle and Strabo, ended in the remote way of such communications: 'One thinks of the field-mouse in the Egyptian story of Sennacherib's disaster (Herodotus ii, 141) and recalls precautions taken in modern India against rat-fleas. I am etc. . . .'

Cabot's notes were made during his travels in 1903–6. They were the starting-point of my own inquiries into the wild-life cycles of Labrador. For it seemed that such violent ebb and flow of animal populations might not have escaped the notice of others besides him. The hunt for records began in 1926, and a weather eye was kept open for them during the next eight years; but nothing much came to light until 1934, when a great harvest of ecological facts from the Moravian Mission and Hudson's Bay Company archives began.

From these new-old records the story of the last hundred years can now be written—only in outline it is true, but continuously and with the main trends clearly established. This reconstruction of past wild-life cycles substantially confirms what Cabot saw or surmised. Apart from the fact that his essay is the basis of the present study, it so vividly draws the reader into touch with the life of Labrador that it is quoted almost in full below:

'Perhaps as many creatures depend upon mice as upon either rabbit or caplin, although people, indeed, rarely eat them. Indirectly they may play as important a part in the concerns of the Indians as the rabbit itself; and this although, in the fur countries at least, one may well touch his hat with respect when the name of the Indians' "Little White One" is mentioned.

'In 1903 my first year in the country, mice were not noticeably plenty. Caribou were abundant through the winter, by early July passing north in large numbers close to the coast. There were some falcons about, the splendid light-colored gyrfalcons, besides broad-winged hawks, dark and almost equally fierce. Both kinds breed in cliffs about the islands. I saw few ptarmigan . . . however, I spent little time inland that year. Foxes, the most important fur game, were fairly plenty. By 1904 mice were distinctly abundant. Hawks were more numerous, the white ones shrilling from many cliffs as we approached their nests. It was that year, I think, perhaps the next, that foxes were noted by the shore people as being scattered and shy; they would not take bait. . . . Ptarmigan were fairly numerous. The wolverene we shot was full of mice. There were no caribou to speak of. We saw a good many wolf tracks, chiefly along the river banks, where mice are apt to be, but heard no wolves at night. There were some hawks and a few owls all the way inland.

'The next year, 1905, was the culminating year of the mice. Sometimes two at a time could be seen in the daylight. Low twigs and all small growth were riddled by them. There was a tattered aspect about the moss and ground in many places not quite pleasant to see. We saw very few mice in the river, but perhaps they swam nights. Falcons had increased visibly, nesting on most cliffs from Cape Harrigan to Mistinipi, a hundred and fifty miles distance. Owls were not many, but had increased somewhat; we only saw one snowy owl. All trout of more than half a pound had mice inside. Ptarmigan were very plenty and the wolves—we may have seen the tracks of two hundred—were silent still. The bear of the trip was full of mice. He was very fat, as doubtless the other predatory animals and birds were. They were in much the situation of some of us Vermont children one year when blackberries were unusually thick; the bushes were hanging with them, and all we had to do was to walk up to them with hands down and "eat with our mouths". Caribou were still scarce, even on George River, and foxes plenty.'

2

Cabot continues:

'In the spring of 1906 the mice disappeared with the snow. The local impression was that they moved away at these times, but such is almost always the prevailing belief, whether as to buffalo, caribou, or fish, in fact any sort of game. It is possible they did move, but if so one ought to hear of their reappearing somewhere occasionally in large numbers, and so far as I learn this is not their way.

'With the vanishing of the mice the change in the visible life of the country was remarkable. The falcon cliffs were deserted, coast and inland. Where the birds had gone none could say. They had seemed to belong to the country. We felt the absence of their superb flights and cries.

'In the trout reaches of the Assiwaban fish were numerous, but they were living on flies now, with what minnows they could get, and were no longer mousey, but sweet and good. No owls appeared; there had, however, never been very many. Our bear of the year was living on berries, and did not smell beary or greasy when we skinned him; the meat was singularly sweet and well flavoured. Ptarmigan were all but wanting, old birds and young. . . . Whether the caribou may not have kept out of the country because the mice were in possession is a question. The ravelled moss and other leavings of the mice were a little unpleasant to our eyes, perhaps also to the sensitive nose and taste of the caribou, as sheep ground is to the larger grazing animals. . . .

'The bearing of the mouse situation on the human interests of the region are [sic] easy to see. It affected all the game, food game and fur. The abundance of mice tended to build up the ptarmigan, which are of vital importance in the winter living of the Indians through the whole forested area to the Gulf. Likewise it built up the caribou herd by providing easier game than they for the wolves. The departure of the mice did the reverse, reducing the deer and ptarmigan, but it may have brought the deer on migration as suggested, giving at any rate an easy year to the hard-pressed Indians of the George. At last they had good food and new clothes and lodges, in all of which necessaries they had gone very low. . . .

'All in all it is hard to imagine any other natural change which would have affected the fortunes, sometimes the fate, of all the other animals of the peninsula, from man to fish, as did the coming and going of the mice during the years from 1903 to 1906. Only fire could have done the like. Nor were the shore people by any means untouched. All their land game came and went, was plenty or wanting, shy or easily taken, according to the supply of mice. . . .

'The year the mice disappeared I was not wholly away from their influence, even at home in New Hampshire. They or their ghosts followed as in the old tale of the Mouse Tower. Whether as a case of cause and effect, that winter a remarkable flight of goshawks, the "winter hawks" of the Labrador, moved down upon the northern states, looking for food. There also appeared, so I read at the time, a wide flight of snowy owls.'

3

Not long ago someone was advocating a *Declaration of Interdependence* as guarantee for the world's political and economic stability. So might the mice in Labrador declare the need for full knowledge of the cycle of rise and decay which brings such harsh reminders of ephemeral prosperity. So might they abandon all naïve belief in the natural balance and justice of nature, yet hope and pray for a constant population, making their badge *Libra*, the Balance, with full communal festival in September.

Cabot's essay plunges us at once into a delicate plexus of animal inter-relation, with only some parts of the pattern as yet clearly showing. He himself realized our main ignorance of these tensions, when he explained the limitations of a casual traveller's insight:

'In time, if whale and cod, wolverine and wolf, Indian and falcon, are not swept from the scene by our remorseless civilisation, the important role of such creatures as have been mentioned, the low food-bearers, may be followed through, and what is casual inference, in many fields, may be demonstrated as true cause and result, or, on the other hand dismissed as unwarranted. We can only put together first coincidences at sight, leaving further observation to determine certainties. The thread of causality traced here is at least more obvious than some outdoor theories that are based upon larger experience, as was, for instance, Spracklin's belief that cod came in well at Fanny's only in years when berries were plentiful on the land. Who shall say? Among the myriad existences of the open there is room for many a thread unseen.'

This introduction is to whet the appetite for more solid fare. Cabot's distilled years of observation are like the bear that he killed in 1906: 'the meat was singularly sweet and well flavoured.' What follows contains more of statistic and a certain reiteration of evidence which is necessary for proof of the periodism of Labrador life.

4

First it is desirable to get a bird's-eye view of the country where these events have been taking place. It is well to go back in mind to the early years of last century, when the Moravian Missions were alone in occupation of the 500-mile strip of coast that lies between Hamilton Inlet (then 'Esquimaux Bay') and the north-east corner at Cape Chidley. Even to this strip they clung a little precariously, ministering to about a thousand primitive Eskimos. To the north lived no white man on the Canadian side except in Ungava for a few years, only 'heathen Eskimos'. Southwards were Hudson's Bay Company posts at Rigolet, and North-West River, in Hamilton Inlet; and a little later Aillik and Kaipokok. The *Arctic Pilot* tells us[18] that

'Eastern Labrador presents to the Atlantic a formidable coastline of steep-to cliffs of Laurentian gneisses, schists, and granites, with occasional Huronian rock, deeply indented by fiords, and studded along all its length by innumerable islands. These are all rocky, and many of them are high. Along continuous stretches of hundreds of miles these islands afford an inside sheltered channel. Only at one spot of this whole rugged and barren coast is there a stretch of sandy beach. The ocean face of rock rises from 500 to 1,000 feet, increasing in height northwards to 1,500 feet at Nain, and continues to rise from Okkak to Nachvak Bay to a height of 3,000 feet.'

Farther north the mountains form the highest land in British North America east of the Rockies—massive peaks of 4–5,000 feet.

'Navigation opens on the southern shore at the end of June, or early in July, but north of Nain the coast is seldom clear of field-ice before the end of July, and all the year round bergs are passing down southwards.'

George Robinson, harbour master at St. John's, Newfoundland, writing in 1889 said[13] that 'The older masters of the ice are inclined to consider that the seasons have become milder subsequent to the year 1860 or about that date, and that the northern ice is later and the volume smaller. The same impression prevails on the Labrador coast'.

This impression is confirmed in the main by the voyages of the Moravian Mission ship *Harmony* (there was a dynasty of ships with that name), recorded in the *Periodical Accounts* of the Mission.[20] In any period, however, the ship was liable to intense hazards of ice and wind during its annual voyage from London or Stromness to Hopedale. In 1826 'her passage through the unusual quantity of floating ice on the coast, which stretched out to sea for three or four hundred miles, was more tedious and dangerous than in former years'. But in 1830 she met with neither ice nor fogs. In 1841 'she fell in with little or no ice, but experienced such a succession of contrary winds and storms, especially as she entered the seas in which that barrier is usually met with, that the Captain was for many days in great doubt whether he would be able to visit any of the stations'. In 1847 'on the 11th of July she fell in with the first ice in Lat. 53° 58' West Long. 52° 32', and with this obstacle she had to contend more or less for the next three weeks. ... On the 29th the wind became favourable, and after passing through a host of ice-bergs of all sizes the vessel came to her anchorage in Hopedale Bay on the 31st.'

5

So far we can visualize a lofty coast of rocks, beset with summer drift-ice, frozen and snow-covered in winter, visited once a year by ship, harbouring one or two thousand souls, administered chiefly by the influence of a handful of German (later English) missionaries. For the material sovereignty of Newfoundland after 1809 has not even to this day brought to the northern coast of Labrador much help or leadership, save once during the brief brilliant rule of Sir William MacGregor.

We can imagine the isolation, the slender resources, the dependence on 'country provisions', and the anxiety with which natural events were watched by native and missionary.

The great table-land lying inland is also inhabited by the fur-bearing animals which are the main interest of this study. John McLean, factor to the Hudson's Bay Company, wrote[11] of this land in 1838, from his northern base at Fort Chimo in Ungava Bay:

'Lakes of inferior note are without number, and the whole country is intersected by small rivers in every direction. . . .'

'Bleak and barren rocks are its distinguishing features, presenting very little variety from Ungava to Esquimaux Bay, a distance of nearly 600 miles; this remark applies to the general aspect of the country, tho' some parts of it bear timber and that of large dimension, yet those parts bear a small proportion to the endless barren waste.

'In the vallies between the ridges of rock the ground is invariably of a marshy nature, bearing small white pine or larch, of from four to six in. diameter: the only variety of the arboreous class the country produces—a few miserable birch are observed beyond the height of land.'

McLean here wrote of the hinterland of Ungava Bay, inhabited by a few wandering Indian bands, miserably poor, and then known only by the tedious journeys that McLean, Erlandson, McKenzie, and other Hudson's Bay Company pioneers made up the George's, Whale, and Koksoak Rivers. These lie west of the main watershed or 'height of land', which an exhausted legislature finally chose as the boundary of political Labrador. The Eskimos of the Moravian Missions seem to have made Labrador itself their chief hunting ground in winter, following inland after the caribou or to trap the fox and marten. Few white men have travelled far into this hinterland. Hesketh Prichard,[12] [(1)] who made a bold summer traverse in 1910 from Nain to George's River, wrote:

'Ridge upon ridge, some of considerable height, roll away seemingly to the world's end. In the valleys and cups of the hills lie thousands of nameless lakes. The winds, during the greater part of the year rage over it. It is sheer desolation. . . . Of dominant notes there are but two, the ivory-coloured reindeer moss and the dark Laurentian stone. . . . A stony wilderness, with here and there some coarse grass growing in the marshes; without a bush or tree of any kind to break the monotonous and dreary prospect.'

6

'Labrador' is used rather variously and sometimes vaguely, so that it needs a little explanation. Geographers and geologists (as A. P. Low and A. P. Coleman[10] in the 11th edition of the *Encyclopaedia Britannica*) expand the word to cover the whole peninsula that is northern Quebec and political Labrador. Likewise the *Arctic Pilot* says firmly[18] that 'Labrador is the north-eastern peninsula of the North American continent, lying between Hudson Bay and the Gulf of St. Lawrence'. Many Canadians would just call this the Quebec Peninsula and make Labrador a part of it. Politically, Labrador is the part that lies east of the height of land and north of about latitude 52°: a northern strip of plateau and a southern region that lies in the water basin of the Hamilton River.

To the Moravian Missionaries, Labrador means northern Labrador—north of Hamilton inlet and up to the north-east point, but not round into Ungava Bay (which is Canadian). To the Grenfell Missions, Labrador means southern Labrador—south of Hamilton Inlet, down to Newfoundland waters. To most Canadians, Labrador—'the Canadian Labrador'—means the north shore of the Gulf of St. Lawrence, locally just 'the North Shore': even as the Eskimos call themselves 'the People'.

Such diverse application is not unlooked for in a name whose origin is still not universally agreed upon; though the most likely explanation would seem to be that a Bristol ship's company named it Labrador after a labourer ('lavrador') from the Azores who was the first man on board to sight the coast.[5a]

There seems to be one rule, however: everyone likes the name and wishes to use it for the region he lives in or travels over. I propose no codification of these pleasant assumptions, but it makes ecological study easier if one knows of their existence. To avoid constant confusion I shall speak usually of the 'Quebec Peninsula' for the whole; of 'Labrador' for political Labrador, and of 'Northern Labrador' for the Moravian part of it. The quotations which are the protocols of this ecological study follow, of course, their own lights according to habit and locality.

The half a million square miles of Quebec Peninsula are a formidable stage for any ecological study. Yet movements of wild life over its high plateau and down the mazy intricacy of its coast-line are on a scale to match this. The arctic fox runs southwards in lean years and reaches both James Bay and southern Labrador, its movements helped no doubt by the southerly drift of ice down the outer coast. In 1922 the white foxes even ran as far as Canadian Labrador and massacred some eider colonies in the Gulf. In the spring of 1923, one, surely the farthest south of this wave of hungry foxes, floating no doubt on floes of ice, was shot on the coast of Cape Breton Island, part of Novia Scotia, not far north of the forty-second parallel, and more than five hundred miles from the nearest point of its Arctic home.[16]

To the caribou also the peninsula is an open wandering ground, and the shifting movements of the great herds are of the greatest moment to the native hunters. Low and Coleman[10] say: 'The Indians roam over the southern interior in small bands, their northern limit being determined by that of the trees, on which they depend for fuel. They live wholly by the chase, and their numbers are dependent upon the deer and other animals; as a consequence there is a constant struggle between the Indian and the lower animals for existence, with great slaughter of the latter. . . .'

The seals, harp and hood and others, also fit the scale with their migrations following in the fall of the year the cold stream that sweeps past Labrador coast southwards. On the ice-floes around Newfoundland they breed before returning on what must be a thousand-mile journey north again. The salmon too move miles up rivers like the Koksoak and Hamilton.

7

Such lavish movements of the population, both animal and man, themselves cause violent fluctuations in a small locality. Imposed on top of these are real increase and then dwindling of the numbers from epidemic disease or lack of sustenance. We need some care to tell which one of these is dominant, where plenty or scarcity is observed. We have to know the boundaries of each trapping region, and if we possibly can, some outline of events in adjoining territories. To set a limit to the trapping grounds covered by one company or one tribe of natives is not necessarily to make a natural frontier for the wild animals they pursue. Often, though, we may expect to find a true coincidence of both, since the peninsula is a network of physical barriers to travel, from the rapid-infested rivers to the mosquito-infested summer lands.

Such considerations lead us to seek some knowledge of Quebec Peninsula as a whole, some frame in which to set the more restricted facts about Northern Labrador and Ungava. Completeness in such knowledge is a mirage, as indeed is all completeness in ecology: it haunts the investigator but is never reached. A few more features will, however, give a balanced outline picture of the country.

Physically the height is greatest eastwards. The high Torngat Mountains up in the north-east corner make a massive barrier whose desolate look and formidable scale can best be realized from seeing air-photographs that Crowley, Brown, and Hubbard of Alexander Forbes' recent expedition were able to obtain.[4] This barrier separates the northern Atlantic coast from Ungava west of it. Running south the high plateau still forms a serious barricade to man, but perhaps less to animals.

Except for William Cabot, and William Duncan Strong, whose work is noticed later on, no naturalist has surveyed this land in comprehensive style. The scientific traveller in summer hugs the coast or spends his energies in passing through the inland plateau still alive. And in winter life is underground or under snow or gone away, and what is left the trapper studies. There have been, it is true, a few museum parties whose collections are a starting-point for deeper surveys.

It is to the geological expeditions of A. P. Low[8, 9] and his companions that we turn for first-class knowledge of the trees and plants and some of the animals. Here is a noble pattern drawn from years of travel and clear insight of the land. We bless the Canadian Government Department of that time, that printed fully what he saw, ravishing the sacred pigeon-holes to do it.

In 1892 Low explored from the Canadian Labrador to the height of land at Mistassinny Lake, and thence by roundabout river routes to the shore of James Bay. Sailing down to Moose Factory, he made his way overland to the Canadian Pacific Railway. With him on this expedition was A. H. D. Ross, who brought back a fine collection of plants.

In 1893 and 1894, accompanied this time by D. I. V. Eaton, who did surveying work, Low began another series of brilliant journeys. Threading their way again from Canadian Labrador to James Bay, they turned and crossed the inland barrens northward to Ungava Bay. Next, starting from Hamilton Inlet, they broke into further unsurveyed country up various tributaries of the Hamilton River, to the watershed.

Such journeys put everything except light Indian travel in the shade. Within two years these two men went nearly three thousand miles in canoes, five hundred with dog-teams, and a thousand on foot all through wild and trackless country. The results are set down in a full, scholarly way, and from the broadest point of view.

Four other explorers add good impressions of the country life. Hind[7] leaves a vivid narrative of the difficult southern wooded hills of the Canadian Labrador. Lucien Turner[15] includes, in his ethnographic studies on Ungava natives, some careful notes about the scenery and resources. Mrs. Hubbard saw much during her traverse from Hamilton Inlet to Ungava in 1905.[7a] And Robert Bell, though he scarcely penetrated the interior of the northern parts, had a varied knowledge of the coasts, gained from his own voyaging and from discussions with many experienced men who had lived long in this part of the north. A natural geographer, almost ecologist, Bell leaves several reviews, one of which[1] is specially valuable, from its map showing the distribution of different species of trees in Quebec Peninsula.

8

The subarctic forest is of two chief species, seven others being there in less abundance. Foremost is the black spruce, which Low thought might be nine-tenths of all the trees. The tamarack or larch is next, and does not shrink in size so much towards its northern limits. With local habits and differing northern limits grow also the white spruce, jack or silver pine, balsam fir (the Christmas tree of the Eskimos), canoe birch, aspen, balsam poplar, and—less often seen—the cedar. Deep *Sphagnum* moss is found in the southern forests—so deep that fires can burn all winter under the snow. The forest undergrowth is chiefly a tangled layer of small heathy shrubs: *Ledum*, the Labrador tea, with rusty-felted leaves and small white flowers, and with it mountain laurel, *Kalmia*, dark glossy leaves and purple flowers. In the lowland swamps and along some river-banks grow small willows and alders. Berry-plants—cranberry, blueberry, and cloudberry or bake-apple grow commonly in more open places.

The northern trends—there is no sharp tree-limit—are fewer and smaller (but often very old) trees, *Sphagnum* giving way to the 'untold miles of crisp white moss' that Hutton writes of, thickets of Arctic willow and dwarf birch, and finally the barren Arctic rocks with crowberry (*Empetrum*), moss, and lichens and several hundred kinds of flowering plants—but little grass. The crisp white moss is mainly *Cladonia*, the reindeer moss, in fact a lichen. Ekblaw writes[2] of the flowers 'nearly all vernal in character, they burst into bloom abruptly, just as breaks the summer'.

The limits of these forests can be found marked down on various maps, which must be at best approximations to the truth, since the growth in the northern barren grounds depends so much on local possibilities. Patches grow here and there in sheltered spots. The line runs roughly from the Nastopoka River mouth, on Hudson Bay, skirting the north side of the Leaf River valley nearly to Ungava Bay, whose line it parallels to the Georges River. It runs in the foot-hills of the Atlantic mountain coast range a little south of Hebron down to Hamilton Inlet. South of here it hems in the coast, but usually hangs back from it some miles.

The seaward islands and the northern coast are bare of trees, which come in valleys somewhat inland. This zoning is described by Wheeler,[17] surveyor of the Nain-Okak coast.

'On the more exposed parts of the islands vegetation is confined to lichens, mosses, grasses, and flowering plants, as in the upland zone. Trees appear only in sheltered places. They are seldom found on the outer islands, where they are badly stunted and contorted. They are generally spruce, though tamaracks occur under favorable conditions.

'Timber line is about 1000 feet above sea level. Thus the deeper valleys of the mainland are wooded, while the adjacent uplands are barren. Trees seldom reach a diameter of three feet, even in the most sheltered valleys, and these larger specimens taper more rapidly than the smaller ones, so that 50 feet would probably be a generous estimate of their height.

'By far the greater number of the trees are conifers—black spruce and tamarack on poor or moist ground, white spruce on dry sandy ground in sheltered parts of valleys, and a little balsam fir in the deeper mainland valleys. Deciduous trees are relatively rare, being chiefly confined to a small birch that may become good-sized on steep valley sides.'

9

The growth of trees is very slow up here. The missionary at Nain records[20] in 1849: 'On examining the pine woods it has been ascertained that there is very little after-growth, and as far as I can judge it requires full 300 years for a tree to attain its full size.' Hesketh Prichard[12] [(2)] passed these woods in 1910 when journeying from Nain across the plateau. He went up Fraser River, and 'the banks for the most part were clothed with spruce on a carpet of white reindeer-moss, which began to be interlaced everywhere with bear paths. . . .' Soon he climbed to 1,500 feet and entered the desolate treeless plateau. Marching over this at 2,000 feet he came down again to spruce and birch near George's River.

North of Hebron the land is Arctic. Hantsch[6] says: 'On my excursions in the northeastern parts of Labrador I found only creeping shrubs, raising themselves only a hand-breadth from the ground. . . .' Elsewhere, he adds an impression of the changes going southward. 'Thick bush of birches and willows, as high as a man, is already found at Rama. In the inner part of the bays south from Hebron a low coniferous growth begins, which at Okak truly reminds one of our forests. . . . But these forests appear only as oases. . . .'

We may leave this plant and forest survey with a note, a first impression written in 1833 by a Hudson's Bay man, Nicol Finlayson,[3] who built Fort Chimo.

'The surrounding country is the most sterile and mountainous imaginable, here and there intersected with ravines, swamps and lakes, with now and then a sandy plain, enlivened with no verdure except patches of dwarfish pines, larch and willows in the ravines and swamps. The coast is also bleak, barren and mountainous. . . . The Interior, as far as we have seen, is equally mountainous, rugged and sterile. . . but variegated with patches of pine and larch which grow to a good size. That on which the Outpost was established grows pine superior to the York [Factory] wood and in quality inferior to none in the country. . . . The Indians never leave the coast, where deer are most numerous, above four or five days journey, and that is when they go to look for birchrind for their canoes.'

10

Climate does not need long mention, though it calls the tune for most activities in the north. Even on the coast, the average temperature may be below the zero point of Fahrenheit. But there is a burst of summer warmth and sun. Extracts from a journal of Davis Inlet,[19] chosen at a venture, run:

1902. 16 June. The ice in the River moved down in a body.
     19 June. The River full of drift ice this evening, coming from the North.
     29 June. The grass getting green in patches only; the willows with buds only yet.
     3 July. The fishermen report the coast clear of ice to the south.
     2 Aug. 'S.S. Pelican' arrived.
     26 Aug. A very good sign of cod in the River now.
     28 Nov. Flower's Bay [ice] is fast.
     3 Dec. Some slob in the River.
     7 Dec. The River fast above the Post.
1903 31 May. 2 feet of snow in the woods about here.
     12 June. No snow about the Post now, though a great deal in the thick woods.
     22 June. To the North it is all fast yet.
     26 June. Ice to the North opened up.

Snow is usually back again in September. Sometimes even this short summer fails. The Okak Mission diary[20] says of the summer of 1860: 'That our garden-produce proved scanty, was scarcely a matter of surprise, as, in consequence of the inclement and stormy character of the summer, even the indigenous berries, such as cranberries and crowberries, did not come to maturity.'

For a pleasant, vivid picture of the northern seasons we may take the Eskimo names for the months that Hawkes[6a] took down. These are the names that Ungava Eskimos use; but they are not very different from those of the people that live on the Atlantic coast:

March:	'month of the young jar seal.'
April:	'month of the young bearded seal.'
May:	'month of fawning.'
June:	'egg-month.'
July:	'mosquito-month.'
August:	'berry-month.'
September:	'fading-month.'
(October):	'month when ice forms round the shore.'
(November):	'inland month' (i.e. inland hunting).
December:	'ice-forming month.'
January:	'coldest month for frost.'
February:	'ground cracked by frost.'

The snow lies thinner in the higher Arctic lands than farther south: much of that which does come down is often blown away by furious winds. Shaw,[14] who studied the weather at Port Burwell in 1885–6, wrote: 'Snow does not seem to stay on the land: it is literally blown out to sea, the ravines and hollows filling up level'. The snow depth varies greatly, and we read of Hebron[20] in the winter 1920–1 that 'the small amount of snow which we got was most remarkable. Whenever it did snow, which was seldom the case, storms very soon swept the countryside clean. . . . There was no track for sledges across the hills.' But in 1925–6 the tale is different: 'April brought with it large quantities of fresh snow, and at one time nearly twenty feet of soft loose snow was measured in front of the Mission-house.' The Reverend George Harp, now in charge of Hebron, told me that the snowfall is really heavy in Northern Labrador but is usually blown away. Much more lies in the south, where very deep drifts accumulate in places.

So much for the framework of the country: its obstacles to white man's travel, its vegetation and climate. We come now to a closer view of the animals, the trapper-natives, and the fur-trade units and their territories. Logic suggests this order, but the opposite order is used because it is best to describe both animals and native peoples in their relation to the fur-trade districts; for these supply the essential facts that are discussed in Chapers XIII and XIV, and are the source of all statistics.

REFERENCES

* Indicates that an abstract is deposited in the library of the Bureau of Animal Population, Oxford. H. B. Co. = Hudson's Bay Company.

1. BELL, R. (1895). 'The Labrador Peninsula.' Scot. Geogr. Mag. 11: 335–61.

1 a. CABOT, W. B. (1912). 'In Northern Labrador.' Appendix: 'Mice.' Pp. 287–92.

2. EKBLAW, W. ELMER (1926). 'Ungava and Labrador.' In 'Naturalist's guide to the Americas', ed. by V. E. Shelford. Baltimore. P. 107.

*3. FINLAYSON, NICHOL. Ungava [Fort Chimo], Report, 1832–3. MS. H. B. Co. Archives, London.

4. FORBES, A. (1932). 'Surveying in Northern Labrador.' Geogr. Rev. 22: 30–60.

4 a. FORBES, A., and others (1938). 'Northernmost Labrador mapped from the air.' Special Publ. Amer. Geogr. Soc. No. 22: 255 pp. and separate folder of maps, &c.

5. GLOVER, T. R. (1931). 'The mice of Labrador.' The Times (London), May 4.

5 a. GOSLING, W. G. (1910). 'Labrador: its discovery, exploration, and development.' London. Ch. 4.

6. HANTZSCH, B. (1928). ['Contribution to the knowledge of the avifauna of North-eastern Labrador.'] Canad. Field-Nat. 42: 8 and 38. Transl. by M. B. A. and R. M. Anderson of original paper (1908). J. Orn., Leipzig, 56: 175–202 and 307–92.

6 a. HAWKES, E. W. (1916). 'The Labrador Eskimo.' Canada, Dept. of Mines, Geol. Surv. Mem. 91 (No. 14, Anthropol. Ser.): 28–9.

7. HIND, H. Y. (1863). 'Explorations in the interior of the Labrador Peninsula.' London.

7 a. HUBBARD, L. (Mrs.) (1908). 'A woman's way through unknown Labrador.' London.

8. LOW, A. P. (1889). 'Report on exploration in James Bay and country east of Hudson Bay, drained by the Big, Great Whale and Clearwater Rivers, 1887 and 1888.' Ann. Rep. Geol. & Nat. Hist. Surv. Canada for 1887–8, 3: 1 J–94 J.

9. LOW, A. P. (1896). 'Report on explorations in the Labrador Peninsula, along the East Main, Koksoak, Hamilton, Manicuagan and portions of other rivers, in 1892–93–94–95.' Ann. Rep. Geol. Surv. Canada for 1895, 8: 1 L–387 L.

10. [LOW, A. P., & COLEMAN, A. P.] (1911). 'Labrador.' Encyclopaedia Britannica, 11th ed., vol. 16, pp. 28 and 29.

*11. McLEAN, JOHN. Ungava District, Report, 1837–8. MS. H. B. Co. Archives, London.

12. PRICHARD, H. HESKETH (1911). 'Through trackless Labrador.' London and New York. (1) 64–5. (2) 44.

13. ROBINSON, G. (1889). 'A report on the movements of the ice, currents, and tidal streams of the coast of Newfoundland and in the Gulf of St. Lawrence.' Blue-book, Hydrographic Office, Admiralty, London. P. 3.

14. SHAW, G. (1887). In 'Report of the Hudson Bay Expedition of 1886 under the command of Lt. A. R. Gordon R.N.' Blue-book, Dept. of Marine and Fisheries Canada (Diary, 17 Nov. 1885).

15. TURNER, L. M. (1894). 'Ethnology of the Ungava District, Hudson Bay Territory.' Smithsonian Inst., Bureau of American Ethnology, 11th Ann. Rep. (1889–90): 167–350.

16. DE VANY, J. L. (1923). 'Arctic fox shot in Cape Breton.' Canad. Field-Nat. 37: 118.

17. WHEELER, E. P. (1935). 'The Nain-Okak section of Labrador.' Geogr. Rev. 25: 240–54.

18. Arctic Pilot (1915), vol. 3, 2nd ed., p. 217.

*19. Davis Inlet Post, Journal, 1902. MS. H. B. Co. Archives, London.

*20. Periodical Accounts of the Moravian Missions, London.

CHAPTER XII

THE PREDATORS

1

ONE does not have to be particularly cynical to gain some measure of amusement and wonder from the ecological spectacle that fur-trade inter-relationships in the north afford. Of the many links some can be seen quite clearly: mouse, red fox, Indian, fur-trader, shareholder, costumier, customer, pawnbroker—at this point the choice of paths grows wider, as we find ourselves farther away from wild life in Labrador, and deeper in the tangled undergrowth of economics. Each organism is damming up for a certain space of time what power it can, and preserving with the greatest care its own skin or that of some other stage below in the chain; but the original thing is created out of plants by mice. With many stages and complexities go many points of view towards the whole concern. There is the confident appeal that higher stages make in assembly of themselves[12]: 'They have kept the flag flying—holding the territory until it became part of the Great Dominion, that "captain jewel in the carcanet", of what we proudly call the British Empire.' There is the outside, impartial, completely cold and abstract scientist who thinks:[6]

'The theory of the preceding section shows that the consumption of one species by another in the population studied is so active that the classical oscillations in numbers are transformed into an elementary relaxation and the coördinates of the singular point around which such oscillations could be theoretically expected are exceedingly small. This fact . . . enables us to predict that were we in a position to reduce the intensity of consumption we could increase the coördinates of the singular point, and in this way observe the classical oscillations of Lotka-Volterra.'

There is the equally theoretical viewpoint[14] of the Indian: 'Nearly every old summer camp of the Naskapi is marked by bears' skulls set on posts, for these Indians perform many rites to appease the spirit of this important animal.' The points of view, if any, of the fox and the field-mouse, have not been recorded, but they would probably both agree with *Nuttall's Standard Dictionary of the English Language* in defining 'predatory' as 'plundering; ravenous', and 'prey' as 'that which is *or may be* seized by violence in order to be devoured'. A hard, expectant life.

The trapper in Labrador has always lived rather near to absolute poverty. If prices fall he has to accept the fact, and so the turmoil of Western city moves and countermoves has little influence on his trapping energies and direction, except when trends are persistent and long. This chapter therefore treats of three kinds of predators only, the fur-trader, the trapper, and the animals they pursue or live among.

2

In such a country we usually find that the fur-traders followed the lines of least resistance. Even the least resistance was formidable: when James Killock[10] and Robert Chilton with other Hudson's Bay Company men left Rupert's House on 28 June 1834 to place a post on Nichikun Lake, they had to make seventy-one portages with their 'outfit' and canoes. The post was reached on 12 August, and during the first winter only two Indians paid a visit—they complained of scarcity of provisions, having already eaten twenty of their beaver skins. Travel inside the country in summer (and that was the only way for trading, as distinct from hunting and trapping parties) was always much at this level of danger and effort. A. P. Low alone of all modern white travellers seems really to have conquered the country year after year. Many others have turned back or starved.

So the districts used by traders of the Company mostly followed the big water-basins of the rivers. In spite of all the hazards of the game, the stress of evil years when hunters have to go great distances, and remembering that the bands from one district sometimes went to other posts in hope of better prices, we can still draw some sort of a map showing the territories that the fur trade followed in the last century, and even now to great extent. The Ungava part is described in more detail in Chapter XVII.

Ungava District had the Koksoak, the Whale and George's Rivers, with some outposts centred on Fort Chimo. Eastmain District (oddly not including Eastmain Post) covered the Big River basin. Esquimaux Bay District had Hamilton Inlet and the basin of the Hamilton River, together with a chain of northern coast posts which challenged those of the Moravian Missions. The latter had Northern Labrador and a fairly faithful flock that traded with its missions. They seldom passed beyond George's River and reached that mainly for the deer hunt. Rupert's River District held a huge domain, including Eastmain River and the central heights with Nichikun and Kaniapiscau, also Rupert's and Nottaway Rivers with the cluster of big lakes that occupies the southern height of land. The gulfward slopes had to eastward the District of Mingan, and to westward the King's Posts (equivalent of the later Bersimis District), separated roughly by the Moisie River. In the last thirty years the details have moved and changed, and many fur-traders, single or in rival companies, have changed the situation. But the map gives a broad idea of the nineteenth-century trading areas, the larger statistical units of our study.

3

Some two or three thousand Eskimos now live along the treeless or nearly treeless coasts of east Hudson Bay, Hudson Straits, and Labrador as far as Hamilton Inlet. They far outnumber white men. Their life is coastal, but for excursions inland after caribou. A hardy, independent people whose character, life, health, and hunting habits are described with understanding and regard by Hutton;[7, 8] and by Binney,[3, 4] the first who ever made for them a comprehensive book of knowledge fitted to their needs and way of life. Originally whale and seal and polar bear and caribou hunters, and fishermen, they learned last century to trap the fox and other furs.

FIG. 13. Map of Quebec Peninsula. The main rivers are marked in order to show the arrangement of valleys and river basins radiating from the centre of the peninsula. Others, and the numerous lakes are omitted. Indian House Lake is an expansion of George's River. Lake Kaniapiscau, not shown here, lies between Nichikun and Ft. Nascopie. It had a post, different from Kanaapuscow. Broken line shows approximate tree limit. Names in small capitals are fur posts: Hudson's Bay Co. posts in present or recent operation are underlined. Others are various older posts now closed.

'There could hardly be two greater contrasts than the Indian and the Eskimo: the one aloof, lithe in intellect, a guardian of forest secrets; the other responsive, supple, and of open countenance.'[3] Binney also draws[3] distinction between the hunting grounds of 'the shrill-voiced Nascopie Indians' who roam the interior after caribou and visit Fort Chimo and Davis Inlet, and the Swampy Crees who go no farther north than Great

Whale River, and hunt the former districts of Eastmain and Rupert's River and also south and west of this.

The distribution of the Indian bands has importance for the handling of fur-trade statistics. The furs from inland posts are brought by Indians to the Hudson's Bay Company posts. A fluctuation in fur returns may mean several things. Is it due to varying abundance of wild life, or varying energy of the trappers ? Do bad years reflect the bad luck of the fox or the bad luck of Indians starving for want of deer or stricken with influenza ? Or again does each band frequent the same post through thick and thin ? The last question can be answered with a certain degree of confidence. But it is not a simple problem, since our knowledge rests so much on vague report and Indian tradition, as well as on the records of explorers and the fur trade.

The work of Speck[13] is the chief modern source of information. Like Strong, who helped him with notes from Labrador, Speck sought for Indian folk-tales and customs. He also made inquiry from many people, including Indian chiefs, aiming at a map of the distribution of each band. His map, as he admits himself, is oversimplified, and must be only a rough and ready approximation to the old Indian hunting and trapping grounds. The separate existence of a few is even doubtful. But this knowledge is the best we have and is enlarged by Speck's thumbnail histories of each band. I can add a little light also from archives of the Moravian Missions and the Hudson's Bay Company.

Besides Speck's inquiries, we have some published notes by Lucien Turner,[16] another American ethnologist, who lived two years at Fort Chimo in the eighties of last century. As ever, Low contributes much, and there is Strong's experience which we have already mentioned.

4

First about the Crees. These extend from James Bay up the west coast of Quebec Peninsula, hunting partly inland also. The rest is country of Nascopies and Montagnais. The former incurred the dislike of the Montagnais over some dim distant war against the Eskimos. From this came the name Nascopie, meaning 'uncivilized', 'heathens', or perhaps quite simply 'those——'. The Nascopie have, not unnaturally, a better name for themselves: Né-né-not, which means 'the ideal type of red man'. (In the same spirit the Indians named their Arctic neighbours 'Eskimo', a term of contempt that means 'eaters of raw flesh'. But the Eskimos call themselves 'Innuit', which means 'the People'. Other nations (all of them) are 'Kablunaet'—'sons of dogs'.[6a] Likewise, while the Prussian called cockroaches 'Russians', the Russians called them 'Prussians', thus satisfying national prestige.) The broad tribal differences between the Indians may be narrower than this would make them seem, and American ethnologists favour the portmanteau term 'Nascopie-Montagnais' which is more correct but lacks the convenience of a portmanteau. The Montagnais are in the southern parts, and we shall here consider only the northern territories, which are Nascopie lands.

The bands have always been few and poor and dogged by bitter catastrophes of starvation. The rough census that Parliament demanded in 1857[24] for its report on the Hudson's Bay Company totalled 3,910 for the Quebec Peninsula. In 1924 the Canadian Department of Indian Affairs reckoned 4,648.[13] This means that to each *Indian* were about 125 square miles of country: perhaps to each *hunter* were over 500 square miles. To a large extent such averages and ratios are mere abstractions; but they emphasize the sparse predatory human population, and no doubt explain the elasticity of the fur-bearing animal numbers, which still yield a large crop even after many years of trapping, though deer have not held up so well.

These Indians achieved a sort of balance which the acquisition of firearms must have changed in large degree but still left possible. The mental equation which the Indians made with the natural scene they lived in has already been hinted at. It has a depth which the white man's commercial exploitation cannot show. Jenness says: 'The Naskapi and Montagnais believed vaguely in a great sky god to whom they occasionally offered smoke from their pipes. Of more concern to them, however, were the numberless supernatural beings whom they postulated in the world around them, and the souls of the animals on which they depended for their food supply.'

Five hundred would be a large band: the nineteenth-century average was below 250, and the same is true at present. Of these only a proportion would be effective hunters. None lived permanently and but few now live on the coasts of Northern Labrador or Hudson Straits. Half a dozen Nascopie bands concern us chiefly here.

5

The limits of the Indian bands doubtless had origins in the natural lie of the land, and now rest on traditional habits and tribal rights. They were, however, affected by the disposition of the Hudson's Bay Company posts, their chief trade centres. Speck's map shows nineteenth-century boundaries: many of these still hold good.

The Ungava band lived in the Ungava country east of Whale River, roaming southward inland to a varying extent; but seldom beyond the watershed. Finlayson's Ungava report[5] in 1833 showed that these Indians chiefly haunted the northern parts where the deer were then in numbers. Duncan Matheson, a later factor at Fort Chimo, confirms this fact in a letter he wrote[11] in 1899: 'The Indians were more scattered and travelled over a greater extent of country than usual last winter, some of them going as far as the site of old Fort Nascopie, and others to the height of land and beyond: and all had the same story to report in the spring—"no martens".'

The Nascopies of the Ungava band therefore ranged for most part in the

Koksoak and Whale River valleys and adjacent uplands, centred on Fort Chimo for their trade. Where they traded in the interregnum when Fort Chimo was closed is not clear.

In eastern Ungava lived the Barren Ground people. Their territory was the George's River Valley up to the head of Indian House Lake—a broad expansion of the river, famous as a caribou hunting place. They wandered as well in the barrens west of Whale River, marching with the Ungava Indian lands. The Barren Ground band traded, if at all, with Davis Inlet. Since the deer failed in 1916 and influenza swept through them in 1919, only a few are left and these have come out now to Nain for trade. It must have been the same band that the Nain missionaries[23] heard of in 1857: 'In the spring some of our people, who were on the rein-deer hunt, met with a tribe of heathen Indians, 150 in number, including women and children. Their camp, according to the report of the Esquimaux, was about the same distance inland, as Hopedale is from Nain, that is, 200 miles.' A little more than this, at right angles to the coast, lies Indian House Lake. In February 1858 over fifty of these Indians came starving to the mission, and it was learned that over thirty others perished. But Indian visits to the coast were very rare in this part of Northern Labrador.[23]

Bordering these to the south another small band had its grounds—the Davis Inlet band that Strong lived with. This was an almost international affair: Speck says its ultimate sire was a Scotch-Cree Indian who married an Ungava Eskimo more than a century ago. One son, mating with southern Indian wives, started the Davis Inlet band. These probably used to trade at North West River, another Hudson's Bay Company post. Davis Inlet post began in 1869, and the journals[18] are available from that date but are not very full of meat, being mostly written in a bald and unrewarding fashion with little eye for background—although many such journals are full of colour and carry a certain impressive power of under-statement. From 1875, at any rate, various Indians came each year to trade, and probably before that too. They numbered in 1930 about 36 in all, but formerly were larger. Strong says that these and the Barren Ground people often camped together.[14]

South again were the North West River band, whose lands were north of Hamilton Inlet, and who hunted west almost to the height of land, by the huge Lake Michikamau. These traded at North West River post. West of these and high up among what Turner called 'the festoonery of lakes looped through the highlands' lived the small Lake Michikamau band: between that lake and Lake Petitsikapau. These used to trade at North West River but now go out to Seven Islands on the Gulf of St. Lawrence. There may also be some tiny bands on other parts of this almost unpeopled central upland, over to Lake Petitsikapau, Kaniapiskau, and Nichikun.

Far west of all these bands were others stretching inland from the Hudson Bay up the great rivers: the White Whale River, Big River, Eastmain, and Rupert's House bands: while south of the watershed were the Bersimis, Godbout, St. Marguerite, Moisie, Mingan, Natashquon, Musquaro, and St. Augustine bands. These seldom influenced the fur returns of Ungava or Northern Labrador, though trading movements and small migrations of families were evidently more common than any rigid map could show, and some of the White Whale River Indians drifted over to Ungava.

6

Predator research needs figures for the predator numbers, but in the case of Indian bands these are hard to come by. Censuses exist, but some refer to Indian visitors to posts, others to total counts of heads; but these may give Canadian tribes and leave out those that now live within political Labrador. It seems that there cannot have been for more than a century past more than two thousand, perhaps only a thousand, souls in the Ungava, Barren Ground, Davis Inlet, North West River, Michikamau, and Petit-sikapau bands.

The 1857 census of *visitors* to Hudson's Bay Company posts gave about 600,[24] and this figure probably left out some of the Ungava people, since Fort Chimo then was closed. A modern census by government, in 1924, which omits political Labrador and therefore presumably all or part of the Barren Ground and Davis Inlet bands, gives Fort Chimo 213, George's River 36, and North West River 308, a total of 557 heads—and this must include the families.[13] The active hunters are a fraction of these. There must have been only a few hundred hunters in these bands.

We leave the native population problem at this point, since anything but real and complete analysis would serve no purpose—and analysis of that sort must fail for figures on which to base it. The main lines can be seen: a coastal Eskimo nation, several thousand strong, settled north of the tree line and along the barren north-east coast. Inland, and pushing to the north and north-west coasts for trade, half a dozen Nascopie bands, each moving within a natural orbit of its own.

White men trap the east coast in places, but little inland. Last century Ungava was wholly native and still is in the main. At the time only a few white 'planters' trapped along the coast of northern Labrador, mostly at the south end and in Hamilton Inlet. In the last thirty years much outside new fur-trading activity has invaded these coasts: Revillon Frères the biggest, but also many small concerns and fluctuating individual efforts.

7

For survey of the wild animal predators one turns to several sources, each of value in a different way. Bangs, American museum enthusiast,[2] first encouraged enough collecting to lay a groundwork for correct classi-fication of the species: he never visited the country himself. Quite recently Anderson of the National Museum of Canada[1] has summed our Museum knowledge in convenient and judicial shape (and with vast experience of field natural history in other regions). This summary is published in *Canada's Eastern Arctic*, where Taverner[15] does the same for birds.

The works of the German naturalist Hantsch (translated into English by the Andersons) and of Strong stand high and almost alone as first-hand studies in the field of Labrador. Hantsch, who gives indeed a conspectus of the life at large of north-east Labrador, had birds as his special interest, but brought a German thoroughness and care to other sides of wild life also. Strong, ethnologist on the trail of Indian lore, gives[14] very vivid notes which tell us much of animal life inside Labrador where he travelled and camped with the Davis Inlet band of Indians in 1928. Low and others also put down useful notes on various animals. And last we have the fur-trade figures and reports. These are good for mapping distribution, movements, and abundance of a great many forms.

If we take the mammals living north of about the fifty-fourth parallel, which runs through Hamilton Inlet, Kaniapiscau Lake, and Big River, we shall have chosen the three old fur districts of Eastmain, Ungava, and Moravian Mission Labrador, the latter covering part of Esquimaux Bay District too. This holds the Arctic, border barrens, and northern parts of the main subarctic forest. Here live (omitting small shrews and such) about eleven predatory land mammals, put in a list below:

Black bear (*Ursus americanus*)
Wolf (*Canis lycaon*)
Coloured fox (*Vulpes ?fulva*)
Arctic fox (*Alopex lagopus*)
Marten (*Martes americana*)
Three kinds of weasel or ermine (*Mustela cicognanii* and other spp.)
Mink (*Mustela vison*)
Wolverine (*Gulo luscus*)
Otter (*Lutra canadensis*)

The bear eats berries, mice, and fish and what else offers. The wolf and wolverine are followers of the caribou, ravening also on the smaller life. The fox hunts small rodents such as mice, and birds, as also does the marten. The weasel also mouses presumably. The mink does not live an open life: its food in Labrador is little known. The otter swims for fish.

Each and all of these may figure in the fur returns of almost any part of the northern country, except north-west, which keeps a more truly Arctic fauna. Such lists from different points are set out below to show the way each region has a bias both in fauna and in hunting practices. The lists are not a mirror image of the wild life: there are several fallacies that require a cautious attitude for interpretation. Thus a ship or native party may call and sell its catch of furs from many hundred miles away. Some furs are hard to get and hardly worth the toil of snaring or shooting and then transporting over many miles of country to the post. Such are wolf and to some extent weasels. But the land is not rich enough in wild life at any time for coats to stay easily on predatorial backs, and we can assume for most of the species that their fur is plundered when the native can.

TABLE 15

Some Typical Fur Catches in Quebec Peninsula

(Totals for ten years: years of production, not of sales.)

	Moravian Mission		Hudson's Bay Company		
	1870–9[22]	1900–9[22]	Davis Inlet Post.[17] 1881–90	Fort Chimo Post. [19] 1918–27	Rupert's River District.[25] 1852–61
Bear, black . .	92	206	90	55	1,384
Beaver . . .	2	0	20	55	47,862
Ermine or weasel .	0	1,042	18	2,655	244
Fisher . . .	0	0	0	0	234
Fox (red, cross, silver) .	3,473	2,414	854	2,484	2,153
Fox (white, blue) .	2,165	4,216	289	20,020	1,344
Lynx	21	2	3	85	7,988
Marten . . .	745	1,521	970	3,563	29,188
Mink	149	635	188	1,188	2,626
Musquash . . .	265	255	5	2,163	20,161
Otter	103	170	156	811	7,809
Skunk . . .	0	0	0	0	1,755
Wolf	29	55	118	2	31
Wolverine . . .	19	102	78	26	56

Arctic hares and snowshoe rabbits omitted because they are not always distinguished in the returns. Caribou skins and a few minor items also omitted.

8

This table needs some guidance and an explanation of some features. The dates of fur returns were chosen partly at random, partly dictated by the records that survive from earlier trading days. The actual numbers read across give a false comparison, since one (Davis Inlet) is taken at a post with a small hunting population but fairly large collecting grounds, another (Fort Chimo) at a post that really centralizes a very large district, while Rupert's River is a district covering several different posts. The lists are rather to be read downwards for each place. This shows the dominant animal caught, different in the Arctic, Subarctic, more southern forests, and Atlantic coast.

In all, the foxes and marten figure very large and important—the marten being the more valuable to trade. The white fox—that is arctic fox—is supreme in the far north, but ranges very far to southward. The catch of ermine does not mean much in these lists so far as life-zones are concerned, as its value and attraction fluctuated in part, it is said, with coronation needs in Europe. The ermine might look forward to a quiet century if this is true.

Some predators that are very rare in the northern region we have been taking for a sample are much more common in the forests around James Bay and in the southern parts generally. This is thought to be due to sparseness of the snowshoe rabbits (*Lepus americanus*) in the North: though these range right up into Ungava, yet few in numbers. Mink, too, are rarer towards the north (practically all the Moravian Mission skins come in to Hopedale), while otters are not too thick. The wolf and wolverine must be relatively more numerous than the fur lists show. South of the line we drew, some other predators begin to filter in: the skunk (*Mephitis mephitis*) and fisher (*Martes pennanti*) among them. But even here the list is not long.

The northern fur lists show bare patches in the predator populations, and this must be partly the effect of poorish rodent and hoofed animal communities that form the prey and food. There are no moose or white-tailed deer. Beaver (*Castor Canadensis*), which swell the lists of Rupert's River and other districts farther south, are almost absent, also musquash (*Ondatra zibethica*) are but a shadow of their swarming colonies in the south. (The Moravian musquash skins mostly come in to Hopedale.) Red squirrels (*Sciurus hudsonicus*) come far north, but flying squirrels (*Glaucomys sabrinus*) and woodchucks (*Marmota monax*) only reach to the skirts of Northern Labrador. In mice, voles and lemmings (also some shrews) the country is, as we know, well furnished in certain years. The outburst of such rich food supply, anomalous in so starvation a country, is what makes mouse affairs so dominant in predator ecology. The situation is rather like a gold-rush for which men will drop their trades and carefully learned habits and turn to the sudden new resource that holds out such enormously high promises of luxury and wealth. The aftermath is not unlike, too.

9

Over most of Canada in the nineteenth century the predatory fur-bearing animals were always outrivalled in amount by the two abundant staple rodents: beaver and musquash. In the ten years from 1871 to 1880 the Hudson's Bay Company sold in London furs as follows: beaver, 1,527,000; musquash, 5,597,000; marten, 721,000; coloured fox, 102,100; lynx, 184,200; otter, 114,900. The lynx and fox and perhaps the marten live to large extent on snowshoe rabbit. The mouse-fox-and-marten chain of wealth stands out as local and peculiar to the Quebec Peninsula, and especially to its northern parts. The fur community is particularly predatory in facies, more so than any other region except pure Arctic, which has the fox-lemming chain—much the same in principle, though the members favour different colours for their coats.

We shall not dwell on the sea predators, although they are a dominating factor in native life. These are polar bear, walrus, half a dozen kinds of seal, and several whales. As these do not live on mice, they only enter the present account by the back door, if possibly the weather fluctuations that affect the ice or currents that they live among, may be similar to the ones that govern mouse affairs on land.

10

Besides the caribou (*Rangifer arcticus*), whose wanderings and fluctuations make a long story by themselves, there are several less distinguished herbivores which are locally esteemed by natives: the porcupine (*Erethizon dorsatum*) for food and quills, and the arctic hare (*Lepus arcticus*) for food and fur. The former comes in wooded parts—it often finds a place in the journals of the Hudson's Bay Company for Davis Inlet[18] and Nichikun.[21] The hare, really Arctic, ranges no farther south than Hamilton Inlet. So far as we know these play no signal part in the fluctuation plexus studied here.

The list of mice, their status and importance, are reserved for Chapter XVI which contains the evidence about mouse cycles and their correlation with the fur returns. There is one more item which probably has some considerable weight in the fluctuation rhythms. This is the game-bird population. It will be considered also when the mice are fully discussed. Also the owls and hawks and shrikes, that cycle with the rest. The chapter following now gives some essential details about the sources of my information, with various acknowledgements of help received; it then dilates upon foxes at great length and with many dates and figures. These dates and figures are worth some care and attention from the reader, since they are the main central pivot on which these Labrador chapters turn.

REFERENCES

* Indicates that an abstract is deposited in the library of the Bureau of Animal Population, Oxford. H. B. Co. = Hudson's Bay Company.

1. ANDERSON, R. M. (1934). 'Mammals of the Eastern Arctic and Hudson Bay.' In 'Canada's Eastern Arctic.' Ottawa. Pp. 67–108.
2. BANGS, O. (1898). 'A list of the mammals of Labrador.' Amer. Naturalist, 32: 489–507.
3. BINNEY, G. (1929). 'Hudson Bay in 1928.' Geogr. J. 74: 1–27.
4. BINNEY, G. (1931). 'The Eskimo book of knowledge.' London.
*5. FINLAYSON, NICHOL. Ungava [Fort Chimo] Report, 1832–3. MS. H. B. Co. Archives, London.
6. GAUSE, G. F. 'The struggle for existence.' Baltimore. P. 137.
6 a. GOSLING, W. A. (1910).' Labrador, its discovery, exploration and development.' London. P. 156.
7. HUTTON, S. K. (1912). 'Among the Eskimos of Labrador.' London.
8. HUTTON, S. K. (n.d.). 'Health conditions and disease incidence among the Eskimos of Labrador.' Poole.
9. JENNESS, D. (1932). 'The Indians of Canada.' Bull. Nat. Mus. Canada, 65: 273.
*10. KILLOCK, JAMES. Report on Nitchequon [Nichikun] Post, 1834–5. MS. H. B. Co. Archives, London.
*11. MATHESON, DUNCAN. Fort Chimo (Ungava) Correspondence, Sept. 10, 1899, to Commissioner, Winnipeg. MS. H. B. Co. Archives, London.
12. SALE, C. V. In Binney, G. (1929). 'Hudson Bay in 1928.' Geogr. J. 74: 26.
13. SPECK, F. G. (1931). 'Montagnais-Naskapi bands and early Eskimo distribution in the Labrador Peninsula.' Amer. Anthropologist, 33: 557–600.
14. STRONG, W. D. (1930). 'Notes on mammals of the Labrador interior.' J. Mammal. 11: 1–10.
15. TAVERNER, P. A. (1934). 'Birds of the Eastern Arctic.' In 'Canada's Eastern Arctic.' Ottawa. Pp. 113–28.
16. TURNER, L. M. (1894). 'Ethnology of the Ungava District, Hudson Bay Terri-

tory.' Smithsonian Inst., Bureau of Amer. Ethnology, 11th Ann. Rep. (1889–90): pp. 167–349.

*17. Davis Inlet Post, Fur Returns, 1881–90. MS. H. B. Co. Archives, London.

*18. Davis Inlet Post, Journals, 1869–76, 1879–98, 1901–9. MS. H. B. Co. Archives, London.

*19. Fort Chimo [Ungava], Fur Returns, 1918–27. MS. H. B. Co. Fur Trade Dept., Winnipeg.

*20. H. B. Co., London Fur Sales, 1871–80. MS. H. B. Co. Archives, London.

*21. Nitchequon [Nichikun] Post, Journals and Correspondence, 1834–44. MS. H. B. Co. Archives, London.

*22. Northern Labrador Missions, Fur Returns, 1870–9; 1900–9. MS. Moravian Missions, London.

*23. Periodical Accounts of the Moravian Missions. London.

24. (1857). Report from the Select Committee (House of Commons) on the Hudson's Bay Company. London. [224–260—Sess. 2].

*25. Rupert's River District, Fur Returns, 1852–61. MS. H. B. Co. Archives, London.

CHAPTER XIII
FURS OF FOX AND MARTEN

1

THE central evidence for recurring and rather regular wild-life cycles in Labrador comes a few pages farther on. The curve on page 268, that illustrates the fox-fur catches for a hundred years, is the backbone of all this evidence. It shows violent ups and downs in fur supplies, and suggests some corresponding fluctuation among the foxes. The business of this chapter is to prove the existence of these fluctuations in supply and establish something of their rhythm.

It will occur to the reader at once that such statistics may be full of traps. I can only say that in all that follows I have tried to emulate the caution of Uncle Remus: 'I ain't 'sputin about it, but I ain't seed um, an' I don' take no chances deze days on dat w'at I don't see, an dat w'at I sees I got to 'zamine mighty close.'

First the sources of information. The evidence is of two sorts: the statistics that annual fur catches provide, and the written or printed notes in journals, letters, and reports. The second give cross-angles that check the first, leading to fairly safe interpretation. Two great organizations furnish nearly all the facts: the Moravian Missions (field agents of the Society for the Furtherance of the Gospel, now a Trust) and the Hudson's Bay Company. The first, whose deepest concern is the spiritual salvation of the native, has also a problem in their bodily needs. Here it meets on common ground the Company, whose care for the bodily needs of its shareholders brings with it an urgent interest in native welfare. It is obviously difficult either to redeem or trade with a people that threatens to vanish from the earth, through starvation or disease.

The Mission archives had not before been thought a field for ecological analysis. But such research leads one down unexpected paths, and the filling in of fox and mouse history for Labrador has been done in places that the biologist might not dream of choosing as his laboratory: a mission hall near Holborn, a scientific conference held in a fishing hamlet on the North Shore of the Gulf of St. Lawrence during the black-fly season, a cellar-library under the pavement of Bishopsgate in London City, Canadian offices where one had casual talks with fur-trade men, a café in London and a quiet house in Malmesbury where mice were discussed with missionaries on leave. Add to these, reports from missionaries, doctors, trappers, traders, and explorers living at a score of distant stations, and some notion can be gained of the way the facts were gathered.

2

Mr. George Binney first suggested approach to the Moravian Missions. Through the courtesy of Dr. Samuel King Hutton, then the London

Secretary, a search was authorized and gave rich harvest of population records, which are all the more valuable in having been set down with no scientific theory to give them bias. The advice and knowledge of Dr. Hutton, and his eight years' experience of Labrador and practice as a doctor there, were a vital help. The kindly attitude of other officials at the Fetter Lane office is also a pleasure to acknowledge. They turned out old cupboards and unearthed a wealth of archives for more than a hundred years past. What promised to be an afternoon's inquiry expanded into a task that covered many days in the next five months. Mrs. Phoebe Jackson helped throughout with transcription, and I am indebted to her speed and skill.

The Moravian Missions first gained solid foothold in Labrador in 1770 and have published a printed report of each year's expedition of supply and the happenings at their stations along the coast. These reports appeared as the *Periodical Accounts of the work of the Moravian Missions*, covering also many stations scattered boldly in other parts, as Surinam, Tanganyika, Nyasa, Cape Colony, Greenland, and Alaska. Although these volumes are printed and published for distribution to the Society's members, whole sets must be fairly scarce. At 32 Fetter Lane they have them nearly all. The parts of interest here are those that treat of Labrador, its food supply, the fur catch, fisheries, seals, weather, and ice conditions out at sea. With these are other entries, telling of outbreaks of disease and various disasters and alarms. We read too of the growing influence of new white visitors, the rare arrival of Indians, and similar incidents of the kind. The whole of these *Periodical Accounts* that deal with Labrador was read and every bit that concerned wild life, fur, and weather was extracted and typed in duplicate. These extracts make a fat volume of two hundred pages, indexed, and available in the Bureau of Animal Population. Relevant entries most often come each year for every post though there are certain gaps.

The descriptions are those of educated, keen observers: German and, later, English missionaries, living close to natural things, in touch with native hunters and trappers, and forced to think intensely of the hazards of life on a bleak coast unvisited for most months of the year. The theme of their writings was in main religious: the partial moulding of a hard-bitten but attractive primitive race into the cast of Christianity; but the natural scene also engaged their interest and is often clearly told with obvious fidelity.

There is a pile of diaries, written in crabbed German script, that cover more fully some of the nineteenth-century times. These have been left for someone better possessed of languages and with phenomenal eyesight. But there may be some valuable wild-life notes in them that would fill the interstices of the history given here.

3

The Missions early realized that outright charity would do no service to a people used to hard and perilous courses. Also the means of supporting the Missions were meagre and without guarantee of continuity. They therefore set up fur trading and some other small industries, so that the Eskimos could earn possessions by barter and contribute to their own security. The furs were sold by auction in London, and the profits went back into the Mission enterprise. In such a remote, ungoverned land, this meant little more than a sensible method of levying a small tax towards the cost of administration, a cost that still had to be met chiefly from subscriptions at home.

The fur returns were collated and duplicated like the other archives. Some are the 'Pelzwaaren' or fur returns of each post, others come in London fur-sale books. They start in 1834 and run almost complete to 1925, when the Hudson's Bay Company took over the fur trade at the Mission settlements. These years are of production: sales came of course a year afterwards. That is to say, a fox living in 1834 was caught in the winter season of 1834–5, and its skin sent home in 1835 and sold that autumn.

The log-books of the Mission ships were also perused to learn the ice-conditions every summer. These books run, with several gaps, from 1889 to 1919, and the relevant facts were extracted in the same fashion as the other archives.

4

The Hudson's Bay Company archives have to be seen in their impressive bulk to be properly appreciated. The journal of a fur post had an entry nearly every day: 365 days in the year may give about 50 to 100 pages in a journal. The post may have been there 50 to 100 or even 200 years, though not all the archives have survived. There are more than 150 posts now, while a host of others opened and closed in past times. The larger districts (a score of them) kept Correspondence Books. There are also Reports, Minutes of Council Meetings, and mountains more.

These archives, until lately scattered still at the posts and offices in Canada, are now safely stored and sorted at the London centre: in sections, companies, and brigades they line in red filing cases the walls of a large basement library. This circumstance gives peculiar advantage to the English ecologist who seeks to graft ecology on to history. But among the tangle of archives one has to choose, and also needs a guide. To the Archivist, Mr. R. Leveson-Gower, I owe a heavy obligation for his almost uncanny knowledge of the whereabouts of the materials, which are quickly falling into ordered shape under his guardianship. Equally I have to thank the Governors (formerly Mr. Charles V. Sale, now Mr. P. Ashley Cooper) and the Committee of Management, and not least the Secretary, Mr. Chadwick Brooks. The Company has taken a broad view about the publication for scientific and general advantage of what used to be guarded secrets; while Mr. Brooks has regulated my access to and use of the facts with courtesy and wisdom. Mrs. Phoebe Jackson and Mrs. Mary Nicholson have given me imaginative and long-continued assistance in transcription, and I wish to make acknowledgement of this help.

The search for Labrador materials was really a side-issue raised by the

Moravian finds. It formed a small part of a four-year study, made possible by the New York Zoological Society and the interest of its President, the late Mr. Madison Grant; afterwards also by a Leverhulme Research Fellowship and a grant from the Government Department of Scientific and Industrial Research. The chief axis of this research was the ten-yearly fluctuation in Canadian forest life.

The books and papers salved from posts in Labrador are not at all complete in series. Those so far read and digested are: journals of Davis Inlet Post (not all preserved) from 1869 to 1909, and of Nichikun Post from 1834 to 1843; some fur returns of Davis Inlet from 1872 to 1928; and for Fort Chimo, reports, journals, and correspondence mentioned fully in a later chapter, and also a fairly full record of fur returns from 1868 to the present day. In addition there are a few records from Nachvack Post, and elsewhere. The annual Fur Trade Inspection Reports from 1887 to 1890 and Annual Reports on Fur Trade from 1891 to 1928 include a general conspectus of main happenings each year in Labrador and Ungava.

These are the chief sources, but there is a comet's tail of small notes and papers that have also been drawn upon, especially in settling points about the dates and history of posts. The seeker should perhaps be warned that his search will resemble dredging deep sands for scattered ingots, or digging clay for diamonds that often turn out to be small or of doubtful colour. The records themselves are usually of good quality, but it is hard to light upon the significant ones. The job takes many months and exacts from the worker a certain quality of imaginative drudgery.

5

As a frame in which to see the fur returns and the relation between the Moravian and Hudson's Bay Company posts on northern Labrador, the following table is included. Some research went into this chronology, and the salient evidence is given in a note at the end of this book.

Hebron, Okak, Nain, and Hopedale, strung out along something like the length of the east coast of Great Britain, were founded before 1834, when the surviving fur-trade record starts. There must have been earlier figures, now lost, and we cannot say exactly when Eskimo fur trade first developed. Gosling says:[2a] 'In 1811 the ship's homeward cargo consisted of 100 barrels of seal oil, 2000 seal skins, 2750 fox skins. . . . This is the only occasion in which the ship's cargo is given in detail.' His remark was based on a full study of the Moravian Periodical Accounts: it shows that trapping was done as early as 1810. Other references suggest that fur trading had already become an established practice. Hopedale writes[10] of the winter season of 1825–6 that 'the Esquimeaux were not successful in their fishery last autumn. . . . They got afterwards a supply of meat, by hunting rein-deer, and taking a great many foxes in traps. They much relish the flesh of foxes.' It is quite likely that the natives always had trapped the fox for food, using their own simple devices. At any rate at some time between 1771 and 1811 there grew up a flourishing barter trade

18

TABLE 16

*The trading posts on the coast of Northern Labrador, including the main
posts on Sandwich Bay and Hamilton Inlet, and all the posts north
of these to the north-east point of Labrador.*

Asterisks mark the Moravian Mission stations, the rest of the posts being of the
Hudson's Bay Company. The posts are arranged in geographical order along the
coast, from Cartwright in the south to Port Burwell in the north. The dates of
opening and closing are given in 'ship-years' or 'outfits', 1866, for instance, being
the season 1866–7. The opening date given as 1866 thus means the summer of 1866;
but the closing date given as 1894 means that the post was abandoned in the summer
of *1895*. This system of dating enables direct comparison to be made with the fur
returns. Note that although the Mission trading establishments were taken over by
the Company in 1926, the Mission stations themselves continued at Makkovik,
Hopedale, Nain, and Hebron.

Post	Opened	Closed
Cartwright	1873	..
North West River	1836	..
Rigolet	1836	..
Aillik	Between 1836 and 1839	Between 1875 and 1878
*Makkovik	1896	1925
Makkovik	1926	..
Kaipokok	1837	1878
*Hopedale	1782	1925
Hopedale	1926	..
Davis Inlet	1869	..
*Zoar	1866	1894
*Nain	1770	1925
Nain	1926	..
*Okak	1776	1925
Nutak (= Okak)	1926	..
*Hebron	1830	1925
Hebron	1926	..
Lampson	1867	1877
*Ramah	1871	1907
Nachvack	1868	1905
*Killinek	1905	1923
Port Burwell	1916	..

which in good years yielded several hundred skins of coloured fox; while
1842 saw one of the biggest shipments (1495) they have ever made.

6

About these years the Hudson's Bay Company, stirred to renew its
northern enterprise, set up shop in Hamilton Inlet. As has been explained,
the older name of 'Esquimaux Bay' can no longer be sustained after the
dying out of the local Eskimos there. But the fur trade knew the district
as 'Esquimaux Bay' until as late as 1901, after which it changed to
'Labrador'.[8] In older days the Eskimos owned this fjord, and earlier still

extended their domain as far south as Belle-Isle Strait.[7] It is generally admitted, even by those who object to the influences of mission life on natives, that the Moravians by their courage and single-minded tenacity have arrested the northward retreat and dwindling of these people by preventing many of the worst effects of white man's 'progress'.

The Esquimaux Bay posts were Rigolet and North West River, set up in 1836. At this time or a little after, smaller posts—Aillik and Kaipokok—were made, on the outer coast, not far from their parent posts. In Ungava also a new foothold had been gained at Fort Chimo in 1830, but abandoned not long afterwards (see p. 341).

Then followed stability again for about thirty years: the Company in Esquimaux Bay and Ungava, the Missions spread out between; while a patch north of Hebron—the northern triangle of Labrador—was no-man's land for fur trade, though held by Eskimo tribes.

Sir George Simpson's views had something to do with the freedom that the Missions enjoyed from trade rivalry in early days. He wrote[9] from Lachine on 24 April 1839, to W. H. A. Davies, the manager of Esquimaux Bay District:

'It is desirable to know if there be any trade on the Labrador coast deserving our attention, as in that case, should it be necessary to send a vessel to Ungava, it would be an easy matter to establish one or two posts on the coast; if this could not be done without interfering with the Moravian Missions, we should rather forego any advantages likely to arise from such a measure, as the Governor and Committee and Councils are desirous to promote the laudable views of that very zealous and inoffensive sect, instead of interfering with them in any manner of way, or acting prejudicially to their interests, whatever benefits in a pecuniary point of view we might derive from such a source. But as their most northerly settlement is situated at such a distance from Ungava as to render it barely possible for them to communicate with some of the intermediate bands of Esquimaux, I should think they would rather encourage than otherwise our forming one or two posts on that inhospitable line of coast.'

It was not until the sixties, a few years after Simpson's death, that the Company renewed its advance on northern Labrador. Two other reasons that must have damped enthusiasm before this were the apparent poverty of the coast, and the closing of Ungava between 1842 and 1866 (see p. 342) which made far northern transport less worth the while.

In the sixties the Mission for one reason, and the Company for another, both began to look northward to this unprovided coast. The Mission planned to establish a house in Saeglek Bay, and the *Harmony* sailed there in 1868 only to find that a Hudson's Bay Company man had forestalled it. 'It was resolved to leave him in undisputed possession of this bay, and advance further north to meet the heathen Esquimoes.'[10]

Nachvack, thirty miles north of Saeglek, was chosen; but two missionaries, going late the same summer to build a house, again found the Company's flag there before them, so they did not remain. In 1871, however, the Mission was able to found Ramah, in Nullatartok Bay—between

Nachvack and the Saeglek Bay establishment (known as Lampson). Nachvack and Ramah remained nearly forty years, but closed down in 1905 and 1907. Lampson lasted only eleven years.

7

Rather similar development was happening farther south: Zoar (Moravian Mission) in 1866 and Davis Inlet (a Company post wedged between Zoar and Hopedale) in 1869. The latter became calling place for the band of Indians of that name, who seldom touched Moravian posts. Cartwright (1873) came also in this second expansion time. All Company posts that we have mentioned in Labrador were 'Esquimaux Bay District'. Fort Chimo was revived in 1866.

The Missions' virtual monopoly of their long coast-line was broken therefore by these new enterprises, and also by the great increase in other white visitors, mostly bent on cod-fishing but not averse to some private barter too. The disposition of all these posts has been told, a historian might think, very briefly. For ecology it may seem too tedious. Yet the posts are the sole source of our statistics, and it is vital to have some notion of the extent of their monopoly and trade.

The twentieth century saw much growth and change, especially in the south. Other traders began to settle. The Mission branched out anew at Killinek (the island that forms the northern tip of Labrador) in 1905. Here the Colonial and Continental Church Society had the boundary of its sphere of influence in Ungava Bay. Makkovik had been set up near the old Aillik post in 1896, a corresponding extension to the south.

The Company had growing opposition in Esquimaux Bay District, as we can read in the Annual Reports on Fur Trade.[8] In 1894 'there is but little opposition in this District'. By 1901–2 competing traders were at Cartwright, Rigolet, and North West River. In 1902 Revillon Frères entered the field. In 1905–6 Davis Inlet still had, and Cartwright once more had, monopoly. In 1906–7 Revillon and other firms were living at Rigolet and North West River, and one trader at Cartwright. In Ungava, Revillon began to trade in 1903.

The relations of the Company and the Mission up to this time are summed up by an inspector (Roy Hall) in 1910–11, who wrote of Davis Inlet: 'The Moravian missionaries have trading stations at Nain and Hopedale, distant 60 miles north and 40 miles south respectively. . . . They have so far only traded in the vicinity of their own stations, and as they and the Company charge similar prices, no serious competition exists. . . . The Company's old policy has been "peaceful cooperation with the Moravians", but now that opposition has established at Makkovik conditions are altered.' The last remark indicates that there was probably an outpost at Makkovik or Aillik, collecting for Rigolet. The fringes of territory had overlapped. In 1914 there is mention of keen competition at Davis Inlet from the Mission at Hopedale; by traders living at Voicey's Bay and Aillik; and from other firms in Hamilton Inlet itself.

In 1926 the final important change took place, when the Company bought over all fur trading at the Mission settlements—a transaction done at the Mission's wish for the native interest.

8

The statistic value of the fur returns can now be weighed. The figures are set out in Tables 17 and 18, and summed into one curve in Fig. 14.

TABLE 17

Coloured foxes taken by the Moravian Missions in Labrador

Dates are years of production, i.e. a year earlier than return of furs to the market.

Year	*Makkovik*	*Hopedale*	*Zoar*	*Nain*	*Okak*	*Ramah*	*Hebron*	*All stations except Killinek, Ramah, Hebron*	*All stations*
1834	..	22	..	78	116	..	60	216	276
5	..	**29**	..	**159**	101	..	**117**	**289**	**406**
6	..	2	..	29	23	..	51	54	105
7	..	16	..	**104**	47	..	38	167	205
8	..	12	..	82	85	..	97	179	276
9	..	**35**	..	**148**	**109**	..	**113**	**292**	**405**
1840	..	8	..	28	6	..	22	42	74
1	..	83	..	256	**215**	..	145	554	699
2	..	**166**	..	**355**	206	..	**668**	**827**	**1,495**
3	..	62	..	49	39	..	162	150	312
4	..	**77**	..	**214**	**131**	..	**251**	**424**	**675**
5	..	42	..	12	8	..	39	62	101
6	..	**54**	..	34	17	..	54	105	159
7	..	**56**	..	**285**	**148**	..	**255**	**489**	**744**
8	..	5	..	9	15	..	51	29	80
9	..	9	..	23	25	..	**93**	57	150
1850	..	78	..	85	39	..	55	202	257
1	..	**151**	..	**161**	**192**	..	**262**	**504**	**766**
2	..	27	..	— }	— }	..	— }	27	27
3	..	14	..	44 }	26 }	..	102 }	84	186
4	..	71	..	100	72	..	178	243	421
5	..	**261**	..	**152**	**101**	..	**227**	**514**	**741**
6	..	22	..	38	24	..	115	84	199
7	..	3	..	5	12	..	66	20	86
8	..	16	..	24	11	..	80	51	131
9	..	**70**	..	**127**	**71**	..	**103**	**268**	**371**
1860	..	7	..	15	2	..	13	24	37
1	..	2	..	27	42	..	**103**	71	174
2	..	26	..	81	41	..	40	148	188
3	..	27	..	**105**	**105**	..	**294**	**237**	**531**
4	..	**35**	..	75	68	..	128	178	306
5	..	9	..	21	21	..	46	51	97
6	..	11	5	30	21	..	35	67	102
7	..	**73**	**94**	**337**	**302**	..	**361**	**806**	**1,167**
8	..	39	17	34	32	..	25	122	147
9	..	22	14	11	6	..	2	53	55
1870	..	**41**	13	**59**	54	..	29	167	196
1	..	31	28	48	**139**	60	**247**	246	**553**

Year	Makko-vik	Hope-dale	Zoar	Nain	Okak	Ramah, Killinek	Hebron	All stations except Killinek, Ramah, Hebron	All stations
1872	..	60	55	116	78	11	39	309	359
3	..	7	25	23	27	0	17	82	99
4	..	28	55	161	111	10	63	355	428
5	..	43	79	234	194	20	118	560	698
6	..	17	42	147	109	0	126	314	440
7	..	26	32	70	33	10	19	160	189
8	..	35	10	19	16	0	3	74	•77
9	..	60	47	123	90	31	83	320	434
1880	..	75	226	383	222	77	117	910	1,104
1	..	18	51	37	29	11	21	134	166
2	..	58	49	158	41	4	13	300	317
3	..	38	96	151	114	23	121	407	551
4	..	28	37	27	41	8	10	132	150
5	..	26	17	31	12	0	10	88	98
6	..	29	29	55	35	1	48	146	195
7	..	43	22	33	29	6	57	126	189
8	..	16	..	29	5	0	0	50	50
9	..	40	..	67	32	8	31	141	180
1890	..	25	..	261	158	65	202	445	712
1	..	28	..	97	42	9	41	167	217
2	..	12	..	27	15	2	9	54	65
3	..	22	..	90	29	5	20	141	166
4	..	13	..	119	83	3	36	215	254
5	..	52	..	173	71	19	56	296	371
6	..	90	..	101	60	0	20	251	271
7	..	103	..	90	52	2	26	245	273
8	..	15	..	17	4	0	4	36	40
9	..	26	..	30	19	0	6	75	81
1900	15	29	..	50	13	..	0	107	107
1	56	102	..	157	60	..	74	382	456
2	28	31	..	67	30	..	22	158	180
3	5	9	..	10	13	..	0	37	37
4	0	33	..	39	10	4	27	84	115
5	21	90	..	254	82	11	81	452	544
6	46	95	..	207	36	38	23	286	347
7	10	17	..	10	2	2	2	39	43
8	29	35	..	70	11	9	0	155	164
9	19	59	..	162	97	7	74	340	421
1910	6	115	..	144	53	29	39	320	388
11	0	12	..	4	6	3	6	22	31
12	9	26	..	77	33	9	31	145	185
13	66	38	..	83	59	28	39	236	303
14	49	202	..	424	148	40	98	824	962
15	4	25	..	51	40	8	15	120	143
16	40	83	..	74	33	2	28	231	261
17	61	92	..	189	162	6	244	512	762
18	40	58	..	133	24	20	16	268	304
19	1	0	..	0	0	0	0	1	1
1920	14	19	..	48	0	6	7	81	94
1	8	63	..	125	10	21	75	211	307
2	26	108	..	91	4	18	45	230	293
3	12	25	..	51	0	20	43	91	154
4	56	38	..	122	61	..	48	277	325
5	149	231	..	309	0	..	344	708	1,052

TABLE 18

Years of maximum abundance of coloured foxes in Labrador, as shown in fur returns of the Moravian Missions

(Dates are years of production.) Differences of 4 skins or less have been ignored.

All stations	All stations except Killinek, Ramah, Hebron	Maklo-vik	Hope-dale	Zoar	Nain	Okak	Ramah, Killinek	Hebron
1835	35	..	35	..	35	? 34	..	35
1839	39	..	39	..	39	39	..	39
..	..	..	..	..	..	41	..	..
1842	42	..	42	..	42	..	..	42
1844	44	..	44	..	44	44	..	44
1847	47	..	46 = 47	..	47	47	..	47
..	..	..	..	..	..	..	..	49
1851	51	..	51	..	51	51	..	51
1855	55	..	55	..	55	55	..	55
1859	59	..	59	..	59	59	..	59
..	..	..	..	..	..	..	..	61
1863	63	..	..	..	63	63	..	63
..	..	..	64	..	..	..	..	..
1867	67	..	67	67	67	67	..	67
..	..	..	70	..	70	..	..	..
1871	..	..	..	..	..	71	? 71	71
..	72	..	72	72	72	..	..	..
1875	75	..	75	75	75	75	75	..
..	..	..	..	..	..	..	..	76
..	..	..	..	..	..	..	77	..
1880	80	..	80	80	80	80	80	80
..	..	..	82	..	82	..	..	..
1883	83	..	..	83	..	83	83	83
1886	86	..	..	86	86	86	..	..
..	..	..	87	..	..	..	87	87
..	..	..	89	..	..	..	..	..
1890	90	..	..	..	90	90	90	90
..	..	..	93	..	..	..	..	..
..	..	..	..	..	..	94	..	..
1895	95	..	..	..	95	..	95	95
..	..	..	97	..	..	..	..	97
..	..	..	..	..	..	99	..	..
1901	01	01	01	..	01	01	..	01
1905	05	..	..	..	05	05	..	05
..	..	06	06	..	..	..	06	..
..	..	08	..	..	..	..	..	..
1909	09	..	..	..	09	09	..	09
..	..	..	10	..	..	..	10	..
..	..	13	..	..	..	..	..	..
1914	14	..	14	..	14	14	14	14
1917	17	17	17	..	17	17	..	17
..	..	..	..	..	..	..	18	..
..	..	20	..	..	..	..	..	..
1921	..	..	..	..	21	21	21 = 22 = 23	21
..	22	22	22	..	..	..	..	..
? 1925	? 25	? 25	? 25	..	? 25	? 25	..	? 25

The history just reviewed allows us to divide them into an early time, 1834–67, when monopoly reigned from Hopedale to Hebron; a second period from 1868 to 1900, when there were many summer visitors, but little serious competition in trade, since the Company kept to its territories and the Eskimos had strong attachment to their Missions (as still they do). From about 1900 opposition must have affected the southern posts, though

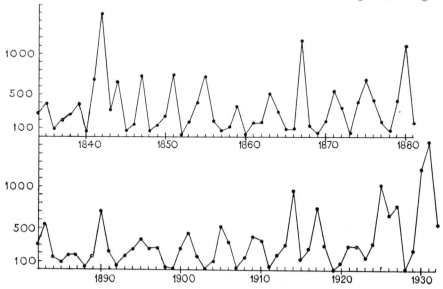

FIG. 14. Coloured fox skins, Moravian Missions, all stations, 1834–1925;
H. B. Co., same area, 1926–32

the coast from Nain to Hebron was very isolated still; and after 1910 the competition became much more general, culminating in a new regional dominance for the Company after 1926.

9

The cycle in fox fur supply hits the eye at once. Its regularity is as remarkable as its scale. During the ninety-two years when the Missions controlled the trade, the intervals between peak years of coloured fox abundance were, in order, these: 4, 3, 2, 3, 4, 4, 4, 4, 4, 4, 4, 5, 3, 3, 4, 5, 6, 4, 4, 5, 3, 4, 4. An Eskimo hunter living between 1847 and 1880 might have reflected that his good and bad luck chased each other with sufficient regularity to amount to a natural law. A statistician may also reflect that 23 cycles in 92 years gives an average of exactly 4 years.

A fluctuation on this scale is indeed a geographical feature. It merits close analysis, both to confirm its reality and to chart its distribution in the north. Such analysis goes as follows: first the broad conclusions to be drawn from the general curve, seen against the background I have tried to sketch. Then resolution into individual posts to see how far the cycles run together at separate distant points. Then comparison with some independent Hudson's Bay Company figures for Davis Inlet. These operations reveal a clear, wider regional cycle in furs collected, suggesting the existence of a vast pulsation in wild life and the elements. Analysis then digs farther down, to find if the archives confirm with their experiences the features of yearly trend in fur catch, and how far these are displaced by hazards of disease, or trade, or other interfering causes. Digging again to lower levels (ground-level in fact) we shall assemble the less copious but just sufficient information about the fluctuations of wild mice or voles and see how these fit the corrected history of the fox curves.

The 'year' in these fur-trade figures is a common pitfall in using records of the sort. The Hudson's Bay Company always worked in 'Outfits', that is the year the posts were 'fitted out' with supplies. The Outfit for, say, 1890 was sent out by ship that summer, and, except for the remotest posts, reached its destination in the autumn. The furs caught in the winter season 1890–1 were sent home in summer 1891. The 'furs returned' in 1891 would be accounted as 'Outfit 1890'. This custom, at first sight confusing, has merits in ecological work. The ecologist wants to know about the fox, Tod himself, not his skin. The fox whose lustrous coat is returned (odd phrase!) to London in 1891 was alive in 1890, perhaps born that year. What is important, too, this fox did not breed in 1891, unless it be a father trapped after it had begot young in the late part of winter.

The Moravian trade year followed the same principle, but was adjusted to times of the annual visit of their supply ship: most often in July, but sometimes August. In this study, the furs brought back in 1891 and caught in the season 1890–1 are listed as 1890—and so with all other years. To summarize: the Moravian trade year ended in July or August, the Company's in April (for Labrador in March, at any rate in the nineteenth century). Both covered the same snow-lying trapping season.

10

The principal coloured fox curve for Moravian stations, Fig. 14, repays some attention before analysis into smaller parts. For one thing it gives surer, since larger, figures: less subject to chance effects than those of the separate posts. But even these figures are not enormously big and we must reckon them liable to some interference, as from the effects of epidemic disease or the climate on trapping. Such will, however, need to be very powerful or very widespread to make serious distortion.

The average cycle, we saw, was four years. This in itself proves little, until we know how much the period varies. Four-year cycles come 13 times out of 23: just more than half the number (54 per cent.). Four-year periods are therefore the commonest, while two and six years (one each) are rarest. In 92 years one peak was never more than six years after the last. Three and five years are commoner, but four is quite dominant, as the percentage frequencies show (Table 19).

Three-, four-, and five-year cycles between them are 92 per cent.; so the chances were 9:1 that the interval between good Labrador fox years would be one of these lengths. A seven- or a ten-year period was unknown.

TABLE 19

Length of cycle . .	2	3	4	5	6	7
Number . . .	1	5	13	3	1	0
Frequency percentage	4	22	57	13	4	0

This regularity, in a biological universe whose savage irregularity and complexity has so far thwarted the hopes of prophets, is an astonishing affair. It encourages a search for still greater regularity. Suppose the cycle is really four years, and nothing else: that the moon or the sun or some surging wave of atmosphere, or natural rhythm of plenty and disease, has just this length and that it controls the foxes. The variations from this four-year period would then be due to chance interference superimposed, but unable to prevent return to the four-year rhythm. We can test this by starting off the actual cycle and the theoretical cycle at 1835 and seeing if the two get out of step. This is how they go:

Real: 35, 39, 42,   44, 47, 51, 55, 59, 63, 67, 71, 75.
Theoretical: 35, 39,   43,   47, 51, 55, 59, 63, 67, 71, 75.
Real: 80, 83, 86,   90,   95.
Theoretical: 79,   83,   87,   91, 95.

So far the two lines fit rather well. There is little sign of the phases getting out of step unless it be in 1842–4. But between 1895 and 1901 comes the six-year gap, which of course has the effect of adding *one and a half periods*, which puts the real and the hypothetical in complete opposition. If, however, we start afresh in 1901 the agreement continues as before:

01, 05, 09,   14, 17, 21, (25).
01, 05, 09, 13,   17, 21, (25).

The reader may feel that this load of inference bears heavily on the small statistics. And yet it is hard to resist a suspicion that a four-year periodicity has underlain the whole phenomenon, and at least once has changed its step. We can throw more light by examining the posts. The figures for separate posts look more slender, and yet show the cycle in full force. There is variation, as in the big curve, but it is similar. Where it differs, it is on lines we should expect, where the chance fluctuations of small statistics are concerned. The frequency of cycles with different lengths, using all intervals that can certainly be read off are shown below. There is one small convention: differences of four skins or less have been ignored (a mild form of smoothing, arbitrary but reasonable for its purpose).

TABLE 20

Length of cycle . .	2	3	4	5	6	7
Number . . .	20	28	48	18	1	0
Frequency percentage	17	24	42	16	1	0

The fours still have it, while three, four, and five together have 82 per cent. Even with these slender figures for posts, the chance that the cycle would come within three to five years was 8 to 1. There is an increase in two-year cycles.

11

The cycle in foxes operates right down the long coast from Killinek to Makkovik. The figures vote rather solidly for this conclusion, if we agree that the few exceptions may be due to chance fluctuations (meaning the lucky haul of skins or the unlucky failure to trap successfully in time of plenty). Such a conclusion rests on other evidence as well: we can examine how much the different stations march in step: that is, how far different parts of Labrador are flooded with coloured foxes in the same years. Something of simultaneity must be happening, else the main curve could not show regular undulations as it does: for the different stations are not so evenly balanced that one of them could wholly dominate and mask the movements of the rest.

A perfect technique for measuring how far the different stations agree is a little hard to devise. The trouble comes in finding a standard free from all objections. Here we use two standards: the main curve just discussed, and the theoretical cycle that seemed to fit it. Taking these as reference for peak fox years in the cycle, we work out the extent that each separate station coincides with the main trend.

TABLE 21

Occurrence of coloured fox peaks at (all) separate stations, 1834–1925, relative to those on the main curve for all stations

Years	-2	-1	0	$+1$	$+2$
Number	3	10·5	88·8	16·3	4·3
Frequency percentage	2·4	8·5	72·3	13·3	3·5

The fractions look a little mysterious. They arise when two or three years tie for right to be called maximum (since four skins or fewer are not given significance). In such cases the honour is divided between the years. Sometimes $+2$ years from one peak is -2 from the next: these being midway between maximum points, half a unit is given in each frequency class. The verdict is clear: that nearly three-quarters of peak years come together with the rest, while only 5·9 per cent. come entirely out of step. This is pretty good proof of a universal fox cycle in northern Labrador. A statistician would point out that the main curve includes the figures we are comparing with it; but a more refined dissection (which can be done from these figures published) is not possible here.

Comparison with the theoretical four-year cycle already suggested gives very similar but not quite such good results. Here, as before, we omit the years 1896–1900.

TABLE 22

Occurrence of coloured fox peaks at (all) separate stations, 1834–1926
(omitting 1896–1900), relative to a theoretical four-year cycle

Years	−2	−1	0	+1	+2
Number	2·5	17·5	67·8	28·3	2·8
Frequency percentage	2·1	14·6	57·0	24·0	2·3

The extent of complete inversion here is 4·4 per cent. instead of 5·9; the amount of exact agreement is 57 per cent. instead of 72·3. The stations therefore vary from expectation (if we can use such an assumptive word) chiefly by one year either way, and seldom more. The agreement has been set forth in these two ways, because each has a fault that the other is free from. In so far as the main curve includes each of the stations, it might be said that we are comparing each station partly with itself. It is a little like giving oneself a handsome testimonial. The answer is that each station forms but a small fraction of the total: the testimonial, though not written by another person, has to fit the opinions of several others. The 'four-year cycle' is free from this bias: but it has no certificate of authenticity and is too rigid to take in small variations.

12

This analysis has so far laid bare a clear cycle, about four years or near it, in the coloured fox catches at Moravian Mission stations for over ninety years. The furs of Davis Inlet have it too (p. 313). The manner in which the cycle colours even small trapping results and comes at places hundreds of miles apart gives it a bold and almost cosmic quality. There must be some very powerful forces behind it. However, we have only shown a cycle in fur returns. There is some way to go before proving a real fluctuation in the foxes themselves. But at the present stage of analysis it is a formidable trade cycle, bringing alternate dearth and plenty to an Eskimo population much engrossed with the chase, and having influence on fur-trade prosperity outside its own country.

Coloured fox has been the chief performer in this chapter. Arctic foxes also get caught along the coast: a few in most years, and hundreds in some. These white fox figures are reserved for the later chapter on the fur trade of Ungava. Here we shall only note that the Labrador white fox cycle, mainly caused by a southward drift from higher north, also averages four years—as it does in Ungava.

13

Sufficient marten furs were also caught at Moravian stations to justify a note on their periodicity. The other species, such as black bear, otter, wolverine, wolf, and weasel, are too few to give any leverage for deduction.

The marten, 'of shy and suspicious nature', is blood brother to the sable of Siberia, and a midway link between wolverine and weasel: Coues[2] called it 'the American sable'. In habits it differs from the fox. According to Comeau, who lived in southern, Canadian, Labrador: 'To trap marten with success, one has to specially select the ground, viz., thick woods and heavy timber, such as spruce or balsam. . . . No other fur of any consequence will be found in such localities.' In Ungava also martens prefer the woods, as is plain from several remarks in Ungava Reports, and from the notes of explorers. This distribution stands out plain from the fur returns, diminishing to the north.

The books of Seton[6] and Hewitt[3] record the marvellous ten-year cycle of abundance and scarcity in the Canadian marten, and equally in the coloured fox. But in Quebec Peninsula the régime is different: no obvious ten-year rhythm in either species, instead a short abrupt fluctuation of three to five years. Somewhere between Lake Winnipeg and Hamilton Inlet this huge wild-life movement changes gear, so that the east has two or three revolutions for each one in the west.

The short marten cycle was known to Pennant,[5] the great eighteenth-century authority on northern quadrupeds. According to him 'once in two or three years they come out in great multitudes, as if their retreats were overstocked: this the hunters look on as a forerunner of great snows, and a season favorable to the chase'. Pennant was right, as the Hudson's Bay Company's sale books show. During the eighteenth century their furs came mostly from posts strung round Hudson Bay and James Bay. The marten figures have an undoubted short cycle, which lengthened and changed in after years, as the trade spread out westwards and tapped different populations.

Hind[4] heard of the short cycle, too, when he travelled in southern Labrador last century. Of the St. Augustine River (flowing out where Belle Isle Straits join the Gulf) he wrote: 'It is on this river that the curious emigration of animals every third or fourth year is particularly observed. The year 1857 was one of these migratory years, and during the winter the hunters on the lower part of the St. Augustine fifty miles from the sea, reaped a rich harvest of otters, martens, and foxes.'

14

Table 23 contains the Moravian Mission marten furs. As the figures are so few, their resolution into periods rests on less sure ground than in the case of foxes. The marten and fox peaks are laid side by side in Table 25.

The catch varies widely. It has not the regular rhythm of the fox, yet the general run is similar. The intervals between peak years occur in the following frequency (again we do not count a difference of four skins or less, while only the record from 1841 onwards is analysed, as the early figures are so minute). (Table 24.)

The result is different from the coloured fox cycles in that the fours are scarcer. But three-quarters of the cycles (76 per cent.) are either three, four, or five, 24 per cent. falling into the twos and sixes. There is here a main dominance of the same short cycles as in the fox.

TABLE 23

Martens taken by the Moravian Missions in Labrador

(Dates are years of production.)

Year	Makko-vik	Hope-dale	Zoar	Nain	Okak	Hebron	Ramah	Killinek	Total
1834	..	8	..	0	0	0	..	..	8
5	..	3	..	3	3	3	..	..	12
6	..	0	..	1	0	1	..	..	2
7	..	0	..	4	0	0	..	..	4
8	..	0	..	0	0	0	..	..	0
9	..	0	..	1	3	1	..	..	5
1840	..	1	..	0	1	0	..	..	2
1	..	0	..	0	0	0	..	..	0
2	..	35	..	2	1	0	..	..	38
3	..	20	..	9	2	0	..	..	31
4	..	0	..	6	9	2	..	..	17
5	..	0	..	0	5	1	..	..	6
6	..	12	..	0	0	0	..	..	12
7	..	14	..	13	6	4	..	..	37
8	..	7	..	0	0	0	..	..	7
9	..	11	..	0	0	0	..	..	11
1850	..	6	..	0	0	0	..	..	6
1	..	16	..	4	16	4	..	..	40
2	..	6	..	0	0	0	..	..	6
3	..	6	..	4	4	0	..	..	14
4	..	27	..	2	2	3	..	..	34
5	..	55	..	19	15	1	..	..	90
6	..	110	..	26	23	12	..	..	171
7	..	15	..	14	11	1	..	..	41
8	..	12	..	6	20	0	..	..	38
9	..	58	..	33	55	6	..	..	152
1860	..	101	..	25	15	7	..	..	148
1	..	5	..	23	6	1	..	..	35
2	..	49	..	17	10	2	..	..	78
3	..	68	..	28	13	0	..	..	109
4	..	54	..	49	15	7	..	..	125
5	..	46	..	25	13	1	..	..	85
6	..	22	2	6	7	0	..	..	37
7	..	65	22	5	6	1	..	..	99
8	..	56	28	4	10	0	..	..	98
9	..	23	26	0	8	0	..	..	57
1870	..	13	114	10	0	0	..	..	137
1	..	11	5	8	10	0	0	..	34
2	..	17	4	1	10	0	0	..	32
3	..	19	4	0	3	0	0	..	26
4	..	0	64	0	0	0	0	..	64
5	..	53	20	10	11	0	0	..	94
6	..	189	0	0	0	0	0	..	189
7	..	33	10	5	4	0	0	..	52
8	..	58	2	2	8	0	0	..	70
9	..	14	18	0	15	0	0	..	47
1880	..	25	80	2	9	0	0	..	116

Year	Makko-vik	Hope-dale	Zoar	Nain	Okak	Hebron	Ramah	Killinek	Total
1881	..	28	114	1	2	0	0	..	145
2	..	13	32	0	0	0	0	..	45
3	..	0	30	0	0	0	0	..	30
4	..	44	273	28	4	0	0	..	349
5	..	78	11	3	7	0	0	..	99
6	..	86	51	3	4	1	0	..	145
7	..	66	11	9	26	0	0	..	112
8	..	34	..	34	0	0	0	..	68
9	..	22	..	12	3	0	0	..	37
1890	..	9	..	15	2	0	0	..	26
1	..	94	..	3	5	0	0	..	102
2	..	13	..	2	17	0	0	..	32
3	..	5	..	3	1	0	0	..	9
4	..	27	..	0	3	0	0	..	30
5	..	54	..	1	5	0	0	..	60
6	..	62	..	5	6	0	0	..	73
7	..	61	..	9	4	0	0	..	74
8	..	27	..	6	4	0	0	..	37
9	..	36	..	44	9	0	0	..	89
1900	15	77	..	42	63	0	..	..	197
1	48	164	..	28	53	0	..	..	293
2	49	102	..	20	32	0	..	..	203
3	19	36	..	13	11	0	..	..	79
4	0	182	..	29	3	0	..	0	214
5	20	80	..	15	1	0	..	0	116
6	65	99	..	13	2	2	..	0	181
7	3	62	..	5	1	0	..	0	71
8	19	9	..	7	7	0	..	0	42
9	27	94	..	0	4	0	..	0	125
1910	19	50	..	13	0	0	..	0	82
11	0	23	..	3	0	0	..	0	26
12	1	23	..	15	0	0	..	0	39
13	0	42	..	0	0	0	..	0	42
14	5	25	..	27	0	1	..	0	58
15	1	4	..	0	0	0	..	0	5
16	2	1	..	0	0	0	..	0	3
17	0	0	..	0	0	0	..	0	0
18	12	1	..	11	0	0	..	0	24
19	0	0	..	0	0	0	..	0	0
1920	7	2	..	0	0	0	..	0	9
1	9	22	..	5	0	0	..	0	36
2	1	32	..	1	0	0	..	0	34
3	0	5	..	8	0	0	..	0	13
4	0	0	..	3	0	0	..	0	3
5	3	1	..	4	0	0	..	0	8

TABLE 24

Length of cycle .	2	3	4	5	6
Number .	3·5	6	4·5	5·5	1·5
Frequency % .	17	29	21	26	7

15

We can test whether bumper years of fox and marten come together by the method already employed for the fox furs at various posts. The total marten furs are compared with the total foxes for all Mission posts except Hebron, Ramah, and Killinek, which lie north of the marten grounds. Table 25 sets these out in detail, and a summary is below.

TABLE 25

Cycles in marten furs in northern Labrador. The peak years of marten (all stations) and fox (all except Hebron, Ramah, and Killinek) at Moravian Mission stations

Coloured fox	Marten	Coloured fox	Marten
1842	1842	1883	
1844			1884
1847	1847	1886	1886
1851	1851	1890	
1855			1891
	1856	1895	
1859	⌠1859		⌠1896
	⌡1860		⌡1897
1863		1901	1901
	1864		1904
1867	⌠1867	1905	
	⌡1868		1906
	1870	1909	1909
1872		1914	1914
1875		1917	
	1876		1918
	1878	1921	⌠1921
1880			⌡1922
	1881		

TABLE 26

Occurrence of marten peak years in Labrador, 1841–1925, relative to coloured fox years (omitting the three northern stations)

Years . . .	−2	−1	0	+1	+2
Numbers . . .	1·5	1	8·5	10	1·0
Frequency % . .	6·8	4·5	38·6	45·6	4·5

The great majority of good marten years either coincided with (39 per cent.) or came one year after (46 per cent.) the corresponding peak in foxes. These two classes together come to 85 per cent. of the whole. From this we may infer that there is probably some common bond between the populations of fox and marten, causing in both a three- to five-year rhythm, and running simultaneously or with a one-year lag. The variations from this general rule may be real or due to fallacies in the figures, which are really very small for the marten.

REFERENCES

* indicates that an abstract is deposited in the library of the Bureau of Animal Population, Oxford. H. B. Co. = Hudson's Bay Company.

1. COMEAU, N. A. (1909). 'Life and sport on the North Shore of the Lower St. Lawrence and Gulf.' Quebec. p. 76.
2. COUES, E. (1877). 'Fur-bearing animals: a monograph of North American Mustelidae. . . .' U.S. Dep. Interior, Misc. Publ. No. 8, p. 81.
2 a. GOSLING, W. G. (1910). 'Labrador, its discovery, exploration and development.' London. p. 286.
3. HEWITT, C. GORDON (1921). 'The conservation of the wild life of Canada.' New York. pp. 226–9.
4. HIND, H. Y. (1863). 'Explorations in the interior of the Labrador Peninsula.' London. Vol. 2, p. 136.
5. PENNANT, T., cited by Coues (2), p. 92.
6. SETON, E. T. (1912). 'The Arctic prairies.' London. p. 103 and ch. 15.
7. SPECK, F. G. (1931). 'Montagnais-Naskapi bands and early Eskimo distribution in the Labrador Peninsula.' Amer. Anthropologist, 33: 557–600.
*8. H. B. Co., Annual Reports on Fur Trade. MS. H. B. Co. Archives, London.
*9. H. B. Co., Outward Correspondence, 24 April 1839, George Simpson to W. H. A. Davis. MS. H. B. Co. Archives, London.
*10. Periodical Accounts of the Moravian Missions, London.

CHAPTER XIV

THE FOX POPULATION

'Hide fox, and all after!' *Hamlet.*

1

SOMEONE said to me: 'The great advantage of ecology over physics is that you *can* see all the units that you are dealing with.' And yet this is not entirely true, even though mice and foxes are so much more convincing than the disturbing, diaphanous table with its lonely whizzing particles that modern physicists love to deduce from the solid oak. In population work we move in a world of deduction from signs and traces and samples. It is true that species of social inclination and respectable bulk, that live in herds, flocks, warrens, or schools, are obvious to the eye, and may with earnest application be watched and counted. Even this work is full of difficulties—for without a marking system it is not easy to count even a wood of trees and make no mistakes. But most wild beasts are small and nimble and elusive. Many live below the ground or come out at night.

The fur returns that made the previous chapter are signs of something happening to the fur trade. They are probably signs of some periodic change in the fox population itself. But the figures themselves do not tell us what this change is: they do not even prove that foxes fluctuate at all! It might be supposed that foxes only go to the bait that trappers lay, when times are hard. The abundance that comes every four years might be but a quadrennial driving hunger. Another possibility would be a periodic outpouring of foxes to the coast, perhaps due to hunger also. An observer on the British coast in August, unfamiliar with our long life and poor powers of reproduction, might postulate a periodic wave of population increase that reached a climax in fine summers, perhaps every four or five years.

Or why not disease? As a later chapter shows, foxes have epidemic bouts of madness. Nothing could be more unwise than to enter a trap. A fourth alternative would be a real change in numbers over the whole country.

There are, too, the human factors. Do prices affect the industry of Eskimo trappers? Periodic epidemics among the natives might have the same effect on fur returns as periodically hungry, nomadic, or insane foxes. This element of distrust is a necessary part of any analysis like the present one. The next step is therefore to assemble all other evidence that can illuminate the meaning of the fur returns, which have to be most carefully interpreted.

2

First we may consider what fraction of the population is caught by trappers. Is the surface skimmed, or do the inroads of trapping seriously drain its resources ? If we knew what proportion was trapped, we should, of course, strike to the core of the whole matter, since we should obviously know the size of the population itself. This might seem impossible to find out, yet there are three points that can be established and which we may now examine in turn. There must have been at least as many foxes each year as the fur returns show. For the whole coast between Makkovik and Killinek (omitting Davis Inlet and other Hudson's Bay Company posts) the number caught varied from 1 to 1,495. Grouped in frequencies the annual catches show thus:

TABLE 27

Number caught	0–250	251–500	501–750	751–1,000	1,001–1,250	1,251–1,500
Frequency (years)	48	28	9	3	3	1

Mostly the catches were less than 500 in a single winter: four-fifths of them were so. But in sixteen of the years they were over 500 and four times above 1,000. Taking peak years alone, the figures are these:

TABLE 28

Number caught	1–250	251–500	501–750	751–1,000	1,001–1,250	1,251–1,500
Frequency (years)	1	7	9	3	3	1

In good years, therefore, the hunters could get between them most often 250–750 foxes along the whole Moravian coast. Adding in Davis Inlet, a post of the Hudson's Bay Company, slightly increases this figure. If we had Nachvack and other old posts the total would be higher still, perhaps nearer 1,000 than 500, but it could scarcely be more.

Unceasing assault on the fox population of Labrador for a century or more has not brought it towards extinction. With each cycle the population returns to the scene with untarnished vigour. Neither the figures nor archives contain any rumour of overtrapping the foxes—though martens have not fared so well, none appearing in the returns of Okak after 1908 or of Hebron after 1914. But the fox stock seems inexhaustible. We can reason from this buoyancy of the population that 500–1,000 is a small fraction only of the peak number, else trapping would have bitten deeper into the reserves of fur. This conclusion might seem hardly worth labouring, were it not for a curious circumstance which suggests that the fraction, though small, is far from minute. This circumstance requires a digression, but is of deep importance in the ecological edifice we are building up.

3

As a species, though not individually, the fox has three coats, from which he gets his name as the coloured fox. There is a common one of brownish-red material, a more impressive one with a handsome black pattern mixed with the brown, and a very select expensive one that is jet black tipped with silver. So important and valuable is the last that thousands of foxes now spend their lives in captivity solely in order to grow this coat that women may wear it. 'They stripped Joseph out of his coat, his coat of many colours that was on him.'

Of these three kinds of fur, the silver is immensely the most valuable in the market. The average price in Canada in the season 1934–5 was about 36 dollars, or a little over £7. Cross fox at the same time was only 21 dollars, or about £4, while red was runner-up at 7½ dollars, or about £1. 10s. Prices before the slump were higher, for instance in 1928–9 about £21, £15, and £6—higher prices but rather similar ratios.[13] This order of precedence has always existed, and is not just the whim of a new fashion.

The three colours or phases of fox are hereditary varieties, and not separate species. There is no colour bar in these fox populations. Silver, cross, and red mate together; whether with equal enthusiasm we do not know, but certainly they do, as is attested by the mixed litters that have been found, and the experience of fox breeders on the farms. All the phases occur down the Labrador coast and carry the graded values. Throughout last century, too, the man who caught a silver fox was in luck.

The fur returns are always split into these three classes of colour phase, and analysis of them brings some interesting suggestions.

Grouping the figures into ten-year periods displays the broad trends in changing proportions of red, cross, and silver during ninety years, 1834–1923. Uniformity of treatment for the figures is preserved by using only the four stations which were in being throughout: Hopedale, Nain, Okak, and Hebron. These four also provide opportunity for geographical analysis. The statistics come in Tables 29 and 30, the calculation of which I owe in part to Mr. P. H. Leslie, whose criticism and advice have been very valuable.

TABLE 29

Proportions of phases of coloured fox furs taken at Hopedale, Nain, Okak, and Hebron, in ten-year periods 1834–1933

Ten-year period	Total	% Red	% Cross	% Silver	Ratio Red/Cross	Ratio Red/Silver
1834–43	4,243	52·11	32·05	15·84	1·6	3·3
1844–53	3,145	56·92	28·55	14·53	2·0	3·9
1854–63	2,879	64·22	24·70	11·8	2·6	5·8
1864–73	2,759	66·51	24·86	8·63	2·7	7·7
1874–83	3,526	70·05	21·84	8·11	3·2	8·7
1884–93	1,813	71·10	22·95	5·95	3·1	11·9
1894–1903	1,939	71·27	21·45	7·48	3·3	9·5
1904–13	2,191	70·56	22·09	7·35	3·2	9·6
1914–23	2,855	69·60	25·22	5·18	2·8	13·5
1924–33	4,316	73·77	21·16	5·07	3·5	14·5

The last ten-year group is based on Hudson's Bay Company figures, together with the Moravian figures of 1924 and 1925.[14]

TABLE 30

Proportions of phases of coloured fox furs taken at four stations, in ten-year periods 1834–1933

HOPEDALE

Ten-year period	Total	% Red	% Cross	% Silver	Ratio Red/Cross	Ratio Red/Silver
1834–43	435	60·00	25·75	14·25	2·3	4·2
1844–53	515	69·71	19·61	10·68	3·6	6·5
1854–63	505	76·24	14·46	9·30	5·3	8·1
1864–73	328	61·28	25·61	13·11	2·4	4·7
1874–83	400	65·75	24·50	9·75	2·7	6·7
1884–93	270	64·81	28·52	6·67	2·3	9·7
1894–1903	476	70·38	23·53	6·09	3·0	11·6
1904–13	520	71·54	21·92	6·54	3·3	11·0
1914–23	675	68·89	25·78	5·33	2·7	13·0
1924–33	1,110	72·16	22·52	5·32	3·2	13·6

NAIN

Ten-year period	Total	% Red	% Cross	% Silver	Ratio Red/Cross	Ratio Red/Silver
1834–43	1,288	52·41	33·15	14·44	1·6	3·6
1844–53	867	55·48	29·41	15·11	1·9	3·7
1854–63	674	61·87	25·22	12·91	2·4	4·8
1864–73	754	66·45	24·93	8·62	2·7	7·7
1874–83	1,483	68·91	23·67	7·42	2·9	9·3
1884–93	717	68·76	24·41	6·83	2·8	10·0
1894–1903	814	72·73	18·92	8·35	3·8	8·7
1904–13	960	67·71	24·17	8·12	2·8	8·3
1914–23	1,188	71·13	23·83	5·05	3·0	14·1
1924–33	1,633	74·22	20·51	5·27	3·6	14·1

OKAK

Ten-year period	Total	% Red	% Cross	% Silver	Ratio Red/Cross	Ratio Red/Silver
1834–43	1,047	50·33	32·00	17·67	1·6	2·9
1844–53	601	53·24	30·62	16·14	1·7	3·3
1854–63	481	61·12	28·48	10·40	2·1	5·9
1864–73	748	68·05	26·87	5·08	2·5	13·4
1874–83	959	72·16	18·56	9·28	3·9	7·8
1884–93	398	70·10	24·62	5·28	2·8	13·3
1894–1903	405	69·14	22·22	8·64	3·1	8·0
1904–13	389	74·29	20·57	5·14	3·6	14·5
1914–23	421	65·08	28·98	5·94	2·3	11·0
1924–33	590	72·71	22·03	5·26	3·3	13·8

HEBRON

Ten-year period	Total	% Red	% Cross	% Silver	Ratio Red/Cross	Ratio Red/Silver
1834–43	1,473	50·78	32·99	16·23	1·5	3·1
1844–53	1,162	54·22	30·81	14·97	1·8	3·6
1854–63	1,219	61·77	27·15	11·07	2·3	5·6
1864–73	929	67·17	22·93	9·90	2·9	6·8
1874–83	684	72·08	20·91	7·01	3·4	10·3
1884–93	428	79·91	15·42	4·67	5·2	17·1
1894–1903	244	71·72	22·95	5·33	3·1	13·5
1904–13	322	72·98	18·01	9·01	4·1	8·1
1914–23	571	70·58	24·69	4·73	2·9	14·9
1924–33	983	75·48	20·14	4·38	3·7	17·2

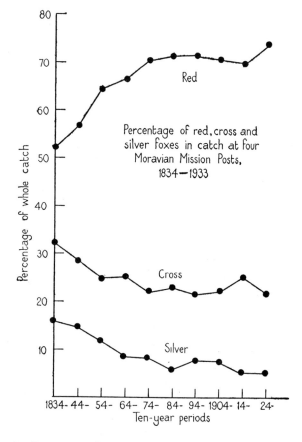

FIG. 15. Percentage of red, cross, and silver foxes in catch at four Moravian Mission Posts, 1834–1933.

4

The balance among the colour varieties has changed in a striking way since the Mission fur trade started. There has been increase in the common red phase at the expense of both the others. It looks as though the furs had survived in the relative scale of their market prices. If this change could be safely assigned to the selective action of man, it would prove that the proportion of foxes caught is appreciably high. If this hypothesis holds

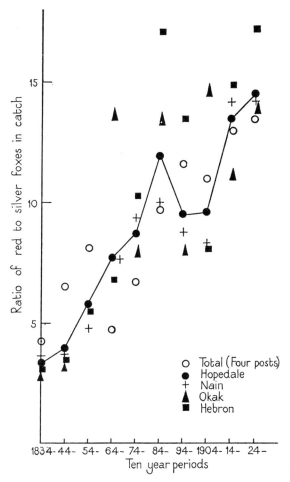

FIG. 16. Ratio of red to silver foxes in catch at Moravian
Mission Posts, 1834–1933.

its ground after proper scrutiny of the figures, we may be able to get at any rate a dim idea of the size of the population from which this appreciable fraction of furs was skimmed. It would mean that the rate of catching hovers somewhere between a negligible fraction and a danger of over-trapping.

The changes stand out more clearly from the curves in Figs. 15 and 16. These illustrate the progression (with some minor irregularities) from

1834–43, when the percentages of red, cross, and silver stood at 52, 32, and 16, through a stage in 1874–83 when they were 70, 22, and 8, to the situation of 74, 21, and 5 in 1924–33. In other words there is now only one silver to every three in early days. Cross fox have diminished less, but still in a marked degree. Before canvassing the causes of this altered balance, we have to be sure that the figures do really contain a significant trend. Each point on the mean curve is compounded of forty separate samples, taken over ten years at four centres. To split each into forty would bring the numbers too small, too much open to random error. We therefore take the four posts, and plot ratios, which form a small constellation around the points of the main curve. The result is a belt instead of a line, the width of the belt giving a measure of the variability of the fox ratios in separate samples. This galaxy of points still shows an obvious upward twist in the ratios of red to silver. The points for single posts are apt to dance about, an activity that we may reasonably assign to the small size of the samples they represent. There are some signs of levelling out in the later years, though this slackening of the climbing curve is rather hard to establish soundly in such a broad and variable belt of points, and there seems to be a strong change still in the recent years. The cross foxes form a similar belt which is for clearness omitted from the diagram, but can be drawn from the tables by anyone who wants to go farther down that particular track. It seems that cross foxes have also decreased in relation to red: again there is a slackening of this trend in the more recent years. In the catch as a whole, cross foxes have increased a little in the last forty years, but this change may not be as reliable as it looks, owing to the variations in the ratios at single posts.

5

We set out to try and discover how good the fur returns are as an index of population change. We have seen that every fox has a price on its head, but one which varies with the colour of the coat. There is at any time a natural balance in the proportions of different inherited colour phases. In Labrador this balance has shifted since the beginning of commercial fox-catching. Although it is theoretically possible that the change is a natural one—evolution caught in the act—the fact that the relative intensity of change follows the relative values of the three colours is strong argument that man has been the chief influence, perhaps the only one. Whichever is true, there is laid before us the interesting spectacle of evolution and selection in operation. It is somewhat amusing to consider that this hundred years of predator-prey evolution has brought probably neither advantage nor disadvantage to the fox (it is still there in force) while the result is disadvantageous to the man who now gets fewer silver foxes in his line of traps. 'Advance no banners up heaven's eastern sides'?

It requires the labours and ingenuity of a geneticist to discover how far this process has still to go. There may be several kinds of limits, hereditary or environmental. The main point here is that for man to change the colour ratios of Labrador foxes by the differential desires of his womenfolk, the number caught must be a fairly good fraction of the whole population. And if that is the case, the figures are probably a reliable sample for showing some of the broad fluctuations. That is to say: one was justified in treating the small figures as seriously as was done in the last chapter. Behind these useful arguments there still lurks the shadow of the possibility that we have stumbled on a natural change in the species, for which Eskimos are being given the credit.

6

There is no doubt that some selection can be exercised by those who pursue the fox. The trap is indeed almost impartial, and I have been told by various fur-trade men that the catch in traps is mainly a product of chance where colour phases are concerned. But both white men and natives also shoot foxes and have done so for many years. They certainly had guns quite early in the nineteenth century, for a letter from Hopedale in 1863[16] complains that: 'The circumstance that the majority of our people no longer harpoon seals, is really a retrogression from their old and good habits. All the young people use fire-arms, so that in a few years the long-established mode will be unknown. The taking of sea-birds by the Esquimaux, in their kayaks, which here, as in Greenland, was formerly performed exclusively by means of hand-missiles, has entirely ceased, and the gun alone is used.' Finlayson wrote[5] in the Fort Chimo report for 1832–3 that: 'Those who winter on the Islands bring only white foxes, but those who are furnished with guns and who winter in the Bays for the benefit of being near the deer, procure coloured foxes as well as white.' In 1835 Finlayson wrote[11] from Fort Chimo that he had traded twenty new guns, some second-hand ones, and all his pistols, to the Eskimo. The natives made these pistols into serviceable guns by fixing them to a better stock for their shoulders. A very recent report (1936) from the missionary at Nain says[16] that: 'Hunting and trapping foxes is no child's play in any winter. Day by day the hunters have to be out in all weathers from dawn till dusk, attending to their traps, and ever keeping a sharp look-out for foxes, which sometimes may be got with the gun while they cunningly avoid the traps.' We might add to these a note in Nachvack Journal.[15] On 23 October 1868 the post manager wrote: 'I saw a black fox today and fired at him, but he was too far for shot.'

So much for the means of selection: its existence strengthens the theory that man has profoundly altered the hereditary colour ratios. It should be possible, by a careful study of prices, to explain some of the irregularities in the trend. I have not the material or knowledge for this, which is a task for economists. The spectacle of a geneticist and an economist joining forces in order to find out how Labrador foxes are evolving would be a pleasant one, of which it is to be hoped that the world will not indefinitely be deprived.

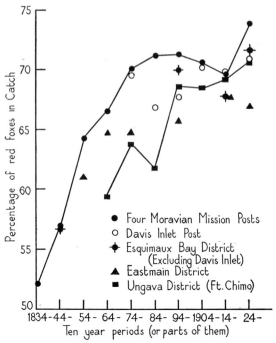

FIG. 17. Percentage of red foxes in the catch in districts of Quebec Peninsula, 1834–1933 (Esquimaux Bay District first point 1840–52).

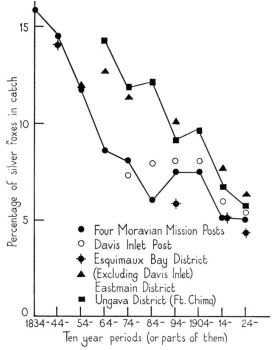

FIG. 18. Percentage of silver foxes in the catch in districts of Quebec Peninsula, 1834–1933 (Esquimaux Bay District first point 1840–52).

7

Northern Labrador is a vast theatre for these studies, but it lies only on the fringe of a hinterland stretching trackless hundreds of miles to south and west. Foxes, like the Indians, may traverse great distances, and in any case must be to some degree in contact with the other foxes farther inland. For the fur-trade districts are only human travel units, with many limits that a fox would easily trot past. We can only guess at the extent of the movements and intermixing of fox populations, but we must be prepared to find them large. It might be, therefore, that the changes in colour-phase proportions were due to influences right outside Labrador itself, in some such way that silver foxes were being drained away by the action of distant trapping centres.

I have not been able to build up from archives the complete fur returns of other districts in this region. It is rather unlikely that they have survived all the hazards of fur trade. The Mission posts stand by themselves in their fullness of record. But there are some Hudson's Bay Company records that give enough of the information we need. They are set out in Tables 31–4. In making groups of years, one has to use whatever happens

TABLE 31

Proportions of phases of coloured fox furs taken in 'Esquimaux Bay District' at various periods between 1840 and 1933

The last two groups calculated from Rigolet and North West River posts—equivalent of the old District. 1897–1900 includes also Nachvack and Cartwright, but Davis Inlet has been excluded.

Period	Total	% Red	% Cross	% Silver	Ratio Red/Cross	Ratio Red/Silver
1840–52 (4 years: 1840, '45, '47, '52)	446	56·73	29·15	14·12	1·9	4·0
1897–1900 (4 years)	698	69·91	24·21	5·88	2·9	11·9
1916–23 (7 years)	996	67·07	27·81	5·12	2·4	13·1
1924–33 (10 years)	4,512	71·46	24·25	4·29	3·0	16·6

to be available: the gaps are due to missing archives. So far as possible old and recent fur returns are arranged to cover similar networks of trading posts. In Esquimaux Bay District the group for 1897–1900 includes a northerly post (Nachvack), but its contribution was probably small.

The main relationships and trends stand out in Figs. 17–19. We can see at once that there has been this decline in proportion of silver fox in Esquimaux Bay District, and in the Davis Inlet area and its hinterland where the band of Indians hunted. Taking only main trends into consideration, these agree quite closely with the Moravian posts. That is to say, the

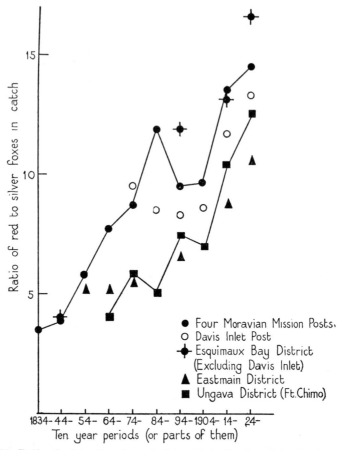

FIG. 19. Ratio of red to silver foxes in the catch in districts of Quebec Peninsula, 1834–1933 (Esquimaux Bay District first point 1840–52).

decline in silver has happened over most of the centre and west of northern Quebec Peninsula (the reader may refer to the map on p. 248), and has gone on up to recent years. Eastmain District is very interesting, as it shows

TABLE 32

Proportions of phases of coloured fox furs taken at Davis Inlet in ten-year periods, 1874–1933[8] (statistics missing for 1874)

Ten-year periods	Total	% Red	% Cross	% Silver	Ratio Red/Cross	Ratio Red/Silver
(1874)–83	562	69·57	23·13	7·30	3·0	9·5
1884–93	997	66·80	25·27	7·93	2·5	8·5
1894–1903	1,341	67·71	24·16	8·13	2·8	8·3
1904–13	849	70·20	21·67	8·13	3·2	8·6
1914–23	470	69·79	24·25	5·96	2·9	11·7
1924–33	1,295	70·89	23·78	5·33	3·0	13·3

TABLE 33

Proportion of phases of coloured fox furs taken in 'Eastmain' or Big River District at various periods between 1854 and 1933[9]

The last two groups calculated on Fort George and Great Whale River posts—equivalent of the old District.

Period	Total	% Red	% Cross	% Silver	Ratio Red/Cross	Ratio Red/Silver
1854–62 (9 years)	3,445	60·98	27·06	11·96	2·3	5·1
1865–73 (9 years)	3,135	64·72	22·62	12·66	2·9	5·1
1874–5 (2 years)	785	64·71	23·95	11·34	2·7	5·7
1895–1900 (6 years)	1,991	65·65	24·25	10·10	2·7	6·5
1915–23 (9 years)	2,775	67·49	24·83	7·68	2·7	8·8
1924–33 (10 years)	5,913	66·92	26·70	6·38	2·5	10·5

TABLE 34

Proportions of phases of coloured fox furs taken at Fort Chimo and its outposts between 1868 and 1933[12]

(Post reopened 1866; figures for 1877, 1878, and 1880 missing.) Figures for three years of the earlier period of occupation are also included, since they confirm the main trends. But as these figures are very small, they have been omitted from the Figure.

Period	Total	% Red	% Cross	% Silver	Ratio Red/Cross	Ratio Red/Silver
1837–9	192	58·33	30·21	11·46	1·9	5·1
1868–73	1,587	59·42	26·28	14·30	2·3	4·1
1874–83 (1877, '78, '80 missing)	3,103	63·78	25·33	10·89	2·5	5·9
1884–93	2,303	61·66	26·14	12·20	2·4	5·1
1894–1903	2,049	68·62	22·31	9·17	3·1	7·5
1904–13	1,950	68·36	21·95	9·69	3·1	7·0
1914–23	1,739	69·06	24·27	6·67	2·8	10·4
1924–33	3,360	70·53	23·82	5·65	2·9	12·5

decline at a similar *rate*, but with a consistent lag following the areas west of it. Ungava District also follows more closely Eastmain than Labrador, until more recent years, when it was intermediate in red fox percentage; though this change in trend may be only an accidental incidence of chance sampling. The Ungava figures show a consistently higher number of silver foxes than the Moravian posts throughout the whole period. These figures can hardly be analysed more finely without a risk of seeing in chance variations some natural law.

8

The distribution of the colours of the coloured fox came in as a digression. To prevent this twig from growing into too large a branch (it perhaps carries already more weight than is safe) we are compelled to break it here. The raw materials for a much larger survey, covering other parts of Canada, exist at Oxford. But the task is large and would lead too far afield. The study here shows well enough that the 'fox spectrum' can be a useful tool in population analysis.

The whole argument may be assembled finally like this. Fox catches fluctuate remarkably. If the fraction caught is large, then the fluctuations are more likely to be an index of some real events and not the vagaries of chance. A century of undiminished catches points to the fraction being small. Against this is a factor which is important when we come to consider voles: a large number of the foxes that enter traps or are shot would in any case have died from starvation or disease. With this idea in mind we can see that a very fluctuating population can produce a higher return and still keep its resilience—that is, up to a point.

The gradually increasing proportions of red phase at the expense of silver, and to a lesser extent of cross, can be explained by man's selection in the order of market prices. Wherever fur trade operated in Quebec Peninsula this change has taken place. To produce the change, it seems that a rather large fraction must be on the average trapped—and this, as shown above, is possible. We do not know how strong selection is, but we postulate that it acts through shooting (which only kills a part of the catch each year); while not all the foxes shot will be picked out selectively. It seems likely then, we cannot at present say more, that selection is really rather small in differential power: its effective action demands, therefore, that the fraction trapped be large.

Let anyone think this out for himself with a bowl of counters, of three colours, and imagine the action of a very small selective power when only small samples are withdrawn. I realize that hereditary factors of the phases make the case not so simple as this, but believe that the principle of this argument is essentially sound.

One is led to ask what this elusive fraction actually is. If 1 per cent. were trapped, and this were not more than 1,000 in northern Labrador in a maximum year of average size, the total population would be not more than 100,000. Ten per cent. gives 10,000. Fifty per cent. gives only 2,000. We have deduced that the fraction is not enormous and yet not minute. It is difficult, without some greater knowledge of the process at work, to venture on any exact determination. But it seems quite likely that the fraction may be more than 10 per cent. and less than 50 per cent., i.e. the total population is between 2,000 and 10,000 (if 1,000 is our datum).

9

We now have to attempt a nearer estimate of the Quebec Peninsula foxes. As a later table shows, the coloured fox catch has risen very much in recent years, and it is therefore not entirely typical of the whole hundred years. But these figures give a good cross-section of present trends. Three sources are used: Moravian Missions, Hudson's Bay Company, and Revillon Frères. Revillons have been strenuous competitors of the Hudson's Bay Company for the last thirty years or so, and at a good many points in the North: at some the chief and at others the only rival. Through courtesy of the Manager in Winnipeg, the Revillon figures are made available.[17] The period 1924–33 is chosen to consort with previous tables of fox colours.

Mr. P. H. Leslie has made computations the results of which appear in Table 35. The districts are chosen to fit natural features of country—mainly, the boundaries follow watersheds.

TABLE 35

Total catch of coloured foxes taken by the Moravian Missions, Hudson's Bay Company, and Revillon Frères, in Quebec Peninsula during the years 1924–33

Figures for other trading concerns are not available. The districts are explained in Table 36.

District	Total coloured foxes
1. 'Rupert's River'	5,815
2. 'Big River'	8,797
3. 'N.W. Quebec'	1,265
4. 'Ungava'	4,078
5. 'Northern Labrador'	5,412
6. Davis Inlet	1,295
7. 'Esquimaux Bay'	5,776
Total	32,438

Their fur output is got by adding up catches for various groups of posts. I have called the old 'Eastmain District' 'Big River', since Eastmain *post* confuses matters by coming in another district. 'N.W. Quebec' covers a great barren land region mostly beyond the trees, and not all hunted even by natives. Apart perhaps, from some very remote central areas, these districts cover a pretty good network. The posts constituting each of the districts are given in Table 36.

TABLE 36

Composition of districts used for Table 35

1. *'Rupert's River.'*
    H. B. Co. posts: Rupert's House, Neoskweskau, Nemaska, Eastmain, Mistassinny.
    R.F. posts: Rupert, Nemaska (Nemiskau), Eastmain.

2. *'Big River' District.*
   H. B. Co. posts: Fort George, Great Whale River.
   R.F. posts: Fort George, Great Whale River.

3. *'N.W. Quebec.'*
   H. B. Co. posts: Port Harrison, Povungnetuk, Cape Smith, Wolstenholme, Sugluk,
        Stupart's Bay, Payne Bay.
   R.F. posts: Port Harrison, Povungnetuk, Wakeham Bay, Diana Bay, Payne Bay.

4. *'Ungava.'*
   H. B. Co. posts: Fort Chimo, Fort McKenzie, Leaf River, Whale River, George's
        River.
   R.F. posts: Ungava (Fort Chimo), Leaf River.

5. *'Northern Labrador.'*
   H. B. Co. posts: (M.M. until 1926): Port Burwell, Hebron, Nutak (Okak), Nain,
        Hopedale, Makkovik.

6. *Davis Inlet.*
   H. B. Co. post.

7. *'Esquimaux Bay.'*
   H. B. Co. posts: North West River, Rigolet, Cartwright, Frenchman's Island.

In these ten years 32,438 coloured foxes were removed and skinned and used for adornment, an average of 3,244 a year; but such averages, in view of the cycle, are somewhat abstract. The real annual figures were these:

TABLE 37

Year	1924	1925	1926	1927	1928	1929	1930	1931	1932	1933
Catch	3,184	7,536	7,320	4,281	246	631	1,384	2,706	1,083	4,067

Thus the production really varied from 246 to 7,536 in different years.

10

If the fraction trapped was between 10 and 50 per cent., the whole fox population would lie between 6,488 and 32,440 on an average, and between 15,072 and 75,360 in the best year of all. Figures such as these lend colour to the hypothesis here put forward, that the foxes of Labrador may be numbered only in a few tens of thousands. This is not a large fur reserve on some hundreds of thousands of square miles. It could be matched by more than one silver-fox farm covering only a few hundred acres.

However, the fox production in the tables is not quite the whole. There are some other traders: these, it would seem, affect almost entirely 'Esquimaux Bay District' and probably would not add more than another thousand or two to the total. Our conspectus covers all that part of the country north of the east–west height of land that runs inland from James Bay to the hills north of Belle Isle Strait.

I may be rash in proposing actual figures: yet it is of great importance to bring the discussion down to definite numbers. These population figures have one great argument in their favour: they may not be true for certain, but they are within the realm of reasonable possibility. If anywhere near the truth, they would carry a vital practical conclusion: that the fur resources of Labrador are not so large or so immune from the consequences of overtrapping as might be supposed. The country seems so vast that the fur resources might appear to have no end; the same was thought of buffalo, fur-seal, chinchilla, and whale.

But from this suggestion arise questions that affect more than the balance-sheets of fur-trade concerns; there is nothing less than the fate of two native races in the balance. On northern Labrador the Eskimo still depends in the main on four resources: fishing, sealing, hunting caribou, and catching fur. The first two are essential sources of his food, but are often precarious things to live by. The fish may come late, or the weather for drying may be bad. The seals are erratic and may be almost missed on migration in certain years. The caribou are also a gamble, and now very scarce over much of the peninsula, and recently the Newfoundland Government has set up restrictions on the hunt in Labrador.

The fur trade is a source of wealth, which gives at any rate the chance of buying food and (if vitamins were used) health also. The fox and marten cycle, though disconcertingly intense, could be forecast and dovetailed to some planned economy of loans to cover times of dearth. The other furs (like bear and otter) are less important in the north. The marten may already be decreasing, as it does not stand up to fur-trade pressure as well as other species.

11

The fox, then, is a master factor in Eskimo life. For Indians the danger is no less, since they are mostly not hunters of the seal, though often masters at inland fishing. If the fox catch is really rather large in proportion to the real population, additional pressure may be disastrous.

Professor Frank Speck put the situation eloquently and, I think, unanswerably, in a recent article,[6] in which he pleaded for the closing of Quebec Peninsula to any more white trappers, and for the creation of a vast native reserve administered by a few officials.

His suggestion is

'to restrict the operation of invaders into the hunting grounds of the aborigines, thus barring the whites from free-land hunting and trapping beyond certain distances from the coast. Game in the interior is too uncertain a quantity to support life for more than a limited number of souls. . . . The annual influx of whites who leave their homes in the coast settlement to invade those of the Indians in the barren hinterland for winter hunting and trapping is an overtax of the country's resources. For this the health, the morale, the vitality of the Indians pay the price with no indemnity—sacrifice entire! . . . Considering the conditions applying to a barren and sub-arctic realm, its resources solely in hunting, colonization by Europeans not even remotely an issue in the case, the equation stands thus. . . .'

20

Speck writes here chiefly with southern Labrador in mind. There some Indian tribes show signs of illness that results from poverty in food and fur. This poverty he traces to the unhindered encroachment of white trappers. The northern tracts might be next to suffer. In this connexion the trend of fox catches should be examined. The table (38) of fur returns shows that there has been a tremendous increase in the Hudson's Bay Company's catches in the last ten years. This may be, for all I know, partly due to their competitors being subdued, but I think it means a real and striking increase in the levy on foxes.

TABLE 38

'Average annual catch' of coloured foxes in various districts, obtained from other Tables

(These are conventional figures, worked out to make comparison possible between different groups of years. In reality the years vary with the cycle.)

Period or part of it	Moravian Mission	Davis Inlet	Esquimaux Bay	Ungava	Eastmain (Big River)
1834–43	424	..		..	?
1844–53	315	..	111	..	?
1854–63	288	..	?	..	383
1864–73	276	..	?	159	348
1874–83	353	62	?	310	362
1884–93	181	100	?	230	?
1894–1903	194	134	175	205	330
1904–13	219	85	?	195	?
1914–23	286	47	142	174	308
1924–33	432	130	451	336	591

12

The idea of creating in Quebec Peninsula a game reserve in which the white man's encroachments upon native resources should be prevented, or at any rate kept inside certain limits, has gone one step towards practical realization by a recent action of the Quebec Government. On 16 January 1932 an order was made by the Minister of Colonization, Game and Fisheries, 'respecting the erection of the whole of the North Region of the Province as a Game Reserve'. The order (for a copy of which I am indebted to the Department of Indian Affairs in Ottawa) runs as follows:

'That, since a few months, the Fish and Game Service has been informed, that, in many instances, white trappers go by aeroplane to the Mistassini regions (James Bay) Abitibi and even to New-Quebec, to hunt fur-bearing animals.

That the considerable expenses necessitated by such trips, impel these trappers to get the greatest possible quantity of fur; and that hunting, thus carried on, in these distant places, where it is impossible for Us to exercise any control, is the cause of numerous abuses, and is greatly detrimental to the Indian population who has no other means of Livelihood;

That certain reports even establish that these white trappers use poison to catch these animals,

That this proceeding, besides destroying everything, endangers the lives of the Indians who are very fond of the flesh of such animals, which they are liable to eat after their having been killed by poisoning;

That, moreover, these white trappers, bringing back their furs by aeroplane, escape the supervision of the department officers and may thus carry their furs to foreign markets without paying the regular dues required by law;

That it is important to take efficient measures to prevent these abuses, and to safeguard, as much as possible, the control of this business, whilst protecting this source of revenue in these distant regions;

Therefore, the Honourable the Minister recommends that, in virtue of paragraph 6 of article 48, chapter 86 of the Revised Statutes (1925) the District of Mistassini, the unorganized part of the District of Abitibi, that of Ashuanipi, and also the whole of New-Quebec, be established as a Fish and Game Reserve where Indians only carry on hunting for the fur bearing animals.'

The real practical test of such a policy, is whether 'in these distant places, where it is impossible for Us to exercise any control' the situation will be changed. It is a commonplace of conservation that game laws are useless without adequate enforcement. It is to be hoped these new ones will be enforced, especially as they affect the practice of fur-hunting by aeroplane, which is a real menace, not only in Quebec but in other parts of Canada also. The aeroplane, equipped with floats that enable it to land on inland waters in the wildest parts of the country, increases the searching power of the trapper to a fantastic degree, as well as taking him out of the sight of game guardians and police.

The new scheme leaves political Labrador, of course, untouched. But here also a start has been made in the exercise of supervision over hunting (see p. 377). Sooner or later the whole peninsula will have to be treated by means of a common plan. Neither the reindeer nor the fox are particularly interested in political boundaries. They do not pause on the watershed of the George's and Hamilton Rivers to fumble for their permits, or wonder how much the royalty on their skins is worth. And the exclusion of the white man is unlikely by itself to prevent the decrease of game resources. Natives, with white man's traps and tools and weapons, can bear just as relentlessly on the animal populations. Such exclusion slows the pace, but does not alter the result. Just as the North Sea is now relatively a pond from which only so many fish can be safely taken every year, and then only through the regulations of international agreement, so Quebec Peninsula, if it is not to become almost sterilized of mammalian resources, will require a common policy.

13

Fur traders should reflect on two aspects of this question: the future of native populations here, and the future of coloured foxes whether trapped by Indians, Esquimaux, or by the 'Caucasian invasion' which Speck refers to. A policy is needed, but first of all we must have a firmer ground of facts to base it on. Three facts are already established: the cycle in numbers, the gradual change in colour phases, and the great jump up in recent catches. The fourth is only as yet a working hypothesis: that the coloured fox, like the beaver, has not infinite resistance to attack, though his cavalry movements are more effective than the walled amphibian sieges of the beaver. Another fact that is undeniable is the prime value of fox trapping to the natives. It becomes therefore of very great importance to apply some test, to see if the hypothesis is really true.

Such testing, by modern ecological methods, is possible and should be undertaken by some commission representing the various interests that are involved.

The method of marking foxes should give first-rate results in a country that has so wide a trapping network to give records of recovery. Marking and ringing has, in recent years, been used a great deal for following migratory movements. Since 1909 some half a million wild birds in the British Isles have been ringed.[7] Similar enterprises have grown up in other countries. The result is a mass of facts that could have been gained in no other way. Similar methods are now being developed for wild mammals. The ringing technique has been adapted for small rodents by Izotov[3] in the Ukraine, and by Chitty[2] at Oxford. Other methods of marking were employed by Johnston[3] for following the movements of North American deer-mice, and by Hamilton[5b] for population studies on voles in New York State. Green[5a] and his team of pathologists banded snowshoe hares in Minnesota in order to follow the fate of individuals and the changing density of the population. A Russian worker opened the way for wild fox marking in 1935, when two arctic foxes on Novaya Zemlya were given numbered aluminium ear-clips and released.[1] We do not know the results of these Russian experiments yet, but Errington and Berry[4] in Iowa have obtained some information about the movements of red foxes tagged in the ears with metal markers. Nineteen foxes were recaptured at distances varying from 2 to 96 miles, the average 30 miles. These were marked as young ones and released some way from their homes. One several months old, in a different experiment, was caught 160 miles away. We can see the large scale on which these animals move about. The technical side of this research has already been explored in the marking of domestic animals for identification. Much of the earlier branding is giving place to metal marking clips, as in the great Australian herds of merino sheep, about which exact information is sought for population and other studies.

Most marking work has aimed simply at recording movements. But it can also give important results in population analysis. An example will make this clear. Suppose that 100 foxes in different parts of Quebec Peninsula are caught alive and marked with numbers and released again. A month or two later 50 are recaptured, perhaps turning up some distance from where they were caught before. It might then be reasonably assumed that the total population in the area studied was about 200. If 100 had been recaptured the total would have been 1,000. The only important assumptions made are that the marked foxes have the same mortality as the others, that there is a good random sampling in the catches, and that there has been no great mortality between the marking and recapture. In any case, there will be most valuable information about migration.

All population research is tedious, and requires a five- or ten-year run if new techniques are to be evolved that will produce safe results. The work should be done in years of moderate abundance, neither slump nor final peak. For great scarcity would prevent any work at all, while peak years might introduce the complication of sudden mortality. Here the forecasting of the cycle assumes importance once more, and we are reminded that the chain of reasoning remains unfinished, subject for a few more chapters.

The marking experiment deserves a serious trial. Who will try it? *Who will bell the cat?*

REFERENCES

* indicates that an abstract is deposited in the library of the Bureau of Animal Population, Oxford. H. B. Co. = Hudson's Bay Company.

1. ANON. (1935). ['Experiment in marking of the arctic fox (*Alopex lagopus*) on Novaya Zemlya.'] Bull. Arctic Institute (Leningrad), No. 9: 281. (In Russian; English summary p. 305; Transl., and specimens of ear-tags, in Bureau of Animal Population.)
2. CHITTY, D. (1937). 'A ringing technique for small mammals.' J. Anim. Ecol. 6: 36–53.
3. For references, see Chitty (2).
4. ERRINGTON, P. I., & BERRY, R. M. (1937). 'Tagging studies of red foxes.' J. Mammal. 18: 203–5.
*5. FINLAYSON, NICHOL. Ungava [Fort Chimo] Report, 1832–3. MS. H. B. Co. Archives, London.
5 a. GREEN, R. G., LARSON, C. L., & BELL, J. F. (1939). 'Shock disease as the cause of the periodic decimation of the snowshoe hare.' Amer. J. Hyg. 30: Sect. B, 83–102.
5 b. HAMILTON, W. J. (1937). 'Activity and home range of the field mouse, *Microtus pennsylvanicus pennsylvanicus* (Ord.).' Ecology, 18: 255–63.
6. SPECK, F. G. (1936). 'Eskimo and Indian backgrounds in Southern Labrador.' The General Magazine and Historical Chronicle (University of Pennsylvania), 38: 143–63.
7. THOMSON, A. LANDSBOROUGH (1936). 'Bird migration: a short account.' London. p. 20.
*8. Davis Inlet Post, Fur Returns, 1872–33. MS. H. B. Co. Archives, London and Winnipeg.
*9. 'Eastmain District', Fur Returns, 1854–1933 (incomplete). MS. H. B. Co. Archives, London and Winnipeg.
*10. 'Esquimaux Bay District', Fur Returns, 1840–1933 (incomplete). MS. H. B. Co. Archives, London and Winnipeg.
*11. Fort Chimo Post (Ungava District) Correspondence. Nichol Finlayson to George Simpson, 10 Sept. 1835. MS. H. B. Co. Archives, London.
*12. Fort Chimo (Ungava District), Fur Returns, 1868–1933. MS. H. B. Co. Archives, London and Winnipeg.

  13. Fur Production of Canada, Seasons 1928–9 and 1934–5. Canada, Dominion
      Bureau of Statistics, Fur Statistics Branch, Ottawa.
*14. Labrador Posts (Hopedale, Nain, Okak, Hebron), Fur Returns, 1926–33. MS.
      H. B. Co. Archives, Winnipeg.
*15. Nachvack Post (Esquimaux Bay District), Journal, 1868–9.   MS. H. B. Co.
      Archives, London.
*16. Periodical Accounts of the Moravian Missions. London.
*17. Revillon Frères, Fur Returns for Posts in the Quebec Peninsula, 1913–33.
      (MS.).

CHAPTER XV

THE NATURE OF FOX CYCLES

1

THERE is still a good deal to be said about the four-year cycle. So far I have only sketched the elements of the matter. Signs and traces suggest a powerful restlessness among these northern animal populations; but we have to work, as it were, with second- and third- and fourth-hand information, gathered on the fringes of a huge hinterland into which, as Doughty said of Arabia, 'a European will hardly adventure with heavy heart to bewilder his feet'. Such materials must be forged with care if they are to make a tough instrument for scientific theory or practical policy. Hence the rather slow pace of this discussion:

> This fight did last from breake of day,
> Till setting of the sun;
> For when they rung the evening-bell,
> The battel scarce was done.

The present chapter puts the cycle again under inspection, examines its credentials, and leaves it at the end with reputation undamaged but a character more clearly defined.

If the last chapter's calculations are anywhere near the truth, there is strong contrast between the sparse numbers of coloured foxes living scattered over the land and the high proportion caught. Fox has not by his efforts cornered more than a tiny fraction of the food built up by plant and mouse and bird. In terms of fictitious averages, there may not be on a square mile more than the equivalent in fox of several small beef steaks. The high catch therefore connotes vigorous movements among the foxes, and among the trappers too. We know that these occur, and so the hypothesis hangs together, and carries the suggestion that the fur cycle is a fair index of population changes.

We have to examine now some of the things that affect the fur returns, introducing errors into their interpretation as index of population density. They fall into natural order in this way:

1. Real variations in the population caused by other factors than the four-year cycle. *Fire* is one cause of these. There may be others.
2. Variations in the fraction caught. Fox *migration* is one cause, *starvation* another. Conditions affecting the *trapping* intensity and opportunity require consideration: changing *areas*, fluctuations of *price*, *disease* in the human community and among sledge dogs, and vagaries of winter *weather*, especially storms and depth of snow. Also the *number of traps* in operation, and the *number of trappers*.
3. Variation in the amount the trader secures from his customers. This can be due to the whim of *shifting native bands*, or to the intensity of rival trader *competition*.

4. Finally, the collected furs are liable to *delay and accident* before they reach the market. This factor seldom counts, as the fur returns are almost always based on the actual collections at the posts. Similarly, errors in *accounting* are negligible, and those of *transcription* reduced to a minimum by careful checking.

This list of influences is fairly formidable. But such sabotage of the evidence for underlying cycles partly carries with it its own remedy. A great many of the factors are local and may be discounted if we study a very large extent of country, for they will cancel out and thus can be classed with the chances that determine the toss of a penny. We have to consider chiefly the things that might affect the whole ecological system in certain years, and it is just these which are most accessible in the records.

When the interfering factors have been surveyed, there is still a large body of archive evidence which enables us to find out what the cycle actually did in different years. But the survey here gives some idea how far the fur returns can be trusted to reflect ecological events, and to what degree their details can be usefully analysed. We should bear in mind the Chinese saying that 'you cannot strip two skins off one cow'. The returns are to be used like any other instrument: it cannot be put to work for which its accuracy is insufficient.

2

Forest fires are a scourge in Labrador. Low[2(1)] wrote in 1896 that 'at least one half of the forest area of the interior has been totally destroyed by fire within the past twenty-five or thirty years. These fires are of annual occurrence and often burn throughout the entire summer, destroying thousands of miles of valuable timber, to the south of the central watershed. The regions thus devastated remain barren for many years, especially towards the northern limits. . . .'

Such fires affect wild animals by destroying them and by sterilizing great tracts of country that become unsuitable as a habitat. They must also cause migration and shifting of the centres of animal population. An impression of the after-effects of fire is given by Davies, a Hudson's Bay Company man, writing[11] in 1840 from Hamilton Inlet, in reference to his travels in the angle of country that lies between North West River, Kaipokok, and the Inlet: 'The country has been extremely ravaged by fires and has therefore a naked and desolate appearance. I however discovered a section covered with wood, which offers a fine prospect of martens and otters; the tracks of both these animals were exceedingly numerous.'

Fire is continually starting new ecological succession in the vegetation. Bell[1] says: 'The process appears to have been going on from time immemorial, and young trees are constantly growing up to replace those destroyed, so that "second growths" of all ages are to be met with at intervals throughout the country.' But we learn from Low[2(1)] that 'the second growth of black spruce, Banksian pine, aspen and white birch is never as good or as large as the original forest'. Probably the martens are hit more hardly than the foxes, for martens like to haunt the well-timbered land, while foxes are cosmopolitan nomads.

The causes of such fires are various, but the chief responsibility rests on the natives. Erlandson, a Hudson's Bay Company clerk, exploring southwards from Fort Chimo in 1832, has left the following note:[13]

'It is not', he wrote, 'at all surprising that this part of the country is in a great measure destitute of fur animals. I see the woods on fire in three different places: this is done by the Indians, and are preconcerted signals to apprise each other of arrivals and departures of individuals and families, or some such trivial occurrences. This mode of telegraphing they practise throughout the summer season, to the evident injury of their own hunting lands. It is in vain to remonstrate with them: they lay the blame on others, and are even credulous enough to believe that an evil spirit sometimes sets the woods on fire.'

On 12 to 14 July this fire approached the site of the new outpost that Erlandson was setting up on South River, and burned the woods to the opposite water's edge. The place was abandoned soon afterwards, but stood on or near the present Fort McKenzie, that is about 170 miles southwest of Fort Chimo, near where the Swampy Bay River joins the Kaniapiscau.

Erlandson adds his impression of a forest fire at night:

'A conflagration in a mountainous country like this is really an awful grand spectacle to behold in a dark night: the trees and shrubs scattered upon the hills, forming each a distinct fire, gives the hills the appearance of being studded with lamps. The valleys and more wooded parts are swept by broad sheets of fire, while the noises of falling burning trees and the immense columns of fire and smoke hurled into the air adds horrors to the scene.'

Low also says[2(1)] that

'the majority of them can be traced to the Indians, who start them either through carelessness or intentionally. The Nascaupee Indians of the semi-barrens signal one another by smoke made by burning the white lichens that cover most of the ground in the interior, and these signals cause many of the fires. The southern Indians signal in a similar manner, but do not practice it to such an extent as their northern brethren, having found that they are rapidly destroying their hunting grounds.'

Such fires are sometimes mentioned in the Fort Chimo archives, even though Chimo lies right at the farthest limit of trees.

There are other records of the kind. Two great fires, later referred to in Canadian Labrador as 'the dark days', on account of the way in which the smoke obscured the sun, were noticed in October 1785 and July 1814.[1c] These must have been of enormous extent. The Moravian Missions noticed another period like this in 1821.[12] John Spencer, manager of Nichikun, a Hudson's Bay Company post far in the centre of Quebec Peninsula, and in the same country that Low travelled in, wrote in his journal[10] on 30 June 1839: 'Hot sultry weather, and we are surrounded by fires in every direction. However, I shall speak to the Indians in the fall about it, for its a most destructive thing, destroying as it must vast numbers of young fur animals such as martens.' And on 27 June 1841:[10] 'A great and valuable part of the green woods in which we have been accustomed to hunt deer in winter is now destroyed by fires, occasioned by the imprudence of Petahtanimiscum, who I intend shall smart for this wanton destruction of our hunting grounds. It's a serious thing to this place, as in all probability we shall have to go such an intolerable distance in search of these animals [caribou], as it's only in the green woods they are to be found in winter.' In a letter written[9] in December 1843, he refers to 'the present awful appearance of the surrounding country, which is so much destroyed by fires that the hopes of procuring deer's meat is almost out of the question, and as for partridges and rabbits there are practically none'.

3

Apart from the carelessness of white settlers and travellers, and lightning or summer heat, there is another agency that Low mentions: fires 'set on purpose by the owners of schooners, who often fire the country along the shore, so as to easily make dry firewood for future seasons'.

What a feast of casual destruction these records witness to! There can be no doubt these fires have been for many hundred years a disastrous feature in the life of animals, including both the fur-bearers and the small beasts they live upon. According to the varying scale of the fires at different times, there must have been appreciable injury to the fur re-sources, which we might expect to find reflected in the returns for certain years.

There is no means of even guessing at the extent of animal life destroyed, for this depends so much on the fire and the chances of animals escaping from it to other regions. Also, we have nothing like a complete record of forest fires in Quebec Peninsula. The notes below contain all the informa-tion I can find.

The early fires in the interior of northern and central Labrador in 1832 and 1839–41 have already been noticed. How far they spread we do not know. But possibly the same fire was felt at Hopedale, three or four hundred miles away. In the summer of 1841 the people noticed[12] much hazy weather, and once 'a strong smell of burning, and an immense quantity of dust, like fine ashes, which was deposited thickly upon the linen that was hanging out to dry . . .'.

That the effects of forest fires could be detected a very great distance from the source is shown by the experience of F. F. Payne,[3] the meteoro-logist of Lieut. A. R. Gordon's Hudson's Bay Expedition at Stupart's Bay on the Hudson Strait in 1886. On 29 and 30 August: 'extraordinary meteorological phenomena noted today, evidently caused by immense bush fires in the heart of Labrador.' Next day 'water taken from a stream, after a fall of rain, tasted so strongly of smoke it was unfit to drink'. Stupart's Bay lies on the Arctic coast far north of trees.

What Low[2(3)] calls 'the greatest fire of modern times' broke out in southern Labrador about 1870 or 1871, sweeping 'the country south of the height-of-land, from the St. Maurice to beyond the Romaine River'. How far north it went is not on record, but the missionaries at Ramah, far to the north, may have felt its influence.[12] On 11 October 1871 they 'observed the air filled with clouds of black smoke . . . the ground, instead of having a covering of white, had assumed a dark appearance as far as the eye could reach. This was the result of a fall of soot and ashes, which retained their peculiar smell for several days. . . . As we afterwards heard, nothing was seen at our other stations.'

A few years earlier, in 1868, the Mission ship *Harmony* ran into fog mixed with smoke, as she sailed up the coast to Hopedale. This smoke 'was supposed to be caused by a great fire of the bush at a considerable distance inland'.[12] But Low says[2(3)] of Hamilton Inlet: 'In this region great fires occur annually; that of 1893 covered hundreds of square miles of the tableland between the Hamilton and Northwest Rivers. Similar remarks apply to the forests of the western watershed, more than half of which have been burnt.'

There are some other notes, but insufficient to tell us whether the fires were local or widespread. Probably no one knew even at the time. There were only casual reports of inland trappers to go upon, such as this from Hopedale[12] in 1861: 'It was very dry and forest-fires took place, which appear to have destroyed many wild animals, especially foxes. The fish are said to have been driven away from the coast by the "bitter smoke" resting on the water.' This suggestion about the fish (also referred to by Cabot) is interesting, and not impossible, in the light of Payne's experience and the undoubted fact that herrings in European waters are diverted from water affected by certain plankton organisms that give off powerful smells.

The whole record of fires in the peninsula is obviously bare and broken. But we can distinguish several very big years of fire outbreak: 1785, 1814, (1821?), 1839–41, 1870 or 71, (1881?), 1893–4. Fire has always been happening to some extent each year. These were some of the biggest outbreaks. Between them were others which either went unrecorded or were less extensive and serious. I can find no influence of the big years of fire upon the northern Labrador fox returns, nor any hint of a regular short periodicity in fire outbreaks. We may consider that the effects of fires were often considerable, especially in causing migration of animals, but that they probably acted at random and not with the regularity of a four-year cycle.

4

When we come to the question of *migration*, we feel again the need for field studies, and in particular marking experiments. Our knowledge at present is misty and vague; it has no framework of numbers and distances; it therefore demands a cautious tone in drawing deductions. The main question is how far fluctuations in the fox catch at one place are due to the waxing and waning populations within a local area, and how far to ebb and flow through movements. The only facts we have at present are the reports of traders and missionaries, based on their own observations and on the working experience of trappers. The field knowledge of such men must by no means be treated lightly; it is built up from tracks in the snow and other signs, from the animals they see about, as well as from the numbers trapped. The trouble comes in the casual way in which such observation is recorded.

There is no doubt that coloured foxes do move about a good deal at different seasons and in different years. When they are hungry, foxes probably cover great distances in search of food. We do not know whether the coloured fox travels hundreds of miles as does the arctic fox. But as the coloured species outstrips his cousin in size and strength, there is no physical reason to stop him from equalling his migration efforts. We might discover from marking experiments the movements of 'a multitude like which the populous North poured never from her frozen loins'. But that hangs on future research.

Hind, over seventy years ago, observed the cycle in southern Labrador and thought it was caused by such movements (see quotation on p. 273). He may have mistaken a real fluctuation for migration, just as the French farmer calls the plague of field-mice on his land an 'invasion'.

Some of the foxes' wanderings must cancel out, one post securing the catch that never reached another. But radial movement from inland to the coast, if it occurs, will exaggerate the amplitude of fur fluctuations, giving a misleading appearance of local multiplication. There may be something of this. No pretence can be made that an index as rough as the fur returns bears any detailed resemblance to a natural curve of population increase in a circumscribed region. The only point is whether migration produces, or at any rate distorts the curve: whether maximum abundance on the coast comes in the same year as it does inland. I think we may conclude, for the present, that migration has some effect but seldom produces a fictitious peak. Several facts support this conclusion. To begin with, trapping is by no means confined to the coast belt. Although exact distances inland are not known, some trappers certainly go fifty or a hundred or more miles into the country. The best example is the Davis Inlet band of Indians which hunted and trapped far inland; and yet the maximum figures of the post returns for foxes follow closely the average for the coast, as will be shown on a later page.

Again, the fur cycle is not a sudden, catastrophic affair. It does not, like the lemmings moving down from the Norwegian mountains, flood the coast only every third or fourth year. The rise is gradual and within the possibilities of natural increase. Finally, the evidence about vole fluctuations in Labrador in a later chapter also lends support.

5

The *hunger* of foxes is a very important element in the business of catching fur, much more important than movements of natives, changing price, or climatic vagaries. When natural food is plentiful the bait is less attractive, and foxes shun the traps, only entering in numbers when food grows scarce. We read in the journal of Davis Inlet,[5] 10 December 1904: 'V. and I. . . . report no foxes caught their way. The cry is they won't take bait: too many mice.' There are a good many other records of this sort. As the chief natural food for foxes in Labrador is mice, the subject is treated more fully in the following chapter.

Trapping factors are not all easy to assess. The *territory covered* by each post in northern Labrador seems to have stayed much the same in the last hundred years. We can picture the trapping territories as being something like a chain-mail of territories overlapping a little, and widely sampled every winter. They may have extended a greater distance inland in the later years.

The *opening and closing of posts* might have an influence on the figures. But if the fur returns on pp. 274–5 are examined, there is obviously little influence from this source. That is because the new post only gradually gets its customers, and because the closing is partly due to a gradual failure of the trade. In no case have events of this kind shifted the incidence of a peak year in returns.

Prices have little effect on trapping from year to year, though they have stimulated the general trend of fur catching. The reason for this is that trading concerns lived by barter and have kept their tariffs constant as far as they can, to avoid a chaotic effect on accounts. I have no details about more recent policies, or of the extent to which the native follows market prices. It is possible that the Eskimo now sits and plans his winter's work by listening to radio announcements of the London and New York market prices—a thought that somehow fills one with a certain amount of horror. But there can be no doubt that, whatever the prices are, the natives will take their traps and get to work when foxes are abundant. The only effect we must be prepared for is a slight exaggeration of the peaks, how much we do not know. But this may be countered by the limited trapping capacity mentioned later.

6

We come now to *human disease*, and its capacity to cripple the little army of trappers in certain years. We should expect that severe disease running through the people would prevent them from working so much in the wind and bitter cold of Labrador winter, or even keep them in bed at home. These diseases fall into three classes: sheer want of food, lowering vitality and resistance; the diseases native to Labrador; and germs brought in by white men from outside. According to all the records, starvation seldom paralysed the natives so much that they could not trap; it simply meant that they worked with belts drawn tighter. There are some accounts of desperate winters, with food shared out by missionary and native, but none which actually incapacitated them; and even the bad cases were usually balanced by good ones elsewhere on the coast. The seal-hunt has always been the major determinant of food supply. The irregular visits, varying numbers, and changing conditions of this hunt are a very important thread running through Eskimo life on the coast. No further mention will be made of seals except to note that there appears no vestige of a four-year cycle in their numbers or migrations, so far as the scattered missionary records are concerned. They do not correlate with fox. Other determinants of food supply—caribou, cod, and salmon—are equally irregular so far as can be seen. I regard Cabot's theory of the caribou wanderings and the mice as still unproven; we need much better materials for its study.

Since disease is only brought in here in order to eliminate it from important cyclical influences on fur, no full exposition will be attempted. Dr. Hutton has summarized his medical observations made at Okak Hospital in a useful but little-known book,[1b] to which the reader is referred. Of the chief and constant Eskimo disease he writes:

'Influenza is endemic on the Labrador coast. It occurs among the Eskimos in pandemic form; the pandemics occur with great regularity twice each year, adhering to an established time of appearance. One pandemic differs from another in severity, and to a lesser extent in type. So far back as history carries us, Influenza has been endemic among the Eskimos; old mission diaries speak of deaths from the prevalent "Eskimo cold", and this is the disease which we know as Influenza. This is one of the diseases which has, obviously, not been imported. . . . The pandemics arise annually in February and August.'

The natives, Dr. Hutton informs me, actually have a special name for influenza ('nuvak') which implies that the illness holds a certain established position in their life. The account now to be given is based on the Mission *Periodical Accounts*.[12]

In 1918 and 1928 there were invasions of the white man's influenza: there may have been earlier ones as well. The 1918 epidemics had ghastly results on two of the northern posts: at Okak every male native died, and it killed 207 out of the whole community of 263. At Hebron two-thirds of the whole congregation died, and six-sevenths of the hundred actually resident there. Makkovik, Hopedale, and Nain escaped. The Makkovik missionary wrote in January 1919: 'The epidemics have not reached our congregation yet. The "Spanish 'flu" has been working sad havoc in the South. We hear that around Cartwright and Rigolet about seventy have died of it.' The northern posts contracted it from a sailor who had it on the Mission ship *Harmony*, although Captain Jackson made every effort to prevent contact with any infection.

7

The immunity enjoyed by certain posts enables us by a rough-and-ready method to analyse the effects on fur catches. The coloured fox returns show peaks in 1917 at every post (except Killinek whose figures

	Makkovik, Hopedale	Nain	Okak, Hebron
1917	153	189	406
1918	98	133	40
% 1918/17	64	70	10

are in any case minute). These posts all fell to much lower figures in 1918 and to zero in 1919. The figures are shown on the previous page.

The places that got smashed up by influenza showed a much heavier drop than the others; but the epidemic missed the peak. We can take this as an example of the greatest effect that an epidemic would ever have.

In 1928 influenza returned to Labrador, part of a North American pandemic. This time it visited Hopedale, Nain, and Hebron, and possibly other posts. Mr. Ralph Parsons informs me that the disease treated mildly the posts as far as Hebron (its limit of spread north in 1918), but had a heavy effect on those that had not previously been visited. This is borne out in Mission experiences. It is very curious that Hopedale and Nain had it mildly though they were not struck before.

A string of foreign diseases has invaded Labrador in the last sixty years: measles, mumps, 'chicken-pox' (or was it mild small-pox ?), scarlet fever, whooping cough, typhoid, typhus, diphtheria—a shower of gifts for which the natives mostly have to thank the Newfoundland fishing fleet. These ships began to come to Northern Labrador about 1859, developing cod fisheries near Hopedale and north of it. By 1869 at least 400 were going up. Syphilis, according to Hutton,[1b] arrived after some Eskimos came back about 1902, from an exhibition abroad. According to Gosling[1a] there were thirty-three of these natives, who were persuaded to go to Chicago and Europe, where they provided entertainment and probably 'educational value' in the great cities. Only six of these poor creatures survived, and these returned with syphilis among them. A previous party of Labrador Eskimos was hired by Hagenbeck in 1881 to go to his menagerie in Germany. All these died in Europe. Another fifty-seven were taken to the Chicago Exposition in 1893. These were tricked of their reward and were ultimately repatriated destitute and unpaid and infected with typhoid. The earliest of these shameful experiments was done by Captain Cartwright, who had, as a matter of fact, the best intentions. This was at the end of the eighteenth century. Here is what one of the Eskimos said after he had been some time in London: 'Oh, I am tired! Here are too many houses, too much smoke, too many people. Labrador is very good; seals are plentiful there. I wish I was back again.' But, with three others, he was dead of small-pox before he saw Labrador. The fifth, who recovered, carried infection to the coast, where there was an epidemic whose scale will never quite be known. The disease does not seem to have become endemic.

This frightful list of scourges is perhaps not so serious as might appear, for few of them have established a permanent population of germs in the fashion that influenza has. Syphilis is not epidemic, but has an insidious action on the native birth-rate which may be very serious in the future years. Tuberculosis (worst for Indians) is another steady drain. Of the epidemics only measles and typhoid need concern this study. The rest, though once or twice severe, either had no huge effects, usually hit only one or two stations, or else attacked (as with whooping cough) chiefly the children.

Measles occurred (one case) at Hopedale in 1828, but not again until 1881, when there was a violent and partly deadly epidemic at Hopedale, Zoar, Nain, and Hebron, missing, however, Okak and Ramah. At Hopedale the disease appeared on 17 August: 'Of the entire population of this station only five or six persons escaped the epidemic.' Nain had it in September, severely. Zoar got it in October, from Nain. Hebron also began then. At Zoar and Hebron 40 people died, and 31 at the other places. The fox-fur cycle was rising to a general peak at all posts in 1881.

Let us compare the fox catches of stations that had and had not the disease:

	Okak, Ramah	Hopedale, Zoar, Nain, Hebron
1880 . . .	121	313
1881 . . .	299	801
% increase . .	147	156

There is no difference in the recovery-rate of fox catches.

A measles outbreak like this is a fairly good test of the effects of human disease on fur trapping. Apart from local outbreaks at Hopedale in 1905 and Makkovik in 1906, there was none apparently until 1916, when a grave Newfoundland pandemic of measles spread via Indian Harbour to Hopedale, where thirteen people died. It also spread to Makkovik (a few deaths), Okak (four deaths), and Hebron. The Hebron missionary noticed that those who had had the disease in 1881 escaped this time. The pandemic skipped Nain. Analysis of fox catches shows again no effects of the epidemic on fur trade (the cycle was then rising to its 1917 peak):

	Nain	Makkovik, Hopedale, Okak, Hebron
1915 . . .	51	84
1916 . . .	74	158
% increase . .	45	88

Typhoid, brought by natives returning from an exhibition abroad, killed 90 out of 300 at Nain in 1894–5, spread to Hopedale in 1895–6; and broke out at Hebron in 1899–1900 and Ramah in 1900–1. Influenza at Okak in 1904 killed 65 out of 300, and also occurred to northward; while in 1844–5 several stations suffered from an undescribed but fatal disease.

8

In every country, *transport* strongly influences the tempo and economic efficiency of local life. The Eskimo's means of transport on land are his legs and his dog-drawn sledge or comatik. The performance of his legs, drawing him out to set or visit lines of traps, depends on the stimulus he has to move them. This stimulus, in the absence of illness, we assume to be fairly constantly provided by the desire for gain. I have already tried to assess the results of epidemics among the natives upon their ability to carry on trapping. We have now to consider the effects of epidemics among their dog-teams. As the subject of sledge-dog disease comes in Chapter XXII, I shall only mention here the facts that bear on validity of the fur returns for interpreting cycles.

In the North there arise in certain years disastrous outbreaks of disease that appear often to spread from one dog team to another, but sometimes seem to happen in different places simultaneously. Some of these outbreaks are small affairs, others are pandemics that sweep the coast. The symptoms have a common character, in that the nervous system is involved, but individual variation is very wide.

Usually, the illness seems to attack the central nervous system, causing paralysis or madness. But in their madness the dogs never bite a human being, except in rare cases by chance. They often run in a curious way, foam at the mouth, and die of weakness. The important feature here is the extreme destructiveness of the epidemics, which can almost obliterate a population of several hundred dogs. Such epidemics cripple dog transport, not only just after they have run their course, but for the several years required to allow a new population to grow again.

Table 39 contains all the records I have collected for Northern Labrador. There are doubtless some that escaped the diarists: for instance the published Moravian Mission accounts ran rather shallow in the nineties of last century, and Davis Inlet journals prove that the Missions had dog epidemics of which they printed no record.

TABLE 39

Sledge-dog epidemics in Northern Labrador, 1800–1934

Unless otherwise indicated, the records come from the Periodical Accounts of the Moravian Missions.

*Sept. 1803.	Okak, and all down coast. Bad ep.
*1835–7.	Nain in autumn 1835, Okak and Hebron in 1836–7. V. bad ep., 90% d. in some places.
*1858–9.	'Whole coast', including Nain, Okak, Hebron. About 95% d.
1861–2.	Hopedale, some d. Hebron, bad ep.
1863–4.	Hopedale, some d.
*1867–9.	Hebron, bad ep. 1867–8. Nachvack, Jan. to May 1869, bad ep.[8]
1873–4–5.	Davis Inlet, bad eps.[5]
1878–9.	Only two dogs left at Rigolet, March 1879.
1884.	Davis Inlet, protracted ep., April to Nov.[5]
*1890–1.	Davis Inlet protracted ep. (July 1890?), April to July 1891.[5] Okak and Nain, bad ep. April to July 1891.
1894.	Davis Inlet, some d., June.[5]
*1898–9.	Okak, Hopedale, Makkovik, New Year to late spring, 1898, bad ep. Hebron, 1898–99 season, 'still dying'.
1902–3.	Davis Inlet, protracted ep., April, July, Sept., Dec. 1902, Jan. to April 1903.[5]
1904.	Nachvack, spring, bad ep.[8]
*1931–2.	Nain, Makkovik, summer, bad.

Known pandemics are marked *.

21

Several times we read of the Eskimos dragging their own sledges, of hardship through checking of the search for game, but never once a suggestion that lack of dogs had crippled the trapping work. But this omission may be accidental, so let us examine the distribution of these dates of dog scarcity in relation to the fox-fur catches. The 1835–6 epidemic at Nain hit the trapping season, yet this was a peak year for foxes there. All the other places were also at a peak, so that the epidemic at Hebron and Okak in 1836–7 coincided with a drop in returns. In 1858–9 the whole coast suffered a bad epidemic. This might have checked the rise to a peak in 1859–60, or even made that fallaciously the peak. But 1861–2, bad dog year at Hebron, was also a high fox year; likewise 1867–8. 1897–8, when many dogs died from New Year onwards at Okak and Hopedale, Hopedale had its peak, though Okak showed little change from the year before.

On the whole the records suggest that sledge-dog disease never exercised a decisive influence on the furring, and that where a drop occurred it was usually a coincidence. There is at any rate little suggestion that the dog epidemics caused a four-year cycle in trapping operations that could have produced an important fallacy in the figures.

9

Diseases (and accidents) form the main obvious check on the Eskimo population, though this may also be influenced as much by more subtle factors of habit and cultural change. The size of fur catch must be partly limited by the *number of hunters*, in turn depending on the population size and structure; partly on the number of traps in use; and partly on the effectiveness with which the trapper does his job (that is, if he can and whether he does). The total native population has changed remarkably little in the last hundred years, as Table 40 shows. It is based on census figures for various dates, contained in the Mission Accounts:

TABLE 40

Population attached to Moravian Missions in Labrador at different periods

| Year | Number | | Total |
	Native	White	
1840–1	..	..	1,075
1843–4	..	..	1,156
1857–8	..	..	1,122
1860–1	..	..	1,163
1863–4	..	..	1,059
1867–8	..	..	1,087
1875–6	1,145	127	1,272
1884–5	1,062	201	1,263
1894–5	c. 1,034	c. 280	1,314
1907–8	c. 1,000	c. 300	c. 1,300
1934–5	..	..	1,080

The white men were few before 1860, and have slowly increased to the present day. The natives have hovered between 1,000 and a little over 1,100 just meeting their liabilities with nothing to spare. I dò not know the proportion that hunts and traps. It cannot be more than a third, since the totals include children. The foxes *average* something from one to four per head of population, the ratio varying from year to year.

Mr. P. H. Leslie has pointed out to me that the limited number of traps in operation may limit the fox catch in very good years. This may sometimes keep down the maximum below its possible size; but the native shoots foxes as well, an extra reserve of catching power for the trapper. The relatively stable Eskimo numbers account for the generally uniform run of the cycle through all this time.

There may have been some general tendency in later years for trappers to work at greater distances from home, with more traps than formerly. The missionary at Nain reported for 1926–7 that:

'The trapping of foxes and other fur-bearing animals was crowned with success. Yet if one compares the number of furs obtained in late years with the lower figures of earlier years, it is necessary to remember the fact that formerly one man rarely had more than six traps to attend to, and that most of the trapping was carried on in the near neighbourhood of the Station; whereas now trappers spend their winter anywhere between the outer islands and the edge of the high plateau in the interior, carrying on their hunt with from twenty to a hundred traps each. So one can only wonder that the furred animals are not exterminated.'

The *winter weather* must have some influence on trapping, but I have no means of weighing its importance in Labrador. To do this properly would need a careful and intimate knowledge of the art and of its application under different conditions. But it can be said that there is hardly a mention in the voluminous Mission records of weather as cause of good or bad fox harvests. This omission must be of real significance, because every phase of Labrador life is touched on at one time or other; and the vivid influence of sea and ice conditions on the seal hunt is often described. But it is well known in other parts of North America that the depth and hardness of snow, the frequency of blizzards, or of extreme cold, matter greatly to the trapper in certain years, so that their influence cannot be easily dismissed. We must also bear in mind that the fox, whose legs are short in a country where snow lies in some winters 10 or 20 feet, may be impeded sometimes in its migration; on the other hand, the winter cold and wind usually make a crust enough to carry its lightly moving body.

10

The *movements of natives* affect the local balance of trade, but as far as the Missions are concerned, there have been hardly any massive changes except when new posts were opened or closed. The religious tie has made for conservative and closely knit communities of Eskimos. The changes, if any, were gradual. One exception was the sudden migration to Hebron in 1847–8: 'Saeglek is no longer a heathen settlement, the 71 Esquimeaux who previously resided there having left that spot and taken up their abode . . . at Hebron. Saeglek is now a fishing place for our people.'[12]

Occasionally the Indians that Davis Inlet desired for its exclusive customers would drop in at Zoar or other posts. The only visits of this kind that I have traced (usually by remarks from both sources)[5, 12] were to Zoar in 1870, 1880, 1881, 1883, and 1884–5; and to Hopedale and Nain in 1904–5. The trading influence seems to have been unimportant, to judge by the figures shortly to be discussed. The other unusual visit (to Nain in 1857) has already been alluded to in Chapter XII: it was an emergency journey by a starving tribe from George's River, and probably carried little trade to Nain. The post-war attachment of the same band to that post is another matter, about which no details are in my hands. The Nain Mission report for 1920–1 notes that 'Indians have for some time past been trading regularly at our store in Voisey's Bay'. They traded for certain in 1915–16, and may have done so before that.

The Indian bands have always been more temperamental in their attachment, partly because their animist religion has no affinity with the West European beliefs that the Company's men grew up in. Another important reason is that these Indians follow the caribou in its wide and unpredictable migrations. This makes them by nature mobile, and capable of long journeys to distant posts. The normal *hunting* territories of different bands seem to have been clearly enough established by custom, but this territorial arrangement did not prevent some individuals from going far afield *to trade* the results of their hunting and trapping. In a special report in 1911 on Ungava posts, H. M. S. Cotter, the experienced northern trader of the Hudson's Bay Company wrote:[7] 'There are about 60 Indian hunters at Ungava just now. They trade with whom and where they please. . . . We have always had the bulk of the Indian furs. . . . These Indians periodically wander out to Davis Inlet, to Seven Islands, to North West River, and to Great Whale River, and sometimes they go to Nitchequon at the height of land. Their wanderings depend on the deer.'

This statement finds agreement in the journals of Davis Inlet,[5] wherein are records of Indians from various bands, noted vaguely as 'Northern' or 'Southern', or less often definitely as 'Ungava', 'North West River', and so on.

11

This discussion leads on naturally to *competition* between rival traders, since this can have exactly the same effect on a post's returns as if the natives have bartered a hundred miles away. The main history of the coast has already been outlined: the live-and-let-live arrangement between Moravian Missions and the Company, at any rate up to 1910, and even after that to a great extent. The chief tension-point lay between the Hudson's Bay Company post at Davis Inlet and its missionary neighbours to north and south. As it happens, the fur returns of that post have survived, almost intact, and these give a chance for examining the cycle at posts belonging to different concerns, and dealing with rather different clients.[4]

Davis Inlet began in 1869 and still goes on. Its furs were from visiting Indians, out of the interior; from white settlers or 'planters' in the immediate district; and from a little trapping round the post and a little casual trade with Eskimos. The proportions from each source probably varied very much, but the journals imply that the Eskimo trade was fractional, at any rate up to 1909 (the date to which they have been abstracted). The Mission trade at Hopedale was with Eskimos, and with a few white settlers, practically never with Indians. At Zoar it was the same, with the rare Indian visits already noticed. The only difference is in late arrivals who bring their furs in May to August. To make the figures match, the Davis Inlet fur returns were adjusted to include in each 'year' the few furs brought in after the Outfit closed and before the ship arrived in summer. In this the figures differ from Hudson's Bay Company fur returns generally quoted by authors. They are in the table following: since the post was set

TABLE 41

Fur returns for coloured fox from Davis Inlet, Zoar, and Hopedale, 1872–1925
(Zoar only to 1887)

Year	Davis Inlet	Zoar and Hopedale	Davis Inlet, Zoar and Hopedale	Year	Davis Inlet	Hopedale	Davis Inlet and Hopedale
1872	99	115	214	1899	68	26	94
3	24	32	56	1900	47	29	76
4	(missing)	83	?	1	177	102	279
5	135	122	257	2	143	31	174
6	33	59	92	3	26	9	35
7	37	58	95	4	23	33	56
8	51	45	96	5	118	90	208
9	53	107	160	6	158	95	253
1880	94	301	395	7	15	17	32
1	20	69	89	8	46	35	81
2	58	107	165	9	82	59	141
3	81	134	215	1910	236	115	351
4	26	65	91	11	105	12	117
5	42	43	85	12	14	26	40
6	42	58	100	13	29	38	67
7	92	65	157	14	68	202	270
8	53	16	69	15	18	25	43
		(Zoar closed)					
9	203	40	243	16	72	83	155
1890	237	25	262	17	93	92	185
1	117	28	145	18	115	58	173
2	50	12	62	19	4	0	4
3	135	22	157	1920	11	19	30
4	137	13	150	1	63	63	126
5	199	52	251	2	87	108	195
6	243	90	333	3	32	25	57
7	225	103	328	4	131	38	169
8	76	15	91	5	269	231	500

between two missions, Zoar and Hopedale, the foxes taken by these are put alongside for comparison, and in a third column all three are summed in order to cancel some of the results of trade rivalry—if any. Zoar, however, lasted through only part of the régime of Davis Inlet, which is still operating.

The cycle stands out sharply in all three columns, being most regular when the three (later two) stations are added together. But the separate resemblance is so striking that the overwhelming influence of the cycle is undeniable. The main discrepancies are in the mid nineties—a period we already found to be rather irregular at all the coast stations. The curves run parallel even after 1910, when we know some active competition started. The explanations are probably that the efforts at rivalry were small, and the effects smaller still, on the principle that 'to every action there is an equal and opposite reaction'—which leaves matters much the same as if no competition existed at all.

12

The Missions from 1859 onwards began to notice rather often another disturbing incursion into the well-ordered communities under their care. In that year the Okak mission wrote[12] that 'as early as the 3rd of July a trading-vessel from Newfoundland arrived here, with the object of finding a suitable fishing-ground; several others have since followed'. In the summer of 1866 there were 30 Newfoundland schooners at anchor in Hopedale Bay; in 1868 there were 108; in 1869 more than 500. From this time onwards the Newfoundland cod fishermen were regular visitors in summer, though the strength of their invasion varied with the fluctuations of fish and ice and weather. The missionaries were chiefly alarmed at the danger to health and morals of their people; but occasional entries suggest also a leakage of furs. At Okak in 1881: 'The number of schooners that visit the more northerly stations is on the increase. . . . These visitors injure the Esquimoes by net-fishing on a large scale just at the mouth of bays which our people occupy, and also by tempting them to make use of every opportunity to dispose of their fish and furs in barter for useless articles of food or clothing.'

The steamship was beginning to come into Labrador life as well, and there was a mail steamer from the late years of last century onwards. All these outside visitors must have had some effect on trade. The Moravian Mission furs show a pronounced drop in the number caught *per capita* after 1875 (for this I used the rough method of dividing ten-year averages by sample years of population). This change may have been caused by the draining away of furs to the Hudson's Bay Company, fishermen, and petty traders—unless it represents a real falling-off in the country's fur supply, which is probably unlikely in those earlier days. The competition from outside must have fluctuated and therefore brought some errors into the interpretation of figures. Thus for 1884 Hopedale recorded that 'the sale of Bibles and other books was very small, as only a few schooners succeeded in making a good haul, and the crews were therefore obliged to practise economy.' Again, in 1901 a large number of schooners returned empty to Newfoundland, because there were very few cod-fish, owing perhaps to the heavy drift-ice that hemmed the coast that summer. It is doubtful, however, if these fluctuations in the numbers or buying power of the summer visitors can have generally influenced the fur returns for the whole coast.

13

The fur is now in the trader's store, and practically safe from further hazards. Even the great fire that destroyed Nain mission houses in August 1921 appears to have spared the furs. The mission ships hold a really astounding record of navigation for nearly a hundred and fifty years. Only once the *Harmony* failed to reach all the stations: in 1853 she was faced with northerly gales that drove her 400 miles out of her course. In that year she got to Hopedale but not to Nain, Okak, or Hebron. Although the three northern stations eventually received their stores, the furs were of course left there for an extra year. The returns for 1854 for these three stations therefore include the ones for 1853, which were not separately entered. The mission ships were famous for their immunity from disaster, which they owed in part to their dynasty of skilful and tried captains. It is related that Lloyds allowed (in the nineteenth century at any rate) a reduction in insurance premiums because the ship was covered by extra divine protection (estimated at 1 per cent.!).

The fur returns have now been put to the test in various ways. The existence of many interfering factors has been recognized, but the verdict is made that these are incapable of producing a rhythmical cycle in fur catches. The most they can do is to cause small deviations in the peak years of the fur returns, but usually at so few places that the total figures are only slightly changed. This verdict rests, however, on the assessment of a number of variables and of their effects, and it has to be admitted that we know comparatively little about some of these variables—for instance winter snow conditions. Fortunately there is some direct evidence about fox abundance and scarcity, contained in archives. These statements are largely independent of most of the interference that we have been discussing. They record the experience of the trappers who have been working at the best of their capacity to catch foxes during the winter.

Instead of describing the years of abundance, I have assembled the statements about years of scarcity. For one thing it is useful to know whether these poor years have been caused by any of the catastrophes that have been detailed in this chapter—fire, pestilence, storms, and the rest. Another reason for choosing years of scarcity is that the written archives seldom distinguish coloured from arctic foxes. As far as they are concerned (except in the fur returns themselves, which are precise) it was 'fox', sometimes only 'fur' or 'the hunt'. There can, however, be no confusion over an absent fox, whatever its species. The maximum years receive some notice in the next chapter.

The records have been selected in the following way. The minimum years of each cycle were determined from the coloured fox curve of all Moravian Mission stations (see Table 17). Reference to fox numbers and the general catch were assembled for these seasons. In doing this only the main or average season of scarcity was considered; that is, no account was taken of the deviations at separate stations. The sources are the *Periodical Accounts* of the Moravian Missions[12] (1834–1925); journals of Davis Inlet (1869–1909);[5] H. B. Co. Annual Reports on Fur Trade (1887–1928);[7] and Ungava District Correspondence[6] (1866–1909, with some gaps): the last was only drawn upon when reference to the surrounding districts was made. It should be remembered that the reports are nearly always a trifle exaggerated, so that 'we have been doing nothing in fur' really means 'fur very scarce': there were nearly always a few pelts in the store by ship-time, even in the leanest years.

1836–7.

1840–1.
  Okak. 'During the whole winter there were few traces either of hares or foxes.'

1843–4.

1845–6.
  Nain. 'Last autumn, few seals were caught anywhere, and on the land, foxes and game of every kind were almost equally scarce.'
  Hebron. 'Few foxes . . . were, however, taken.'

1848–9.
  Nain. 'Of foxes, few were to be seen or caught.'

1852–3.

1857–8.
  Hopedale. 'The autumn of 1857 was very unproductive, and, during the whole winter, no foxes and but few ptarmigan were to be met with.'
  Nain. 'Foxes were scarcely to be met with.'

1860–1.
  Okak. 'What tended to increase the prevailing distress, was the fact, that foxes were also exceedingly scarce.'
  Hebron. 'Shortly before Easter some small parties came for purposes of trade. They were in poor circumstances, and complained of the paucity of foxes, —a circumstance which has also been noticed here.'

1865–6.
  Hopedale. 'Scarcely any foxes were taken.'
  Nain. 'Scarcely any foxes . . . were killed during the winter.'
  Okak. 'The scarcity of foxes and seals in the spring.'

1869–70.
  Davis Inlet. 9 Dec.: 'Foxes and fur of all kinds very scarce in the bags.' 16 Dec.: 'Lane and Ford have done . . . very little with fur.' 7 Jan.: 'Lane and Ford came . . . from *Hopedale*, no fur.' 20 Jan.: 'Received letter from *Hopedale*, no fur as far south as *Eyelick* [Aillik].'
  Okak. 'Foxes were very scarce.'

1873–4.

Hopedale. 'Very few foxes.'

Davis Inlet. 3 Nov.: 'No signs of foxes after the snow.' 9 Dec.: 'W. Edmonds arrived: he has done nothing [i.e. caught nothing] this fall: only one marten and one mink.' 18 Dec.: 'W. Edmonds and A. arrived: no foxes caught at *Zoar*.' 27 Dec.: 'Foxes scarce, not one silver caught at *Nain, Hopedale,* or *Zoar* as yet.'

Nain. (Scarcity of foxes.)

Okak. 'Foxes and ptarmigans were also remarkably scarce.'

Hebron. 'Foxes, hares and ptarmigan have also been scarce.'

1878–9.

Zoar. 'Some of the Esquimoes had a poor year, as scarcely any foxes were caught.'

Hebron. 'No foxes . . . were caught.'

1881–2.

Davis Inlet. 18 Nov.: 'There are very poor signs of any fur-bearing animals round here.' 2 Dec.: 'Very poor prospects of getting much fur this winter.' 4 Dec.: 'Edward Brown arrived from *Hunt's River*: he brings rather discouraging news, viz. that Lane and Broomfield have not caught a single skin of fur.' 7 Dec.: 'Edmunds came and left, they have caught nothing in the way of furs up at *Shango*. He says there are some signs of foxes, but they will not take bait.'

Nain. 'During the winter, no foxes have been taken, and very little game of any kind, not even ptarmigan. . . . Very few foxes were seen.'

Okak. 'Neither foxes nor hares were to be had.'

Hebron. 'Soon after the New Year some walruses were killed by our hunters, which were most welcome, as foxes seemed to have disappeared for the season.'

1885–6.

Davis Inlet. 25 Jan.: James Ford arrived from *Paul's Island*. . . . They have got 94 seals but only two foxes.' 29 Jan.: 'They have done well at *Nachvak* with seals and white whales, but nothing in furs.'

Nain (written 18 March 1886): 'The prospects as to furs are poor.'

Ramah (written 20 March 1886): 'Fox trapping has been rather unsuccessful. . . . The winter is not a very severe one.'

1888–9.

Davis Inlet. 15 Nov.: 'No deer, no foxes, and probably no seals.' 26 Nov.: 'L. and B. . . . have killed about 120 deer. On the other hand they have scarcely done anything in furs and seals.' 17 Dec.: 'A young man has been at *Zoar* from *Nain* and reported quite a failure in seals, no deer, and only three foxes . . . among all the people there.' 3 Jan.: 'Indians came down and traded for about a hundred dollars worth in deer skins etc. No fur of course. . . . As for furs, every hope of getting any now before I close the books is given up.' 5 Jan.: 'No foxes seem to have been caught anywhere about.' 31 Jan.: 'At *Okak* and *Hebron* they have done remarkably well with seals. . . . With foxes nothing at all is done, only one white at *Okak*.' 5 Feb.: 'Indians brought about 70 martens, 4 otters, one wolverene, one wolf, 4 beaver etc.' 24 Feb.: 'Received a letter from *Nachvak* dated the 6th of Jan. . . . they have done nothing scarcely in anything and not a single fox on hand.' 2 April: 'At *Nachvak* they have only two foxes on hand.'

1892–3.

Davis Inlet. 28 Nov.: A settler 'brought very poor reports: only one fox got amongst the gang over there.' 10 Dec.: 'No one seems to have caught any foxes.' 10 Jan.: 'W. M. Edmunds came. . . . No sign of foxes up his way. I suppose this is the worst winter for fur that has ever been here. Up to date I have only 6 foxes.' 5 Feb.: 'No fur of any account has been caught to the South, but the little that has been caught I purchased, only six foxes' (this resulted from a buying trip to *Hopedale, Island Harbour, First Rapid, Kibokok, Makkovik, Flounders Bite, Aillik,* and *Big Bay.* Indian visitors also brought apparently little or no fur).

1898–9.

Makkovik. 'Fur of all kinds was, as elsewhere, very scarce in this district. . . . How poor the fur catch was will be better understood when we say . . . that the whole Makkovik congregation together did not catch more than one man does in a fairly good year.'

Davis Inlet. 4 Feb.: 'I returned from South . . . with a very poor collection of fur, in fact the trip was a failure as nothing worth while had been caught.'

Nain. 'Foxes and reindeer were fewer than for some years past; ptarmigans and hares likewise.'

1903–4.

Davis Inlet. 12 Dec.: 'T.E. has caught nothing since he was here last, and he reports no sign of foxes; there is going to be a dearth in the fur line this year.' 16 Dec.: 'T.E., J.E. and D.H. . . . brought no fur and have caught none; and none has been caught, so far as they can hear, to the North—not a very bright outlook.' 18 Dec.: 'Arrived G.W., R.F. and T.P. No foxes is the cry, none caught and no sign.' 20 Dec.: 'S.B. and son arrived with the same report: no foxes. This fall's hunt comprises of one solitary red fox.'

Nain. (No foxes caught in the autumn.)

1907–8.

Makkovik. 'Great scarcity of fur-bearing animals.'

Hopedale. 'There were next to no foxes. . . .'

Nain. 'Fur . . . has been very scarce this winter.'

Okak. 'Foxes are conspicuous by their absence.'

Labrador District. (Annual Report on Fur Trade, includes here Ungava and Esquimaux Bay Districts): 'The returns of *Cartwright* post are nearly equal to those of the preceding year; but at all other posts a very large falling off is apparent. This . . . is entirely attributed to the scarcity of fur-bearing animals and the comparative failure of fisheries.'

Ungava District. (Letter, 31 July 1908, G. B. Boucher to P. McKenzie): 'The fur throughout the entire country was a complete failure. From Wolstenholme . . . to as far south as *Rama,* the reports are all the same. At *Rama* station they did not get during the entire year one fox.'

Killinek. 'There were no foxes.'

1911–12.

Makkovik. 'In the autumn and winter neither seals nor foxes were in evidence.

Nain. 'The fur catch is practically nil.' 27 Dec. 1911: 'Furring and sealing are almost blank. Not one fox has been caught in the whole Nain district. . . . William Ford, who has had connection with Nain Store for something like forty years, has never known such a poor year during the whole of that time.'

Okak. 'Abia, our Okak patriarch, summed the matter up in terse words: "the poorest year since the sixties".'

Hebron. (Foxes very scarce.)

Killinek. 'In the autumn . . . there were but few foxes.'

Labrador District. (Annual Report on the Fur Frade, including Ungava and Esquimaux Bay Districts): 'Temporary disappearance of those fur-bearing animals which comprise its principal returns.'

1915–16.

Makkovik. 'Fur-bearing animals seem to be very scarce.'

Hopedale. 'Fur is scarce. I don't think more than a dozen foxes have been trapped or shot all the autumn.'

Nain. 5 Jan. 1916. 'Last year there was an abundance of foxes, and we did not think they would stay away all of a sudden. However, the trappers found last autumn that apparently the foxes had emigrated, very few indeed being left behind. Very few of the people have been so fortunate as to get a fox either by trap or by gun. . . . Severe cold having set in, there seem to be more foxes about.'

1919–20.

Nain. 'Almost total absence of foxes.'

Hebron. 'There was a complete absence of foxes.'

1923–4.

Makkovik. 'Fox trapping was also very poor.'

Hopedale (26 Jan. 1924). 'The fur catch is very poor. In the early autumn foxes appeared to be plentiful, but with the opening of the trapping season and the advent of the cold weather, foxes disappeared. Other fur-bearing animals were equally scarce.' Annual report, summer 1924: 'Furring showed no improvement during the whole of the winter.'

Nain. 'Fox trapping was rather below the average.'

14

Allowing that these remarks left by missionaries and traders are not all of equal evidential value, yet they leave a deep impression of reality. Brief as they are, there is often in them a whole winter of expectation and worry and disappointment. We can imagine a little of the daily inquiry, the fruitless miles of searching for fox tracks in the dry cold winter weather, the trial of new places for the traps, and the growing certainty that (as many Hudson's Bay Journals have said) 'the fur simply is not in the country'. The periodicity of the minimum years is similar to that of the peaks, with the same frequency of intervals. With the establishment of a real periodic cycle in coloured foxes we are led to deeper analysis of its underlying forces, of which mouse seems the strongest. Let us come back to mouse fluctuations.

REFERENCES

* indicates that an abstract is deposited in the library of the Bureau of Animal Population, Oxford. H. B. Co. = Hudson's Bay Company.

1. BELL, R. (1895). 'The Labrador Peninsula.' Scot. Geogr. Mag. 11: 335–61.

1 a. GOSLING, W. G. (1910). 'Labrador: its discovery, exploration and development.' London. pp. 234–41, 309–13.

1 b. HUTTON, S. K. (n.d.). 'Health conditions and disease incidence among the Eskimos of Labrador.' Poole.

1 c. LLOYD, H. (1938). 'Forest fire and wild life.' Mimeographed release, National Parks Bureau, Ottawa.

2. LOW, A. P. (1896). 'Report on explorations in the Labrador Peninsula, along the East Main, Koksoak, Hamilton, Manicuagan and portions of other rivers, in 1892–93–94–95.' Ann. Rep. Geol. Surv. Canada for 1895, 8: 1 L–387 L. (1) 36 L.   (2) 43 L.   (3) 37 L.

3. PAYNE, F. F. (1887). In 'Report of the Hudson Bay Expedition of 1886 under the command of Lieut. A. R. Gordon, R.N.' Blue-book, Dept. of Marine and Fisheries, Canada. p. 49.

*4. Davis Inlet Post, Fur Returns, 1872–1933. MS. H. B. Co. Archives, London and Winnipeg.

*5. Davis Inlet Post, Journals, 1869–1909 (incomplete). MS. H. B. Co. Archives, London.

*6. Fort Chimo Post (Ungava District), Journals, 1866–1902 (incomplete). MS. H. B. Co., London.

*7. H. B. Co., Annual Reports on Fur Trade. MS. H. B. Co. Archives, London.

*8. Nachvack Post (Esquimaux Bay District), Journals, 1868–1905 (incomplete). MS. H. B. Co. Archives, London.

*9. Nitchequon [Nichikun] Post (Rupert's River District), Correspondence, 1834–44. John Spencer to Robert Miles, 1 December, 1843. MS. H. B. Co. Archives, London.

*10. Nitchequon [Nichikun] Post (Rupert's River District), Journals, 1834–44. MS. H. B. Co. Archives, London.

*11. North West River Post (Esquimaux Bay District), Correspondence, 1839–40. MS. H. B. Co. Archives, London.

*12. Periodical Accounts of the Moravian Missions, London.

*13. South River Post (Ungava District), Journal, 1832–33. MS. H. B. Co. Archives, London.

*14. Ungava District [Fort Chimo] Correspondence, 1834–40, 1869–1909 (incomplete). MS. H. B. Co. Archives, London.

*15. Ungava District [Fort Chimo] Reports, 1832–4, 1836–8. MS. H B. Co. Archives, London.

CHAPTER XVI

VOLES IN LABRADOR

'. . . and the fowls shall summer upon them, and all the beasts of the earth shall winter upon them.' Isaiah 18: 6.

1

THERE is nothing like such a fine record of fluctuations in mice as there is for foxes; but just enough for our purpose of correlation. The 'mice' that perform these fluctuations are mainly short-tailed field-mice, that is, voles. Authorities (as Anderson) consider that the chief actor is the large Labrador vole (*Microtus enixus*). But other species of small rodents live in Northern Labrador, the following being recorded in the list by Anderson:[1] at least two voles or meadow-mice (*Microtus enixus* and *M. pennsylvanicus labradorius*), two red-backed voles (*Clethrionomys gapperi ungava* and *C. g. proteus*), a false lemming-mouse (*Phenacomys ungava ungava*), a lemming-mouse (*Synaptomys borealis innuitus*), a banded lemming (*Dicrostonyx hudsonius*), and a white-footed deer-mouse (*Peromyscus maniculatus maniculatus*).

Most of these species range as far north as Port Burwell and Fort Chimo; some of them come (perhaps somewhat different in race) south of Hamilton Inlet. Even the lemming, inhabitant of Arctic tundras, is found far south of the true Barren Lands, but chiefly or only on the hill-tops that rise above the trees (as at Hamilton Inlet, where southern forms begin to creep in).[2]

Davis[3] suggests that *Microtus enixus* is only a northern race of *Microtus pennsylvanicus*, to which it lies very close. This is the common central and eastern vole of North America. Similarly, *Microtus fontigenus* may be a race of *pennsylvanicus*: *fontigenus* in turn seems close to *labradorius*, apparently occupying the south-east parts of Quebec Peninsula and giving place to *labradorius* in Ungava Bay. There seems some ground therefore for believing that two different stocks of voles have spread to the Barren Lands, by eastern and western routes, and that they mingle at any rate in Ungava.

Much exploration and careful collecting is still the need: our knowledge still rests on a comparatively small nucleus of skins and skulls from a few spots along these coasts. How far all these species follow vole cycles we hardly know. But the exodus of predators in years of vole scarcity implies that the other rodents either share the cycle (as happens in Norway) or else have a negligible density of population. Either alternative makes it practicable to use rough records of 'mice' as the peak years of vole.

2

The records of vole fluctuations between 1832 and 1925 are collected together in the large Table 42. Nearly all refer to the Northern Labrador

coast. (I have some more for Canadian Labrador which make another
story that is too incomplete to be worth presenting here. The Fort Chimo
evidence is reserved to keep company with the arctic fox materials in
Part IV.)

TABLE 42

Records of mouse abundance in Northern Labrador between 1832 and 1925

(P.A. = *Periodical Accounts* of Moravian Missions.)

1832. *Okak.* 'On the 30th of July, our potatoes were completely frozen; and a very
fine flower-bed was soon after robbed of its contents by the mischievous
mice, which would have done yet further damage, but for the interference
of our cat, the only animal of her species which we have hitherto been able
to retain in Labrador. To the weasels that infest our poultry yard she is
also a formidable enemy.' (P.A.)

1837. *Hopedale.* 'Our potatoes were frozen on the 1st of July; and our other vegetables, which have not been devoured by the innumerable mice, seem to
grow smaller every day.' (P.A.)

1838. *Nain.* 'All we have just now to complain of is the damage done by the swarms
of mice.' This refers to the late summer. (P.A.)

   Hebron. Great abundance: see below.

1839. *Hebron.* 'The winter proved cold and stormy; but the quantity of snow which
fell was extremely small. This circumstance was the means of ridding us of
the countless swarms of mice which had hitherto [1838] infested the land
like a plague, destroying the vegetables in our gardens by wholesale. At
present [1839] not a single one is to be seen.' (P.A.)

1841. *Hopedale.* 'Mice have also done much mischief in our gardens.' (P.A.)

1846–7, Winter. *Okak.* 'The mice committed serious ravages on our stock of potatoes. . . . As for our enemies, the mice, they were not permitted to enjoy
undisturbed the booty they had collected for the winter; for the Esquimaux
children broke into their store-houses, and plundered their contents.' (P.A.)

1853, Summer. *Hopedale.* 'For some time past, we have observed that our potatoes
and other vegetables have been attacked by mice.' (P.A.)

1874, Spring. *Zoar.* 'The large number of mice, which appeared in spring threatened
to cause great damage, but, fortunately, they only destroyed a few young
plants.' (P.A.)

1874–5, Winter. *Ramah.* 'The take of foxes had been smaller than was expected
owing no doubt to the abundance of mice, which supplied them with food,
without going near the traps.' (P.A.)

1874, 13 Oct. *Nachvack.* 'Sutherland digging up the turnips in the garden. . . . We
did not get more than one barrel, the same time I expected three to four.
Nearly half was eaten by the mice, which are unusually plentiful this year.'
(H. B. Co. Journal.[8])

1875. *Hopedale.* 'The mice, which are a veritable plague, have done great mischief.'

1888, 5 Nov. *Davis Inlet.* 'John reports some sign of mountain mice and ermines on
the hills.' (H. B. Co. Journal.[6])

1903. Not very common. (Cabot, 1912, see quotation in Chapter XI. The exact
region is not clearly stated.)

1904. Abundant. (Cabot, loc. cit.)

1904, 10 Dec. *Davis Inlet.* 'V. . . . and I. . . . report no foxes caught their way. The
cry is they won't take bait: too many mice.'

   14 Dec. 'T. E. . . . and G. W. . . . report no fur: the foxes won't take the bait
   is the cry.'

   28 Dec. '5 North Indians (arrived) . . . report . . . good sign of foxes. The

troubie seems to be among them they won't take bait: too many mice.' (H. B. Co. Journal.[6])

1904–5, Winter. *Okak*. 'There were also a good many foxes about; but they found such quantities of mice to feed upon that they seldom fancied the dainties that were placed in the traps to entice them.' (P.A.)

1904 & 1905. *Okak*. 'In the years 1904–05 the berry crop failed, presumably because the mice and lemmings had eaten the young shoots. . . .' (Hutton.[4a]) '. . . The failure of the berry crop in 1904—because a plague of mice had eaten the young shoots in the springtime. . . .' (Hutton.[4])

1905. Very abundant. (Cabot, loc. cit.)

1906. Very scarce. (Cabot, loc. cit.)

1908. *Okak*. 'I remember definitely that mice were plentiful at Okak . . . in 1908 and again in 1913. These are two years in which I travelled home from Labrador, and on each occasion I remember trying to bring live specimens over to England, and had no difficulty in getting plenty of them from the Eskimo ·boys.' (Dr. S. K. Hutton, letter to C.E., 4 July 1932.)

1908–9, Winter. (Letter dated 5 March 1909.) *Nain*. 'The hunters say there are a number of foxes about, but they find so many dead sea-birds on the ice, and so many mice on the land, that they will not take the bait from the fox-traps.' (P.A.)

1909–10, early Winter. (Letter dated 27 Dec. 1909.) *Hopedale*. 'There was every prospect . . . of their catching a good many foxes. But, unfortunately for them, the country is suffering from a plethora of mice; in consequence of which the foxes decline to be lured into the traps. The tracks of the foxes are exceptionally plentiful, but in spite of our diligence in setting the traps and hunting with the gun, comparatively few have been killed.' (P.A.)

1909–10, Winter. *Hopedale*. 'Although foxes were plentiful in the winter, compara-tively few were caught, owing to the fact that they found plenty of mice to live on, and accordingly took no notice of the bait placed in the traps for them.' (P.A.)

1910–11, Winter. (Letter dated 2 Jan. 1911.) *Hopedale*. 'As mice are scarce this winter, foxes are frequently trapped.' (P.A.)

1913. *Okak*. Abundant. Many were caught to feed a captive buzzard during the summer. (Information from Dr. S. K. Hutton, see also letter above under '1908'.)

1916–17, Winter. *Hopedale*. 'Furring has not proved a success either. Foxes seem to be fairly plentiful, but mice are so abundant that foxes find plenty to eat and so will not take the bait from the traps.' (P.A.)

1917–18, Winter. *Nain*. 'Foxes turned up in specially large numbers; but at first they were not easy to catch, as mice were so plentiful. . . . In February and March, when a thick coat of ice covered the ground and the foxes found it most difficult to appease their hunger with mice, they were pretty frequently attracted by the bait in the traps.' (P.A.)

1920–1, Winter. *Nain*. 'Foxes though fairly plentiful refused to be tempted into the traps, even by the best of bait, for mice of all kinds abounded and were easily caught by the foxes, as there was practically no snow to hide them.' (P.A.)

1924–5, Winter. *Makkovik*. 'There had also been a few foxes about during the present winter, some of the men making quite good catches. . . . Others, again, had obtained hardly any fur, as the foxes in their neighbourhood had found plenty of mice to devour, and had therefore fought shy of the traps that had been set for them.' (P.A.)

Hopedale. 'The fox trappers, too, had a poor time,—not, they say, because foxes are scarce, for there is a very good sign, but mice and berries were so plentiful, and the land was so long free from snow, that foxes would not look at the bait round the traps.' (P.A.)

1925–6, Winter. *Makkovik.* 'Fur-bearing animals, foxes above all, were plentiful last winter; but the hopes of the hunters and trappers were not always realized, because an unusual number of mice provided the foxes with sufficient food, and accordingly the bait in the traps had but little attraction for them. Still, everybody secured some pelts—a few of the men even a good number.' (P.A.)

? 1926, Spring. *Grand Lake*, head of Hamilton Inlet. Considerable migration of greyish-brown voles in spring, probably this date, at any rate during the peak abundance for that district. A good many dead mice about, but mainly large numbers of tracks in the snow in a north-south line. (Information, Jan. 1929, from Mr. N. Henry, H. B. Co. post manager, North West River.)

1926–8. *Nain.* 'At Nain, Labrador, in the summer of 1926, the mice were everywhere. In order to collect them it was only necessary to dig a hole in the ground the size of a bucket. During the night from thirty to fifty mice would fall into the hole. It is significant that late in the season several mice were found dead in the nests. Food was abundant and hence starvation was not the cause of their death. In July 1927, there were no mice. None of the various baits or traps was able to catch more than a few and collecting was given up. In the summer of 1928, however, the mice were becoming common. The effect of the disappearance of mice on other members of the fauna was marked. In 1926, there were twelve nests of the rough-legged hawk at Indian Harbor. In 1927 and 1928 there were no nests. . . . In the summer of 1928 only three hares and only one snowy owl were seen. The arctic foxes were forced to feed on fish. In the winter of 1927–28 about seventy-five furs were brought in. Almost all of these came from one place where the foxes had been able to find fish. The normal catch is about fifteen hundred. The great horned owl and the raven were not affected.' (A. C. Weed, of the Field Museum of Natural History, Chicago, published by Davis.[3a])

These intermittent notes on mouse abundance, spread over a century, are obviously not all of equal value for the investigation of cycles. They require some stiffening, which can be given by observations in the next ten years—the period of Hudson's Bay Company operation at the Moravian Mission stations. These recent records will therefore be treated before a correlation between mice and foxes is attempted.

3

The Company's fur returns for 1926–34 extend the fox fluctuation curve whose interpretation we are seeking. There may have been some change in methods that would have affected the level of returns. The vigour of trading and the number of traps have probably become greater. The record from 1925 is given below, together with the last Mission figure, for 1925. The figures are sums of coloured fox returns for Makkovik, Hopedale, Nain, Nutak (the new name for Okak), and Hebron, and they probably form a fairly homogeneous series.[7]

Outfit	1925	1926	1927	1928	1929	1930	1931	1932	1933	1934
No. coloured fox	**1,033**	663	**784**	17	108	450	**559**	117	931	**2,226**

The periodicity during these years was less regular than the average.

The rise, a temporary recovery, in 1927 was apparently widespread, for it happened at Makkovik, Hopedale, Nain, and Okak (though not at Hebron). There seems to have been no special catastrophe in 1926 that could account for the figure being lower than the one for 1927—unless, as is reasonably possible, the change of management produced some fall-off in custom during the first year.

If the peak years are accepted to be 1921, 1925, 1927, 1931, and 1934 (the last is substantially confirmed by reports of a falling-off in 1935, though I have not the actual figure), they give a period sequence of 4, 2, 4, 3. If 1926 was not really a minimum, the sequence is 4, 6, 3. Either involves a reversal of phase in the four-year cycle, such as happened in the nineties.

4

The yardstick established, we may turn to mouse abundance in these years (noting in passing that the largest coloured fox collection ever made at these posts in 101 years was that of 1934: it was 49 per cent. greater than the next highest, which fell in 1842). Observations on the foxes are so mixed up with those on the mice that the two are tabulated together. There are three sources of information. The *Periodical Accounts* of the Moravian Missions, still full and valuable annals of life in Labrador, are supplemented by some letters received from the same missionaries in the last few years, and by some others from the Grenfell Missions farther south. There are also a few published notes by scientific explorers. Since 1925 there has been an increasing annual crop of reports from Hudson's Bay Company posts, written out in reply to a special set of questions. It is convenient to set out the missionary and explorer records in one table (43) and the Company's reports in another (44); and the greater continuity of the observations justifies a grouping by stations instead of years. Where no special reference is given, the information comes from letters, filed at Oxford.

TABLE 43

North West River (Hamilton Inlet). (Dr. H. L. Paddon, International Grenfell Association Mission.)
1930–3. '*Mice* abundant 1930. Almost extinct 1931. Increasing 1932. Abundant 1933. . . . All agree that these mice were more abundant in 1933 than in 1932 in Hamilton Inlet.'
1934–5. '*Mice* reached maximum abundance in the year ending May 1934; becoming far more local in 1934–35. Foxes reached apex in (season) 1934–35.'
Makkovik. (Rev. G. W. Sach.)
Winter, 1932–3; summer, 1933. '*Mice*, foxes and owls scarce.'
Winter, 1933–4; summer, 1934. '*Mice* normal; foxes plentiful; snowy owls more than previous year; hawks normal.'
'In some parts of the country hunted by our men, fur-bearing animals have been a little more plentiful.' (P.A.)
Winter, 1934–5; summer, 1935. '*Mice*, foxes, snowy owls less than previous year; hawks scarce.'

22

Hopedale. (Rev. W. W. Perrett.)

Summer, 1933; summer 1934. '*Mice* very numerous in 1933 and in 1934.'

Winter, 1933–4. 'Foxes have been somewhat more plentiful this year than last, though they were far from abundant.' (P.A.)

Winter, 1934–5. 'Better catch of fur than has been the case for some years.'

Inland from Davis Inlet. (Strong.[5])

June 1927–Sept. 1928. 'Like all northern regions, Labrador is subject to periodic fluctuations in the abundance of animal life and the winter of 1927–28 marked a very low ebb in the numbers of all species, resident as well as migratory. The country was lifeless beyond description, and it was not at all unusual to travel fifty or sixty miles a day in the utterly uninhabited interior and not see a single bird or animal track, let alone any living creature. In spite of constant hunting only two snowshoe rabbits and no arctic hares were killed by the Indians. Willow ptarmigan, rock ptarmigan, and spruce grouse were likewise very scarce, and the fur-bearers, as would be expected, were very rare. This lifelessness extended to the birds of prey, small birds of all sorts, squirrels and *mice*. Needless to say, the Indians were terribly pressed for food, and if several small herds of caribou had not been encountered, in addition to the trout secured in nets under the ice, many of these people would have starved to death. These periods of want are of frequent occurrence in Labrador, and the mortality from starvation among the Indians who live in the Peninsula is still quite high. Formerly, when there were no trading stations and the hostile Eskimo prevented access to the coast, their sufferings at such times were even more extreme.' (Strong travelled much in the interior, partly with the Davis Inlet band of the Nascopie Indians, while serving as a member of the Rawson-MacMillan Subarctic Expedition of the Field Museum of Chicago, during the period June 1927 to Sept. 1928.)

Nain.

1931–4. '*Mice* were scarce in 1931, more plentiful in 1932, abundant in 1934.' (Rev. F. M. Grubb.)

Winter, 1933–4. 'Foxes were a little more plentiful this season, and some of the hunters got a few; but mostly *mice* were too numerous and the foxes wouldn't take bait, so were hard to catch in traps.' (P.A.: Rev. F. M. Grubb.)

Winter, 1934–5. Good trapping season. (P.A.: Rev. F. M. Grubb.) 'During the year 1934 *wild mice* were abundant, but in 1935 they were less so. It has been noticeable that the *lemming* has disappeared. This autumn (1936) nothing has been seen of *meadow mice* or *lemmings*; the long-tailed, big eared *house mice* are however much in evidence. Foxes were most plentiful in 1934, but much less so in 1935. This autumn they are apparently numerous, but the Eskimos expect that they will migrate when the berries, which at the moment provide them with food, are covered with snow. The snowy owl is always plentiful in years when *mice* are abundant. . . . During the winter of 1934–35, while travelling, Mr. Hettasch in one day saw twelve snowy owls on sea ice.' (F. W. Peacock and Rev. P. Hettasch.)

Hebron. (Rev. George Harp.)

1929 and 1930. Very great abundance of *voles* in the summer of 1929 and winter of 1929–30. *Voles* gradually dwindled in numbers in the summer of 1930. Description of *voles* tallying with *Microtus*. 'Fox trapping has been a total failure.' (P.A. 1929–30.)

Winter, 1932–3. 'Foxes have been very, very scarce.' (P.A.)

1934–5. 'During the month of October (1934) there was great excitement among the Eskimos because there was a good sign of foxes.' (P.A.)

1935 and 1936. 'The *mice* were not very plentiful last summer (1935) but you should see them this. They are numerous: very numerous indeed, and the whole place is full of them. . . . Foxes were plentiful last fall (1935) . . . many were to be seen after the trapping season.'

5

Since 1926, when Mr. Charles V. Sale initiated the system, reports have come from a good many posts of the Hudson's Bay Company. Labrador posts did not send many until after 1932, from which date the record is fairly complete. The post manager puts down his opinion as to whether various animals have been more abundant or less abundant than in the previous year, also (a much less reliable measure) whether they have been exceptionally abundant or scarce. The Outfit is used, because it conveniently covers twelve months ending 31 May—a breeding season and a non-breeding season. Additional remarks, often of good natural history value, are added to many of the routine replies; while the whole report rests on the information gathered from others besides the manager himself, and covers usually a considerable body of observation over a wide area. In the following table I have included, in addition to the northern posts, some on Hamilton Inlet and just south of it. 'More' = 'More abundant'. 'Less' = 'Less abundant'. 'Ab.' = 'Unusually abundant'. 'Sc.' = 'Unusually scarce'. In practically every report these symbols follow closely the fur returns where coloured fox is concerned.

TABLE 44

CARTWRIGHT

Outfit	Mice		Coloured fox	
1925–6	More.	Average.	More.	Ab.
1926–7	Less.	Sc.	More.	Ab.
1927–8	Less.	Sc.	Less.	Sc.
1928–9	More.	Ab.	Less.	Sc.
1929–30	'None.'		More.	
1932–3	More.		More.	Ab.

'Foxes, though so abundant were exceedingly difficult to trap; their cunning seemed greatly increased; no fear for human tracks on trap line, but shied off from traps.'

1933–4	More.		More.	
1934–5	Less.	Sc.	More.	

'Coloured foxes: no epidemic observed, though the number of "samsons" greatly exceed the average, and several, though fully prime were the size of kitts. Something apparently affected the growth of their full winter coat. All trappers report no mice in the country.'

1935–6	Less.	Sc.	?	

'Coloured fox: better signs in the country, although all trappers report them chary of traps. Landward, scarcer than last year, only a few being caught in the fall and early spring.'

NORTH WEST RIVER

1932–3	More.		Less.

'Mice ab. on the South side of Hamilton Inlet, but not on the North.'

1933–4	More.		More.

'The foxes were reported plentiful everywhere, North and South. . . . Quite a few owls were noted during the winter, which is not usual in

Outfit	Mice	Coloured fox
	this vicinity. Mice were very plentiful in certain districts, chiefly South of the Post, along the Grand River.'	
1934–5	Less. Sc.	More. Ab.
	Epidemic in coloured foxes, Dec.–April. . . . They 'have been more ab. this Outfit than ever before at this post. . . . One of our trappers trapped about 300 . . . a feat never before heard of. . . . The total catch is also away over any other year as far as the oldest inhabitant can remember.'	
1935–6	Less. Sc. early in year. No change.	
	'Mice . . . were thought to be somewhat more ab. during the spring.'	

RIGOLET

Outfit	Mice	Coloured fox
1927–8	Less. Sc.	Less. Sc.
	Mice: epidemic Nov.–Dec.	
1932–3	More. Ab.	Less. Sc.
1933–4	More. Ab.	More. Fairly ab.
	'Mice were numerous all over the territory indicated (i.e. South to Fish Cove, North and East to Tilt Cove and Bluff Head, West to Valleys Bight and English River). . . . Coloured foxes were reported fairly plentiful all over the section, but very difficult to catch, due probably to the abundance of mice and rabbits.'	
1934–5	More. Ab.	More. Fairly ab.
1935–6	Less.	More.

MAKKOVIK

Outfit	Mice	Coloured fox
1932–3	?	Less. Sc.
1933–4	?	More. Ab.
1934–5	More. Ab.	More. Ab.
1935–6	Less. Sc.	Slightly less.

HOPEDALE

Outfit	Mice	Coloured fox
1932–3	Less. Sc.	Less. Sc.
1933–4	More. Ab.	More. Sc.
1934–5	More. Ab.	More. Ab.
1935–6	Less. Sc.	Less. Ab.

DAVIS INLET

Outfit	Mice	Coloured fox
1932–3	More. Ab.	Less. Sc.
	Coloured foxes disappeared in spring 1932.	
1933–4	More. Ab.	More. Average, not ab.
1934–5	More. Ab.	More. Ab.
	'Coloured foxes were very plentiful all through the Outfit.'	
1935–6	Less. Sc.	Less.
	'Foxes were very fat all the year round. . . . Putting in a good appearance in April and May (1936).'	

NAIN

Outfit	Mice	Coloured fox
1932–3	More. Ab.	Less. Sc.
1933–4	More. Ab.	More. Ab.
	'Due no doubt to the abundance of lemming and wild mice, it was found very hard to get the foxes to take bait of any description.'	
1934–5	Less. Sc.	More. Ab.

NAIN (*cont.*)

Outfit	Mice	Coloured fox
1935–6	Less. Sc.	Less. Sc.

'In early fall signs of coloured fox were numerous; but as winter wore on, they gradually disappeared. . . . In early spring, just after trapping was over, it was observed that there was a trek of the foxes to the outside land, in fact they were apparently more numerous at that time than they had been all winter.'

NUTAK (OKAK)

Outfit	Mice	Coloured fox
1932–3	Less.	Sc.
1933–4	More.	More.
1934–5	Less.	More. Ab.

'Foxes seen towards the close of the Outfit looked to be in very poor condition and noticeably without any great amount of pep.'

1935–6	More. Ab.	Less. Sc.

'Two coloured foxes were picked up dead during the month of May.'

HEBRON

Outfit	Mice	Coloured fox
1932–3	(See note.)	Less. Sc.

'Lemming and wild mice excessively scarce during winter, but reported to be plentiful during spring 1933.'

1933–4	More. Ab.	More. Ab.

'The cycle is on the up grade.'

1934–5	More. Ab.	More.
1935–6	More. Ab.	Less. Sc.

6

We can now compare mouse abundance with the years of plenty among coloured foxes. The first way of comparison is to tabulate the peak years shown in the catch of coloured foxes for Northern Labrador side by side with the recorded years of 'mouse' abundance (or scarcity, shown in brackets) along that same stretch of coast. For several reasons it is convenient to take the region from Hopedale (in the later years from Makkovik) to Okak. In omitting Hebron on the north and Hamilton Inlet on the south, we reduce the materials a little. But there is reason for thinking that the central stretch of country is more homogeneous, and we already have its fur catch tabulated in Table 17. For the years 1926–34 the peaks already described are not altered by subtracting Hebron. Accepting 1934 as a fox-fur peak we can use all the records from 1834 to 1936. It has to be realized that 'mouse abundance' does not necessarily mean the *maximum* abundance in a cycle of voles. Where the record is isolated we have to accept it at its face value. But in recent times there are often sequences of records which enable us to define the peak year: here only the peak is used. The Mission and Company reports are not entered twice, provided they agree at the same place. If they disagree each is allotted half a unit, in order that statistical justice may be maintained. The results ought at any rate to give some notion whether high fox catches go with 'mouse' abundance.

TABLE 45

Fox peaks (fur returns)	'Mouse abundance' (or scarcity)
1835	..
..	1837
..	1838
1839	..
..	1841
1842	..
1844	..
..	1846
1847	..
1851	..
...	1853
1855	..
1859	..
1863	..
1867	..
1872	..
..	1874
1875	1875
1880	..
1883	..
1886	..
..	1888
1890	..
1895	..
1901	..
..	(1903)
..	1904 (2 records)
1905	1905 (2 records)
..	(1906)
..	1908 (2 records)
1909	1909
..	(1910)
..	1913
1914	..
..	1916
1917	1917
..	1920
1922	..
..	1924 (2 records)
1925	1925
..	*1926
1927	(1927) (1927*)
..	(1928)
1931	(1931)
..	(1932, 2 records)
..	1933 (2 records)
1934	1934 (3 records) (1934, 1·5 records)
..	(1935, 3·5 records)
..	(1936)

7

A condensation of these lists of dates is given in Tables 46, where the frequency of mouse abundance and scarcity records is summed in relation to the peaks of the fox cycles, '0' being used for the peak year, '—1' for the year before, and so on.*

TABLE 46

'*Mouse Abundance*' (*chiefly peaks*)

Years	.	.	.	—2	—1	0	+1	+2
Number	.	.	.	2·5	14	9	0	1·5
Frequency%	.	.	**9·3**	**51·8**	**33·3**	**0**	**5·6**

'*Mouse Scarcity*'

Years	.	.	.	—2	—1	0	+1	+2
Number	.	.	.	0·5	0	3·5	8·5	1·5
Frequency%	.	.	**3·6**	**0**	**25·0**	**60·7**	**10·7**

When we remember that these figures are the sum of a number of separately and carefully recorded historical events, their fewness assumes less importance than if, let us say, they were the casual tossings of a penny 27 or 14 times. I mean that the errors in each set of observations are probably small, so that correlation between them is justifiable. The truth of this contention stands out from the lists of dates, where the relation of mouse abundance to the fox-fur peak and the year before it is shown again and again. This repetition of a characteristic grouping gives great additional strength to the relationship shown by the summarized percentages.

One feature of this relationship is of singular importance. The majority of mouse abundance years come *one year before* the peak in fox-fur returns. The next largest percentage is in the same year as the fox peak; but also in this year come some records of mouse scarcity, although the latter are mainly one year later.

This discrepancy can be explained in two ways. It may be due to local variations in the occurrence of peaks, which would give a fictitious impression in the summarized figures. This occurs to a small extent, as anyone can find out from the tables already given. The other explanation is that foxes are caught in larger numbers when they are starving, and so enter willingly into traps for the sake of the bait. I believe this to be a master factor influencing the fur returns, and it is supported by three different bits of evidence.

First we have the repeatedly expressed regrets that foxes avoid the traps when mice are abundant. We find this mentioned in several places, in various years: Ramah, 1874; Okak, 1904; Nain, 1908, 1917, 1920, 1924, 1933; Hopedale, 1909, 1916, 1924; Davis Inlet, 1904; Makkovik, 1925;

* Weed's observations at Nain, 1926–8, given on p. 324, were found too late to include in Table 45. They agree with the results.

Rigolet, 1933. The same observation was made by Captain Cartwright[5b] on 15 March 1779: 'Great plenty of foxes had been going everywhere, but the traps were all drifted up, and they kill such plenty of grass mice, that they are not very eager for dead baits.' These are enough to knock out any suggestions that the hypothesis comes from one person only. It is, to put it at the lowest, a widespread conclusion from field experience.

The second line of evidence runs through the more recent reports, in which a sequence of one or two cycles can be followed at several posts. In a majority the foxes are clearly reported still abundant, and usually to have increased, a year after mice have become scarce. If we accept the reports as, on the whole, reliable estimates, the phenomenon seems real enough.

There is a third fact which probably plays an important part in the abundant phase of the fox-fur cycle. It was shown in an earlier chapter that Labrador foxes are taken both with the gun and the trap. On the relative importance of these two methods would depend whether the peak fell in the 'mouse year', when more are shot; or in the year after, when the traps are filled.

8

The evidence that we have collected so far—the casual notes of a hundred years, built during the last decade into a fairly regular system of observation—leaves us with some assurance that Cabot's description of the mouse cycle and its results is fairly drawn. There is a cycle in wild life; it has some regularity; its period varies around four years; the foxes and martens have it; the ebb and flow is real; it has gone on for 100 years; it is regional and often coincides over many hundred miles of country; with it go vole fluctuations; the foxes follow these; the peak year of foxes often comes in the year after that of the mice; but not always: they sometimes coincide.

This is the outline that we have sought to establish. Some of it is solid fact. The rest we may best treat as a sound working hypothesis—to repeat Cabot's remark: 'We can only put together first coincidences at sight, leaving further observation to determine certainties.'

Several points of weakness require special testing. In particular, we have only the barest information about the voles. What density do they reach? What are their breeding seasons, sex ratios, reproductive rates, and length of life? What variation in these from year to year? What is life like for a rodent in winter, under 10 feet of snow? What parasites and diseases? Which month does the decrease come in? What kills the voles? What food is normal? Do they make stores of food? How many voles to an acre is needed by a fox? Ask all these questions for the fox and marten, and the field for scientific research expands. The fox has disease. Does this come from the voles to the fox? The dogs too. Do they get ill through the fox or the vole or the lemming? What cycles in weather? How far afield do these act, and whence their mainspring of periodicity? Does the ice go with the weather along this coast?

Further enlightenment must come through the research of at least one trained ecologist, living in Labrador, and adopting for Labrador problems the technique and ideas that are being developed for vole research in England, Russia, and the United States. The time is past when research on the living fabric of the world can be pursued only in the organized and calm routine of central places of learning, or by passing expeditions. Population research will take its place with astronomy and meteorology; and it will become as natural to maintain ecologists in Labrador, as it is to maintain six stations on latitude 39° 08′ N. in order to measure the earth's period of nutation; or the high Arctic weather stations in Siberia. This leaves another cat to be belled.

9

We have hunted the fox through several chapters, but the reader will have detected a preponderant and underlying interest in voles and mice. I hoped to be able to use the fox as an indicator of Labrador voles, for correlation with European cycles. Although the fox figures give a reliable *general guide* to the populations of fox and vole, there is the difficulty that the peak year in fur is *not an absolute index of maximum population*. It may be the peak, or the year before. Occasionally it may mislead altogether. This must be realized when correlation is attempted. We already have something from England, Scandinavia, and Labrador. There is more to come from the Canadian Eastern Arctic before the assembly of North Atlantic voles, mice, lemmings, and foxes is complete.

Apart from the fox cycle, and the hints and observations contained in Cabot's essay, we know almost as little about the consequences of the vole cycle as we do about its causes. This outburst of mouse meat undoubtedly spreads a feast for the predatory birds and animals, and must have some effect upon their survival, and perhaps upon their reproductive efficiency and, in the case of mammals, the qualities of their fur. And the richness of this natural food supply may affect the willingness of wolverines and wolves and other fur-bearers to take the bait in traps, as it seems to do with the foxes.

All these radiating chains of influence need to be studied, and it is not to be forgotten that some of the causes of the vole cycle may act directly on carnivorous species. For instance, climate may alter the efficiency of breeding in certain years. The periodically high density of fur-bearers itself probably has consequences of a far-reaching kind. One is the appearance of disease in foxes and in sledge-dog teams, believed (though not yet scientifically proved) to spread long distances by the migrations of the first and the normal journeyings of the latter. This subject is treated in Chapter XXII, and I will here only mention the belief among Eskimos, both in Labrador and Baffin Island, that wolves and even caribou are hit by the same epidemic that affects the foxes and sledge dogs. Whether such wide mortality arises from the spread of infection or from some physiological deficiency due to starvation or lack of essential protective food factors, it would be eventually traceable to the mouse cycle.

10

The last suggestion receives some support from Hutton's observations[4] on 'kallak', a pustular eruption of the skin that the Labrador Eskimos get in certain years. His study was made at Okak Mission Hospital in 1904–6. The disease, to have a special native word applied to it, must have broken out at intervals for many years. Hutton says (p. 9): 'The Eskimo is a meat eater: the vegetable part of his diet is a meagre one. Be ries ripen in profusion on the hillsides in the autumn, but only the small black watery berry, *Empetrum nigrum*, is eaten to any extent by the natives. These berries are gathered by the Eskimos into bags and barrels and allowed to freeze for a winter store. In spring the buds of the *Sedum roseum* and the young shoots of the willow, *Salix argyrocarpa*, are gathered and eaten.' He adds that the people grow no vegetables, and only a few of them shared the Mission garden produce. *Empetrum* is what we call the crowberry: it is common enough on our own hills, and in the Arctic regions it comes farther north than other berries, and is found all over the barren grounds of Canada. High in the Arctic, however, as in North Greenland and the remote islands of the Canadian Arctic archipelago, it loses the capacity to bear ripe fruit and can no longer live.

'In the years 1904–5 the berry crop failed, presumably because the mice and lemmings had eaten the young shoots; and during those two years this valuable constituent was absent from the dietary' (p. 20).

The outbreak of kallak began in October 1905, and was also noticed at the same time at other points along the coast. Its symptoms may be read in detail in Dr. Hutton's book. He was able to prove that it was not true scurvy, or scabies (a mite-caused skin itch); or any of the ordinary contagious diseases that affect the skin (this outbreak was strictly limited to the natives), and he concluded that it was due to food factor deficiency, and that the voles had ultimately caused this by eating down the crowberry plants. If man can suffer, so also may reindeer and ptarmigan. Perhaps even the meat of the voles themselves may vary in richness, and influence the life chances and reproductive rates of predators.

11

The vole cycle profoundly influences some predatory birds, as the quotation from Cabot has already described. These changes are reflected in the southward migrations of several species, recorded by naturalists in southeastern Canada and north-eastern United States. In Chapter XXII we shall see how the snowy owl (*Nyctea nyctea*) flocks down periodically from the Arctic, at intervals corresponding with those of the arctic fox (and therefore lemming) cycle. The owls appear in greater numbers on southward winter migration at times when their food is scarce in the north.

There is some good information also about two other predatory birds, connected with the zone in which Northern Labrador lies: the northern shrike (*Lanius borealis*)—a forest species; and the rough-legged hawk or buzzard (*Archibuteo lagopus*)—a bird of the barren grounds. The northern shrike is scarce enough in ordinary winters for its southward incursions to be easily recognized. Shrikes or butcher-birds are a family of Passerine birds that have taken to a predatory life, catching and killing small birds and mammals, as well as insects, and often impaling the prey on thorny bushes to form a larder. Taverner[5a] remarks: 'Shrikes are bold and spirited and quite as daring and capable in proportion to their size as any of the true birds of prey.'

The summer quarters of the northern shrike are in the northern conifer forest belt, but a certain number migrate southwards in the winter and turn up in cultivated country, and even in villages and towns, where they have been seen to prey (to the satisfaction of American farmers) on the introduced English house-sparrow. The breeding range stretches across Canada, and includes that part of Quebec Peninsula which is mainly covered by coniferous woods. The species is found, for instance, around Hamilton Inlet.

Davis[3a] used as an index of shrike incursions the results of winter census counts done in the north-eastern United States. This species cannot be confused in winter with the only other American shrike, the loggerhead shrike (*Lanius ludovicianus*), which at that season has moved farther south. The basis of the evidence for periodicity is the Christmas Bird Census, organized by the American journal *Bird Lore*, partly as a means of interesting naturalists in bird populations and partly as an attempt to make a standard record in many districts on the same day. Davis does not say exactly from what area his figures are derived, indicating simply the north-eastern States. Also he combines with them, without giving an analysis of the details, another Christmas census for the years 1900–10, done by the Maine Ornithological Club. We are, in fact, given the elements of the recipe, without the exact quantities of each. The results are shown as the number of individual northern shrikes seen per census. These range from about 'half a shrike' to eleven. Within this range there is a very strongly pronounced periodicity, which evidently has some validity, because it is based on a large number of different censuses covering a fairly wide area of country.

This record is confirmed by a certain number of observations made on earlier shrike incursions. For instance, one naturalist notes that in the district of Cambridge, Massachusetts, shrikes were abundant in 1901, but scarce in 1902, 1903, 1904. This Davis takes as proving that the small hump in his curve for 1903–4 did not indicate a real peak. It is certain, in any case, that the earlier census figures are less reliable than the later ones.

All the peak years, except the one in 1903–4, correspond with years of abundance of voles in Northern Labrador already discussed, or at least (where the vole evidence is meagre) of corresponding abundance in the enemies of voles like the fox. Since the northern shrike depends partly on mice and voles for food, it seems very likely that the southern emigrations are caused by the crash of the northern cycle. Davis makes this correlation, with the aid of the cycle in arctic fox at Fort Chimo, cited by Gross and discussed in Chapter XX. These dates, used by Gross, as will be shown there, represent in most cases the real peak years of the arctic fox population in the region of Ungava. But since the shrike is not an Arctic bird, it is better to compare its migrations with the cycle in Northern Labrador foxes living in the same forested or semi-forested region. We can now also compare them with the more limited records of vole years in Northern Labrador.

12

Speirs[4b] has analysed the rich records accumulated by the Royal Ontario Museum of Zoology's observers, and finds in them evidence of periodicity in certain birds arriving in winter in the Toronto Region. His periodicities are worked out from the number of records of occurrence, partly amplified by actual numbers of individuals seen. He does not give the actual data on which the years of cycle are based, but the years for the northern shrike invasions agree closely with those of Davis.

TABLE 47

Coloured fox peak N. Labrador	Northern shrike invasion		Great vole abundance (and scarcity) N. Labrador
	Toronto	NE. United States	
1890	1889–90	..	..
1895	1895–6	..	..
1901	1900–1	1900–1	..
..	..	..	(1903)
1905	1904–5	..	1904, 1905
..	1905–6	1905–6	(1906)
1909	1908–9	1909–10	1908, 1909
..	..	..	(1910)
1914	1914–15	1913–14	1913
1917	..	1917–18	1916, 1917
1922	1921–2	1921–2	1920
1925	1926–7	1926–7	1924, 1925, 1927
..	..	..	(1927, 1928)
1931	1930–1	1930–1	..
..	..	..	(1931, 1932)
1934	1935–6	1934–5	1933, 1934
..	..	1935–6	(1934, 1935, 1936)

Allowing for the facts that the peak years shown in the fur returns do not always represent the actual peak in population, and that the years of vole abundance are not all confirmed by subsequent scarcity as being the actual peaks, there is a very strong agreement between the shrikes and the voles. The conclusion we draw is that the shrike invasions in the south occur in the winter after a vole abundance in Northern Labrador and (where the records exist to prove this) before a vole scarcity. In other words, the birds do migrate when their food has disappeared, or become unavailable during the winter—or at least that is what it looks like. The correlation cannot be absolutely proved until continuous field studies have been done in the North. But even as a correlation, the cycle is of great interest, and shrike invasions could certainly be used as a very valuable index of the state of the rodent cycle in the northern forests. One proviso should be made: we have no direct proof that the shrikes that visit New England come from Quebec Peninsula, since the range of the northern shrike extends to Alaska. The four-year cycle in voles may be found to have a wider extension, and the need for marking experiments is again obvious. But it seems a reasonable assumption that a large number of these shrikes come from Quebec Peninsula, and that the vole cycle there controls this movement, and probably also the building up of fresh shrike populations in each cycle. How many shrikes return north again we do not know.

Davis points out that the average cycle since 1900 is 4·2 years, and that the length of this cycle is greater than in earlier years (as indicated by the Ungava arctic foxes). This greater length is brought about by having fewer three-year intervals, and more four or five. But we can equally pick out a series of years between 1847 and 1880, when the Labrador red fox cycle was on the average 4·2. Although it is probable that there are real changes from time to time in the length of the cycle, I do not propose to analyse this problem any further here.

13

Speirs also has some records for the rough-legged buzzard. Of this bird Taverner says: 'It is a mouse-hawk *par excellence*', and mentions that 40 out of 45 stomachs examined contained mice. It nests on the northern barren grounds right across the continent, and is almost entirely a winter visitor to southern Canada. In the Toronto Region there were peak numbers seen in 1917–18, 1926–7, 1930–1, 1934–5, and 1937–8. These again correspond in general with the Labrador cycle.

Speirs makes the important point that such peak years may be caused by two different things. There may be abnormal exodus of shrikes or buzzards from the north (or they may fly abnormally far south) in certain winters when their food is scarce or inaccessible. But there is also a cycle in their numbers through natural increase, so that there will be more birds actually present, and therefore more to be noticed, on migration in the peak years. Probably both these things occur together.

Although we know so little about the nature of this cycle in Labrador, we can define its geographical distribution a little further: which brings us to a consideration of wild-life cycles in Ungava.

REFERENCES

* indicates that an abstract is deposited in the library of the Bureau of Animal Population, Oxford. H. B. Co. = Hudson's Bay Company.

1. ANDERSON, R. M. (1934). 'Mammals of the Eastern Arctic and Hudson Bay.' In 'Canada's Eastern Arctic'. Ottawa. pp. 67–108.
2. BANGS, O. (1897). 'On a small collection of mammals from Hamilton Inlet, Labrador.' Proc. Biol. Soc. Washington, 11: 235–40.
3. DAVIS, D. E. (1936). 'Status of *Microtus enixus* and *Microtus terraenovae*.' J. Mammal. 17: 290–1.
3 a. DAVIS, D. E. (1937). 'A cycle in northern shrike emigrations.' Auk, 54: 43–9.
4. HUTTON, S. K. (1912). 'Among the Eskimos of Labrador.' London. p. 285.
4 a. HUTTON, S. K. (n.d.). 'Health conditions and disease incidence among the Eskimos of Labrador.' Poole.
4 b. Speirs, J. Murray (1939). 'Fluctuations in numbers of birds in the Toronto Region.' Auk, 56: 411–19.
5. STRONG, W. D. (1930). 'Notes on mammals of the Labrador interior.' J. Mammal. 11: 1–10.
5 a. TAVERNER, P. A. (1928). 'Birds of Western Canada.' Bull. Nat. Mus. Canada, No. 41.
5 b. TOWNSEND, C. W. (1911). 'Captain Cartwright and his Labrador Journal.' London. p. 260.
*6. Davis Inlet Post, Journals, 1869–1909 (incomplete). MS. H. B. Co. Archives, London.
*7. H. B. Co., Fur Returns for Labrador Posts (Makkovik, Hopedale, Nain, Nutak, Hebron), 1926–34. MS. H. B. Co. Archives, Winnipeg.
*8. Nachvack Post (Esquimaux Bay District), Journals, 1868–1905 (incomplete). MS. H. B. Co. Archives, London.
*9. Periodical Accounts of the Moravian Missions, London.

WILD-LIFE CYCLES IN UNGAVA

CHAPTER XVII

THE UNGAVA SCENE

1

FORT CHIMO, trading post of the Hudson's Bay Company, stands on the east bank of the Koksoak River, twenty-seven miles from where it flows into Ungava Bay,[14a(1)] and is 'surrounded by a country that presents as complete a picture of desolation as can be imagined'.[10(1)] The first of the Company's ships, the *Nonesuch*, passed through Hudson Straits in 1668, to establish Rupert's House on Hudson Bay. But, although ships went every year through Hudson Straits, it was over 140 years before Ungava was visited by any white man.

In the beginning of the nineteenth century missionaries and traders began to explore Ungava Bay, which previously had been avoided because of its uncharted sunken reefs, its huge range of tides, and treacherous swift currents. Low estimated a mean rise and fall of tide of 40 feet in the bay, with some spring tides as high as 60 feet.[7 (1)] At Fort Chimo itself the usual rise and fall, so Turner records, is 10 feet, and sometimes up to 31.[14a(2)]

Up to 1931 the biggest island in the bay, Akpatok, a cliff-bound, barren mass of limestone forming one of the prominent features of the bay, had only once been visited voluntarily by any white man, and then only for a few hours. When it was charted by English explorers in that year, the existing map was found to have no relation to the island's real shape or size.[2]

We have here a region, as yet hardly mapped at all, except by the rough traverses of occasional explorers, yet offering a rich store of archives from which its wild-life fluctuations can be pieced together. Fort Chimo forms the central point of these studies. The Ungava wild-life cycles require as a background some history of this post, its native customers, its fur-bearing animals, and the fortunes of its trade. We shall here encounter similarity with the elements that have already been described for Labrador: Ungava is the northern sector of the general background that was outlined in those chapters. Repetition of these features will so far as possible be avoided, except when we come to consideration and analysis of their influence on one another.

There is an observation by Andrew Graham[4] (whose 'Notes on Hudson's Bay', written in 1768, have never been published) that explains the meaning of Fort Chimo's name. Of the Eskimos he says: 'When they discover the sloop, they come off to us in canoes, whooping and making a frightful noise, and when they come along side they rub their breast with their open hand, calling in a pitiful tone Chimo! Chimo!, which is a sign of peace and friendship.' It is good to know that the fur trade did afterwards bring some peace to this people, for it stopped much of the traditional fighting between Indians and Eskimos, also some of the tribal feuds within each race.

For the history of Ungava there are five chief sources. John McLean, a Hudson's Bay Company factor who combined great energy, endurance, and skill with a somewhat polemical disposition, and who discovered the Grand Falls on the Hamilton River in Labrador, and published a spirited record of his life in the fur trade.[10] The first-hand observations of Low,[7, 8, 9] geologist and traveller, and of Turner,[14, 14a] ethnologist for two years in Ungava; the compiled history of posts by White;[16] and a number of unpublished archives of the Company examined by myself (see Chapter XIII), give the chief information on the subject. The papers of the Labrador Boundary Dispute provide a little further material.

2

In 1811 two Moravian missionaries, Kohlmeister and Kmoch, moving northwards among the uncharted heathen Eskimos, explored Ungava Bay and reported well of it.[7(2)] As a result of this report the Company, under the driving energy of its new Governor, George Simpson, laid plans for trade.[10(2)] It was not until about 1824 that the expedition was arranged, and it did not get away until 1828, when Dr. William Hendry struck inland from Hudson Bay and made the first official traverse of Ungava Peninsula. (This journey is said to have been the basis of R. M. Ballantyne's book *Ungava*.)

Low saw Hendry's sketch-map at Moose Factory and made a copy for the Geological Survey; but he had not seen the narrative,[19(3)] which is preserved in the London Archives of the Company. Hendry made his way from Moose Factory to Richmond Gulf in June, through various difficulties of wind and ice. His Indian guides were afraid of meeting Eskimos, but were persuaded to go on.

The route is described by Indian names, but the sequence, and Low's interpretation, show that the party ascended to Clearwater Lake, making twenty-two portages to do it. From there they got across to Seal Lake and into the North or Larch Branch of the Koksoak River. On 14 July they had reached tidal water coming from Ungava Bay, and saw white whales and seals, but no natives of any kind, only some traces of Eskimos.

At this time a racial feud still separated the Eskimos and Indians. Hendry reported:

'Having seen no recent traces of Indians I cannot think there is any likelihood of a Post near the mouth of the River being visited to advantage by this class of people; in this part of the country the population cannot be so numerous as must have been imagined, otherwise in some situation or other we must surely have met with greater proofs. Mr. Atkinson has frequently expressed that to his knowledge and the opportunity he has had of acquiring information Indians are scarce throughout the country and believes there are very few but who either visit the Company's Posts in person or send in their furs by others, and such as do not are mostly superannuate for active labors. He also acquaints me that the Indians personally known to himself and who frequently resort to Nepeethjee and parts of the country southd. seldom now go beyond the height of land to the eastward.'

Hendry also made a few notes on the woods, the scarcity (during his traverse) of caribou, the river trout, the signs of porcupine-eaten trees, of foxes and partridges. Although he saw only one deer, the numerous wolves and wolverines were evidence of large herds, which had probably passed to the northern coast for the summer.

3

Hendry did no more than prospect the country, and he returned almost immediately to Hudson Bay, which was reached on 20 July. His report was not particularly encouraging, but it proved the existence of natural resources. In 1830 a more solid expedition set out to establish a trading post. This time Nichol Finlayson was in charge.[19(4)] He had to make the same route as Hendry, and was to be met in Ungava Bay by the Company's supply ship, *Montcalm*. There was the same series of difficulties, made worse by the dry state of the Clearwater River:

'We carried through it over portages sometimes in deer paths, sometimes over rocky hills and ravines where there is scarcely footing for the rein deer which browze on them. I own that I had serious thoughts of returning here, my party were getting crippled in the portages and the Indians refusing to proceed at every point; but the N.E. expedition since first it became a subject of conversation was looked upon with much terror in the Southern Department by the labouring class. Had I failed in this attempt I knew it would be a death blow to it, at least in making another attempt from that quarter. Therefore I determined to proceed and succeed or perish in the attempt.'

The party arrived at the Koksoak River site on 1 August, and set to work at once. By 1 September, four houses were built from wood rafted down the river. By 13 September the ship seemed overdue. 'We were beginning to look with terror on the barren rocks that surround us when blessed be the Father of Mercies, the Brig appeared in the River and dispelled all our doubts and fears.'

Finlayson had already met some Eskimos:

'I have only seen two parties of Esquimeaux consisting of about ten families; but as they had visited *Okkak*, the nearest Missionary Settlement, in the course of the sumr., [they] had nothing to trade. Our meeting was friendly in the extreme and when I told them by the interpreter that they would be supplied with every necessary for furs, oil etc. etc. their joy was unbounded. Foxes they say, of colour as well as white, are plentiful, but the fear of meeting any of the Inland Indians prevents them from going into the Interior in search of other fur animals.'

They also told him that: 'Foxes of all colours are here, but the white in greater numbers, but for want of traps they cannot kill many of them.'

These Eskimos were those that Kohlmeister and Kmoch wrote about: 'Some of the Ungava people have come to Okkak, and carry on a trade between their countrymen and that place. They are a kind of middle men, bring fox and bearskins, and exchange them for European goods. These they carry back, and sell at a very advanced price in the Ungava country. They spend two years on such a trading voyage.'

We see here the early stage of that process which gradually drew all the natives of Ungava into a vital dependence on the fur trade. Hendry mentions finding a cache of things left by the Eskimos. Among them were iron barbed arrows, an iron-pronged fish spear, and 'a fine British-made clasp knife, half worn and the haft set with mother of pearl or imitation'.

But there were other native bands still unversed in fur trading. In 1832–3 Finlayson wrote[18(1)] that 'the Esquimeaux from Cape Hopes Advance to Richmond do not at present hunt any foxes except for the purpose of ornamenting their clothing; but were they aware of a market to take these to, they would undoubtedly preserve them for market'. And there was much searching before the first Indians were encountered, in September 1831.[18(1)]

The trade, such as it was, developed quickly. In 1838, McLean relates,[10(3)] some Eskimos arrived at Fort Chimo with fox skins, who had been nearly two years on the way. The Indians also scoured their inland hunting grounds for fox and marten. And yet the project bore heavy losses, and staggered under difficulties of supply that caused it to be abandoned after eleven years of effort. In 1842 McLean evacuated Fort Chimo,[10(4)] which was not reoccupied until 1866.

4

Although this book is not a history of trade and posts and exploration, but is focused on population changes in wild life, it is impossible entirely to separate the history from the animals, since history created the conditions under which the observations and records of animal life were made. And, although we cannot reconstruct for this early period any complete account of wild-life cycles, the notes that the traders left are very vivid and interesting to the ecologist, and help to explain the origins from which the later, rejuvenated fur trade grew.

Apart from economic factors at head-quarters and in the home market, which cannot be followed here, the overriding difficulty of maintaining Fort Chimo at that early date was in supplying it and taking out the furs each year. Sometimes a ship called only every second year. The main supply ships of the Bay never risked a call; if any ship came, it had to be chartered specially or extend the range of the Labrador round of visits. Such special shipping was costly, and we find Simpson constantly goading his traders to establish an inland route, by which the furs and stores could be moved from Fort Chimo annually to and from Hamilton Inlet (then known as Esquimaux Bay). 'That difficulty', he wrote[19(1)] in 1837, 'will be in great measure removed by supplying it [Fort Chimo] from Esquimaux Bay through inland navigation, the distance not exceeding 4 to 500 miles. . . . This mode of transport must be continued until the trade of [the] District becomes sufficiently important to send a vessel there every second year.'

Obediently following these instructions, the Fort Chimo men performed a series of extraordinary journeys through the hinterland of Ungava and Labrador, reaching Hamilton Inlet several times. Considering how few white men have ever travelled successfully in that country, we can only be astonished at the journeys these men made in the ordinary course of their trading business.

Their travels were not done without excessive hardship. They established several important facts. A man might go from Chimo to North West River; and canoes could make the journey owing to the endless rivers and lakes that seam the plateau, but, heavily laden with stores, their transit was almost an impossibility, owing to shallow water and rapids. It was also found that both Indians and beavers were scarce inland, and that sources of 'country provisions' in fish and fowl and game were erratic and often meagre. One of the most important discoveries of this period was that of the Grand Falls above Hamilton Inlet, by McLean.

During this early pioneering time the traders established several posts in the interior, but none of them prospered. They were chiefly built on the two main highways for canoes: the Koksoak and George's Rivers. The Company's men at Hamilton Inlet were pushing inland also, and Fort Nascopie, established in 1840 on the high land between Ungava and the Hamilton River basin, survived after the northern posts had been abandoned. The details of these early posts have little direct importance here. They formed, however, the framework of a district organization that was to be built up again in later years. And the journeys described by Finlayson, Erlandson, McLean, and Kennedy supplied the first reconnaissance of the land.[18, 19]

The people at the fort seem to have traded almost entirely furs, deerskins, and eiderdown from the natives, since the irregularity of the supply ship made any idea of exporting fish and the oil of whales impossible. The trade fluctuated with the cycles of abundance and migration of wild animals, and with the rather erratic visits of the natives, especially the Indians. For these natives did not regularly attach themselves to the post, but roved also to Esquimaux Bay, and even to Seven Islands and Mingan (on the Gulf of St. Lawrence).

In Outfit 1835 the fur returns included a large fraction brought in by visiting Indians from Eastmain on the coast of Hudson Bay. In Outfit 1837, McLean records[18(3)] that 'for some time past the Trade has been on the decline in consequence of the defection of the inland Indians, two thirds of the tribe having entirely abandoned this part of the country and gone across to Esquimaux Bay, where they traded to much greater advantage to themselves than at this place. However, there exists no difference between the tariffs at present and the natives have all returned to the District. . . .'

5

We can now see pretty clearly some of the reasons why the first assault on Ungava failed: no regular supply ship, an intractable hinterland, native tribes unused to trade and still nomadic to a high degree, the hazard of living on country food, no profit to be made from the sea's resources. Finally, perhaps a strong human factor—the mistaken persistence of head-quarters irritating McLean's impatient, practical mind.

And yet Fort Chimo combined, from the point of view of fur-trade strategy, impressive advantages. Like Hamilton Inlet, Ungava Bay was an avenue for ships far into the country. The Koksoak River was huge enough to receive a fairly large ship up to Chimo (indeed, the name Koksoak means Big River). The fort was on the borders of two native territories, each rich in its own way, giving variety and therefore greater stability to the trade. To the north were Eskimos, from whom came the larger hunts of white fox. South were Indian lands, from which came martens and other inland furs.

In the rivers within reach of the fort were rich supplies of salmon and other fish, and white whales—giving a summer seasonal industry which could alternate with winter trapping. Inland were huge herds of caribou, erratic it is true, but followed by nomad Indians. Southward also was timber, mostly of use for fuel, which could be rafted down the river.

A place that combined so many strategic advantages for the trade could not long remain unused. The next promoter of the scheme was Donald A. Smith (better known as Lord Strathcona), then one of the Company's traders on Labrador,[16] but who later promoted still greater strategy in his planning of the Canadian Pacific Railway. As a result of his representations the steamer *Labrador* was built for the Labrador and Ungava trade,[14a(3)] and Fort Chimo was re-established by Joseph MacPherson on 29 September 1866.[20]

Trade almost at once revived quite briskly, both with the Indians and the Eskimos, and Turner in 1894 was able to write[14a(3)] that 'since 1866 the post has been a paying station, and in later years a good profit has been made'. The chief reason for this change was that the visiting ship could now take home supplies of oil and salted (even a little frozen) fish, which greatly swelled the total of returns[1,21]. In prosecuting these new lines of trade, outposts were soon opened at George's River (the old Fort Sivewright) and Whale River, where posts have operated up to recent times.

A letter from P. McKenzie, manager of Fort Chimo in 1886,[21(1)] gives some account of the outposts or stations. George's River was 'established principally for salmon and seal fishing. . . . Trade with Esquimaux does not amount to much, and I do not want the Indians to go there.' The Forks was a hunting post in winter and used for wood-cutting. It lay seventy miles south of Chimo, at the same place as the old South River House.

Whale River, thirty miles overland and sixty miles by water from the Fort, also had no fur trade. 'This River does not freeze over until about the end of January. . . . The only business there [is] to be the catching of and curing of salmon, whale fishing . . . and hunting in winter. There is no trade. . . . We fished whales there this season for the first time and got ninety.'

The salmon and trout fisheries have gone on up to the present day. (Ungava is about the farthest point that the Atlantic salmon go to on migration from the sea, but trout come abundantly also in rivers to the west.[1a, 7(3)])

The whaling did not do so well, and it was believed that the white whales gradually became so shy that it was too difficult to drive them into the nets. H. M. S. Cotter, in a special report on Ungava posts in 1910–11[22(1)], summed up the whaling situation as follows: 'At one time we carried on a white whale or porpoise fishery at Ungava, Leaf River, and Whale River, but the whales got killed out, and very shy [sic], and the business became unprofitable.'

6

The records I have examined (a fairly complete assortment of journals, correspondence, reports, and fur returns from 1866 to 1928) leave no doubt that, up to 1908, Fort Chimo was the sole important fur trading-post of the Company in this region. Between 1866 and 1908 there was, with the exception of Revillons' competition, to be discussed later, no change in the distribution of Ungava posts. From Cape Wolstenholme in the west, to beyond George's River in the east, practically all the fur bartered by the Company from Eskimos was traded at Fort Chimo. A small amount came in from the outpost at George's River, but these returns were usually included with those of the parent post.

If one could get the fur returns for Fort Chimo and also those for Revillons, it seemed that one would be able to combine them into an index of cycles for the whole Ungava region during these earlier years. But there is a very important proviso that has to be made here. The furs that came in depended on somewhat irregular movements of native hunters, and their irregularity operated in two cumulative ways. In the first place, any particular band of hunters did not always come in every year, and secondly, the furs that they brought were not always caught in the same localities. Such variability in the provenance and delivery of the furs is a serious error that has to be treated in a later chapter. It is best discussed when the notes on abundance (got by the traders from these visiting hunters) are reviewed.

These considerations show that 'Ungava District', in spite of the bleak solidity of its topographical shape, in reality fluctuated somewhat according to the hunting ranges of native tribes that visited the central post. The trade had not the constancy that we saw in the faithful Eskimo congregations of the Moravian Labrador coast. But as the years went on, the natives must have settled more and more firmly into regular trading relations. One factor was the disappearance of disturbance due to tribal feuds.

Another was the growing dependence of natives on the white man's things
—ammunition, tools, nets, blankets, flour, and tea. The big ship became
an annual event of tremendous interest. And missionaries, invading
Ungava, also contributed a stable element. In 1884 the Rev. E. J. Peck,
of the Church Missionary Society, paid a flying visit in order to convert the
people of Ungava.[11] By 1897 the Eskimos at Fort Chimo were holding,
on their own initiative, three church meetings on a Sunday.[20(1)]

The Indians did not become so easily christianized. The Chimo Journal
for 11 June 1899 gives a pleasant picture of a summer Sunday there:
'Barometer risen since yesterday, quite warm and pleasant in the afternoon. River as calm as glass this afternoon. The Indians were having a
big feast this afternoon; they had the drum going all the time. Esquimaux
having church. Other 6 or 7 canoes of Indians arrived today.'[20(2)]

In this short sketch of the history of Ungava trade up to a few years
before 1914, we have been able to distinguish two separate periods. In
the first, from 1830 or so to 1842, the traders were groping their way
towards a knowledge of the country's possibilities. It was a time of strenuous exploration and experiment that failed to create a settled trade in furs.
Its chief interest otherwise for the present study is in the glimpses it gives
of Ungava ecology a hundred years ago. The second period, from 1866 to
the first decade of the twentieth century, was one of steady consolidation,
with Fort Chimo paramount in a district two or three times as big as the
British Isles.

But great changes were beginning towards the end of this stable era,
caused in particular by two new developments. One was the entry of a
French rival trading company, Revillons Frères, into this northern field.
The other was the entry of the white fox into the field of high fashion, with
the result that within twenty years from 1908 a great network of new
trading posts had sprung up and covered all parts of the Canadian Arctic
where any Eskimos could be reached.

7

Before describing the history of this final period, which brought an
important redistribution of the local channels of trade, it is convenient to
take stock of the conditions that existed in the middle period of about
forty years. For this period gives some very important evidence about
fox cycles, for the interpretation of which we need to know something
about the ecology of Ungava and its inhabitants.

First, the country and its natural limits to the travels of fox and man.
Turner remarks[14a(3)] that 'the district of Ungava is a huge amphitheatre
opening to the North'. For a broad view of the disposition of its inhabitants,
we may imagine the higher levels occupied by a sprinkling of wandering
Indian families, the lower ones by small settlements of coast-living
Eskimos, both moving in orbits that had Fort Chimo as their focus. The
amphitheatre is drained by two great rivers, the Koksoak and the George's,
together with several others, of which Leaf River is the largest.

The watersheds of these rivers were really the limits of the district to the east and south and west. Eastwards the barren and almost impenetrable high mountains of Labrador cut it off from the Moravian territory along the Atlantic coast. Southwards, however, there is such a vast tangle of lakes and the undetermined springs of rivers on the high central plateau that a definite geographical line could hardly be drawn. Rather there was a rough limit set by the normal boundaries of Indian hunting grounds and possibilities of family travel in a single season. The same thing is true of the lower wild undulating barren lands that form the north-west block of Quebec Peninsula. The northern limit was Hudson Strait. Natives practically never passed southwards from Baffin Island during this period. McLean[10(5)] at Fort Chimo was visited in September 1839 by a party of Eskimos, who crossed the strait on a drift-wood raft at great peril, in search of proper wood for their boats. Later, in 1895, a party is mentioned as crossing northwards from Wolstenholme.[21(8)] Such journeys can have had no significant influence on the trading records. Whether the arctic fox also finds Hudson Strait a barrier to his travels is a very vital question that will be discussed in Chapter XX.

8

Before the significance of variations in the fur returns can be assessed, we need to know a little about the distribution of the native hunters. With the exception of a few skins trapped here and there around Fort Chimo by the men in residence, and a small contribution from the post at George's River, practically everything was brought to Fort Chimo by the natives. Often, as we shall see, these native expeditions travelled great distances to trade. There was none of the practice, which often existed in the southern districts, of sending out parties every year to meet the natives and bargain with them. The lack of competition from other traders, and rigours of the land and rivers and weather of Ungava, explain why the people at the fort seldom left it for more than a day, except on occasional business journeys to George's River, or in search of deer for food, or on exploring expeditions.

According to Low:[7(4)]

'In 1857, there were seven trading posts in the interior of the peninsula [i.e. Quebec Peninsula], and at present there are but three, Waswanipi, Mistassini, and Nichicun. Fort Chimo . . . was not then opened. The policy of the Hudson's Bay Company was then to keep the Indians away from the coast and contact with opposition traders; this has now been changed, and the great body of the natives travel annually to and from their hunting grounds in the interior, to the various coast posts.'

We are fortunate in having some authoritative knowledge of the Ungava people—not complete, it is true, but ample for the present purpose. The chief scientific source is the lavish report by Lucien Turner.[14a] This contains experience of over two years that he spent at Fort Chimo, working for the Smithsonian Institution, in 1882 to 1884. Low's reports add a good deal about the Indians, whom he knew; but he relied mostly on Turner for the

Eskimos. The Ungava archives also provide a mass of rather disjointed notes and a few comprehensive reviews of the district that are very valuable. Knitting together published research, and drawing upon a large store of information obtained in recent years from native tribes and white people living in contact with them, is Speck's summary,[12] which was confirmed by Strong's investigations. It is somewhat condensed, but gives an invaluable framework into which the earlier information fits quite well. Hawkes's useful monograph on the Eskimos should also be mentioned.[5]

Three kinds of Eskimos traded at Fort Chimo, living along different sections of the coast. The first group, the Suhinimiut includes also the Eskimos of Northern Labrador. The Suhinimiut, had the following distribution. In Turner's time, about eight families lived along the north-east coast between Cape Chidley and George's River. A few lived at the latter of which McKenzie wrote[21(2)] in 1889: 'There are only Esquimaux attached to this post: no Indians go there.' Together these two groups numbered only about fifty people. According to Turner, the coast from George's River to the Koksoak was uninhabited, but about thirty Eskimos lived on the Koksoak itself.

Although these Eskimos are usually spoken of as being strictly littoral, except in the caribou hunting season, some of the Koksoak people certainly went quite a long way inland. H. M. S. Cotter's report for 1910–11[22(1)] stated that 'a good many families winter on the Koksoak or Ungava River, going up about 70 miles from the mouth; some are on the Whale River and a few on the False River, both east of Fort Chimo'. Speck also discusses these people.[12(1)] The constant references to Whale River Eskimos in the post journals evidently apply to these inland camps.

The second main division was the Tahagmiut, whose territory began at Leaf River and extended up the west side of Ungava Bay and along the northern coast westwards to Cape Wolstenholme. These were known to the traders as 'the Northerners'. Their customs were different, they spoke a harsher dialect, and they had a passion for gambling. Although Turner includes the Leaf River Eskimos among the 'Northerners', this was not the usual custom in the post journals, where the Leaf River Eskimos were usually mentioned as a separate group. They occur constantly in the records of visitors to Fort Chimo from 1866 onwards, while the Whale River and Koksoak natives are also mentioned quite often.

Two groups of 'Northerners' began quite soon to visit the post with furs, though they were irregular at first. These lived at Apelook and Stupart's Bay; and some of them later went to Cape Wolstenholme. Turner's description[14a(4)] of their journeys to Ungava Bay is fascinating:

'The distance . . . is so great that only three, four, or five sledges are annually sent to the trading post for the purpose of conveying the furs and other more valuable commodities to be bartered for ammunition, guns, knives, files and other kinds of hardware, and tobacco. Certain persons are selected from the various camps who have personally made the trip and know the trail. These are commissioned to barter the furs of each individual for special articles, which are mentioned and impressed upon the mind of the man who is to effect the trade. The principal furs are those of the various foxes. Among them are to be found the best class of silver foxes, and wolverenes and wolves. Those to be sent are procured the previous winter, and when the snow falls in November or early December the line of sleds starts out for the trading post . . . when all is in readiness a southern course is traveled until the frozen morasses on the south of the hills are reached. Thence the course is toward Leaf River and across to Fort Chimo. By the last week of April or the first week of May the visitors are expected at the trading post. They usually bring with them about two-fifths of all the furs obtained in the district; indeed, the quantity often exceeds this amount. . . . The homeward journey is more frequently made along the coast, as there the snow is certain to remain longer upon the ground. It is not infrequent that these travelers experience warm weather which detains them so long that they do not reach the end of their journey until the middle of the summer or even until the beginning of the next winter.'

9

This description has been rather fully quoted, because it contains several facts of great importance to this study, in particular the lag in fur deliveries from the northern coast, and their large amount. It is therefore also important to know when the first northerners came to Fort Chimo, and whether they kept up a regular trade. As early as Outfit 1870 there are references in the Chimo journal.[20(3)]

23 Jan. 1871. 'Six cometics [sleighs] of Esquimaux arrived . . . from the North: twelve men and a number of women and children.'

25 Jan. 1871. 'These are all Esquimaux who have never been here before. They have come from a long distance.'

Others arrived on 30 January, 2 February, 22 April, all 'from the far North', strangers who brought furs with them. In a letter in 1871 P. McKenzie reported[21(3)] that: 'A great number of strangers visited us last winter, more than ever was here before, but returned without giving in their most valuable fur.' (The trade that winter suffered from want of ammunition.) Notes are rather meagre until 1883, when K. McKenzie wrote:[21(4)] 'The Esquimaux from the North brought a considerable number of foxes last spring.'

On 28 September 1887, P. McKenzie wrote[21(5)] that the Eskimos from Stupart's Bay were irregular visitors to Fort Chimo. In the winter of 1886–7 they could not come, because their dogs had died from epidemic. Later on they became more regular in their visits. By September 1900 we find the manager, Matheson, writing[21(6)] that 'the Northern Esquimaux were in as usual in March, some coming from near Cape Wolstenholme'; and in September 1901[21(7)] that 'the Stupart's Bay Esquimaux came in as usual in March'.

Some of the Stupart's Bay Eskimos changed their camping quarters in 1895, which was a bad fur year that upset the life of several other tribes of natives in Ungava. Matheson wrote:[21(8)] 'These Esquimaux are to pass the coming winter in the neighbourhood of Cape Wolstenholme. . . . The families who formerly lived at and about Cape Wolstenholme moved across the Straits 3 years [ago] but are expected to return this fall and will probably come in here in course of the winter.' Also in 1897–8 'some of them passed the winter near Cape Wolstenholme'.[21(9)]

The great delay occasioned by these long journeys to the post, and some other considerations, led to the establishment of a post at Cape Wolstenholme in 1909, after which the trade at Fort Chimo became more circumscribed.

A third group of Eskimos, the Itivimiut, sometimes visited the post. These came overland from the coast of Hudson Bay, and were known as the Little Whale River Eskimos. Turner says:[14a(5)] 'They trade, for the most part, at Fort George, belonging to the Moose district. Each year, however, a party of less than a dozen individuals journey to Fort Chimo for the purpose of bartering furs and other valuables. Those who come to Fort Chimo are usually the same each year.' These were a very distinct tribe, superficially influenced by missionaries, but little used to fire-arms, and dependent for the chase upon their own ancient practices. They are mentioned in the Chimo journals for 1866 and 1883, and possibly in some others that have not been completely studied. It may have been this band of which Matheson wrote in 1904:[21(10)] 'The Esquimaux known as the "Whale River Band" did not turn up this spring. . . . They have not failed to come in for the last 15 or 20 years.' Or they may have been from the local Whale River.

10

This completes the survey of one or two thousand miles of Arctic coast, on which were these scattered settlements, mostly of one or two families together. As to their total numbers, we have the report, relayed by Low,[7(5)] of

'Mr. R. Gray, who was for upwards of ten years clerk at Fort Chimo, and is well acquainted with the Eskimo of Ungava Bay:—From Cape Chidley to Hope's Advance, 51 families; about Hope's Advance, 30 families; from Stupart Bay to Cape Wolstenholme, 80 families; from Cape Wolstenholme to Great Whale River, 80 families. The average Eskimo family is small and rarely exceeds five persons. Taking this as the average, the total population west of Cape Chidley would be 1200 persons. This estimate is probably excessive, and 1000 persons would be nearer the number, if not still above it.'

These figures were apparently for 1894. They give a maximum possible number of families (i.e. hunters) trading to Chimo, of about 170. McKenzie in 1886 wrote[21(1)] that Eskimos, including in both tribes men, women, and children, came to 360 for the district; remarking in the same letter that 'all the furs caught by the Esquimaux and Indians between this and Little Whale River are either traded here or at that post'.

In 1888 he wrote[21(11)] that 'I find that Lieut. Gordon [of the Dominion Exploring Party at Stupart's Bay] is quite correct about the number of Esquimaux in the vicinity of Stupart's Bay: I have got the names of over sixty families of them.' These two figures (allowing three or four to a family) add up to about the same numbers that Gray gave to Low, so that McKenzie's 360 most likely applied to Ungava Bay itself.

H. M. S. Cotter, in his report for 1910–11,[22(1)] gives the number of Eskimo names on the Chimo books as 50, with another 40 going to Revillons. Thirty hunters were expected at Wolstenholme post in 1911–12. These figures together add up to 120 hunters, and perhaps as many families. This population squares with Low's other census,[9] compiled on the cruise of the *Neptune* in 1903–4, which gives 400–450 Eskimos on the south shore of Hudson Strait. If all these figures are reliable, the population must have fallen to about half, between 1894 and 1904. This fall in numbers is confirmed by the intermediate figure given by Low[8(1)] on the basis of his travels in 1896: 'The Eskimos trading at Fort Chimo are about 140 families, or 700 persons in all; but less than half of these visit the post.' He explains how the furs are sent in by specially commissioned representatives of the bands.

That the decrease was real, and not just due to the extremely approximate nature of these population estimates, is confirmed by a remark of McKenzie's in a report[21(1)] on Ungava for 1886–7: 'The Esquimaux seem to be dying off very fast.' Partly there were epidemics, whose nature is not very clear, partly starvation due to lack of caribou. Nineteen starved to death at George's River in 1889–90,[21(13)] and 18 to 20 others, whose home is not recorded, in 1897–8.[21(14)]

Mr. J. W. Anderson writes from the Hudson's Bay Company, in 1938: 'The present day Eskimo population from Cape Chidley (Port Burwell Post) to Port Harrison is estimated at 1,780 men, women, and children. . . . There are undoubted indications that the Eskimo population has increased in recent years.'

11

Something was said about the Indians in Chapter XII, in a sketch of the life of Quebec Peninsula as a whole. Except for the annual visits of the Davis Inlet band to that post, and in later years of the Barren Ground people to Nain, the Indians played a minor part in the fur trade of the Atlantic coast north of Hamilton Inlet. That is, their direct influence was small; but indirectly Indian hunting may have helped to deplete the stocks of caribou that the northern Eskimo settlements count on for food and clothes.

At Fort Chimo, on the other hand, the Indian trade ranked equally with the Eskimo. Perhaps it is less dominant nowadays, when the soaring values of arctic fox skins have made the Eskimo trade of such great importance, and Indian tribes are shrunk to smaller size than they were. The Indian then, by his ability to catch large numbers of red, cross, and silver foxes, and also martens, bears, &c., was an important person in the trade. He also supplied, in those early days, a vital quantity of deer meat and skins, besides helping in other activities of the post. The Indians of Labrador are usually described as a degenerate and rather poor branch of the race, inferior in many respects to the Eskimos. This opinion has come from the traders, who seem to have expected an independent nomad people to alter at once its ways of life in order to help the trade; from ethnologists, hoping to discover new and complicated customs and beliefs; from explorers, wanting wild hunters to turn to canoeing and packing for wages; and from missionaries, whose attempts to introduce monogamy and a strange theology have usually failed to penetrate far below the surface of the Indian mind.

In spite of these opinions, and without any first-hand acquaintance with the people, one hesitates to put in a low class of humanity a race that possesses such a remarkable pow r of assimilating itself to a country where most white travellers have been hard put to it to survive at all. Turner's fascinating account of their simple but ingenious material culture and folk-stories, and the sympathy that Strong, who lived among them, felt, confirm one's impression. The astounding journeys made by some of these Indians in search of fur and game witness a tough fibre and woodcraft of a very high order; while, to an ecologist interested in animal populations and the conservation of living matter, there is something very arresting in the Nascopie belief that killing animals makes no difference to their total numbers, since the spirits go on existing after death!

Speck's convenient and concise account of the Indian territories in Ungava is confirmed by the first-hand authority of Strong, who explored in this region in 1927–8. These contain some gaps that can be partly filled from the Fort Chimo archives.

There were four elements in the Indian trade. The main band was that known as the Ungava Indians. These lived usually in the middle part of the Ungava amphitheatre, in the thinly-wooded barren country drained by the Koksoak and its tributaries. In this vast hunting ground, over 60,000 square miles in extent, a few hundred Indians roamed in the tracks of deer. They seem often to have visited the head-waters of Whale River, and sometimes joined temporarily with other neighbouring bands. For instance we read in a letter[21(10)] September 1904: 'Most of the Indians wintered near George's Lake and found abundance of deer. . . .' George's Lake was the head-quarters of another band, the Barren Ground Indians, and is now known as Indian House Lake.

12

There seems to have been a fairly well-recognized frontier between the Indian and the Eskimo lands, at any rate in the western parts of the country. Low[7(6)] states categorically: 'The northern limit of their territory is marked by the Koksoak River, from its mouth to the Stillwater Branch, and by this stream westward to its head on the neighbourhood of Clear-water Lake, and thence westward to Richmond Gulf on Hudson Bay. This line divides the Indian territory from that of the Eskimo, and the boundary is well observed, the latter keeping far to the north of it, when hunting deer inland, and the Indians rarely crossing it from the south-ward.'

Speck[12(1)] has a note on this subject and gives evidence that hunting sometimes went north of Koksoak River. Flaherty, whose travels in this region are referred to more fully in the next chapter, gives a similar account of the situation. Although the precise statements on the subject are not very common in the Fort Chimo archives, I have found no record to suggest any violation of this broad frontier across the base of Ungava Peninsula. One that confirms it is mentioned by Matheson[21(10)] in 1904, the year when most of the Indians had wintered at Indian House Lake: 'Some 4 or 5 families went up the North branch of the Koksoak, and but for the scarcity of deer, would have made excellent hunts, martens being fairly numerous on both sides of the River.' And Cotter[22(1)] (1911) mentions the Eskimo hunting territories farther to the north-west.

We get a glimpse of what this Eskimo country was like, a hundred years ago, in McLean's unpublished report[18(3)] for 1837–8:

'Donald Henderson returned from his exploring expedition on the 25th August [1838], having proceeded to some distance beyond the Bay of Hopes Advance [i.e. Leaf Bay]. . . . He entered a large River flowing into the Bay of Hopes Advance, which he ascended in the boat about a distance of twenty miles, then struck off into the interior. Not a vestige of any description of timber was discovered. He describes the navigation as exceedingly dangerous. . . . Several of the natives were seen, who appeared as usual very friendly disposed, and bartered a few fox skins and ivory. The happy dogs [meaning the natives] appeared to luxuriate in the midst of abundance, the inland country abounding with deer and the sea with marine animals.'

It is safe, then, to say that the Ungava Indians left the north-west peninsula to the Eskimos. Exactly how much overlapping happened within the valleys of the Koksoak and Whale Rivers it is hard to know. All the evidence suggests that there was some degree of geographical over-lapping in the lower region, due partly to the presence of the trading post there; but the two races kept strictly separate, and there were only rare intermarriages. On the other hand, each race mated to some extent with whites.

To the southward there was not always a clear boundary, though Speck gives the limits with a good deal of sharp definition. He adds, however:[12(2)] 'Shift of residence is constantly being caused by decline in population, by intermarriage, and by the changing conditions of the life of the game . . .' and we might also include the opening and closing of trading posts. When we come to the consideration of yearly variations in fur supply, we shall see that in bad fur years, or when deer were scarce, the Ungava Indians scoured this desolate land as far as the central watershed. And in some years a few of them visited Davis Inlet, North West River, Eastmain, and even posts on the Gulf of St. Lawrence. But very few of these journeys seem to have been mass movements of whole bands, which confined their erratic wanderings to the main basin.

13

The east part of Ungava is occupied by the valley of the George River (always referred to in the old accounts as George's River, but shorn of its apostrophe on modern maps). McLean wrote[18(3)] about it in 1838, in one of his unpublished reports from Fort Chimo:

'George's River, falling into this Bay about eighty miles to the eastward, is described as a large but rapid stream and deemed to be navigable to its source in a large lake near the height of land. A singular circumstance is mentioned as characteristic of this River: it runs so still at intervals as scarcely to indicate which way the current leads, then all of a sudden forms into strong rapids, flowing in this manner throughout its whole course in alternate rapids, or as it were lakes. The only large lake on this side of the height of land is within seventy miles of this establishment. It is forty miles in length, its medium breadth two and a half. Lakes of inferior note are without number, and the whole country is intersected by small rivers in every direction.'

This enormous river has seldom been explored except by the pioneer traders of the Company a century ago. One of them was Erlandson, who established Fort Trial on Indian House Lake, the great lake described by McLean.[16, 19(2)] To this lake also Hesketh Prichard travelled in his adventurous traverse from Nain in 1910. Most travellers in the region have been too busy in remaining alive to make extensive notes. For this reason we should have little information about the people living in the valley, but for Strong, who knew its head-waters well, and some of the Indian people. Low,[8a] the Hubbards,[6] Wallace,[15] and Wheeler[15a] add a little more. We must also refer to the numerous journeys of W. E. Clyde Todd of the Carnegie Museum and his associates both to the coasts and the interior of Quebec Peninsula: a remarkable record of biological survey almost every year since 1901, but still locked in the Museum's files. Even so, the details of numbers and history are rather obscure.

Ranging around and east of the head-waters of George's River was the Davis Inlet band. The country up there was described by Erlandson to Finlayson[19(5)] in 1834 as 'by no means a poor fur country; but to the N. and N.E. of this tract extremely barren and mountainous, but deer plentiful. But on the opposite direction S. and S.W. well wooded and comparatively flat and abounding consequently in martens, beaver and other furs'. The band that hunted in this intermediate country was the one that supplied most of the furs to Davis Inlet, at any rate in later days. It scarcely concerns us here, as it practically never came in contact with Fort Chimo, although it no doubt knew the Barren Ground people lower down the valley.

In September 1899, however, Matheson reported:[21(12)] 'The Indians who formerly traded at North West River are now located at and around George's Lake, as are also some from the Gulf posts. Several of them visited us in the spring, but they had very little to trade, there being as great a scarcity of fur-bearing animals there last winter as elsewhere.

These Indians would prefer coming here to going to Davis Inlet, could we pay as high for fur and sell our goods at Davis Inlet prices.'

This visit evidently was an isolated occurrence, but it was followed by a certain amount of restlessness among the Ungava Indians. A report in 1900 states:[21(6)] 'Some nine or ten Indians from here went over to George's Lake in March and took their furs to Davis Inlet.' And the Annual Report on Ungava for 1902–3 remarks[22(2)] that: 'For two or three years there seems to have been a leakage from the Returns of Ungava District through Indians carrying their hunts elsewhere.' Some even went to the Gulf of St. Lawrence.

These incidents show that these nomads, as the Nascopie Indians have always been, moved to a small extent from post to post. Fortunately for the interpretation of fur returns, such movements were only of a small fraction of the Indians attached to Ungava District, and furthermore, it can be shown that many of them took place in years when fur was very scarce. The very factor which often drove them far afield prevented the loss to the fur returns from being large.

14

There is another band, whose history and movements are not as well known as we could wish. These were the Barren Ground Indians, of whom Speck wrote in 1931:[12(3)] 'The valley of the George River, the barrens westward to Whale river and to the head of Indian House lake, are the hunting limits of this now much reduced but still most interesting group of the typical Naskapi. . . . The barrens of the interior in this part of the peninsula are so desolate as to have earned the name they bear among the natives—mucwáo, "land of nothing", as they translate it—which term is likewise applied to George river . . . the band has remained one of the most remote and uncontaminated.' He does not say whom they traded with, and the Chimo archives contain only a few remarks about them. Perhaps they are the 'North Indians' frequently mentioned in Davis Inlet journals as visitors to the post.[17] In September 1889 McKenzie wrote,[21(2)] as a result of his visit to George's River post: 'I think it might be possible to get the Indians who frequent the inland lakes of that River to go down and trade there, instead of going to Davis Inlet and other places on the Atlantic coast. There are about twelve families of them: some of them formerly belonged to this post.' The journal for 20 July 1899 recorded:[20(4)] 'Seven Indians and one squaw . . . arrived. . . . 5 men are newcomers: they are the George's River Indians. They were 10 days in coming, and have left their canoes somewhere up Whale River. Their women have all been left at George's Lake. Any amount of deer are crossing the Lake now, though they (i.e. the Indians) were hungry during the winter.' On 16 July 1900: '17 Indians arrived from George's Lake.'[20(5)] There is no more mention of them at Fort Chimo (at any rate up to 1910), and we may conclude that their influence on the trade was negligible. Indeed, some of these Indians may have belonged to the Davis Inlet band and not to the

Barren Ground people at all. The possibility of this being the band that visited Nain in 1853 has already been mentioned in Chapter XII. That is where they now live, since the failure of deer drove them out of the interior[13, 12(4)] in 1916.

15

We come now to the last band. The Little Whale River Indians (not to be confused with those Ungava Indians who lived round Whale River in the east) had a territory stretching from the coast of Hudson Bay across to Ungava itself. To judge from the limited information that we have, these people used to hunt on the coast slopes of Hudson Bay, but have moved eastwards on account of the scarcity of deer.

The earliest reference to them at Fort Chimo that I have noted is in 1883, when McKenzie wrote:[21(4)] 'Several families of Little Whale River Indians came here last winter: they had nothing but a few deerskins to trade, and they reported many deaths among their party from starvation.' They came in April 1883. Although little more is said about them, Turner[14a(6)] gives a sketch of them (he was there at the time). They had different temperament and habits from the Ungava Nascopies, and especially they were much better boatmen and skilled in catching whales, whose flesh and fat they were fond of eating. They were often employed to hunt white whales, and they used harpoons not unlike those of the Eskimos, on the borders of whose land they lived. 'The reindeer have in recent years become so scarce in the vicinity of Fort George [on Hudson Bay] that many of the Indians have left that locality and journeyed to the eastward, dwelling in proximity to the Naskopies, or even with them. . . . Their purchases are made with furs of the same kinds as those procured in the Ungava District. The black bear is procured in great numbers by these Indians.'

Evidently some of the Little Whale River Indians traded with Fort Chimo in the eighties, but those that migrated into the central valley region probably assimilated themselves, in hunting and trading practice, with the Ungava Indians. According to the reports received by Speck the tribal organizations have largely remained distinct.

16

This condensed history of the Nascopie bands within reach of Fort Chimo is incomplete in many ways, partly because some of the facts we want are now lost for ever, and partly because an ecologist dependent on published literature for his work cannot hope to obtain an entirely balanced picture of the situation.

However, this survey does bring out two things that strongly affect the study of fur fluctuations. It gives quite a clear verdict about the Indian bands. We can say that the chief, and always essentially constant, band in the Ungava fur district was that of the Ungava Indians. Although the valley of George's River was officially within Ungava District, its contribution must have been at all times small. Neither the Barren Ground nor the

North West River bands were of any direct importance to Ungava trade. Secondly, the contribution from the Little Whale River Indians, though probably fairly regular, must have been a small fraction of the whole returns, except in so far as these Indians helped to catch white whales and so swell the profits from oil.

We may dismiss the influence of the more remote Indian bands living to the south and south-west as negligible. Journeys were made from Eastmain and from the Gulf of St. Lawrence, but only by a few individuals, bringing, as often as not, little fur at all. On the central height of land natives were always few and poor, and traded east or west, not to Ungava.

There is a note on the question of southern visitors by McKenzie in 1887:[21(1)] 'Seven Islands, Mingan Indians and Esquimaux Bay Indians sometimes come within six days march of this Post in quest of furs, but never reach the place. They invariably return to the Gulf or Esq[uimau]x Bay [i.e. St. Lawrence and Hamilton Inlet] and most likely sell the greater part of [their] hunts to petty traders.' This statement requires the qualification that visitors travelling up from the St. Lawrence and other southern districts did occasionally arrive at Ungava Bay, but it shows that their influence on the trade can be ignored. Only in July 1867 eight Indians from the height-of-land brought in their spring hunt of deerskins and over 300 marten skins to Fort Chimo, because the central post of Fort Nascopie could not fill their wants.[20(6)]

Having narrowed down the matter to a single main band of Indians, we can draw a second conclusion of value. Many statements are made in the archives about the abundance and scarcity of fur and deer in the interior, and we can now apply these to the hunting lands of the Ungava band, which have been shown to lie within certain limits in the Koksoak and Whale River basins. This is a huge area to use as a unit of study, yet we can be pretty confident that the whole of it was usually covered in the search for food and fur. In very bad years the range expanded, but there are usually special notes whenever this happened, also in the seasons when the range contracted because Indian movements were paralysed or hampered by starvation or illness.

As a corollary to this distribution: Ungava District was a good deal more out of touch with the coast of Labrador than might have appeared from a casual look at the map. This isolation was caused by the almost impenetrable mountain wilderness in the interior of the north-west, and by the comparatively little contact between Indians in the George's River Valley and Ungava itself. The archives show that hardly any news came through from the Atlantic coast to Chimo, except when ships called.

17

There is now a third point to be considered: the numbers of the Indian population dependent on Ungava District. On this question some rather scattered information has been gathered; but it gives a fairly clear conclusion. In these early days there was no official census, and we rely, as usual,

24

on the Hudson's Bay Company archives, and upon Turner and Low. Unfortunately, Fort Chimo was closed at the time of the official report of 1857,[23] in which the Company rendered an account of its state to Parliament, and which included rough estimates of natives attached to the posts. Speck conveniently tabulates these figures for the Quebec Peninsula in his recent paper, but we cannot get much evidence from them about the numbers in separate bands.

The first note I can find is in Turner's monograph,[14a(7)] where he gives 350 as the total number of Ungava District Indians, not including the Little Whale River Indians whose numbers were not ascertained. This figure evidently applies to the Ungava band itself. In 1886, according to McKenzie:[21(1)] 'The Nascopies do not appear to decrease any. Barren ground Nascopies, branch of the Cree Nation, about 400.' Here he refers without doubt to the Ungava Indians, not to the 'Barren Ground Band' which practically never visited the post. His higher estimate might be due to several causes; but the most likely is that counts were usually based on the known number of hunters and a rough multiplication converted these into families. Or the number of families was known, and an equally rough estimate made which depended on the assumed average size of a family. A similar method is used by the Rupert's River Indians to estimate the number of beavers in a pond: it contains an obvious range of error, which has to be accepted as inevitable.

In 1896 Low stated[7(7)] that 'seven years ago [i.e. in about 1889] there were ninety families of Indians trading at Fort Chimo'. Since in another place he gives the population as 350 for the district in 1892, the number reckoned by him for a family seems to have been about four. The winter of 1892–3 was a black one for the natives. Low records that:[7(4)] 'At Fort Chimo the famine of 1892–93 reduced the number of Indians in that district from 350 to less than 200 persons.' Elsewhere he mentions[7(7)] that of the ninety families trading there about 1889 nineteen starved to death in 1892–3 in a body, and in another place six families were lost. 'Besides these, all the other Indians were throughout the winter in a state of chronic starvation, and many died, so that out of a population of two hundred and fifty persons, less than a hundred and fifty survive.'

It would seem as though Low's 250 here is a misprint for 350. Matheson[21(15)] put the total losses at nearly 200, also noting that the famine came from absence of the deer that winter. This frightful disaster, which halved the Ungava band, was a particularly severe example of a common danger to the Indians living up there. There are many notes of the vicissitudes brought by failure to find the deer, or by the changes in migration of the herds in certain years.

In 1896, when Low returned again to the fort during one of his expeditions, he ascertained[8(1)] that 'the total number of Indians trading at and dependent on Fort Chimo is about one hundred and fifty'. An echo of the famine year comes from H. M. S. Cotter[22(1)] in 1911: 'There are about 60 Indian hunters at Ungava just now. . . . In 1892/93 a great many of the

Indians perished—all the good hunters—from starvation; but there are many boys and lads growing up, so that in a few years there will be as large a population as before.' The context makes it plain that these 60 hunters included both the Company's and Revillon's customers.

The recovery forecast by Cotter seems to have been fulfilled, for a census by the Canadian Department of Indian Affairs in 1924 gave the populations as: Fort Chimo, 213; George's River, 36; Whale River, 57; and Port Burwell, 152. According to information from the Hudson's Bay Company, these Port Burwell Indians probably came from George's River. The total figure of 458 presumably includes some of the immigrant Little Whale River Indians.

Some recent figures given me by the Hudson's Bay Company suggest that the population is now a good deal lower than it was in 1924; though the figures supplied do not enable an exact comparison to be made. This decrease is attributed mainly to the great scarcity of caribou in recent years. The whole cycle of events may be summarized as follows:

In 1883 there were 350.
In 1886 there were about 400.
In 1889 there were about 350–360.
In 1892 there were about 350.
In 1892–3 150–200 starved to death.
This left in 1893 less than 200.
In 1896 there were about 150.
In 1911 many young people were growing up again.
In 1924 there were 458, including immigrants from the west.
In 1938 there were fewer than this again.

We see here the Indian population suffering a slow cycle, lasting over a generation, in much the same fashion as the shorter cycles of wolf, lynx, fox, and marten. It is to be supposed that such cycles among the caribou hunters had from the earliest times helped the elasticity of the hard-pressed herds, a subject which will be entered upon in the next chapter.

We can now see on what base the pyramid of Ungava fur trade stood, between 1866 and 1908. There were some 400–1,000 Eskimos and from 150 to 400 Indians: altogether not more than a few hundred actual hunters, forming a thin but surprisingly strong and unbreakable thread between the animals of Ungava and the London auction rooms. These hunters were, and still are, almost the only means of tapping the organic resources of a hundred thousand square miles of country. They are important to the white man; and they have a life of their own to lead, which has been made so dependent on the fur trade as to create an inescapable responsibility.

REFERENCES

* indicates that an abstract is deposited in the library of the Bureau of Animal Population, Oxford. Dates of archives are those of the 'Outfits', e.g. 1900 means 1900–1. H. B. Co. means Hudson's Bay Company.

1. BELL, R. (1884). 'Observations on the geology, mineralogy, zoology and botany of the Labrador Coast, Hudson's Strait and Bay.' Rep. Geol. and Nat. Hist. Surv. and Mus. of Canada for 1882–3–4. 1–62 DD. (1) 16 DD.

1 a. BINNEY, G. (1929). 'Hudson Bay in 1928.' Geogr. J. 74: 1–27.

2. CLUTTERBUCK, H. M. (1932). 'Akpatok Island (Hudson Strait): The Oxford University Exploration Club's Expedition, 1931.' Geogr. J. 80: 211–33.

3. FLAHERTY, R. J. (1918). 'Two traverses across Ungava Peninsula, Labrador.' Geogr. Rev. 6: 116–32.

3 a. GORDON, A. R. (1887). 'Report of the Hudson's Bay Expedition of 1886. . . .' Canadian Govt. Blue-book. 131 pp.

*4. GRAHAM, A. (1768). 'Observations on Hudson's Bay.' MS. H. B. Co. Archives, London. P. 126.

5. HAWKES, E. W. (1916). 'The Labrador Eskimo.' Canada, Dept. of Mines, Geol. Surv. Mem. 91 (No. 14, Anthropol. Ser.): 1–235.

6. HUBBARD, L. (Mrs.) (1908). 'A woman's way through unknown Labrador.' London.

6 a. KOHLMEISTER, B., & KMOCH, G. (1814). 'Journal of a voyage from Okkak to the coast of Labrador and Ungava Bay.' London. P. 47.

7. LOW, A. P. (1896). 'Report on explorations in the Labrador Peninsula, along the East Main, Koksoak, Hamilton, Manicuagan and portions of other rivers, in 1892–93–94–95.' Ann. Rep. Geol. Surv. Canada for 1895 (New Ser.), 8: 1–387 L. (1) 21 L. (2) 15 L. (3) 329–30 L. (4) 41 L. (5) 42 L. (6) 44–5 L. (7) 122–3 L.

8. LOW, A. P. (1898). 'Report on a traverse of the Northern part of the Labrador Peninsula from Richmond Gulf to Ungava Bay.' Ann. Rep. Geol. Surv. Canada for 1896, 9: 1–43 L. (1) 22 L.

8 a. LOW, A. P. (1899). 'Report on an exploration of part of the South shore of Hudson Strait and of Ungava Bay.' Ann. Rep. Geol. Surv. Canada for 1898, 11: 1–47 L.

9. LOW, A. P. (1906). 'Report on the Dominion Government Expedition to Hudson Bay and the Arctic Islands on board the D.G.S. "Neptune", 1903–1904.' Ottawa. P. 134.

10. McLEAN, J. (1849). 'Notes of a twenty-five years' service in the Hudson's Bay Territory.' London. Vol. 2: 25–166. (1) 30. (2) 32–3. (3) 65. (4) 97. (5) 81–2.

11. PECK, E. J. (1886). 'Across Labrador: notes of journey from Little Whale River to Ungava Bay.' The Church Missionary Intelligencer & Record, 11: 510–12.

12. SPECK, F. G. (1931). 'Montagnais-Naskapi bands and early Eskimo distribution in the Labrador Peninsula.' Amer. Anthropologist, 33: 557–600. (1) 571. (2) 597. (3) 595. (4) 596. (5) 598.

12 a. SPECK, F. G. (1935). 'Naskapi: the savage hunters of the Labrador Peninsula.' Norman, Oklahoma. 248 pp.

13. STRONG, W. D. (1930). 'Notes on mammals of the Labrador interior.' J. Mammal. 11: 1–10.

14. TURNER, L. M. (1887). 'On the Indians and Eskimos of the Ungava District, Labrador.' Proc. Trans. Roy. Soc. Canada, for 1887, 5 (Sect. 2): 99–117. (p. 117.)

14 a. TURNER, L. M. (1894). 'Ethnology of the Ungava District, Hudson Bay

Territory.' Smithson. Inst., Bur. of Amer. Ethnology, 11th Ann. Rep. (1889–90): 167–349. (1) 167. (2) 171. (3) 168. (4) 177. (5) 179. (6) 182–3. (7) 183.

15. WALLACE, D. (1907). 'The long Labrador trail.' London.

15 a. WHEELER, E. P. (1935). 'The Nain-Okak section of Labrador.' Geogr. Rev. 25: 240–54.

16. [WHITE, J.] (1926). 'Forts and trading posts in Labrador Peninsula and adjoining territory.' Ottawa. (Contains a very convenient map.)

*17. Davis Inlet Post, Journals, 1869–76, 1879–98, 1901–9. MS. H. B. Co. Archives, London.

*18. Ungava District (Fort Chimo), Reports, 1831–4, 1836–7. MS. H. B. Co. Archives, London. (1) 1832. (2) 1834. (3) 1837.

*19. Ungava District (Fort Chimo), Correspondence, 1828, 1830, 1834–40. MS. H. B. Co. Archives, London. (1) Norway House, 30 June 1837: George Simpson to John McLean. (2) Fort Trial, 1 Sept. 1839: J. McLean to George Simpson. (3) Moose Factory, 1 Sept. 1828: William Hendry to J. L. Lewis. (4) Fort Chimo, 20 Sept. 1830: Nicol Finlayson to the Governor, H. B. Co.

*20. Fort Chimo Post (Ungava District), Journals, 1866–72, 1874–6, 1883–5, 1895–6, 1898–1900. MS. H. B. Co. Archives, London. (Some others are available, but have not been examined.) (1) 11 Apr. 1897. (2) 11 June 1899. (3) 23, 25, and 30 Jan., 2 Feb., 22 Apr. 1871. (4) 20 July 1899. (5) 16 July 1900. (6) 11 July 1867.

*21. Ungava District (Fort Chimo), Correspondence, 1869, 1871–3, 1882–97, 1899–1912. MS. H. B. Co. Archives, London. (Some later letters exist, but have not been examined.) (1) Aug. 1886: P. McKenzie to the Commissioner, Winnipeg. (2) 3 Sept. 1889: P. McKenzie to J. Wrigley. (3) 27 Sept. 1871: P. McKenzie to Donald A. Smith. (4) 6 Sept. 1883: K. McKenzie to S. K. Parsons. (5) 28 Sept. 1887: P. McKenzie to J. Wrigley. (6) 9 Sept. 1900: D. Matheson to the Commissioner, Winnipeg. (7) Sept. 1901: D. Matheson to the Commissioner, Winnipeg. (8) 16 Sept. 1895: D. Matheson to C. C. Chipman. (9) 9 Sept. 1898: D. Matheson to the Commissioner, Winnipeg. (10) 4 Sept. 1904: D. Matheson to P. McKenzie. (11) 11 Sept. 1888: P. McKenzie to J. Wrigley. (12) 10 Sept. 1899: D. Matheson to the Commissioner, Winnipeg. (13) 2 Feb. 1890: Robert Gray to P. McKenzie. (14) 9 Sept. 1898: D. Matheson to P. McKenzie. (15) 12 Sept. 1893: D. Matheson to P. McKenzie.

*22. Hudson's Bay Company, Annual Reports on Fur Trade. MS. H. B. Co. Archives, London. (1) In Rep. for Outfit 1910, Supplementary Rep. on Ungava Posts, by H. M. S. Cotter. (2) Outfit 1902, Labrador District.

23. (1857). Report from the Select Committee (House of Commons) on the Hudson's Bay Company, London. [224–260—Sess. 2.]

CHAPTER XVIII

CARIBOU HERDS AND MODERN TRADE

1

THIS faintly outlined history provides some material for the assessment of fur fluctuations. We have to be careful to allow for certain variable movements of the Eskimo and Indian bands, not all of which are known. But there was no trade competition before 1903, and we know roughly the regions within which the fur was collected. To these general standards we shall add, in the discussion of each cycle, a mass of detailed record which, linked with the fur returns, goes a long way towards establishing the real years of abundance and scarcity.

Besides these short fluctuations in the fur population, some very interesting changes in the caribou herds are on record. Although these do not directly affect the short cycle story, they matter indirectly in two ways. The changing numbers and distribution of caribou have caused migration of whole native tribes into new quarters, and often privation and death. Taking a long view, these changes are of tremendous importance to the future life of Quebec Peninsula, since deer have for centuries been the fount of spiritual life and the source of clothes and food to the interior Indian bands. The immediate profit that may come to traders from the sale of European food as a substitute for deer strenuously sought in a vast barren land can only be justified on a short and limited view. It is possible that the continued existence of a healthy and natural Nascopie culture depends on a knowledge of caribou ecology, while this culture guarantees the continuance of an interior fur hunt by the Indians.

Some of the greatest changes in deer occurred in the first years of this century, and their discussion falls naturally to this chapter, in which are notes on the later expansion of Ungava trading as a whole, with which went a narrowing of the territory of Fort Chimo itself.

How the native had become gradually dependent upon trading posts has already been explained. As early as 1896 Low reported[10(1)] that some Indians wore European clothes and relied to some extent on provisions bought at the traders' stores. The George's River Valley Indians still kept to their own reliance on deer meat and deerskin clothes.[10(2)] But we can see the early stage of that process by which the tribes were to be drawn gradually into the tail of the comet of an industrial civilization. The story is always the same in its elements, whether the people are Samoyeds, Aleuts, Lapps, Arawaks, New Hebrideans, or Eskimos and Indians. There are benefits, some real (tools; tea; credit for starvation years; sometimes shelter; freedom from superstitious fear; and medical help), some sham or doubtful (literacy; guns; clothes; houses); and there are hideous drawbacks (influenza, tuberculosis, syphilis, and the weary list of diseases; the demoralization of wild, sudden wealth; the decay of heart-felt belief in nature worship; missionary hell; and sometimes drink).

Usually the drawbacks beat the benefits, and often the new spiritual theories brought to the natives destroy old ones that alone provide a resistant core to the double blandishments of material wealth and eternal salvation. The Eskimos seem to have a tough quality that yet admits of adaptation to good elements in civilization, the Nascopies less so. The prime conditions of their survival are health (which is a matter purely of organization and education), and the supply of natural animal food (which demands in addition, and as a preliminary condition of action, real knowledge of the animal populations which are the food). To this second object the ensuing digression on caribou history is dedicated. If it only serves to bring attention to a problem and some approaches to it, a step may have been gained. One would wish the Eskimos and Indians of Ungava and Northern Labrador to join that select academy of uncrushable small peoples that includes as distinguished members the Lapps, the Faroese, the people of Tristan da Cunha, some Arawaks and Dyaks, and the Mexican Indians.

2

It may seem remarkable that we can say anything about the movements of caribou in such a huge theatre of operations. The story is certainly rather obscure in many places, and has to be pieced together from what observers saw at various scattered points and learned from native visitors. Most of the sources are those we have already used: Turner, Bell, Low, Flaherty, Strong, and the little army of Hudson's Bay Company and Mission writers. The chief assumption we have to make is that the natives really told truly what had happened. This seems safe enough so long as their story was concerned with happenings rather than the causes of them. Another assumption is the essential integrity of the three great herds described by Low[10(3)] from Indian information. We cannot actually prove that these herds never mingled, or that small remnants of one were not drawn into the main body of another. We must take the existence of three main populations (whether always completely separate or not) as a reasonable working plan to explain the other evidence.

The best evidence for separate herds is that each had different Indian bands in attendance. West was the herd that travelled up and down along the coast-hills of Hudson Bay, ministering to the Little Whale River Indians and others south of them. Then came the central herd that the Ungava Indians followed. East, on the upper George River and Atlantic highlands and coast, was the third, on which depended the Barren Ground and Davis Inlet bands and others around the Hamilton Inlet region. These two Indian bands, as we saw, hardly ever descended to the northern coast—additional evidence that the deer they followed were separate from those of the Ungava herd.

There is, then, a general geographical basis and a corresponding human grouping for the three herds, which I shall refer to for convenience as the western, central, and eastern. This classification, however, is meant to leave still open the possibility of interchange and intermingling, to an extent which may perhaps never be ascertained. We have to look now more closely into the records of this distribution, and some of its later changes. These records lead us partly outside the Ungava District itself, but only to illustrate principles of importance to the study. As far as I know, the evidence has not before been assembled into one place.

3

Low knew well the country and some of the Indians of the western region, by Hudson Bay. After describing the two other herds he mentions[10(3)] 'a third, which passes northward from the vicinity of Richmond Gulf and Clearwater Lake, and summers along the highlands of the northeast coast of Hudson Bay. Of late years, this last herd has become very small, and many of the Indians who lived on it have migrated from Hudson Bay to Fort Chimo, while the second herd was undiminished.' This note was in 1896, the result of journeying in 1893-4.

Without undertaking a complete examination of archives for this part of the country (a task which would be interesting and quite possible) it is not easy to say exactly when the decrease of this herd originally began. There are several pieces of information about ten years earlier that prove it to have been already in progress then. Turner's reference (from 1884 experience) has already been quoted, also the incident of the starving Little Whale River Indians who came over to Fort Chimo in 1883 (p. 356). Peck, the adventurous missionary who canoed and portaged across the Peninsula from Richmond Gulf to Ungava Bay, leaves a few impressions of the country—in spite of his strong philosophical belief that 'surroundings, comparatively, are nothing'.[13]

With four Indians he travelled first up through a chain of smaller lakes, by which he saw (July 1884) several deer-tracks. On the watershed he visited two very large lakes, Clearwater and Seal (the latter being from his description the one known now as Lower Seal Lake). These lie in the direct line of the old caribou migrations. At Clearwater Lake he saw deer on a large island, and of Seal Lake he noted that 'it is quite studded with islands, which are the favourite haunts of the reindeer, especially in the winter months'. (He also saw a seal in this lake.) From Seal Lake he passed into 'a rather large lake, the river from which continues its course to Fort Chimo'. In the upper parts of this river (the Stillwater or parallel branch of it) deer trails 2 to 3 feet wide were frequently seen. These traces of deer were noticed for several days, as he went down that part of the river lying above the main forks of the Larch and Koksoak Rivers. Also wolf-tracks were with those of the deer.

From Peck's observations it would seem that in 1884 there was still a large part of the western herd in existence. Some of the Larch River notes may have been, however, on the outlying members of the central herd.

About the same time as this, the Hudson's Bay Expedition sent out under the command of Lieut. Gordon by the Canadian Department of Marine and Fisheries, was making investigations along the coasts of Hudson Strait. F. F. Payne, a meteorological observer who lived for thirteen months at Stupart's Bay in 1885–6, has left some fine notes on animal life that are seldom referred to.[12] Much of his information came, of course, from the 'Northerner' Eskimos of the place, but he, like most other observers, appears to put high reliance on the Eskimo knowledge of wild life.

Of the caribou, Payne states: 'Only a summer visitor to the coast, arriving in the early part of April, and leaving again for the interior in November.' In April and May the Eskimo went inland for about six weeks to hunt the deer, which served them for clothes and bedding, spear- and arrow-heads, and fat and meat. The young, they said, were dropped in June. Owing to the attractions of the coastal seal hunt in June and July, the deer were little molested until August, when the hunt was on again. He adds: 'They are not so numerous as formerly.'

There are also some notes on the wolf and wolverine, both close attendants of the caribou herds. At Stupart's Bay, the natives said, few wolves were taken, though they used to be very numerous: their fur was sought, both for clothing and for the trade. Wolverines and wolves were, however, often trapped to the westward, where they were to be seen throughout the year. (Bell's rather vague notes[1] on deer at Stupart's Bay may be discounted, since he did not live ashore there and presumably got his information through Payne's party.) In 1896 Low[10(4)] referred to the growing scarcity of wolves on the Hudson Bay coast, especially in the south, on account of the extermination of caribou; though the latter were 'still plentiful' in the barrens and semi-barrens.

Piecing these scattered notes together, we find evidence that the western deer were fairly abundant along their old trails in the eighties of last century, although several people were aware of their decrease in numbers. It does not seem very likely that this herd had changed its migration and found any sanctuary, unless it had moved to the central region. We assume here that Payne's deer were part of the western herd.

4

To Great Whale River, the Company's post on Hudson Bay, came Eskimos from inland and from the north, and Indians who hunted inland also, but farther to the south. From the reports of these two peoples we can get some idea of the course of the northern and southern movements of the caribou. Some notes made by Donald Gillies,[24] manager of this post in the nineties, give a valuable clue to the changes in the herd.

> 1890–1. '*Indians*. Deer also were rather less plentiful than usual on this coast last winter. Usually they abound in the spring months in particular.' (Report for Outfit 1890.)
>
> 1893–4. '*Indians*. Owing to a scarcity of deer in past winter, our furthest off hunters have not been quite so successful as they might otherwise have

been. Owing to forest fires, the deer have apparently abandoned their usual winter feeding grounds. Whether they have done so for good remains to be seen.'

['*Esquimo*.] A large number [of] northern and inland Esquimo visited the place in spring and brought fairly good hunts of deerskin.' (Report for Outfit 1896.)

1897–8. ['*Indians*.] Owing to a scarcity of deer inland in past winter, some of the best hunters have fared very badly and for a time had a hard struggle to eke out a bare subsistence. The deer have probably been driven North by forest fires, which raged in this quarter nearly all last summer.'

['*Esquimo*.] The Esquimo . . . brought good hunts of hairy and other deerskins.' (Report for Outfit 1897.)

Low, who crossed by the Leaf River route in 1896,[11(1)] saw rather few deer, though he attributed their scarcity to the migration which took them farther north in the summer. At Natuakami Lake the Indians were killing caribou, which had come to the fly-free islands of that lake. This was in the Stillwater River region, near the Eskimo-Indian hunting frontier.

Robert Flaherty made some notes[4] on the old caribou hunting grounds during his traverses of the Peninsula in 1912. In the spring of this year he sledged (with Eskimos) to Ungava Bay, from White Whale Point up to Lake Minto, a main head-lake of the Leaf River, which he followed down to the sea. He saw one very old Indian tepee frame along the shore of this lake, and notes that:

'The Indians, from their tree country to the south, used to make hunting excursions into this country in summer, in the olden days of the caribou migrations. Nor were their excursions altogether for caribou; they also made raids on the defenseless Eskimos, who, attracted like themselves by the prospect of deer, ascended the Leaf River from Ungava Bay in kayaks. . . . Defenseless in the sense that they were not armed with firearms, as were the Indians. Since the time, however, that the Eskimos also have been able to secure firearms from the fur men, they have proved themselves more than a match for their hereditary foes.'

According to the Eskimos, the land north of this line of traverse is treeless and Arctic, a rolling hilly plateau with innumerable streams and lakes. The Eskimos used especially to hunt caribou around the head-waters of the various rivers, as at Lake Minto, coming both from east and west to do it. The Payne River valley, along which Flaherty canoed the first part of his return traverse, was a favourite Eskimo route, and he saw a great number of ancient fording trails and stone deer decoys used in former days by the natives.

Flaherty's intimate knowledge of the Eskimos, among whom he lived for many months, is specially valuable here. Among other places, he visited the Belcher Islands, known vaguely for several hundred years, but never explored by white men until his expedition in 1912 revealed a great archipelago ninety miles long and over fifty miles wide.[5] On these islands a small Eskimo tribe had lived, in isolation except for annual visits to the

Hudson's Bay Company post at Great Whale River. They made this trip during the short time when the sea-ice was safely frozen in early spring.

Until within thirty-five years of the time he was there (that would be about 1877) the Eskimos believed there had been large herds of barren-ground caribou. Flaherty saw many bones. Some of the people had never seen a deer and were very excited when he showed a film that he had made in Baffin Island. The native explanation of their disappearance was that they starved to death one winter when heavy rains froze and covered up the vegetation with an impenetrable glaze. The Hudson's Bay Company has a similar record, through Mr. N. Ross, their manager at Great Whale River, though some of the traditional dates are different. In 1938 he wrote:

'Harold Udgarden, the pensioner at this Post, who came here first during the year 1884, states that the old Eskimos who were wont to come over from Belcher Islands then, told him that the last caribou were killed on the Islands about 40 years previous to his arrival. This would set the date of the last caribou seen on the Islands at around 1840–50.

'The reason given by those Eskimo for the dying out of the herd was that a great thaw, with heavy rain, occurred around the month of January, causing a flooding of the caribou feeding grounds (the moss). It then, after a few days, set into winter weather again, when the water covering the moss froze solid, resulting in a great food scarcity for the caribou, which eventually killed them off by starvation.

'The death of the herd, as stated above, would appear to be quite logical, as there seems to have been no apparent migration of caribou from the Islands to the mainland. The caribou was reported to have been on the islands during the whole twelve months of the year. There might have been a migration of caribou from the Belcher Islands to the mainland during the food shortage, but this seems to have never been put forward by the natives.'

Apart from a discrepancy of some thirty years in the date (native dating is always vague for long past events) the two accounts agree.

Mr. Robert Cruickshank, for six years manager of the Hudson's Bay Company's new post on the Belcher Islands, has given me some further information on this subject. Every year that he was on the islands (1933–8) alternate rain and snow in the autumn and early winter produced heavy glaze sheets that covered a great part, if not all, of the tundra. Under this cover the lemmings continued to live immune from foxes, which had to seek other supplies of food. This glaze would make it impossible for caribou to survive at the present day. Mr. Cruickshank suggests that the caribou remains that are still to be seen in many places were from an unusual migratory herd that perished after crossing from the mainland, and that there never was a permanent population of deer on the islands.

5

To reconcile these divergent views one may suggest that there are fairly long intervals during which the climate would allow caribou to live on the islands, and that there have been recurrent periods of more severe climatic stress in which any deer that had colonized the islands perished.

Flaherty adds:[5]

'At about this time, however, the mainland herds also disappeared, changing their migration to the eastern slope of the Ungava Peninsula, since which time they have never as a herd reappeared along the Hudson Bay slope south of 60° N. This shifting of the mainland migration is the more probable explanation of the disappearance of caribou from the islands, particularly when one considers the ease with which they could cross the field ice connecting the islands with the mainland in winter.'

One may doubt whether such a venture so far out on to the ice would happen very often. Also the sea, as Flaherty found, is open round the islands for much of the winter. But it is likely that the Belcher Island deer were an outlying branch of the western herd that was recruited occasionally, and it is very interesting to know that it disappeared just before the mainland relatives had begun diminishing also. The disappearance was a hard blow to the Island natives, whom Flaherty found wearing the feathered skins of eider-ducks and black guillemots for winter clothes. Similarly when he wished to film the natives at Cape Dufferin, there was difficulty in getting good caribou-skin clothes for them to wear in order to show the former native dress.[6]

The decrease on the mainland is also referred to by Cotter in 1911, in his account[25(1)] of the Eskimos trading with Fort Chimo:

'Others, again, trap about the head waters of the Leaf and the intervening country between there and Little Whale River in Hudson's Bay. Excellent fox hunting is reported in this section; we have lately had some big hunts from there, but owing to the failure of the caribou it is not so popular a hunting ground as it once was. During the eighties and early nineties, by far the greater number of foxes came from these inland hunting grounds, and were caught for the most part by Hudson's Bay Eskimo.'

The general drift of this evidence points to diminishing numbers in the last twenty-five years of the nineteenth century, and great scarcity in later years.

An important statement[27] on this subject comes from Mr. J. W. Anderson, who used to be district manager of the Hudson's Bay Company for James Bay, and has had recent experience of Ungava. He writes:

'It is quite possible for caribou to wander from the mainland on to the Belcher Islands. The crossing between the islands and the mainland can be made from about the 10th February until the end of April. In the last forty years, it is only once that we have a record of the crossing not freezing over, but this had been known to happen.

'We doubt very much if the sale of modern rifles had anything to do with the depletion of the caribou herds. In the 90's, the H.B.C. had a monopoly in James Bay District, and all natives were using old-fashioned muzzle-loading guns, loaded with ball, for caribou hunting. In all truth, it was little better than a bow and arrow, for the hunter had to get quite close to his quarry before shooting. Modern rifles were not introduced into James Bay until the advent of the competiton of Revillon Frères about 1903 or 1904.'

The reasons for the decrease must therefore remain fairly obscure. Forest fires, migration into central Ungava, death after glaze storms, are all possible elements in this tangle of population histories. The effect of native slaughtering, even without the aid of rifles, is given weight by Mr. N. Ross, who writes:

'As to the shortage of caribou in the Great Whale River Area, this is blamed, on the whole, upon the Fort Chimo or Nascopie Indians, who, it is said, were wont to lay in wait for the southward migration of the herd as it passed through some pass towards the Northern point of the "Height of Land", and kill them off in great numbers. This depleted the herd considerably and resulted eventually in the herd changing their migration route. Only a small proportion of the usual numbers migrated down into the Great Whale River area. Lately, however, there seems to be a slight increase in caribou in this area.'

A few extracts from police reports and from the annual zoological reports of Hudson's Bay Company posts in recent times illustrate how this scarcity still exists, although the caribou are still there, and therefore could presumably increase again if conditions were favourable, as perhaps they are doing already.

In the winter of 1927–8 Constable J. Murray of the Royal Canadian Mounted Police was stationed at Wakeham Bay with an air survey party. His notes[31] on caribou, obtained from inquiries, are interesting and confirm those just quoted. 'The hunting ground for them is about 100 miles to the south, and then only found in small numbers. The natives inform me that they are getting less in numbers as years go on, and that they [i.e. the natives] have to go further south every year.' In February 1928 he made a patrol westward to Sugluk post (on Little Sugluk Inlet). This has always been a famous place for walrus. But 'caribou are very scarce, the hunting ground for them being about 150 miles inland. At one time they were very plentiful, but of late years very few have been seen, then only in herds of 10 to 12 and less.'

The next information is from Hudson's Bay Company posts:[26]

Great Whale River. '1926–27: None close to the Post, but a few are killed each summer and fall, in the far Interior, probably about 200 animals all told. 1927–8: No deer has been seen near the post for years past. Far inland, near the Fort Chimo side, the Indians killed about 400.'

Port Harrison. '1929–30: Deer very scarce in this locality, and, if anything, there were less met with this year. 1930–31: Eleven only killed during the year. 1932–33: Were seen in greater numbers this Outfit than last Outfit. 1933–34: Very scarce during the year. 1934–35: Very plentiful during spring; many were killed by the Eskimo.'

Stupart's Bay. '1933–34: Scarce throughout the year, but have probably been more plentiful than last year. 1934–35: During spring 1935 were fairly abundant, much more so than in last Outfit.'

Povungnetuk. '1934–35: A great deal more plentiful this winter and spring than they were last year. Tracks were reported quite near the Post, and the deer seem to be travelling southwards.'

6

Leaving the central herd to the last, we come now to the eastern caribou. Low[10(3)] made some notes on this herd. They summered on the highlands between Nachvack and Nain, and they were hunted by several Indian bands, the northern members congregating especially for the autumn slaughter along the upper part of the George River (about a hundred miles below Lake Michikamau). Here the deer moved across south-westwards into the shelter of wooded country, and for a week or two ran the gauntlet of the Indian hunters. In the spring these deer returned to the north-east plateau, but in smaller bands, and at a season when they were not so easy to catch.

Analysis of the Moravian Mission records[28] of last century shows that deer fairly frequently came out to the coast at Nain and Zoar and Davis Inlet, but were mostly hunted inland; also that the whole herd did not leave the highlands in winter. These movements, again, varied very much from one year to another. The journals of Davis Inlet[20] give clear evidence of the herds passing southwards in autumn and northwards in spring. From the fact that autumn arrivals near the post were much more frequently recorded than those in the spring, we may conclude that the deer kept more to an inland or northern route in spring. They seem to have come much less commonly to Hopedale and Makkovik, though the natives of these southerly posts were often successful with the inland hunt. The evidence for these statements is full and convincing, but as it would fill too many pages here, it is relegated to the copied archives at Oxford.

How far the herds moved inland beyond George's River in winter we simply do not know. But it is natural to suppose they sought the watershed and the more sheltered valleys leading to Hamilton Inlet. A small population visited or lived on the hills between the Inlet and Sandwich Bay.[10(3)]

In the north, Indian House Lake (an expansion of the George River) was a famous crossing place where Indians waited for the caribou herd every autumn. From Strong's field work[15] in 1927–8 we learn something of this migration, and of the collapse of the southern movement in recent years. 'The Naskapi say that the caribou herds have decreased very rapidly in the last ten to fifteen years. Prior to that time it was quite usual for them to kill a thousand or more deer with spears as they swam across Indian House Lake. The main caribou herd formerly appeared there in October moving from the north and east, crossed the lake, and passed on to the south and west. In May it came back up the east side of the George River moving to the north east.' In 1905 Mrs. Hubbard noted the rapid decrease, which she put down to over-hunting and forest fires. Strong continues: 'The complete cessation of this migration across Indian House Lake seems to have come in 1916, when the Barren Ground people deserted the Indian House Lake region to go to the coast.' This was when they settled near Nain.

The failure of the caribou also hit the Davis Inlet band, whom Strong was with. At that time a few herds still roved the barren table-land inland from Nain and Hopedale, small herds of one to fifty. In 1927–8 the Davis Inlet Indians killed two of these little herds, one of thirty-two and one of six, eighty miles west of Davis Inlet.

7

The archives I have examined throw some light on this period of recession. As Mrs. Hubbard saw, the scarcity began before 1916. Here is the record, from various posts on the coast of Northern Labrador. The notes, unless they read otherwise, refer to the results of inland hunting into the plateau, often for a hundred miles or more. They are from the *Periodical Accounts* of the Moravian Mission[28] and from the Hudson's Bay Company Journals of Davis Inlet.[29]

1895–6. 'Large herds . . . frequented the neighbourhood of *Hopedale* the whole winter through, some coming also to *Nain*. . . . A special feature of the year has been the large number of reindeer that have been killed. But here again the south has fared better than the north.' *Hopedale* got 800. *Nain*, *Okak*, and *Hebron* a good many, *Ramah* very few. The deer were seen out on the sea-ice, among the islands, which was unusual.

1897–8. 'At *Hebron* . . . a fair number of reindeer . . . but not nearly so many as in the previous year.' 500 were killed in the spring of 1898. The hunt was also good at *Nain* in the 1897–8 season. *Davis Inlet*, 28 Apr. 1898: 'The deer hunters killed just what they liked.'

1898–9. 'Soon after Easter, most of the *Okak* men left the station for the purpose of hunting reindeer. . . . They were fairly successful, though not anything like as much so as in former years.' At the end of April 1899 Stecker saw two small herds near the Ablorilik River, on his tour to Kangiva and Ungava. *Davis Inlet*, Nov. 1898: Deer out at nearby inlet on 4th, 59 killed at Shango (also near) later in the month.

1899–1900. *Hebron*: Good hunt in spring 1900. *Okak*: 'Quite as successful as those at Hebron—if not more so—whilst out reindeer hunting.'

1900–1. *Okak*: 'After Easter a large number of reindeer were shot by the hunters.' *Davis Inlet*, 22 Apr. 1901: 'a load of venison.' 8 May: 'deer plentiful to the north of Nain.' 1 July: 'D. brought the news that deer were plentiful in his bay.'

1901–2. *Okak*: 'In April reindeer appeared.' *Davis Inlet*, 28 Apr. 1902: 'A good many deer reported killed back of Nain.' 1 May: 'J. L. and V. have killed a lot of deer in Voisey's Bay.' 13 May: 'The men arrived back . . . with 7 deer; they saw great numbers.' 23 May: 'B. arrived from deer hunting, with 6 deer; and his companions killed 35.' 22 July: (Four visitors had killed many deer.)

1902–3. *Davis Inlet*, 13 Nov. 1902: Report from two visitors that 'deer out at Daniel's place, they having killed 50 odd each, and J. L. also 50'. 19–20 Nov.: These deer left for the south. 6 Dec.: 'W. E. has . . . killed 136 deer.' 8 Dec.: 'A. . . . has also killed 90 odd deer.' 30 Dec.: 'Deer over in Big Bay yet.' 23 Jan. 1903: 'A herd of deer came up the Inlet.' 23 Apr.: 'I hear there are a good many deer out about Nain.'

1903–4. *Hebron*: 'Reindeer and seals were scarce.' *Nain*: 'A large number of reindeer were shot near this station about Easter this year' (1904).

Hopedale: 'The settlers living north of Hopedale were fortunate in procuring a good many reindeer, a large herd having come down to the coast. . . . Nearly all the men secured some . . . and one man had the good luck to shoot over one hundred.' *Davis Inlet*, 16 Nov. 1903: 'Plenty of deer out at Opetic. E. has killed 18 and O. 12.' 11 Dec.: 'G. and D. returned from Shango with a load of deer; saw a large band on the way.' 24 Dec.: 'A small band of deer crossed the Run.'

These notes prove that up to 1902 the deer could still be found both at the northern and the southern stations. There is a dearth of records for 1903–4, but in 1904–5 began suddenly the failure of southern migration of the deer.

1904–5. Okak: 'Between 500 and 600 reindeer were shot by the *Okak* men, the skins of which are in part used for tent coverings by the natives, in part sold in Newfoundland and Europe for glove-making and other purposes.' *Nain*: 'A number of Indians who reside in the interior, but come down regularly to the coast to trade at the Hudson's Bay Co.'s post at Davis Inlet, last winter stayed on the coast, as there was a scarcity of reindeer in the uplands.' (Store goods ran out at the post, and the Indians came on to Nain and Hopedale.) *Hopedale*: 'The deer that had been expected [by the settlers up the coast] did not come down to the coast from the interior.' *Davis Inlet*, 28 Dec. 1904: 'Five North Indians . . . report no deer inland since last summer.' 7 Jan. 1905: 'Two South Indians in a state of starvation: no deer inland.' (More Indians drifted in, starving, during the next two or three months.) 14 Apr.: '3 North Indians . . . report no deer to the North.' But on 13 May: 'Deer hunters returned. . . with a load each.'

1905–6. Nain: 'Nor were there many reindeer to be had in the spring. The first of our men to go inland in search of deer returned empty-handed. Others who started later succeeded in getting quite a number. . . . Many of our people looked upon the lack of reindeer herds in the year under review as a just punishment for the indiscriminate slaughter of the animals on the part of some of their number during the previous year. As is well known, the sinews of the back of the reindeer are used by the Eskimoes as thread in the manufacture of sealskin boots and other clothing. For the sake of these sinews many animals were shot at the time in question—the skins were possibly also taken—but the flesh was left lying on the ground. A great deal has already been said to the people about this pernicious custom; but now and again we still hear of its having been done.' *Hopedale*: 'There were no reindeer at all.' *Davis Inlet*, 7 Dec. 1905: '5 North Indians. . . . They report no deer inland and all the Indians very hungry.' 8 Mar. 1906: '3 North Indians also arrived starving, and report a large crowd camped at Opatik.' 22 Mar.: 'Post full of Indians.' (Others arrived during the following days, often starving.)

1906–7. Nain: 'Only about 20 reindeer were killed in May' (1907). *Hopedale*: 'The deer have failed' (P. Hettasch, 1907, *Moravian Missions*, vol. 5, p. 107). *Makkovik*: 'Deer . . . exceedingly rare.'

1907–8. Hopedale: 'No reindeer at all.'

1908–9. Makkovik: 'Since the beginning of March, over 40 deer had been killed by the Makkovik people. This was exceptionally good for Makkovik and neighbourhood.'

1909–10. Hebron: 'After Easter some of our people went deer-hunting but returned empty-handed. However they tried again later and this time were successful. Although they did not shoot hundreds of reindeer, as in some years previously, still they got enough to satisfy their wants.' *Okak*: Reindeer hunters returned on 28 April with nothing; but later, in May, they got plenty near Hebron. *Makkovik*: 'In November there were deer in Kippokak Bay, and 26 were killed. We also had three deer in our Bight on November 3rd.'

1911–12. Nain: 'Early in May . . . news arrived that deer were fairly plentiful about two days' drive from Nain. . . . The deer continued to work out towards the coast and before long they could be reached in one day. . . . Deer were abundant.'

1912–13. Hebron: 'No reindeer were killed during the whole of the year.' *Okak*: 'Our people are becoming poorer from year to year. Sea and land no longer offer them the needful for their support. Seals and reindeer are on the decrease. . . . Reindeer have been very scarce of late years.' *Makkovik*: 'At times a few reindeer were killed.'

1913–14. Okak: 'During Ascension Week some of our people got a few reindeer.' *Nain*: 'Deer have . . . been in abundance near Nain. . . . All of our men went off and killed a sufficiency, 200 or more, for their wants.'

1914–15. Hebron: 'During the winter . . . half a dozen reindeer . . . were killed at the far end of the Bay. . . . After Easter some of the men went reindeer hunting, but only a few of them brought home any spoils. Later on they were more successful.' *Okak*: 'During the winter fresh meat has been very scarce . . . a few deer.'

1915–16. Nain: 'Early in the month of April some of our people started off to hunt reindeer, Okak people who came here on a visit brought the news that a small stray herd of reindeer had been seen somewhere between Nain and the Kiglapait Mountains. . . . This winter, again, Nascopi Indians made their appearance at this station, this time with their families.'

1916–17. Hebron: 'A few reindeer were captured in the course of the winter.' *Okak*: 'Those of our people, too, who went out reindeer hunting got a good many.'

The absence of any references to deer in the Davis Inlet journals from the spring of 1906 to March 1910 (the last date to which I have read them) is probably significant, although the Company's men were very variable in what they chose to notice, outside the immediate daily round of work and the state of the weather.

8

Taken as a whole, the evidence leaves little doubt that the failure of deer began in 1905, and largely continued until 1916—the year when the migration was last seen at Indian House Lake. The notes also give an impression that scarcity was just as serious at the northern stations of Hebron and Okak as it was at the southern ones. Occasionally, it seems, a small stray herd would turn up near one of the stations and provide a temporary supply to the natives. If deer were so scarce both in the George

River valley and in the plateau country inland from the coast stations, they must either have diminished to very low numbers or else found sanctuary in uninhabited country far to the northward.

That the herds may have remained in the northern barrens was believed by Strong[15] and the Indians he was with. The Indian theory was wrapped up in the tissue of religious myth. The Caribou God, chief of all the deer, lived up in the north-eastern barrens, on a high mountain known as 'ah-tee-which-oo-ap', or Caribou House. Here the deer were supposed to summer. When the god was informed of the smell of deer bones left around Indian House Lake after the annual slaughter, he refused to let the herds come south any more. The Indians, since the time of failure, have steadily and carefully kept the proper rites, in hope that the god will relent and send the deer south again.

Strong based his views on more material evidence. 'North and east of Indian House Lake', he states, 'is a tremendous stretch of barren grounds into which almost noone penetrates.' The Indians, according to him, will not eat raw meat and therefore stay where there is fuel, and they also use wood for their equipment. 'As a result, the caribou occupying this vast range must have been very little molested by man. The Moravian missionaries all say that for many years caribou have been exceedingly numerous to the west of the mission stations at Okak and Hebron, the Eskimo killing all they wanted only a short distance from the coast. This was certainly the case in May, 1928, when I visited these stations.'

Strong's theory is really the same as that of the Nascopies, namely, that the herd had retired into barren fastnesses in which it could recuperate. Only he makes no attempt to explain why the southern migration stopped. But the Moravian Mission evidence does not fit in with the idea of a large flourishing herd staying in the north, when it might have gone south. We have seen how Okak and Hebron suffered with the rest. And to show how far inland the Eskimos ranged in search of deer, we may quote the evidence of Hutton,[9] given in 1921 to the Privy Council during the Labrador Boundary Dispute. This description gives a good definition of the country in which the northern elements of the herd were hunted.

'In the spring of each year, a large band of Eskimos went inland from Okak at varying distances, up to 200 miles, in quest of caribou. The trip would occupy up to two or three weeks. About the same time, other bands of hunters from Nain, Hebron and Ramah (until the station was closed in 1908) went inland for the same purpose. They all made for the deer country, from 70 to 200 miles inland, and they frequently met in this region. . . . Apart from this main deer hunt, individual groups of Eskimos from these settlements, went varying distances inland, at frequent intervals during the winter and spring, for fur trapping and deer hunting. . . . From the Eskimos, I learned that this annual deer hunt had continued for generations, and that the practice was to go inland until they found the deer, however far that might be.'

The range of native hunting territory indicated by Hutton apparently reached as far as George's River, and the Rev. F. M. Grubb, Moravian missionary at Nain, also informed me in 1934 that they hunt and trap far inland, and that they do reach this lake. Assuming that such journeys were made in the years of deer scarcity after 1905, there does not seem to be a very large area in which the main herd could have been hidden away, except the northern wilderness of high mountains into which Nachvack Inlet penetrates.

One may doubt whether there was a single integral hidden sanctuary (though one hesitates to make a categorical statement about so large and untrodden an area). It would seem more likely that the deer gained a great measure of protection against man by staying in these comparatively inhospitable regions, and avoiding some of the destruction caused by the spring hunt, when the young were still unborn.

9

It seems also quite likely that the deer were considerably fewer at this time all over this range, and there is a curious piece of evidence to support this view, which incidentally suggests another thread of connexion (Table 48). There was an extraordinarily great falling off in the collections of wolf and wolverine skins at the Moravian stations after about 1906.[29] These creatures follow and skirmish around the caribou herds, on whom their chief dependence is thought to be. Grouping the fur returns for the whole coast into ten-year periods, we find a steady high level in the second half of the nineteenth century, but falling steeply to practically nothing just at the time that deer became so scarce. The falling off in deerskins was also marked—though of course these skins were only the surplus not used for clothes.

TABLE 48

Caribou, wolf, and wolverine skins traded at Moravian Missions (all stations)[29]

(No caribou returned before 1867 or after 1911.)

	Caribou	Wolf	Wolverine	Wolf and wolverine
1834–43 . .	..	70	20	90
1844–53 . .	..	56	84	140
1854–63 . .	..	135	101	236
1864–73 . .	..	40	12	62
1874–83 . .	5,518	95	51	146
1884–93 . .	9,575	100	42	142
1894–1903 .	13,567	76	55	131
1904–13 . .	2,650	43	80	123
1914–23 . .	0	8	10	18

Note. The majority of caribou skins were traded at Hebron and Okak, also a few at Nain and Zoar, very few at Hopedale and Ramah. All traded after 1903–4 were at Hebron and Okak. After 1907–8 only 210: 60 at Hebron in 1909–10, 150 at Okak in 1910–11.

10

So much for the decrease of the eastern herd after 1904, which we may accept as being partly a real one in the total population, as well as due to

changed radius of migration. There is some evidence that the winters
during this period were milder and set in later than in previous years. The
dangers of interpreting subjective records that have no instrumental background is well recognized. And yet we cannot ignore the fact that Mission
records after 1908 persistently mention the subject. The late freezing did
not happen every year: it was more that the frequency of mild winters was
greater than usual for the twenty years after 1908. Three examples may
be given,[28] which suggest that the subject would be worth further exploration, to ascertain how far the deer may have stayed north when the conditions were milder.

   1910–11. Hopedale: 'As, during the last few years, the state of the ice at
   Christmas time was still very unfavourable for communication by sledge
   between the southern stations, the date for the despatch of the New Year's
   mail has been postponed for a fortnight, into the month of January. Last year
   the H.B.C. sledge from Rigolet did not reach Makkovik until January 12th
   instead of January 1st. For this reason January 15th has been fixed as the
   date on which the Rigolet and Hopedale sledges shall meet at Makkovik. . . .
   This year . . . we had "open water" for a very long time, and, except on
   the smaller bays in the neighbourhood, ice did not begin to form properly
   anywhere until just now at New Year' [letter dated 2 Jan. 1911].

   1915–16. Nain: 'We have had an exceptionally long and mild autumn. In
   the 28 years I have been here, I have never experienced so late a winter.'
   Hopedale: 'We have had a remarkably open autumn and early winter, the
   like of which has not been known, I believe, for upwards of thirty years. . . .
   On New Year's night the sea partly froze over, but the ice is not really safe
   yet' [letter dated 4 Jan. 1916]. At *Makkovik* there was no ice for travelling
   to the Watch-Night Service before New Year, a very unusual event. *Okak*:
   'The winter has been very short and mild for this land. We have really
   been only frozen in for four or five months. Our oldest inhabitants do not
   remember such a mild winter for forty or fifty years.'

   1916–17. Hopedale: 'The warm summer was followed by a mild autumn. . . .
   The sea did not freeze up till about the New Year.' *Makkovik*: 'We are
   having another late winter. . . . We are still without ice. . . .' [letter dated
   11 Jan. 1917]. *Nain*: 'The sea too remained free of ice for an unusual
   length of time—for not until after Christmas did it freeze over in our
   neighbourhood, whilst elsewhere it was much later. Indeed, as late as the
   end of January, the post-sledge had difficulty in getting to Makkovik.'
   Hebron: 'The past winter was very much like the one before. Not till the
   end of January was the sea-ice fit for sledging purposes. . . .'

These statements give some backing to the theory that stoppage of the
caribou migration across Indian House Lake in 1916 coincided with two
remarkably mild winters all down the outer coast. The possibility that,
having broken their routine cycle of behaviour, the deer did not resume it
at once, even in face of less favourable winters, is worth further investigation.

Mr. J. W. Anderson informs me that a similar change to milder winters
was also noticed on the other side of Quebec Peninsula during this period:
'In James Bay all evidence pointed to milder winters after 1908. As an

illustration of this it was the custom, previous to about 1908, for the final dog team trip to be made between Moose Factory and Rupert's House, arriving at the latter post about the 1st May. Since 1910 it has never been possible to accomplish this trip by dog team in May, and at the present date dog team travel to Rupert's House must be finished early in April.'

11

Finally, there is the evidence for recent recovery of this eastern herd. It seems from Mission records that the abundance Strong mentions for the northern stations (i.e. Okak and Hebron) did not exist much before 1920. It developed therefore during the next eight years. Now, these deer had been, according to the Game Laws of Newfoundland, protected in certain ways for many years. That this protection had no practical existence we may presume from the killing that went on, from the absence of any police or ranger control, and from some trenchant and amusing statements made by settlers in Hamilton Inlet at the time of the Labrador Boundary dispute.[30]

But about 1919 things changed, and serious attempts were made to enforce the law, as may be seen from these sample entries in the Periodical Accounts:[28]

1919–20. Hopedale: 'Venison, which was our main stay in days gone by, is now practically prohibited for us, as the Newfoundland Game Laws are enforced in these parts, and the tinning of venison is absolutely forbidden.'

1920–1. Nain: 'The deer-hunting, which used to fill the gap between fox-hunting and spring seal-hunting, is illegal now, and while all feel the injustice of it, they do not like to transgress the law.' There was scurvy, in consequence, until open water in summer brought fresh trout again. *Hebron*: 'It is as good as impossible for us to obtain deer-meat, on account of the Game Laws.'

In 1922 and 1923 courts were held at Hebron to convict natives who had killed deer out of season. The matter was often referred to by missionaries,[28] as at Nain in 1926–7. As far as can be made out, the chief restriction was upon the spring hunt, made before the young deer were born. A limited hunting occurred at other times, but the spring prohibition was a serious thing for communities dependent at that time on deer for fresh meat.

By 1935 there were several rangers placed on the coast to supervise the conservation of game.[19(1)] By this time also deer had become quite abundant. In 1932–3 a herd came down near to Nain:[28] 'For well over twenty years deer have not been so plentiful close to salt water. . . .' The Hudson's Bay Company report[26] for Nain confirms this account: 'Caribou exceptionally abundant in the winter and spring of Outfit 1932, further south and closer to salt water than usual.' Two other reports from the Company, for 1934–5, are also suggestive of caribou recovery. *Hebron*: 'Deer were numerous inland. Wolves were exceptionally numerous, due, we think, to the plentifulness of deer.' *Makkovik*: 'Deer more plentiful than last winter.'

We may now take a final glance over the whole history of this eastern herd, as far as we know it. Abundant until the beginning of this century, and the natural prey of Indian, Eskimo, settler, trader, wolf, and wolverine. Diminishing suddenly after 1904, perhaps through overhunting, and the deadly efficiency of the repeating rifle, perhaps also through other, more natural causes. With this decrease a slump in wolves and wolverines, migration of Indians to the coast, much hardship among natives, and an increase in sales of European foods. Then the stoppage altogether of migration in 1916, coinciding with scarcity and two very mild winters, possibly also with forest fires to south. The retreat to partial sanctuary of the barren hills of the Northern Triangle. Then final protection (probably interrupted by some poaching), and the recovery at the present time.

12

The central herd was the one that used to pass near Fort Chimo every year. We do not know the whole story of its movements, but a little can be pieced together. It was mentioned by John McLean[21(1)] in 1837–8:

'Rein Deer. Those animals pursue an undeviating migratory course every year, generally making their appearance in this quarter in the month of March, directing their course to the eastward, where they bring forth their young, then pass through the interior to the westward, where they remain in the most barren parts during the early part of winter. Very few are found detached from the main body unless old bucks, whom their youthful competitors compel to retire. When thus expelled they form into separate herds by themselves.'

Elsewhere in this report he writes about the herds passing in the spring and summer, and estimates that a small establishment could get sufficient meat to last eight months of the year. But he also realized that the deer did not always arrive in large numbers, so that this resource could not be relied upon alone.

Turner,[16(1)] for 1884, gives much the same story of the seasonal movements:

'In the months of September and October they collect from various directions. During the spring the females had repaired to the treeless hills and mountains of the Cape Chidley region to bring forth their young on those elevations in early June or late May. After the young have become of good size the mothers lead them to certain localities whither the males, having gone in an opposite direction, also return. They meet somewhere along the banks of the Koksoak river, usually near the confluence of that river with the North or Larch. While thousands of these animals are congregated on each bank small herds are continually swimming back and forth, impelled by the sexual instinct.'

He describes in a spirited style the swimming deer, bodies high in the water, their crowded antlers seeming like the branches of floating trees, the silent onrush of the Indian canoes, the driven herd doubling back, the careful thrust to wound mortally but not to kill before the animal reaches shore, the stripping of skins and meat, the titbits of meat and rancid fat and marrowbones, the stored dry meat for the winter. Sometimes a herd would be surprised on land and shot—perhaps the whole herd massacred in a few minutes. Another method was to drive the deer into a deep snow-bank and finish them with the lance. Against this terrific slaughter the deer had only the defence of their own erratic movements through a land which had very few hunters, depending on luck for their chase.

It seems rather unlikely that the does with fawns returned from such a distance as Cape Chidley or the Torngat Mountains. More probably they were on the coast-belt between there and Ungava.

The herd must have been large at that time, and still in the nineties when Low wrote:[10(3)] 'Wide paths, caused by a single passage of the deer, were met with along the Koksoak River as far south as Cambrian Lake, and smaller paths as far as Lake Kaniapiskau, where a small number of the reindeer appear to remain throughout the summer.'

Towards 1900 there began to be more frequent reports of scarcity. Not just the local scarcity caused by the variable migration path of the herd, but general scarcity that was to become a permanent feature in later years. As late as 1895–6 'deer had been reported numerous all the summer on the North Branch of the Koksoak River'.[25(2)] But Low[10(1)] records for about this period that: 'Owing to the extermination of the caribou in many parts of the country and to an insufficiency of other game, the greater number of the Indians are now obliged to purchase a considerable quantity of flour, and carry it inland to their hunting grounds.' In 1895–6 there is a note[25(3)] that 'the disappearance of deer from this part of the country has had a serious effect upon the expense for the maintenance of the posts'.

In 1900–1 'the continued scarcity of country food which has prevailed in the country hunted by the Ungava Indians for some years has caused much suffering amongst the people and been a great hindrance to the successful prosecution of the hunt; but . . . the reports coming to hand begin now to be more favourable'.[25(4)] The last remark may only refer to the fur animals, for Dillon Wallace[17] was told of the scarcity by Duncan Matheson when he arrived from the interior at Fort Chimo in 1905. Wallace states that

'formerly the migrating herds pretty regularly crossed the Koksoak very near and just above the Post in their passage to the eastward in the early autumn, but for several years now only small bands have been seen here, the Indians meeting the deer usually some forty or fifty miles farther up the river. . . . Of late years, . . . owing to the growing scarcity of reindeer, it is said the Indians have learned to be a little less wasteful than formerly, and to restrict their kill more nearly to their needs, though during the winter I was there [1905] hundreds were slaughtered for tongues and sinew alone.'

Although Wallace's statements on some matters, such as historical dates, are often inaccurate, this note on the deer bears a convincing stamp. The miserable tale is continued by H. M. S. Cotter,[25(1)] who wrote in 1911: 'Although there are large herds of deer in the country yet, there is no doubt they are decreasing. The repeating rifle is responsible for this.'

13

In 1916 the Hudson's Bay Company established a new outpost of Fort Chimo, far up the river—Fort McKenzie. This move was partly dictated by the stress of competition, but there was also another reason, connected with the caribou.

'The country 150 miles inland from Chimo has, owing to caribou and furs having migrated further inland, become untenable for Indians; and if they wished to trade at Chimo they would have to take enough provisions from the Post to last them until they reached their hunting grounds, which would be practically impossible. The result was that very few of the Ungava Indians ever reached far enough inland to obtain sufficient deer to allow them to hunt furs, and they were nearly always in a starving condition. Now that there is an outpost at Fort McKenzie, there is no necessity for them to come near the coast. Fort McKenzie is easy of access for the Seven Islands and Great Whale [River] Indians, and is a great convenience to them.'[25(5)]

The last sentence contains, incidentally, an unconscious tribute to the travelling abilities of these people.

We see that in the twenty years between 1890 and 1910 the central caribou herd had been decimated or removed itself to other regions. Knowing the great scarcity that developed in the western herd also in these years, and in the eastern herd after 1905, there does not seem to be any place to which large numbers of deer could have retreated. It is true the central high plateau, the watershed of Quebec Peninsula, offered certain refuges from man. Yet these were ravaged by fire and hunted by a fair number of Indians. There must have been a real, tremendous decrease in the herd, and there is not a doubt that the deer gradually stopped migrating in large numbers to the northern coast. This ceasing of the complete migration may itself have played a part in further decrease of numbers, since in the old days the northern coast east of Chimo was the refuge where the hinds went to bring forth their young.

Mrs. Hubbard journeyed in these parts in 1905, and was told by Peter McKenzie, who had vast experience in the Hudson's Bay Company's northern work, of the tremendous changes in the herd. 'Many years ago while in charge of Fort Chimo he had seen the caribou passing steadily for three days . . . not in thousands, but hundreds of thousands. The depletion of the great herds of former days is attributed to the unreasoning slaughter of the animals, at the time of the migration, by Indians in the interior and Eskimo of the coast. . . . The fires also which have swept the country, destroying moss on which they feed, have had their share in the work of destruction.'[8]

This scarcity has continued until now, as the annual reports[26] from Hudson's Bay Company Posts bear witness:

Fort Chimo Post. 1927–8 and 1928–9: 'No deer in this vicinity.' 1929–30: 'Deer scarce.'

George's River Post. 1930–1 (from Fort Chimo report): 'In the vicinity of George's River caribou have been more abundant during this outfit than for a number of years.' 1933–4: 'Deer very scarce.' 1934–5: 'Deer very scarce, by reports having migrated to Labrador. Wolves being scarce the past winter, no doubt are following the deer.' 1935–6: 'Deer, the past winter, have been exceptionally scarce. In April a herd of 20 had been seen, and sign of others; this has been the biggest herd that has been seen the past two years, by reports [were] coming from a westerly direction. Wolves the past winter have been exceptionally scarce: two had been seen to the coast, and tracks of three inland, directions west.'

14

Interwoven with this gradual decline in the numbers of Ungava deer were smaller fluctuations, caused by erratic movements rather than sudden changes in the total population. We should not expect a long-lived animal like the barren-ground caribou to decrease and then recover quickly within the space of two or three years. The apparent abundance or scarcity in different years were much more often due to the element of chance in the calculations or guesses of the Indians hunting the wandering herds. McLean was aware of this in 1838 when he wrote[21(1)] of the Nascopies: 'They are addicted to an erratic life, depending solely on the chace for a subsistance. They follow the migrations of the deer from place to place, keeping generally together in large camps, a circumstance which frequently subjects them to starvation, the game being soon destroyed or driven to a distance from them.'

One of the most important variables in the deer migration was commented on by Low:[10(3)]

'Periodically, the reindeer omit to return to the wooded areas from the barrens, and when this happens the Indians depending on them are left in a most lamentable condition, being largely without food and clothing. Many die of starvation in consequence unless outside aid is given. The death of over 150 persons along the Koksoak River during the winter of 1893, is but one of several such calamities which have happened during the last fifty years. In the evidence given before the committee of the Hudson's Bay Company, 1851, a letter was read from Wm. Kennedy as follows: "Starvation has, I learn, committed great havoc among our old friends the Nascopies, numbers of whom met their death from want last winter; whole camps of them were found dead, without one survivor to tell the tale of their sufferings."'

This variation in migration is illustrated by the contrasting seasons of 1868–9 and 1869–70 recorded in Fort Chimo journals.[22]

1868.

    3 Oct. 'Two Nascopies arrived. . . . Traded 33 deer skins from them. They say that deer are very scarce in the interior.'

    11 Oct. 'Two Indians arrived. . . . They say that deer are very scarce: it is some time since they killed any.'

    16 Oct. 'Three skin boats arrived from up the River this evening, as full as they could swim with Esquimaux. They are very hard up for food, no deer at all up the River, they have killed none for some time. . . . They are on their way to the Coast to try and kill seals.'

4 Nov. 'The deer are passing in great numbers towards the Coast at and near False River' (several were shot from day to day).

9 Nov. 'Saw one herd of 20 . . . travelling very fast to the south-westward.'

13 Nov. 'Out all day looking for deer, but saw no signs of any. They must be about done passing for this season.'

16 Nov. 'The blacksmith arrived from False River this afternoon. . . . Deer are . . . plentiful at the River.' (A fair number of deer were shot within reach of Fort Chimo during the second half of November and the early part of December.)

14 Dec. 'Went towards False River to look for deer; we walked 30 miles and saw nothing, only one fresh track. They have taken leave of us altogether.'

17 Dec. (The men started out to hunt deer on the 'Big Plains'.)

24 Dec. 'They killed only 7 deer . . . tho' they say there are any number to be seen.'

1869.

8 Jan. 'Returned . . . from the Big Plains. We did not see a single deer, not even the fresh track of any.'

3 Feb. 'A band of deer passed not far from the house.'

10 Feb. 'Two Nascopies arrived from their hunting grounds. They bring hardly anything: they say they are very short of provisions. There are no deer where they are hunting.'

17 Feb. 'A number of Nascopies arrived from the Interior. They are bound down to the Big Plains near the Coast to hunt deer; they say that there are none at all in the interior.'

27 Feb. 'We returned this afternoon from the Big Plains. We saw a considerable number of deer.'

28 Mar. 'A herd of deer passed within shot from the house.'

5 Apr. 'A herd of deer passed down on the ice late this evening.'

9 Apr. 'One herd of deer crossed the River.'

(Also on 10, 11, 24 Apr., and 5 May.)

17 Apr. 'There are now very few deer on the Big Plains.'

These notes leave no doubt that a large number of deer stayed around the northern coast during this winter, also that any deer moving southwards in autumn were unusually late in departing, and were hard to find in some parts of the interior valley. In May and June, parties of Nascopies coming from the interior had a few deerskins, but had passed a poor winter. The winter of 1869–70 was different.

1869.

17 Sept. 'An Esquimaux came down the River. . . . He says there are plenty of deer.'

8 Oct. 'Returned from an unsuccessful hunt, having killed only two deer. There are none at all now in that part of the country: they have all passed to the southward.'

14 Oct. 'Some Esquimaux arrived from the Interior, where they had been deer hunting.'

6 Nov. 'Shot 3 deer.'

15 Nov. (Had shot 10 deer since the 12th.) 'There are very few deer so far.'

25 Nov. 'R. arrived from False River . . . as there are now no deer to be got there.'

14 Dec. 'Indians . . . report that . . . deer are very scarce.' (Report from several visitors.)

1870.

6 Jan. 'There is no sign of any deer anywhere within reach from the Post.'

1 Feb. (Killed five deer on the Big Plains.) 'Deer are rather scarce in the Big Plains.'

1 Mar. 'Returned from the Plains . . . having killed nine deer among us.'

5 Apr. 'Several herds of deer passed while I was away' (they had been on the Big Plains and shot 12 deer) .

10 Apr. 'A herd of deer passed close to the house.'

18 Apr. 'Went deer hunting. Saw a herd and shot 4.'

22 Apr. 'Saw a herd and shot three young bucks.'

(Other herds passed near or crossed the River on 13, 14, 15, and 18 May.)

This account shows that big herds were not to be found around Fort Chimo during the winter, although they passed in autumn and spring. The presumption is that the deer went into the interior that year.

15

Variations of this kind were recorded in other years; but an analysis of them would fill a book. They influenced the Indians more than the Eskimos, since the latter had a reserve of meat and blubber to be taken from the sea. The Indians, however, were very loth even to look upon salt water, they had not the certainty of feathered game, were not always skilful fishermen, and had no large population of snowshoe rabbits or beavers to rely upon. Their main alternatives were caribou or the traders' provisions. There was a certain conflict between the chase of caribou and the pursuit of fur. This affected the marten hunt perhaps more than the fox hunt, because martens had a more restricted habitat within the woods, which could not easily be reached if the caribou had wandered to another quarter.

This conflict varied in intensity with the movements of the deer, and but for the increasing use of white man's provisions would eventually have curtailed trapping by the Indians. There was also a movement in policy of the Company away from granting the Indians credit, to which Low[10(1)] attributed much of the suffering in the end of the last century, including the disaster in 1893. How far this is true is a question for historians. It is pretty obvious that a measure of provisioning must now be necessary, when deer have become so scarce. Associated with these changes was the establishment of Fort McKenzie inland in 1916, which has already been described.

These three histories reinforce one another. Considered together they take away the possibility of decrease having been due simply to emigration from any one of the three territories. The western herd was declining in the eighties and nineties, the central herd in the late nineties onwards, the eastern herd after 1904. In all three regions the caribou have altered their ways, keeping respectively to the north-west peninsula, the central plateau and upper parts of the Ungava basin, and the north-east mountains and plateau. There were exceptions, wanderers at random or moved by conditions in certain years. But the main situation is vastly changed from what it was fifty or sixty years ago, when three recurrent drifting swarms of caribou made in most years their northward and southward migrations.

It is easy to suppose that changes in numbers alone could bring about these altered habits. A rather parallel history has been observed by Dugmore[3] among the wild buffalo herds of Africa. In the nineteenth century this species was abundant, and moved about in herds by day, swaggering in the open places. A frightful reduction occurred when rinderpest swept the country at the end of last century. For some years afterwards the buffalo changed its ways, retiring to thick forest during the day, and feeding chiefly at night. After a little while, however, the herds were recruited again, and there was a return to bolder habits.

One of the strangest features of the change is that two herds stayed in the north, while the other stayed in the south. It is as if the swallows from Ireland and Germany ceased to fly south in winter, while those that used to visit England never left South Africa. This phenomenon suggests to us that the migration circuit was not entirely necessary for the survival of the species, being perhaps a by-product of dense numbers and the accompanying differences in the psychology and ecological needs of the herd. For analogy we may take the locusts that live in quiet local groups until the population increase abruptly changes their reactions to swarming and mass migration. Analysis of the causes of decrease would need much more solid information than we possess. The organization of a deer herd is a delicate and intricate affair, the reactions of this organization upon reproduction and the attacks of predators, disease, and accident still more complicated. But a few influences can be pointed out as probably being vital, although they are not the only ones at work.

16

The acquisition of fire-arms by natives, combined with the heavy commissariat of the trading posts, must have played a dominant part. Rifles have increased terrifically the speed and range of native killing power, while white men have added to the number of good marksmen. Guns the natives had for over a hundred years, but the modern repeating rifle came on the scene during the later period of decline. In Turner's time[2] (1883) there were no rifles.

'The guns used . . . are the cheapest kind of muzzle-loading single-barrelled shotguns. The balls used are of such size that they will drop to the bottom of the chamber. No patching is used, and a jar upon the ground is deemed sufficient to settle the ball upon the powder. The employment of a ramrod would take too much time, as the Indian is actuated by the desire to kill as many as possible in the shortest time. They do not use the necessary care in loading their guns, and often the ball becomes lodged in the chamber and the gun bursts when fired. When shooting downhill the ball often rolls out. . . . The Eskimo is far the better marksman.'

The Fort Chimo journal[22] for 16 February 1898 notes that six Indians who arrived all wanted rifles. On 13 April: ['The Esquimaux] have fair hunts and almost every one of them wants a rifle, which we are unable to supply, our stock being almost out.' In 1910 Cotter wrote[23(1)] that 'when . . . the natives as now are supplied with modern repeating firearms'. And in 1911 he attributed the decrease of caribou in Ungava to this cause.[25(1)] These statements should be compared with Mr. Anderson's remarks already quoted (p. 368).

We may take an analogy from some laboratory experiments performed by the Russian ecologists, Gause, Smaragdova, and Witt.[7] They kept small microcosms in which one species of mite, a predator, pursued another one, its prey. Most combinations of numbers failed to produce any equilibrium, but caused fluctuations: the prey population would multiply, followed by the predator population, which would catch up and overwhelm the prey, forcing it down to such a low density that the predator partly starved and allowed recovery in the prey again. Or there would be too many predators, so that after a time nothing remained to eat, and every individual starved. But an important condition of the experiment was the medium in which this process of hide-and-seek went on. In flour the small mites could hide more successfully than if they were living among grains of millet or semolina. The population curves were quite different, and the experiments showed how the end-result could be calculated from two considerations: the relative numbers of predator and prey to start with, and the amount of cover or refuge. Even with small initial predator numbers, the end was bound to be extinction of prey unless some of them could escape for long enough to breed successfully. In other words, all systems of predator and prey depend for their continued existence upon a nice balance between the effectiveness of search and the ability of the prey to avoid or take cover from its enemies. No predator can afford to be too efficient.[3a, 3b]

In most of these systems a steady balance is never attained. Instead, there are fluctuations. These fluctuations are further complicated very often by other influences, such as the interaction of parasites with their host to cause disease in both the predator and the prey. Gause has done also experiments with other small animals in artificial microcosms, demonstrating in practice the previous theories of Lotka, Volterra, and Nicholson.

In the system formed by the Indians and the caribou there have been fluctuations and ultimate limits of this sort. For hundreds of years the Indian population must have starved at intervals, giving the deer opportunities to increase, then killing deer heavily until another failure to cross their erratic tracks caused more Indians to starve. This, crudely expressed without the many qualifications that are obviously required, was the position before traders began to dominate the native economy.

At first the fur trade added an unconscious contribution towards the conservation of caribou, one which is seldom mentioned. The killing of wolves and wolverines for their skins doubtless saved indirectly many deer that would have been destroyed by them. In just the same way, man may partly compensate for killing Arctic seals by killing also polar bears that chiefly live on seals. And, after all, this is how man, the predator, has been able to live on sheep and cattle and domestic fowls—by taking the food that formerly went to wolf, wolverine, lynx, eagle, polecat, and (in most civilized countries) fox.

The introduction of fire-arms may have extended the 'searching power' of the Indians enough to send the deer population tobogganing down. Only in Labrador, some curious change occurred that broke the migration circuit and allowed the deer to rebuild their numbers within the double refuge of the northern Labrador fastnesses and the rather casual game laws of the Newfoundland Government.

17

There are many other influences also to be examined; climatic changes, fear of man with his new explosive noises, forest fires and their relation to vegetation and its stages of succession, disease, or the difficulties of re-creating herd traditions that have once been smashed. These need study, along the lines of Fraser Darling's researches[2] upon the red deer herds of Scotland. Perhaps the wave of anxiety about conservation that is agitating North America will reach the House of Parliament in Quebec, and bring some bold measure of reconstruction to the caribou. The way has been cleared of certain political obstacles that other provinces bow beneath, by the exclusion of white hunters from northern Quebec Peninsula (Chapter XIV).

There are encouraging movements in this direction in other parts of North America, as the beaver reserve of the Hudson's Bay Company on Rupert's River; the growing herds of domestic reindeer watched by their Eskimo masters in Alaska; the new Canadian Government venture of the same sort in the McKenzie River region; enlightened Federal research by the Porsilds and Clarke on caribou and musk-ox ecology west of Hudson Bay; and the growing interest (under its new Commissioners) of Newfoundland in the Labrador herds. One wonders, however, if it is with wisdom or as an optimistic gamble that a new company is proposing to introduce a thousand domestic reindeer into the hinterland of Hamilton Inlet.[19(2)]

This ecological plexus needs good research, practical imagination, and bold statesmanship if it is to keep its best value, perhaps if it is to go on at all.

18

Some other changes in the Ungava framework must now be mentioned before we leave it. They arise from quite a different reason—the high modern values of fur in general and of the arctic fox in particular. The main points can be quickly mentioned.

In 1903 Revillon Frères set up a post near Fort Chimo and began an intense campaign to secure the native trade. There is no point in following all the moves and counter-moves that occurred. The result was much what we might expect: the trade became more or less divided between the two concerns, with fluctuations in proportion that were large enough sometimes to hinder interpretation of the fur returns. Another result was a certain amount of demoralization among natives, finding themselves for the first time in a position to dispense favours. And there was an increase in sale of repeating rifles.

From 1903 to 1912 the archives provide a commentary by means of which corrections can be applied to the fur story. After 1912 we have, through the courtesy of Messrs. Revillon Frères, the records of their furs for amalgamation with those of the Company.

Both companies had begun, before the War, to send out expeditions further afield, tapping new Eskimo communities for fur. By 1928 most parts of the inhabited Canadian Arctic were under the influence of these concerns, or of other, smaller traders. The history of this expansion in Ungava and on its borders is summarized in Table 49. It will be seen that Revillons closed Fort Chimo in 1930, but kept some other posts in operation, although by then the ultimate financial control of the two companies had been combined.

During these years the sphere of influence of Fort Chimo itself was shrinking, as the old outposts became posts or new ones were built. By 1925[26] its range was only '25 miles from the mouth of the Koksoak River to 80 miles up the River on either bank, and the barren country between Leaf River and Fort Chimo'. The neighbouring posts of Leaf River, Whale River, and George's River controlled their respective river valleys. Westwards a string of posts divided the coast Eskimos between them, while inland was Fort McKenzie and its interior Indians.

With this sketch of the country, the native peoples, their caribou herds, and the framework of fur-trade posts, as a background, we may proceed to the next figures in the story—the arctic fox and the coloured fox.

TABLE 49

Notes on some Ungava fur posts

(Dates are Outfits, unless otherwise stated.)

Fort Chimo. Re-established 1866 (see Chapter XVII). In 1903 Revillon Frères started a rival post (see this Chapter), which was closed at the end of Outfit 1929.

George's River. This began as an outpost of Fort Chimo on or near the site of the old Fort Sivewright. K. McKenzie, in a letter from Fort Chimo, 13 June 1884, orders John Ford to take charge of new buildings there. A report from Fort Chimo to the Commissioner of the Company, Winnipeg, Aug. 1886, says that George's River was principally established for salmon and seal fishing; but later on we begin to read of notes on fur trading. For many years it was treated as an outpost, in the sense that its fur returns were included with those of Fort Chimo. Since 1925 it has been a separate post.

Whale River. This was at first only an outpost of Fort Chimo for the white whale fishery and winter hunting. In the 1886 report it was stated that 'there is no trade', meaning fur trade with natives. The first whale fishery was in summer 1886. Since 1927 it has been a separate post.

Wolstenholme. Established 1909 (see Chapter XIX).

Stupart's Bay. Established 1914 (shown by fur returns).

Port Burwell. Established 1916 (see Appendix).

Fort McKenzie. Established 1916 (see this Chapter).

From 1920 onwards more posts were established along these coasts, and eventually Ungava fur district covered a larger area than the old district. The detailed history of these posts is not relevant to the present book. From 1910 onwards Revillon Frères also established a number of rival posts.

REFERENCES

* indicates that an abstract is deposited in the Bureau of Animal Population, Oxford. Dates of archives are those of the 'Outfits', e.g. 1900 means 1900–1. H. B. Co. means Hudson's Bay Company.

1. BELL, R. (1884). 'Observations on the geology, mineralogy, zoology and botany of the Labrador Coast, Hudson's Strait and Bay.' Rep. Geol. & Nat. Hist. Surv. & Mus. Canada for 1882–3–4: 1–62 DD.

2. DARLING, F. FRASER (1937). 'A herd of red deer: a study in animal behaviour.' Oxford and London.

3. DUGMORE, A. R. (1924). 'The vast Sudan.' London. P. 274.

3 a. ELTON, C. (1938). 'Animal numbers and adaptation.' In 'Evolution: essays on aspects of evolutionary biology presented to Professor E. S. Goodrich . . .'. Ed. by G. R. de Beer. Oxford. Pp. 127–37.

3 b. ELTON, C. (1939). 'On the nature of cover.' J. Wildlife Management, 3: 332–8.

4. FLAHERTY, R. J. (1918). 'Two traverses across Ungava Peninsula Labrador.' Geogr. Rev. 6: 116–28.

5. FLAHERTY, R. J. (1918). 'The Belcher Islands of Hudson Bay: their discovery and exploration.' Geogr. Rev. 5: 433–58.

6. FLAHERTY, R. J., & FLAHERTY, F. H. (1924). 'My Eskimo friends: "Nanook of the North".' London.

7. GAUSE, G. F., SMARAGDOVA, N. P., & WITT, A. A. (1936). 'Further studies of interaction between predators and prey.' J. Anim. Ecol. 5: 1–18.

8. HUBBARD, L. (Mrs.) (1908). 'A woman's way through unknown Labrador.' London. p. 169.

9. HUTTON, S. K. (1926). [Evidence in the Labrador Boundary Dispute.] Vol. 8: 4209.

10. LOW, A. P. (1896). 'Report on explorations in the Labrador Peninsula, along the East Main, Koksoak, Hamilton, Manicuagan and portions of other rivers, in 1892–93–94–95.' Ann. Rep. Geol. Surv. Canada for 1895, 8: 1–387 L. (1) 49 L. (2) 48 L. (3) 319–20 L. (4) 313 L.

11. LOW, A. P. (1898). 'Report on a traverse of the Northern part of the Labrador Peninsula from Richmond Gulf to Ungava Bay.' Ann. Rep. Geol. Surv. Canada for 1896, 9: 1–43 L. (1) 11 L, 14 L, 15 L.

12. PAYNE, F. F. (1887), in 'Report of the Hudson's Bay Expedition of 1886, under the command of Lieut. A. R. Gordon, R.N.' Pp. 70–83. Blue-book. Dept. of Marine & Fisheries, Ottawa.

13. Peck, E. J. (1886). 'Across Labrador: notes of journey from Little Whale River to Ungava Bay.' The Church Missionary Intelligencer and Record, 11: 510–12.

14. Prichard, H. Hesketh (1910). Geogr. J. 36: 691–2.

15. Strong, W. D. (1930). 'Notes on mammals of the Labrador interior.' J. Mammal. 11: 1–10.

16. Turner, L. M. (1894). 'Ethnology of the Ungava District, Hudson Bay Territory.' Smithson. Inst., Bur. of Amer. Ethnology, 11th Ann. Rep. (1889–90): 167–349. (1) 276–9. (2) 279.

17. Wallace, D. (1907). 'The long Labrador trail.' London. pp. 210–11.

18. Wheeler, E. P. (1930). 'Journeys about Nain: winter hunting with the Labrador Eskimo.' Geogr. Rev. July, pp. 454–68.

19. The Beaver Magazine (H. B. Co.). (1) Dec. 1935, p. 65. (2) Dec. 1937, p. 64.

*20. Davis Inlet Post, Journals, 1869–76, 1879–98, 1901–9. MS. H. B. Co. Archives, London.

*21. Ungava District (Fort Chimo), Reports, 1831–4, 1836–7. MS. H. B. Co. Archives, London. (1) 1837.

*22. Fort Chimo Post (Ungava District), Journals, 1866–72, 1874–6, 1883–5, 1895–6, 1898–1900. MS. H. B. Co. Archives, London.

*23. Ungava District (Fort Chimo) Correspondence, 1869, 1871–3, 1882–97, 1899–1912. MS. H. B. Co. Archives, London. (1) 14 Mar. 1910: Cotter to Romanet.

*24. Great Whale River Post, Correspondence, containing Reports by Donald Gillies for 1890, 1893 & 1897. MS. H. B. Co. Archives, London.

*25. Hudson's Bay Company, Annual Reports on Fur Trade, 1888–1928. MS. H. B. Co. Archives, London. (1) Rep. for 1910, Supplementary Rep. on Ungava Posts, by H. M. S. Cotter. (2) Rep. on Ungava District, 1895. (3) Ditto 1896. (4) Ditto 1900. (5) Ditto 1916.

*26. Hudson's Bay Company, Annual Zoological Reports from Posts.

*27. Hudson's Bay Company, Letter to Bureau of Animal Population from the Fur Trade Commissioner, Winnipeg, 2 Feb. 1938.

*28. Periodical Accounts of the Moravian Missions. London.

*29. Moravian Missions, Fur Returns for Labrador, 1834–1925.

30. [Evidence in the Labrador Boundary Dispute], 8: 3736–51.

31. Rep. Royal Canadian Mounted Police for 1927–8 (1929), pp. 83–7.

CHAPTER XIX

UNGAVA FOXES

1

IN the Labrador fox story the cycle in fur returns was analysed first, and was then given ecological reality and confirmed by the recurrent periods of scarcity given in the archives. This arrangement of evidence rested on the comparatively stable numbers and trading habits of the Atlantic coast Eskimos attached to the Moravian Mission stations, and on the fairly complete monopoly of the Hudson's Bay Company at Davis Inlet over their Indian trade.

The last two chapters have shown how different the trade at Ungava was, in every respect except its monopoly in the earlier years, and its concern in the same cycle of fur-bearing animals. We have the wandering deer; the wandering Indians whose fur hunt depended so much on their success with the deer; the hazardous travels and irregular visits of distant Eskimo bands; the epidemics in man or dog that sometimes increased this irregularity; and violent competition in later days.

So, for Ungava, it is best to study the archive entries first, and then see how true a reflection of this cycle record the fur figures give. Fortunately much of the record is rather full, at any rate better than we might expect from an era in which zoologists were still enclosed in a pre-Galilean concept of animal populations, and traders lived much in the daily round of immediate labour.

The earlier part of the story comes from the correspondence, journals, and reports of the Hudson's Bay Company (see p. 260) for the two occupations of Fort Chimo. The first period, from 1830 to 1842, gives only one clear cycle fragment: the rest is unsatisfactory for the assessment of fluctuations. From 1866 to 1916 the records are fuller, but after that I have only a thin thread of facts until 1925. There is still a large bulk of papers that must be examined some day; but this has not been done, and I have to acknowledge the concession that the Company made in making such comparatively recent archives open to research and publication. Their normal limit is 1870. I am particularly fortunate in having had the comments of Mr. Ralph Parsons, the Fur Trade Commissioner, who developed much of this northern trade in the last twenty-five years; and of Mr. J. W. Anderson, who read this book in manuscript on behalf of the Company. Mr. Anderson served in various parts of James Bay District from 1912 to 1937, was District Manager from 1931 to 1937, and then became the Manager of Ungava District. Besides this private information of the Company, now fortunately released for science, there is a sprinkling of explorers' observations, of varying texture and reliability.

In 1925 a new period, based on a new outlook, began. From then to the present time many of the Company's posts have furnished annual reports on the fluctuations of wild life within their observation or that of trappers coming in to the posts. This series of reports was only once broken, in 1931–2, when the wave of economy engulfed them, along with some other new things meant to endure. The Labrador chapters have already used some of the useful results of this system, initiated and finally designed by Mr. Charles V. Sale, and extended in recent years by Mr. Ralph Parsons and his staff in Winnipeg.

In these later years there have been several other sources of information: the published annual reports of the Royal Canadian Mounted Police; a special inquiry on sledge-dog and fox disease in 1929–30, done by the Company and co-ordinated by myself; the published papers of Gross upon snowy-owl migrations; and some information about lemmings that Dr. R. M. Anderson has collected and given to me; and a little more.

Finally, the union of conservation ideas with administrative responsibilities, led the Canadian Government's Northwest Territories Administration to begin an annual inquiry designed to give 'staff maps' of the population trends of lemming and fox and owl and sledge-dog and ptarmigan for the whole Canadian Arctic, East and West. The Hudson's Bay Company joined in with this inquiry, so that there is now a pooling of information, all of which is put together in the Bureau of Animal Population. The first report was for the season of 1935–6. One advance that came with this modern intelligence system was a method of indicating *areas of observation*, a method adapted from earlier experiments in charting snowshoe rabbit cycles in Canada. More is said of this work in Chapter IV.

2

Some early notes fix 1833 as a year of great fox scarcity in Ungava. Finlayson wrote[5(3)] to head-quarters on 3 March 1834: 'There was not a single fox to be seen in our vicinity last season.' On 25 and 26 July 1834 a report stated:[4(2)] 'Seven boats and upwards of thirty kyacks arrived; they brought but few [furs] as they say foxes were extremely scarce [i.e. in the winter of 1833–4].' On 2 August:[4(2)] 'Six kyacks arrived from the E[ast-wa]rd, two of them strangers. . . . They did not trap a fox last winter.' On 17 August:[4(2)] 'A skin boat and five kyacks arrived from Cape Chudley, where they wintered: brought only two otters, 2 foxes and some deer and seal skins, which they said was their whole winter's hunt, foxes being scarce.'

Next season things improved, for Finlayson wrote[4(2)] on 14 February 1835: 'Foxes were so scarce last year that they [the Eskimo] brought but few. . . . Foxes are not so scarce on the Coast as they were last season.' On 18 August 1835 he noted:[5(1)] 'The Esquimeaux have done pretty well in foxes last season; some "knowing" men of them are turning traders and travel west in search of foxes and make sometimes a handsome profit in this way.'

The fox trade at this time, as at the present day, included both white and coloured, as is shown by the following statement[4(1)] in a report for

1832–3 in which the Eskimo trade is mentioned: 'Those who winter on the Islands bring only white foxes, but those who are furnished with guns and who winter in the Bays for the benefit of being near the deer, procure coloured foxes as well as white.'

From 1866 to 1887 we rely only upon the Ungava District archives, but from 1888 onwards the Annual Reports on Fur Trade begin to add a good deal or polish the raw materials of the other papers. For these reports are, of course, based on the same Ungava archives (mainly the letters). They have a value, however, in filling periods in which the original letters are not available, or in giving a current interpretation which may have more value than our own at a much later date.

The use of these records involves selection, but it is not very hard to avoid the ordinary snares that a preconceived conception of cycles tries to lay. The summary given in this chapter reflects the real trend of recorded events, and has been made by following the situation in each year, regardless of whether the cycle seemed to be 'doing what it ought to do'. The reader, also, should bear in mind the stratification of evidence that these extracts give. The best type of statement is this: 'The Eskimo say that signs of foxes are very scarce this winter', or 'We have seen many foxes about the Post this month, especially white ones.' Another type that is still useful is: 'The Eskimo have caught very few foxes this season.' But this is not so good, because the Eskimo might have been busy searching for food, had few traps or little ammunition, or been ill, or lazy, and so the statement needs some other confirmation. Taken with another record of the first type, the evidence would be valuable in confirmation: but there would still be the chance that a different tribe was being referred to. These comments apply equally to reports which mention the number of foxes traded by various native bands. Our object being to offer some reliable critique of fur returns, we have to avoid any danger of arguing in a circle.

In the event, we shall find that the evidence has to be taken as an interlocking whole. The statements that foxes are absent or scarce are often confirmed by reports about the failure of native hunts, which may not be enough by themselves to prove that foxes have decreased. The positive figures of good hunts show at any rate that a certain number of foxes were running about the country in that year. We must remember, finally, that there are always two species to be considered: the coloured and the arctic. These mingle and fluctuate together in Ungava, yet may have important differences from one another in certain years. Records that 'foxes are scarce' obviously cover both the species. But records of abundance, unless the species is mentioned too, need caution for their interpretation. Except where the matter is discussed, the story applies to 'fox' in general.

3

There is not much information about the seasons of 1866–7 and 1867–8, partly because the renewed trade had still to find its feet. The Eskimos brought a few white and coloured fox skins during the spring months of

1867, and on 1 August a boat of Leaf River Eskimos brought in fifty white and four coloured foxes.* 14 Oct. 1867: 'White foxes, tho' numerous on the other side of the River, appear to be very scarce on this side.' Several Eskimos were trapping not far from Fort Chimo. 30 Oct.: (Three Eskimo) 'continue to get a good many white foxes, but only one cross.'

During the winter and spring more foxes were brought by various Eskimos (there do not seem to have been many visitors yet):

	White (and blue) fox	Coloured fox
1868		
10 Jan.	39	3
27 Jan.	38	4
3 Feb.	10	7
(Little Whale River)		
4 Mar.	30	9
1 May	12	1
(Leaf River)		
31 Aug.	(a few)	

These are samples. They show that there were at any rate some white foxes to be had: they were not extremely scarce. The lean years that follow now prove that foxes descended from a peak that must have been earlier than the winter of 1868–9, and probably than that of 1867–8. (So many extracts have been given in the next pages that I shall adopt a certain telegraphic style that dispenses with some of the introductory and connecting phrases.)

These statements speak for growing fox scarcity. 28 Oct. 1868: Two men hunting across the river 'have only killed two white foxes so far. They say there are a few tracks.' 16 Nov.: 'The blacksmith arrived from False River . . . he reports foxes numerous but they won't touch bait.' (The fort hunters said the same in October about the foxes refusing bait, though there were not many round that part.)

A crowd of Eskimo came from across the river on 25 Jan. 1869. They brought among them at least 16 white and 2 coloured foxes. On 9 Feb.: 'Traded a few foxes from the Esqx. that arrived yesterday. They have very little: they say there are very few foxes this winter.' On 26 Apr.: 'Two Esquimaux arrived from Leaf River, they brought only 21 foxes.' In May and June some parties of Indians arrived from up country, but brought hardly a skin except some of deer.[6(1)]

P. McKenzie's remark[7(1)] that 'there were very few white foxes, I believe, compared to the year previous' refers to this winter season of 1868–9 and obviously to the foxes themselves, not their skins, whose numbers he knew well enough. We can draw the inference from these rather meagre statements that whatever foxes may have still been in some places

---

* Where no reference number is given, the information comes from the Fort Chimo Post journal of the date mentioned.

in the early part of the winter, disappeared or became very scarce before the spring. The winter following was worse for furs.

1 Jan. 1870: 'Traded with Esquimaux. Got only one fox, one wolf, and half a dozen deer skins from them. They report that there are no foxes at all to be got anywhere.' 5 Feb.: 'Trade with the Esqx. They brought nothing but deerskins: there are no foxes at all to be had.' 13 Feb.: 'No foxes to be seen anywhere' [i.e. near the Post]. 18 Feb.: 'Traded with the Esqx. Got only 2 foxes and a few deer skins.' 9 Mar.: 'An Esquimaux arrived from the North . . . brought 1 silver and 4 white foxes.' 26 Apr.: 'Traded with Esqx. Got 2 silver foxes and a few red and white ones from them.'

In the season of 1870–1 there was some improvement in the fox trade. 24 Jan. 1871: 'Trading with the Esquimaux all day. Received a number of white foxes, but only one silver.' (These people came from the north, probably from Leaf River, six comatics of them.) On the 30th two more families came 'from the far North', new visitors that brought a few white foxes. On 3 Feb. three strangers arrived, also 'from the far North', with a few white foxes. These records mean that there were some white foxes to the north-west, along the coast of Hudson Strait. Also on the Big Plains, within reach of the post, there were plenty of fox tracks on 27 Mar.; and again on the 29th, though the beasts were shy of traps. But on 9 Apr., seven young Indians came from the interior, and reported martens and other fur-bearing animals very scarce. On 22 Apr. two more far Northern Eskimos came, with a few fox furs.

This is McKenzie's summary of the Outfit:[7(2)] 'The hunts have been very poor, with both race of native. . . . A great number of strangers visited us last winter, more than ever was here before, but returned without giving in their most valuable furs.' Of course, white fox was little esteemed in these days, and the trader chiefly sought for martens (from the Indians) and silver fox (especially from some of the distant Eskimos). We might venture to fix this season as one of recovery after scarcity, a conclusion that is confirmed by the following winter's records. 1 Jan. 1872: 'Some foxes are going about.' 15 Feb.: 'Men getting more foxes than during last month.' 1 June: 'Men made pretty good hunts of foxes [i.e. last winter]. Quite a number of Esquimaux have been in and brought very good lots of foxes. The Indians have also done very well in comparison to past years.'

The 'men' referred to are always the Company's servants, trapping not far from the post. If any went farther afield, the fact seems usually to have been mentioned. Their hunt was for foxes (when it was not for food, as ptarmigan or deer). Although the journal for this season is rather barren, these few records prove that a good many foxes were to be caught. Some letters in September 1872 confirm this idea.[7(3)] 'The trade of last Outfit has been tolerably good: all my stock of goods was sold out, there was barely enough, but no furs escaped me. The servants have also made pretty good hunts. . . .' The foxes had been 'travelling South all last spring'.[7(4)]

That autumn and the following winter of 1872–3 foxes were still abundant, but there is some suggestion that the periodic disappearance set in during the winter. 16 Sept. 1872: 'Foxes are reported abundant just now.'[7(4)] Again: 'there is a good appearance of foxes on the Coast just now.'[7(3)] 7 Oct.: 'Four Indians arrived from Whale River side. . . . They say that there are great appearances of foxes about.' 19 Oct.: The men who had gone up to the Forks of the Koksoak on 26 Sept. reported 'a good number of fox tracks all over'. 5 Nov.: Two men trapping across the River from the Fort 'report that there are plenty of tracks but they [the foxes] won't go near the traps'. 6 Dec.: 'Two Esquimaux arrived from George's River side. They report plenty of deer on that side. Also a good appearance of foxes.'

4

At the end of 1872 the foxes became scarcer in some places. 17 Dec.: Two men from across the river 'say the foxes are all done, they see no more tracks. They have caught in all as follows: 15 white, 6 red and 3 cross foxes.' 19 Dec.: 'R. arrived from the branches [i.e. the Forks] of the River. He brought only 1 silver fox, 2 white, and four martens. He says there are no foxes: they all went away soon after the snow remained on the ground.' 27 Dec.: Four Indians from Whale River brought some foxes. 5 and 6 Jan. 1873: 'Some Indians arrived from up the River. . . . Received over one hundred foxes from them, besides other furs.'

That the decrease was not universal is shown by this: 1 Feb. 1873: 'G. got one red fox . . . and a cross one yesterday. He has caught several since the 10th ultimo. . . . Several Indians have arrived and are gone back to their hunting grounds. They brought in rather better hunts in foxes and martens than formerly at this season. They report foxes numerous but very shy. The steel traps are also very bad: they break almost invariably and let the foxes escape.' Of course trapping was supplemented by the gun. 20 Feb.: 'D. arrived from Whale River: says there are no foxes. Has caught one silver, 1 red and four white in all.' In March some Eskimos brought in 82 and 19 foxes, and a party of Indians 47.

McKenzie's comment on this season:[7(5)] 'The trade of Outfit 1872, except in silver foxes has been . . . somewhat better than for Outfit 1871. The servants also got a few foxes.'

There are no useful indications of abundance for 1873–4 or 1874–5, but 1875–6 has a good many notes.

The table on the next page shows fox furs well up in numbers, the heavy contribution being white foxes from the Whale River Eskimos. And these archive records are almost certainly incomplete. They form a minimum statement of returns.

Another thing the figures show is the preponderance of arctic foxes in the Eskimo catches, and of coloured foxes in the Indian catches, though the Indian contribution extracted here is small for both species.

We come now to a gap in the records. There is little relevant information for 1876–7. only a few notes proving that the men at the post were still catching white and coloured foxes in November 1876. And on 2 Dec.: Two men 'have been killing a few foxes'. In the blank that occurs between 1877 and 1880 in the written records an index is fortunately provided by some fur returns (referred to in the next chapter). These show a peak in 1879 that was followed by decline.

		Coloured fox	'Fox'	White and blue fox
1875				
21 Dec.	(Whale R. Esk.)	30	..	3
1876				
3 Jan.	(5 George's R. Ind.) . . .	18	..	1
4 Jan.	(5 North Esk.)	26	..	65
7–8 Jan.	(Indians)	2	..	..
7 Feb.	(Whale R. Esk.)	10	..	..
16 Feb.	(2 men of Post)	..	59	..
17 Feb.	(Esk.)	9	..	22
10 Apr.	(2 Esk.)	2	..	26
14 Apr.	(2 North Esk.)	..	..	43
15 Apr.	(Ft. Chimo Esk.)	..	..	9
20 Apr.	(3 North Esk.)	20	..	129
22–6 Apr.	(12 comatics [sleighs], Whale R. Esk.)	some	..	nearly 700
27 Apr.	(Indians)	18	..	10
29 Apr.	(3 Leaf R. Esk.)	6	..	46
6 May	(2 comatics of Whale R. Esk.) .	..	100+	..
12 May	(Indians)	13	..	1
19 June	(Indians)	29	..	1
Total	(Eskimos)	103+	100+	1,043
Total	(Indians)	80	..	13
Total	(all sources)	183	159+	1,056+
Total Foxes (both species) . . .			c. 1,400 or more	

5

By 1882–3, when written notes are sufficient to define the trend, foxes were abundant. 'The Esquimaux from the North brought [a] considerable number of foxes last spring [1883], and altogether the returns of Outfit 1882 compare very favourably with other years.'[7(6)] On 20 April 1883 four comatics of these people traded 526 foxes. But the Lower Whale River Eskimos, who also arrived early in April, had little to trade. 'They report no fur inland, and some of the Indians sick and unable to hunt (4 Apr.).' Another party of them 'had very few skins, and chiefly white foxes' (9 Apr.). Another 'had about 50 foxes' (17 Apr.). There is no information about Ungava Bay itself, so we can only say that the coast of Hudson Strait had foxes abundant in 1881–2 or 1882–3, according to which season the skins were trapped. But farther west there was scarcity in 1882–3.

There were not many foxes within reach of Fort Chimo in 1883–4. 28 Nov. 1883: 'Very poor hopes of a good catch this year.' 18 Feb. 1884:

Eskimos who arrived from the North (? Leaf River) reported 'poor signs of foxes'.

Though foxes were perhaps not abundant in 1884–5, we find Robert Bell noting[1] that arctic foxes 'or indications of their existence, were found at every place touched at by the expedition, in the Labrador, Hudson's Strait and Bay'. This was the Hudson's Bay Expedition of 1884 under Lieut. A. R. Gordon. It set down observers at Nachvack, Port Burwell, Ashe Inlet, Stupart's Bay, Nottingham Island, and Digges Island, and left them to make meteorological observations during the winter and following spring.

Bell's observation is independently confirmed by the diaries of these wintering meteorologists, from which abstracts were published, in the report[2] of the Second Hudson's Bay Expedition in 1885. From H. M. Burwell at Port Burwell on 23 Oct. 1884: 'A number of white foxes seen.' From W. Skynner, at Nachvack (on Labrador) 4 Dec. 1884: 'White foxes come to the door of the Station.' While Sir Frederick Stupart informed me in 1928 that he noticed both arctic foxes and lemmings numerous at Stupart's Bay in the season of 1884–5. Bell saw foxes abundant also on Nottingham Island in Hudson Strait, in the summer of 1884.

Though foxes were noticed at these scattered stations in 1884–5, they cannot have been generally very abundant. Fort Chimo recorded[7(61)] on 11 Feb. 1885: 'We have very few foxes near the Post this winter; but the Indians are getting a few at Whale River and up this one.' And the report[7(7)] for this season said: 'Our returns in furs are only fair. . . . Foxes were scarce; only 17 silvers, the least ever got in a year at this place.'

This scarcity was still noticeable in 1885–6, but P. McKenzie[7(8)] explained it by the cycle: 'I do not think the fur bearing animals are decreasing in this quarter. Foxes have been scarcer for the last few years than for some time before; but I think it is only owing to their migrations. They are never numerous for more than a year at a time, in these parts. Then they are scarce for several years. They may be as numerous as ever in a year or two.'

This is the first clear statement of the existence of the short-period fox cycle in Ungava that I have come across. But it must have been well enough known to the men who lived there. The scarcity must have already turned to recovery, for: 'The Esquimaux brought in more white foxes this year, but no colored ones.'[7(9)] The Indian collection of furs would have been much better if they had not been almost starving.

From the valuable notes kept by F. F. Payne that winter at Stupart's Bay we can fix the abundance and decline of foxes there: 'In the early part of September [1885] the white fox began to appear in large numbers upon the coast; and shortly afterwards those of other colours, which are rarer, were reported as having been seen. . . . Spring traps were kept set throughout the winter, and a number of red and white foxes were taken. . . . After 1st February foxes became very scarce, and few were taken, the last being seen on the 10th May.' Payne explained this disappearance by saying that there is a strong annual migration of foxes to the interior; but very likely this winter marked the turn of the cycle.

1886-7 was a black season for the natives. The Indians suffered, and some died from starvation;[7(10)] while the Stupart's Bay Eskimo lost their dogs from disease and were not able to make the journey to Chimo.[7(11)] I have no notes on fox numbers that year.

6

1887-8 was a good fur year on the coast, but the Indians still starved, and inland furs were scarce. 'The Esquimaux had plenty of deer all the time on the Barren Grounds, and did very well in foxes, mostly white ones. I got all the furs from Stupart's Bay this winter, about 400 white foxes [a few went before to the Dominion Expedition]. The natives from there report white foxes more numerous than for some years past, and that they are gradually coming this way; but have not, so far as we can see, at present reached this quarter yet. . . . Colored foxes are very scarce.'[7(12)] This year seems to have been a peak in the cycle.

In the season of 1888-9 the foxes were declining in numbers:[7(13)] 'Foxes are very scarce near the coast. The few that we have got are poor and mangy. Some disease has been killing them off. The natives tell me that they frequently find carcases of them on the hills. Today I got three silver foxes from an Indian, and one cross. Two of the silver were mangy and also the cross. All were recently trapped and should have been quite prime. . . . White foxes have disappeared altogether from these parts.' This was written from Fort Chimo by K. McKenzie on 6 Feb. 1889. On the same day he wrote[7(14)] to the manager at George's River: 'I am sorry to hear that there are so few foxes your way: it seems to be a general failure, for we are not getting any either.'

His report[7(15)] for the season confirms this situation: 'Foxes of all kinds are considerably below last year's catch, particularly white ones. North of this there were none to speak of. Those that we have received were trapped the winter before last [presumably by the far Northern visiting Eskimos]. We found that some disease resembling the mange in dogs has been killing off both foxes and wolves, and in consequence several of the skins we are now sending [back], although caught in the middle of winter are not at all good, the long hair looking as if it had been singed off, leaving the under-fur exposed in patches. . . . I visited George's River in April last. . . . Scarcity of foxes.'

The next winter, 1889-90, K. McKenzie died, and the letters came temporarily from Robert Gray:[7(16)] 'Three families of Esquimaux are supposed to have starved at George's River, in all 19 people. . . . They have had no deer and no foxes this year so far. . . . Foxes we have now on hand about 200, and all the hunts to come in yet.' In September 1890 Duncan Matheson came up from Mingan to take over Ungava District. His reports for the next sixteen years provide a very good commentary on cycles. On arrival, he wrote[7(17)] (from information supplied at the Post):

'The fur returns are . . . considerably better than those of last Outfit. The principal increase is in white foxes, which are said to have been more numerous last winter than for many years.'

In the following season, 1890–1, foxes were still up in numbers:[7(18)] 'The returns . . . are better than those of Outfit 1889; the principal increase in furs is in white foxes, which were pretty numerous last winter.' Another report[8(1)] stated that the district had made a large gain in foxes of all colours, especially white ones. Foxes, particularly white ones, were much more numerous than for several years past.

But 1891–2 was not so good for fur. 12 Jan. 1892:[7(19)] 'Foxes are not near so numerous as last winter. . . . Several parties of Indians were in lately, they reported game and fur-bearing animals as very scarce. . . . There are no deer or foxes at Georges River, [where] the natives are passing a hard winter.' This trend was confirmed in September 1892:[7(20)] 'Our fur returns are considerably less than those of Outfit 1890. The principal falling off is in white foxes, which were very scarce last winter. . . . The Esquimaux, from whom we get most of the white foxes, suffered also from want of food. . . . The Esquimaux from the Straits came in as usual in April, but their hunts were only a moiety of what they have been in former years. They reported having found a great many dead foxes on the ground after the snow had disappeared in the spring of 1891. . . . At George's River foxes and deer have not been so scarce since the Post was established.'

From this and the following record, we may safely conclude that this cycle, rising from scarcity in 1888, recovered in 1889 and 1890, and fell again in 1891 and 1892. The peak in returns was in 1890, but here we have no means of knowing how much of the white-fox fur belonged to the northern contribution trapped in 1889. And if we had, Labrador analysis warns us against any assumption that peak returns were necessarily peak populations. We leave it, then, that there was a complete cycle in these years, without attempting further definition.

In 1892–3:[7(21)] 'Our returns are considerably less than those of Outfit 1891. The falling off is owing to the great scarcity of fur-bearing animals and deer, and the consequent destitution among the natives.' This was the black winter when 200 Ungava Indians died of starvation. According to another report:[8(2)] 'The returns have very considerably fallen off. . . . The principal cause of this . . . was the great scarcity of foxes and deer. . . . The trade with the Esquimaux, also, was not so good, principally due to the scarcity of foxes, among which they state some disease has broken out, and which they do not expect to be plentiful again for the next year or two.'

7

By 1893–4 recovery had set in in Ungava.[7(22)] 'Our returns are better than those of Outfit 1892: foxes were pretty numerous last year. But deer and partridges were very scarce and the Indians had to abandon their usual hunting grounds and go far inland in search of food. Had they been able to remain on the River and about the Forks, as in former seasons, our collection of foxes would be much larger.' That winter only a third of the usual number of Eskimos came from Stupart's Bay. They had had severe influenza:[7(22)] 'most of them being laid up all winter, their hunts were much less than usual.'

In 1894–5 foxes had disappeared again.[7(23)] 'Foxes and other fur-bearing animals, as well as deer, were very scarce last winter. . . . Formerly the country about the Forks of the River was excellent hunting ground, but since the deer migrated to the North and South foxes have entirely disappeared from that part of the country.' Of the Eskimo:[7(23)] 'Owing to the scarcity of foxes, their fur hunts were much below the average. Most of the Esquimaux from Stupart's Bay visited the Post in April, but their collection of skins was the smallest for many years, foxes having been as scarce there last winter as in other parts of the country.'

In 1895–6 there was still a scarcity of white foxes:[7(24)] 'The Esquimaux hunts last winter were unusually poor owing to the scarcity of white foxes.' This information is amplified in the journal. 29 Mar. 1896: '4 comatics [arrived] from Stupart's Bay. They are fully 3 weeks ahead of time. . . . The hunt over there has been a failure. . . . Two sleds from Apelook also arrived.' 31 Mar.: 'Finished trading with the Eskimos. . . . They had nothing: 14 foxes and 2 bear skins.' 3 Apr. 1896: 'Six sleds arrived from the North. . . . I believe one of the sleds comes from the far North, the men never being in here before. They all say they have very little fur, foxes being unusually scarce in their part of the country during the past winter and fall.' 4 Apr.: From trade with these visitors, '73 foxes in all, 8 of them silvers'. 21–2 Apr.: Three sleds of Eskimos had 'very little . . . 10 white foxes and three bearskins comprised their fur'. 4 May: 'Trading with the Eskimo. They had small hunts, in fact exceedingly so.'

But the coloured foxes around Ungava seem to have been quite abundant: 23 Oct. 1895: 'The signs of coloured foxes at present are very encouraging around here, the tracks being very numerous.' At False River, 4 Nov., where the men had set traps: 'Signs were most encouraging, foxes being at all of the traps.' 14 Nov.: 'B. and I were off to ours at False River but got nothing: although the signs were numerous, the foxes don't seem to be hungry and won't take bait.' 16 Nov., the same place: 'Signs were numerous, but as the mice are plentiful the foxes are not hungry and the result is they won't take the bait. However, when the cold weather sets in it may be different.' 30 Dec.: 'Edmonds [from False River] had a grand hunt: he has 50 prime reds, 19 cross, 13 whites and 5 silvers.' 15 Jan. 1896: 'We also saw good signs of foxes' [at False River]. 19 Feb.: 'Edmonds . . . has caught no less than 30 foxes since New Year's.'

Outfit 1896 brought comparative scarcity once more. In September 1897 the report[7(25)] was: 'Foxes, especially coloured, were scarce all over the country, and more so towards the North . . . than around the Post.' There are details in the journal. 31 Oct. 1896: Two natives 'report good signs of foxes down below. It is a good thing, for they are absolutely none

around here'. 4 Nov.: 'Signs of foxes are few and far between' (after a
visit to False River). 23 Nov.: 'Went to our traps in "Hunting Bay" . . .
got a silver fox. Signs were also numerous.' Also numerous signs now
appeared at False River (25 Nov.).

14 Dec.: 'Agnatook arrived . . . from near Leaf River. He brings very
discouraging accounts of the hunt in that quarter. He has very few foxes,
and the other Esquimaux who are with him have little or no foxes.'
24 Dec.: 'Went to my traps at "High Fall Creek", but got nothing. The
signs were good, but the foxes won't look at the bait.' Still by the 29th
he had no success, though two other men brought in a few coloured fox
skins. 16 Feb. 1897: 'Agnatooke . . . reports no deer on this side of Leaf
River and very few signs of foxes.' 24 Feb.: An Eskimo from Leaf River
'brings discouraging news: no deer or foxes, and people hungry'. On the
25th six Eskimos came in: 'They had little or nothing.' Their trade was
only about 30 foxes. On 28 March the Stupart's Bay Eskimos arrived:
'They have very little fur: say that foxes were exceedingly scarce.'
30 Mar.: The Eskimos from Stupart's Bay and Leaf River gave in their
furs: 'All put together they did not have more than 25 foxes.' But next
day an Indian brought a good hunt of 32. In April Eskimos came into
the post with small or fair hunts, from Apelook, Whale River, and elsewhere.[6(2)]

8

Recovery again in 1897–8:[7(26)] 'Our collection of furs is larger than
that of last year. The hunt, notwithstanding the great scarcity of deer
and partridges during the past winter, was fairly successful. . . . The
Stupart's Bay Esquimaux came in in April . . . with better hunts than for
some years back. Some of them passed the winter near Cape Wolstenholme. . . . They reported white foxes as pretty numerous. . . . The 4 families who wintered on Apatock arrived on the 14th of August [1898] with
64 white bears, some white foxes, and oil. . . . They reported bears, white
foxes and walrus as very numerous all over the Island.'

This abundance does not seem to have extended to the Fort Chimo area
or inland, as the following entries show. 4 Nov. 1897: 'D. and W. S.
arr[ive]d from False River. . . . They report . . . few or no signs of foxes. . . .
Saw but two fox tracks.' 16 Nov.: 'D. arrd. from False River . . . got
neither foxes or partridges.' A few, very few, coloured and white, were
secured with the gun or trap during November, at various places (White-
fish Lake, Hunting Bay) not far from the post.[6(3)] This went on through
December, though on 28 Dec.: 'G. [from the Forks of the Koksoak] has
made a fair hunt, having in all 20 foxes, three of them being good prime
silvers. . . . He reports P. [an Indian] as having done nothing [i.e. had no
success] since the cooper came down: got neither deer nor foxes.' 29 Dec.:
Various Eskimos arrived. 'They say, got no deer, and but very few foxes.'

17 Jan. 1898: 'The two Indians who arrd. last night . . . come from
Whale River country. They brought very few skins: five foxes and a few
martens. They report no deer, and furbearing animals scarce.' 26 Jan.:

Two men from the post 'went all the way to George's River setting traps as they went along, and picking them [up] on their way back. They got nothing and report having seen very few tracks.' 11 Feb.: 'E. and T. arrived from Whale River. They report no signs of either deer or foxes.' 5 Mar.: An Indian 'brought in his fur . . . 30 foxes, all white except one com. [common] cross'.

This story brings out the comparative scarcity of foxes around Ungava Bay and in at any rate parts of the interior. There were evidently only a few patches of moderate abundance here and there. The increase in returns of fox came from the white ones brought in from the north in the spring of 1898. 26 Mar.: Various Eskimos arrived from Apelook. 'They had a good collection of foxes, over 200 of all sorts.' 12 Apr.: 'Seven comitiques —all Whale River Esquimaux except one—arrived. . . . They report having passed a hard winter, deer and other game being scarce.' Nevertheless, in the trade next day: 'The Esquimaux have fair hunts.' It seems probable that these were the Little Whale River people, as foxes had been so scarce along towards George's River, and this band usually arrived in spring.

1898–9 was a low year in the cycle:[7(27)] 'The fur returns are greatly below that of Outfit 1897. The falling off is entirely owing to the great scarcity of fur-bearing animals last winter. . . . The scarcity was not confined to one section of the country, but was general from Hudson's Straits to the Height of Land to the south of here. The Esquimaux believe that a disease broke out among the foxes in the spring of 1898, and this belief is strengthened by dead foxes being found all over the country during the summer. . . . The Stupart's Bay Esquimaux came in as usual in the spring: the scarcity of foxes in that quarter was as great as in other parts of the country.'

There are other notes for the spring of 1899. 7–8 Apr.: 'Four commetics from Stupart's Bay. . . . They have had a poor hunt. Altogether their foxes came to very little over the hundred, and most of them all white, with the exception of a few red.' 11–13 Apr.: 'Four commetics of the [? Little] Whale River Eskimo arrived. . . . Two other lots of the Whale River Eskimo arrived. . . . They had very little fur.' Then on 21 July the unusual visit of Indians from George's Lake: 'They have the same old story: fur scarce.'

The fur-trade annual report remarks[8(3)] with philosophy that 'the disappearance of fur-bearing animals is that of the usual periodic occurrence'. Remembering that the nineties showed in the Labrador fox cycles some curious irregularities, we shall not be surprised if there were also local differences in Ungava and Hudson Strait. These will be discussed later on. We have the cycle at its bottom everywhere in 1898, having shown one or more periods of abundance since 1890. We now have to follow the development of another cycle to its peak about 1901.

The reports for the season of 1899–1900 contain a further reference[7(28)] to the cyclical nature of the fox numbers in Ungava: 'The collection of furs is less than that of last year, owing entirely to the scarcity of fur-bearing animals; the Indians were more scattered and travelled over a larger extent of country than for many years back, and from all parts visited [the same stories] were brought in: "no foxes or martens." It is well known that fur-bearing animals decrease every two or three years, and that then an increase may be looked for. The scarcity has now extended over two winters, so that I am of opinion that the minimum was reached last year. . . . The Northern Esquimaux were in as usual in March, some coming from near Cape Wolstenholme; foxes were as scarce along the Straits as elsewhere. . . . I visited George's River in March: foxes and deer were as scarce there as here.'

In another letter[7(29)] Matheson defines the area of this scarcity: 'The scarcity of fur-bearing animals last winter was unprecedented and extended all over the country from Hudson's Straits to the height of land at George's [i.e. Indian House] Lake. The Indians travelled over a larger extent of territory than usual, some of them going to Nitchequon, Rupert's River, and others to old Fort Nascopie, and from all quarters the same news were brought in: "no martens or foxes".'

This story of dearth of fur could be annotated by many entries from the journal of 1899–1900. Only a few need be mentioned. 2 Mar. 1900: 'M. went to see his traps today, and got one red fox, which he found lying dead, but not in a trap.' 19 Mar.: 'Trading with one of the Esquimaux. . . . He had no fur to trade, only one white fox; and from what they tell us, no one else seems to have got any, or next to nothing.' 28 Mar.: From a party of Leaf River Eskimo, 'only ten foxes'. On 27 April only 40 white and 4 red foxes were traded by seven comatics of Eskimos, some from the north.

9

Things were better in 1900–1.[7(30)] 'The Stupart's Bay Esquimaux came in as usual in March and had a fair collection of white foxes. . . . Last fall [i.e. in the autumn of 1900] the outlook was very promising, and but for the scarcity of deer the hunt would, notwithstanding sickness and the plague of mice that infested the whole country, have been much more successful.' There are some details in the journal. 19 Oct. 1900: 'D. returned from the Pine Woods this evening. He reports seeing a good many fox tracks, in fact, a better sign than has been for some time.' 13 Nov.: 'Mr. G. and W. S. returned from False River this evening. . . . Saw a very good sign of foxes.' 15 Dec.: Two men 'report no foxes caught, but very good signs, the weather being too mild and too little snow for them to take the bait, and the country overrunned with mice'.

But there were also a few adverse reports. The seven families of Eskimos who wintered on Akpatok found no foxes (and not so many polar bears or walrus as there had been three years earlier: perhaps there was some dependence of fox on bear).[7(30)] And a man from Whale River on 26 Dec. 1900 said that foxes were not very plentiful there.

1901 was the peak year, and a good harvest was taken in the winter of

1901–2. As early as 20 Jan. 1902, Wilson (in charge while Matheson was on leave) sent a dispatch[7(31)] to announce good news: 'The prospects of a large collection of foxes are very bright indeed. Up to date we have 1,253 foxes in the store here: 13 blue, 30 cross, 72 red, 11 silver, 1,127 white. Edmunds at Whale River has about a hundred more; and there is a fair number among some Esquimaux who are hunting in that neighbourhood and to the Eastward of that River. The foxes have been caught . . . entirely in this neighbourhood—that is between Leaf River to the Westward, and Tuktuluk to the Eastward, and not more than a distance of three days walk inland. . . . None of the Indians who are hunting well inland have yet been out to the Post. . . . Mr. John Ford arrived from George's River on the 8th inst. He did not bring such good reports from that quarter as I had expected. Up to the time of his leaving there were about 80 foxes in the store. . . . Foxes were quite numerous all over that part of the country, but they would not take bait. The majority of those in the collection had been shot.'

Various hunters, Eskimo and white, found good signs of foxes during the early winter of 1901–2. Foxes even turned up around the buildings, and the dogs killed a white fox there on 6 January 1902, and others on 3 and 9 February. The Northern Eskimos from Stupart's Bay and Wolstenholme came in in the spring of 1902, but in smaller force than usual, because of an epidemic among their dogs. 'While their hunts of foxes were very good, still they maintain that the migration proper had not reached their part of the country.'[7(32)] The same annual review stated that: 'The Indians, too, had all a few foxes, some, indeed, making good hunts.' A note[7(33)] from Matheson, on his return to Fort Chimo in September 1902, adds: 'My anticipations of an increased catch of foxes has been realized. . . . The returns [this means all furs, but not fish and oil] are the largest since 1876.'

Next year decline set in:[7(34)] 'Foxes, which appeared to be plentiful last fall [1902] migrated south immediately after snowfall, and other fur-bearing animals were scarce all over the country.' But at George's River 'the catch of foxes was nearly equal to that of 1901'.

Decline led to extreme scarcity once more in 1903–4:[7(35)] 'The collection of furs is the smallest in many years, mainly owing to the unprecedented scarcity of foxes and other fur-bearing animals during the past season. The prospect in the fall and up to the beginning of winter of an average hunt was really promising; but, immediately after the first fall of snow, all signs disappeared, and a fox track could not be seen in a day's march. Our own three men trapped from 1st Nov. to Jan. between the Rapids and the Forks of the Ungava [i.e. Koksoak] River, and their total catch consisted of five white foxes and one red one. At Whale River Edmunds got three white foxes: two years ago his catch was over 200 [for the whole season].' At George's River there was similar dearth of foxes [7(35)] 'The Stupart's Bay Esquimaux [came] in in April, but not in such numbers as usual, having very little to bring in. We secured all they had.'[7(35)]

'The scarcity of foxes was unprecedented, the oldest hunters not being able to recall such a dearth; and the scarcity was not confined to any one locality, but was general all over the country from Hudson's Straits to the height of land at George's Lake.'[7(36)] It seems that Revillons, who came in 1903 to Ungava, got very few foxes from the natives, although they had a share of martens.

10

Yet from this scarcity the resilient foxes began to come back in 1904–5. 4 Jan. 1905:[7(37)] 'White foxes are pretty numerous along the coast, but unfortunately all the [Ungava] Esquimaux, with the exception of eight or nine in the employ of the French Co., went inland last fall, most of them wintering up Whale River, three days travel from Edmund's place, and have made no hunts, the run of foxes being confined to the coast. . . . As soon as I heard of the scarcity of foxes at Whale River, I sent for the best hunters to come back and hunt along the River here. Six of them came and are trapping between here [Fort Chimo] and the mouth of False River, and getting a few foxes.' The Eskimos who went to Akpatok only got 80 white foxes, also 40 polar bears.[7(38)] At George's River 'white foxes were more numerous than last year, and the catch, though not large, is a great improvement on that of [Outfit] 1903'.[7(38)]

In the autumn of 1905 'white foxes appear to be fairly numerous along the coast'.[7(38)] And the report for the season of 1905–6 stated:[7(39)] 'The collection of furs is larger than last year: the principal gain is in white foxes, which were pretty plentiful along the coast, but very scarce inland. There is also a gain in martens and other furs, the only falling off being in otters.' This meant that coloured foxes were abundant, as well as white. At George's River the total fur returns were less this season.[7(39)]

This was the prelude to another cyclic crash. Already in the autumn of 1906 the signs were discouraging for trade. (From now on we have the rule of Cotter at Fort Chimo: his reports are as incisive as those of Duncan Matheson, and give the same impression of wide knowledge of Ungava.) 19 Oct. 1906:[7(40)] 'The prospects of a good hunt are discouraging at the present time: foxes, reported plentiful some weeks ago, seem to have disappeared.' 26 Dec.:[7(41)] 'The prospects of even an average catch of foxes are none too bright. Only on the lower reaches of the Koksoak and the Upper Whale Rivers have any foxes been trapped, and then not in any great numbers. The best hunt is 40 foxes. . . . Several of our good men have not a single fox to date, others again have from two to six each. Edmunds, whom I saw at Whale River two weeks ago, had only 15, which is a poor record for him at this season. The Indians hunting between the False and Whale River have very few foxes also. Millar and Gordon have nine between them, so from this you can judge of the scarcity in this neighbourhood.'

3 Jan. 1907:[7(42)] 'Mr. Ford writes me from George's River that there are no foxes in the country. He has 20 in store to date.' For the whole season the white fox catch at George's River was only 113, and this was

27

their chief fur.[7(43)] But coloured fox returns there were slightly up in 1906–7.

This is the general summary of that season:[7(43)] 'The fur hunt throughout the country has been a failure. Along the coast from Wolstenholme to Cape Chudleigh, the same reports come of the scarcity of foxes. It would appear that they had migrated south, as I believe they were fairly plentiful in the country hunted over by the Indians going out to Davis Inlet. On this [the Koksoak] River the fox hunt was practically nil, except for a few caught near the mouth in the early fall. The same may be said of the other rivers flowing into the Bay. Very few foxes were brought in from Hope's Advance [Leaf River], Stupart's Bay, and the Straits generally. The Eskimo from that neighbourhood were more or less in a destitute state, and did not arrive here till June, coming part of the distance on foot, in fact several did not put in an appearance at all.' The Indians also had bad fur hunts, whether especially of fox is not related.

11

We are now in the trough of the cycle. In the summer of 1907:[7(43)] 'Very few tracks and signs of foxes are reported about the rivers and coast yet.' 7 Oct. 1907:[7(44)] 'Eskimo trade: which trade is confined chiefly to foxes, is likely to be poor, as no fox tracks are to be seen.' 2 Dec.:[7(60)] 'The prospects are very discouraging. The signs of fur-bearing animals, especially foxes, being very scarce.'

With the fox slump in 1907–8 came the usual lament of the trader:[7(45)] 'The worst year that Fort Chimo Post has had for many a year back. . . . Our salmon fishery for '07 was a complete failure, and our fur returns are comparatively speaking nothing. The fur was not in the country. . . . The Whale River gang of Indians, generally our best hunters, did not get between them more than 100 or 120 pieces [of fur]; for the bulk of the little fur that we did get we are indebted to the Ungava or Gulf Indians. . . . The Eskimo hunts were even worse than [those of] the Indians. This was partly owing to the great scarcity of white foxes around the Ungava River, Leaf River, and Whale River. As for example, Edmunds, our best trapper, had over 60 traps set and for the whole year only got three red foxes. In an ordinary good or even [average year] he would have given us anywhere between 70 and 100 foxes.' The post manager also explains that the Northern Eskimo from Leaf River, Stupart's Bay, and Apelook were induced by the French Company to hunt near Ungava that winter, and that they, knowing this part of the country little, did nothing useful. He adds: 'As a rule these people generally bring us anywhere from 500 to 1,000 foxes. The fur throughout the entire country was a complete failure. From Wolstenholme . . . to as far south as Rama the reports are all the same. At Rama Station they did not get during the entire year 1 fox. On all the rivers running into the Bay, the scarcity of fur-bearing animals has been remarkable.'

At George's River, during this Outfit: 'The fur returns . . . were practically nil. This was owing entirely to no fur being in the country, and to no fault of the Postmaster in charge. Fur was never known to be [so] scarce. For weeks at a time the hunters would not even see a track.'[7(46)]

The season of 1908–9 saw slight recovery in the fur collections, but there was still marked scarcity:[7(47)] 'Although the collection of furs is not large, it compares favorably with last year; with the exception of marten and mink, all other descriptions show increases. . . .' But the report also remarks: 'A poor season was experienced for furs: the hunt from the Northern Eskimo was better than last year, though no very large individual catches came from that quarter. Many of the local Eskimo did [i.e. caught] practically nothing.' At George's River the situation was similar:[7(47)] 'There is a better showing in furs than last Outfit, though there is much room for improvement yet. The Eskimo of this Post are poor trappers, devoting most of their time to seal hunting.'

12

For the summer of 1909 we read:[7(47)] 'The reports to hand from the Coast are encouraging as regards white foxes.' And on 11 Jan. 1910:[7(48)] 'Foxes are very plentiful again and all the Huskies [i.e. Eskimos] are doing well. . . .' 'To the North there is an excellent sign and the hunters in that direction are doing well. I have had no report of the Indian hunt yet. . . .'[7(61)] The annual report[7(49)] to head-quarters records a successful season. 'The fur returns compare favorably with the collections of the past three years. Foxes of all descriptions show the most important increases, particularly whites; but there is a general improvement in all other peltries. . . . The greater number of white foxes were, however, caught on the Coast north of this River. To the Eastward—Whale River and George's River—foxes were not very plentiful till towards spring, when the trapping season was nearly over. 1,200 foxes were obtained from Hudson's Straits: practically the entire hunt from that section.' In spite of the comparatively less successful catch at George's River there was an 'improvement in the collection of foxes at this Post'.[7(49)]

Farther away there had also been a good fox catch, for Revillons got over 3,000 foxes from the Eskimos at Cape Dufferin, on the coast of Hudson Bay, on the other side of Ungava Peninsula.[7(50)]

Of the season of 1910–11, the records give a clear account. 5 Jan. 1911:[7(51)] 'Foxes were reported plentiful at Wakeham Bay last fall.' 6 Jan. 1911: [7(52)] 'The prospects of a good catch of furs reported by the ship is not being realized. As soon as the cold weather set in, the white foxes disappeared, and up to date, though we have heard from all points, the hunts are poor. There is, however, a fair sign of coloured foxes, and the collection at this date compares well with any previous year. . . . The intelligence from inland is not very encouraging regarding martens, though the Indians report a fair sign of coloured foxes, indeed there appears to be an unusual number of silver foxes among the band.' 20 Jan. 1911:[7(53)] 'Since writing you . . . we have traded quite a number of coloured foxes.

There are 22 silver foxes on hand now, which is a remarkable number for this time of year. We have from 500 to 600 foxes on hand altogether.'

By 22 Mar. 1911 we read:[7(54)] 'The white fox hunt is a failure; we have, however, secured a fair share of colored foxes. We have over 40 silvers, and hope to reach 50.' There seems really to have been a very big year of coloured fox. The year's summary remarks:[7(55)] 'Not for thirty years has such a large number of cross and red been caught, and the number of silver foxes—52—is much above the average. Indeed, with the French Company's collection a total of over 80 were trapped, which is a record for Ungava since 1868.'

The white fox collection was not up to this standard, and this decline seems to have been partly due to the growing scarcity and partly to accidents of trade:[7(55)] 'White foxes, although good signs were reported at the beginning of the season, suddenly disappeared, and the collection was a very poor one in consequence. It has to be taken into consideration, however, that no trade was done with the natives from the Straits this year, as not a single hunter came in from there, and it is feared the French company have secured all the trade at Wakeham Bay. The white fox hunt from the Straits usually ranged between five to fifteen hundred pelts.'

The report also notes that 'many thousands of traps are in use now, and the fox hunt is pursued most vigorously'. But 'the local white fox hunt was very poor, many good trappers not securing more than ten pelts each. A party of trappers well fitted out was sent to the Leaf River to hunt, as the signs of white foxes in the spring of 1910 were very good indeed at that place; but the hunt proved a failure, not more than 40 skins being taken all winter. Most of the silver and other coloured foxes came from Whale River to the Eastward, and from the inland Indians.'

<h2 style="text-align:center">13</h2>

Meanwhile Ralph Parsons had established a new post for the Company at Cape Wolstenholme in 1909. That season most of the Straits Eskimo who did not trade with Revillons came in to Chimo as usual, because they had not heard of the new post. Still in 1910–11 little native trade had developed. An annual report[8(4)] states: 'Comparing this year's returns with that of the previous Outfit, there is a marked increase in white bear, silver, cross and red fox. Although we trapped over a much larger strip of country, using about a hundred more traps than last year, and white foxes seemed to be as plentiful, we secured 120 less. The foxes were not hungry and would not go to the traps. This is the only reason for the decrease I can give. . . . Last winter being a very bad year for foxes at Wakeham Bay. . . .'

From these very clear accounts we can conclude that 1910–11 was a high year for coloured foxes eastward and inland from Ungava, a year of crash for arctic foxes in Ungava Bay and as far west at least as Wakeham Bay, but that the latter were still present and provided with natural food in the north-west corner around Wolstenholme.

The next season, 1911–12, the cycle had once more come to the bottom. 9 Dec. 1911:[7(56)] 'There are signs of very little fur about. . . . This year will be without exception one of the worst years ever experienced at Fort Chimo, country food being also very scarce.' 12 Feb. 1912:[7(57)] 'There are simply no white foxes on the coast at all. I do not think that both Companies together could muster 75 white foxes.' 17 Apr.:[7(58)] 'Two Indians belonging to Seven Islands arrived here last night, having in their search for fur and country food, wandered too far to the North. . . . They report both fur and country food as being very very scarce. This report is the same from all over. . . . The reports from Rigolet and all along the coast are the same.' The year's summary[7(59)] said: 'There has been no fur at all [obviously a dramatic exaggeration]. Only eight silver foxes were killed in the whole District, and we got five out of the eight.'

14

The story runs rather thinner for the next ten years, but it is possible to learn the general run of cycles from annual reports on the fur trade, which condense a larger body of archives that I have not examined. A fuller account could be constructed when someone has time to dig into these original sources. We left the cycle at the point of universal scarcity in 1911–12. By 1914–15 it had run nearly another full course, as can be deduced from the report for Outfit 1914:[8(5)] 'The collection was very small, foxes being the chief variety. Although signs indicated good prospects in the fall of 1914, as soon as winter set in the animals disappeared, no doubt from the lack of natural food such as mice, seal meat etc. . . . [In] October 1915 there was absolutely no sign of anything in the fur line. But it still may be a good fur winter as there was plenty of natural food around.'

The report[8(6)] for 1915–16 confirms this decline, from what must have been maximum abundance in 1913 or 1914: 'The fur collection of Outfit 1915 is, with the single exception of 1911, the smallest on record. . . . Practically the whole of this was purchased from Indians. The Esquimaux catch of white foxes was nil. . . . At George's River there was an absolute dearth of fur.'

The same decline, apparently delayed a year, had taken place on Hudson Strait:[8(6)] 'At Stupart's Bay all fur-bearing animals were remarkably scarce during the Outfit [1915], white foxes, of which there were good prospects during the fall, completely disappeared . . . when the trapping season came, and did not again make their appearance until the latter part of April, when their fur is of no use. . . . At Wolstenholme, white foxes show a decrease of 50%.'

Next season, 1916–17, some recovery was noticeable. In Ungava:[8(8)] 'the Eskimo hunt of white foxes . . . was very small; but the Indian hunt of other classes of fur was the highest for ten years. The inspector accounts for the increase of collection by (1) furs being slightly more plentiful than last year, (2) the addition of Fort McKenzie Outpost, which practically obtained the whole of the Indian hunt, whereas Messrs. Revillon Frères obtained 50% of it in former years, (3) our opponents not being so active in competition as in former years.' Fort McKenzie, as we have seen (p. 383), tapped an important south-central part of Quebec Peninsula.

There was recovery of the fur returns along Hudson Strait:[8(9)] 'On the south side of the Straits, during the past summer, furs were considerably more plentiful than during the previous Outfit [1915].'

Although the fur returns show a strong peak and decline, and then another peak in 1921, I have no details to give about the signs of foxes in the snow, and their real abundance. But the journal of Fort Chimo (of which I have examined a few passages[6a] for 1922-6) notes the scarcity in Outfit 1922. 13 Nov. 1922: 'Natives report fox signs very scarce.' 16 Dec.: 'Fur signs at this date very scarce.'

There followed a strong increase that gave a huge haul of white fox furs in 1925-6. But after this decline occurred. The journal makes clear how scarce foxes were, especially in the late winter of 1926-7.

At this point we come into the modern period in which special zoological reports began to be made at the posts. These give the cycle in foxes, and also the correlation of fox with lemming, a subject that requires a special discussion later. It is convenient therefore to take stock of the evidence up to 1924, before going further into the consideration of its causes. This is done in the next chapter.

REFERENCES

* indicates that an abstract is deposited in the Bureau of Animal Population, Oxford. Dates of archives are those of the 'Outfits', e.g. 1900 means 1900–1. H. B. Co. means Hudson's Bay Company.

1. BELL, R. (1884). 'Observations on the geology, mineralogy, zoology and botany of the Labrador Coast, Hudson's Strait and Bay.' Rep. Geol. & Nat. Hist. Surv. & Mus. Canada for 1882-3-4: 1–62 DD. p. 49.

2. GORDON, A. R. [1886]. 'Report of the Second Hudson's Bay Expedition under the command of Lieut. A. R. Gordon, R.N., 1885.' Blue-book, Dept. of Marine & Fisheries, Ottawa.

3. GORDON, A. R. (1887). 'Report of the Hudson's Bay Expedition of 1886, under the command of Lieut. A. R. Gordon, R.N.' Blue-book, Dept. of Marine & Fisheries, Ottawa.

*4. Ungava District (Fort Chimo), Reports, 1831–4, 1836–7. MS. H. B. Co. Archives, London. (1) 1832.

*5. Ungava District (Fort Chimo), Correspondence, 1830, 1834–40. MS. H. B. Co. Archives, London. (1) 14 Feb. 1835: N. Finlayson to J. G. McTavish. (2) 18 Aug. 1835: N. Finlayson to Gentleman in charge, York Factory.

*6. Fort Chimo (Ungava District), Journals, 1866–72, 1874–6, 1883–5, 1895–6, 1898–1900. MS. H. B. Co. Archives, London. (Special references are only made to those passages for which no date is given in the text.) (1) 15 May, 10 & 12 June 1869. (2) 12, 19, 20, 21 Apr. 1897. (3) 19, 20, 23 Nov. 1897.

6 a. Fort Chimo, Journals, 1922–6. MS. H. B. Co. Archives, Winnipeg.

*7. Ungava District (Fort Chimo), Correspondence, 1869, 1871–3, 1882–97, 1899–1912. MS. H. B. Co. Archives, London. (1) 23 Sept. 1869: P. M. McKenzie to D. A. Smith. (2) 27 Sept. 1871: P. M. McKenzie to D. A. Smith. (3) 16 Sept. 1872: P. M. McKenzie to D. A. Smith. (4) 16 Sept. 1872: P. M. McKenzie to

Henry Connolly. (5) 10 Sept. 1873: P. M. McKenzie to D. A. Smith. (6) 6 Sept. 1883: K. McKenzie to S. K. Parson. (7) 1 Sept. 1885: P. McKenzie to W. Davie. (8) Aug. 1886: P. McKenzie to the Commissioner. (9) 31 Aug. 1886: P. McKenzie to S. K. Parson. (10) 15 Sept. 1887: K. McKenzie to S. K. Parson. (11) 28 Sept. 1887: K. McKenzie to J. Wrigley. (12) 11 Sept. 1888: K. McKenzie to J. Wrigley. (13) 6 Feb. 1889: K. McKenzie to S. K. Parson. (14) 6 Feb. 1889: K. McKenzie to John Ford. (15) 3 Sept. 1889: K. McKenzie to J. Wrigley. (16) 2 Feb. 1890: R. Gray to P. McKenzie. (17) 16 Sept. 1890: D. Matheson to J. Wrigley. (18) 18 Sept. 1891: D. Matheson to S. K. Parson. (19) 12 Jan. 1892: D. Matheson to S. K. Parson. (20) 17 Sept. 1892: D. Matheson to C. C. Chipman. (21) Sept. 1893: D. Matheson to C. C. Chipman. (22) 15 Sept. 1894: D. Matheson to P. McKenzie. (23) 15 Sept. 1895: D. Matheson to C. C. Chipman. (24) 11 Sept. 1896: D. Matheson to the Commissioner. (25) 7 Sept. 1897: D. Matheson to W. Ware. (26) 9 Sept. 1898: D. Matheson to the Commissioner. (27) 10 Sept. 1899: D. Matheson to the Commissioner. (28) 9 Sept. 1900: D. Matheson to the Commissioner. (29) 8 Sept. 1900: D. Matheson to P. McKenzie. (30) Sept. 1901: D. Matheson to the Commissioner. (31) 20 Jan. 1902: J. A. Wilson to P. McKenzie. (32) Sept. 1902: J. A. Wilson to P. McKenzie. (33) 17 Sept. 1902: D. Matheson to W. Ware. (34) 18 Sept. 1903: D. Matheson to P. McKenzie. (35) 4 Sept. 1904: D. Matheson to P. McKenzie. (36) 10 Sept. 1904: D. Matheson to P. McKenzie. (37) 4 Jan. 1905: D. Matheson to P. McKenzie. (38) Sept. 1905: D. Matheson to P. McKenzie. (39) Aug. 1906: D. Matheson to P. McKenzie. (40) 19 Oct. 1906: H. S. Cotter to P. McKenzie. (41) 26 Dec. 1906: H. S. Cotter to P. McKenzie. (42) 3 Jan. 1907: H. S. Cotter to P. McKenzie. (43) Outfit 1906, Reports on trade of Fort Chimo & George's River. (44) 7 Oct. 1907: G. B. Boucher to P. McKenzie. (45) 31 July 1908: G. B. Boucher to P. McKenzie. (46) 10 June 1908: G. B. Boucher to Officer in charge, Montreal. (47) Outfit 1908, Report on trade of Fort Chimo & George's River. (48) 11 Jan. 1910: H. M. S. Cotter to the Moravian Missionary, Hebron. (49) Outfit 1909, Reports on trade of Fort Chimo & George's River. (50) 14 Sept. 1910: H. M. S. Cotter to M. R. Grahame. (51) 5 Jan. 1911: H. M. S. Cotter to R. Parsons. (52) 6 Jan. 1911: H. M. S. Cotter to M. R. Grahame. (53) 20 Jan. 1911: H. M. S. Cotter to M. R. Grahame. (54) 22 Mar. 1911: H. M. S. Cotter to M. R. Grahame. (55) Outfit 1910, Reports on trade of Fort Chimo & George's River. (56) 9 Dec. 1911: A. Alston to the Secretary, London. (57) 12 Feb. 1912: A. Alston to M. R. Grahame. (58) 17 Apr. 1912: A. Alston to M. R. Grahame. (59) 18 Sept. 1912: A. Alston to Y. C. Ingrams. (60) 2 Dec. 1907: G. B. Boucher to P. McKenzie. (61) 11 Feb. 1885: P. McKenzie to W. Davie.

8. H. B. Co., Annual Reports on Fur Trade, 1888–1928. MS. H. B. Co. Archives, London. (1) 1890. (2) 1892. (3) 1898. (4) 1910 (Wolstenholme Post). (5) 1914. (6) 1915. (7) 1916.

CHAPTER XX

CYCLES AND MOVEMENTS OF FOXES

The main issue was fully enough for me, and it was only in passing flashes that I followed the play of the warring under-currents.' ERSKINE CHILDERS in *The Riddle of the Sands.*

1

THE last chapter contains all the evidence that I have yet obtained (there is certainly a good deal still awaiting exhumation) about the real numbers of foxes in Ungava between 1830 and 1924. This long period is not at all equally productive of evidence. The fox scarcity of 1833 stands isolated by thirty-five years from the next indications of any value, which begin in 1867. (There were no white men to record anything between 1842 and 1865.) Even in the sixties and seventies the story is rather unsatisfactory and broken by gaps. But from 1882 it runs more strongly, based on the well-written observations of the two McKenzies, of Matheson and Cotter, and their satellites. When the last ten years has been added, in a later chapter, we shall have a continuous run of cycles for analysis, stretching from 1883 to 1935, with only a few doubtful and shadowy patches. With this period of fifty-two years we can find out a good deal about the length and behaviour of the cycle. But first we have to make quite sure that the cycle exists.

The whole of the present study arose from Hewitt's discovery that the white fox fur returns of the Hudson's Bay Company from about 1850 to about 1914 show a pronounced cycle of nearly four years. 'The numbers appear to fluctuate very considerably over shorter periods than is the case with the more southerly red fox and its colour phases. . . . The average periodical cycle occurred in 4·2 years; 4 years was the actual length of the periodic cycle in the majority of the periods.' These white-fox furs came mainly from the Ungava district, and so reflect the cycle in that region in a general way. In 1924 and 1925 I correlated these Canadian figures with the cycle in Norwegian lemmings, and believed that I could show them to be broadly synchronous in rhythm, and pointed out that some climatic cycle must be invoked to explain this parallel phenomenon on opposite sides of the Atlantic Ocean. Although I still think it highly probable that this theory is correct, it has since become evident that there are technical difficulties in arriving at a proper correlation between the two sets of figures. The chief difficulty, which will come out in following chapters, and which has already been discussed in connexion with the Labrador cycle in voles and coloured foxes, is that the fur returns of fox are not an *exact* index of the peak year in rodents. This slight variability in the index makes correlation difficult. And yet, there does seem to be a considerable amount of agreement which further work may prove to be due to something more than chance.

Anyone who has read with endurance the cumulative history given in the last chapter will probably have by now accepted the existence of a short fox cycle in Ungava; and may, incidentally, have reflected on the high quality and intelligence of many of these reports, compiled for a trading business by a dynasty of hard-bitten men. It is certainly fortunate that their notes have in so many cases been saved for study.

In tabulating the evidence for analysis we have to make certain decisions, depending on considerations that were discussed on p. 299, and earlier, in connexion with Labrador. The table that follows is divided, a little arbitrarily, into geographical divisions, corresponding to the different sources of information.

'George's River and Cape Chidley' covers the barren coasts east of Ungava Bay, hunted by Eskimos. 'Ungava Bay' means the coast strip hunted in winter by Eskimos: its data are Eskimo reports. 'Ungava Inland' includes the Indian reports. There must be some overlapping between these last two categories: the race of native has been used here to give a rough geographical division into coast and inland. It is impossible, however, to convert this into an exact and constant boundary; though the general situation of the tribes has already been discussed in Chapter XVII.

The 'North Coast' presents a special problem. It may be remembered that the Tahagmiut Eskimos, described by Lucien Turner, often came in from a great distance, bringing furs that had been trapped a year before. The distant bands (as Stupart's Bay) had to start their trading expedition as soon as the first snow was good for travel, that is, just when fox trapping would be getting into full swing. The furs caught in 1891–2 would leave in the early winter of 1892–3, arriving at Fort Chimo in April or so of 1893. So an arctic fox born in the spring of 1891 at Wolstenholme parted with its skin in the following winter; this reached the trading post in the spring of 1893, and the London auctions in the winter of 1893–4.

In all this we rely chiefly on Turner; but all the other evidence supports his account. We have to be careful, then, not to get wrong in the seasons of abundance, where the Northerners' fur catch is concerned. On the other hand, some of them undoubtedly must have brought in furs trapped the same season: these would be Eskimos from north of Leaf River, or even farther off. The number of skins brought in by the Northerners is therefore not a safe criterion of fur years, unless the place they came from is specified. We have adopted the convention (which it is hoped is near the truth) that furs brought to Fort Chimo from Wolstenholme, Stupart's Bay, or Apelook were caught over a year before; or generally, the furs from 'Hudson Strait'. Anything from Leaf River is assumed to have been caught in the same season as it was brought in. Furs brought in before March are taken to be other than Hudson Strait catches.

But, as the Eskimos passed from camp to camp, they presumably picked up the latest fur news. Their *reports* (as distinct from the furs they carried) are assumed to apply to the season in which their journeys were done.

In Table 50 this confusion has been deliberately ironed out, and the northern fur catches placed in their (presumed) real year of provenance. All the horizontal columns are in this way made easy to read straight across.

TABLE 50

Summary of fox cycles in Ungava, 1833–1924

'Years' are ship-years, e.g. 1833 = 1833–4. Ab. = Abundant, Sc. = Scarce, V. = Very, F = Fox (white or coloured or both, i.e. unspecified), WF = white fox, CF = coloured fox. For scarcity F is expressed as WF & CF. Where no symbol for state of abundance, foxes were reported present, not scarce, but degree of abundance not specified. D = Decrease during winter, M = Mortality noted.

Year	George's R. to C. Chidley	Ungava Bay	Ungava Inland	N. coast (reports)	N. coast (furs)
1833	WF & CF V. Sc.	WF & CF V. Sc.	..	..	..
4	..	WF & CF Sc.	..	..	..
1867	..	WF	..	..	..
8	..	WF & CF Sc.	WF & CF Sc.	..	WF ? Sc.
9	..	WF & CF V. Sc.	..	..	WF Sc.
1870	..	WF	WF & CF V. Sc.	..	..
1	..	F Ab.	F Ab.	..	..
2	F V. Ab.	F V. Ab. D	F V. Ab.	..	..
3	..	..	..	..	..
4	..	..	..	..	WF
5	..	WF & CF	WF Sc. CF	..	..
6	..	WF & CF	..	..	..
7	..	..	..	..	..
8	..	..	..	..	..
9	..	..	..	..	..
1880	..	..	..	..	..
1	..	..	..	..	F
2	..	..	WF & CF Sc.	..	..
3	..	WF & CF V. Sc.	..	..	..
4	WF Ab.	WF & CF Sc.	F	WF Ab.	..
5	..	WF & CF Sc.	..	WF & CF V. Ab. D	..
6	..	..	..	..	WF
7	..	WF Ab. CF Sc.	WF & CF Sc.	WF Ab. CF Sc.	WF
8	WF & CF V. Sc.	WF & CF V. Sc. M	..	WF & CF Sc.	..
9	WF & CF Sc.	WF	..	..	..
1890	WF ? V. Ab.	WF V. Ab. CF	..	M	WF
1	WF & CF V. Sc.	WF V. Sc.	WF & CF Sc.	..	..
2	WF & CF ? V. Sc.	WF & CF V. Sc.	WF & CF V. Sc.	..	..
3	..	F Ab.	F	..	WF & CF Sc. (influenza)
4	..	WF & CF V. Sc.	WF & CF V. Sc.	WF & CF V. Sc.	WF & CF V. Sc.
5	WF ? Sc.	WF Sc. CF Ab.	..	WF & CF V. Sc.	WF & CF V. Sc.
6	..	WF & CF	F	WF & CF Sc.	WF
7	WF & CF V. Sc.	WF & CF V. Sc. M (Ab. Akpatok)	WF & CF	WF Ab.	..
8	WF & CF V. Sc.	WF & CF V. Sc.	WF & CF V. Sc. M	WF & CF V. Sc.	..
9	WF & CF V. Sc.	WF & CF V. Sc.	WF & CF V. Sc.	WF & CF V. Sc.	WF
1900	..	F (Sc. Akpatok)	..	..	F Ab.
1	F Ab.	WF & CF Ab.	F	..	..
2	F Ab.	WF & CF Sc.	WF & CF Sc.	WF & CF ? Sc.	WF & CF Sc.
3	WF & CF V. Sc.	WF & CF V. Sc.	WF & CF V. Sc.	WF & CF V. Sc.	..
4	WF	WF Ab.	WF & CF Sc.	..	..
5	..	WF & CF Ab.	WF Sc.	..	WF & CF Sc.
6	WF V. Sc. CF	WF & CF V. Sc.	WF & CF V. Sc.	WF & CF V. Sc.	..
7	..	WF & CF Sc.	? F	WF & CF Sc.	F
8	? F	WF & CF Sc.	..	..	WF Ab.
·9	F	WF Ab.	CF ? Ab.	F Ab.	..
1910	CF	WF Sc.	CF Ab.	CF Ab. summer, Sc. winter, WF Sc. & Ab.	..
11	WF & CF V. Sc.	WF & CF V. Sc.	WF & CF V. Sc.	WF & CF ? Sc.	..
12	..	..	..	..	..
13	..	..	..	..	..

Year	George's R. to C. Chidley	Ungava Bay	Ungava Inland	N. coast (reports)	N. coast (furs)
1914	..	WF & CF Sc.	..	..	..
15	WF & CF V. Sc.	WF & CF V. Sc.	..	WF & CF V. Sc.	..
16	..	WF Sc.	CF	F	..
17	..	..	..	..	..
18	..	..	..	..	..
19	..	..	..	..	..
1920	..	..	..	..	..
1	..	..	..	..	..
2	..	WF & CF Sc.	..	..	..
3	..	..	..	..	..
4	..	..	..	..	..

2

So far as possible no bias of theory has been introduced into the abbreviation of these reports; but there may be a few misinterpretations that are unavoidable. After a long course of reading these archives one has, however, a rather solid and convinced faith in the general reliability of the reports themselves, whether from white man or native. Several things can be seen at once from the table: the alternation, usually every three or four years, of scarcity and abundance (the latter sometimes coming up rather suddenly); the way different parts of the district have usually (but not invariably) kept in step—this shows best in the scarcities; the occasional disagreement in cycles of white and coloured fox; and the general confirmation that the north coast furs (put to the previous year) give to the north coast reports. It is fair to say that the table fits reasonably into the conception of a wide regional arctic fox fluctuation similar in extent and length of cycle to that of the coloured fox in northern Labrador.

Having marshalled the reports, we have now to bring along and set against them the fur returns for Ungava District (Table 51). There are certain snags about these figures which make them unsuitable for fixing the exact peak years of the cycle. But they have the great advantage of giving a continuous record. The reports are a better reflection of field conditions, but there are gaps. Together they fortify each other's weaknesses.

TABLE 51

Abundance and scarcity of arctic foxes in Ungava District, 1867–1924

For explanation of 'years' see text. Maxima (where known) are in heavy type. Fur returns include white and blue foxes. Figures in brackets are incomplete. Figures with asterisks are from a different source than the rest, but comparable (see text). (Ab.) or (+) means fox species not defined in reports. Wolstenholme omitted after 1908, Stupart's Bay after 1913.

		Reports		
Year	Fur returns (whole district)[16]	George's R. to C. Chidley	Ungava Bay	North coast
1867	?	..	+	..
8	395	..	Sc.	..
9	118	..	V. Sc.	..
1870	385	..	+	..
1	1,008	..	(Ab.)	..

TABLE 51 (*cont.*)

Year	Fur returns (whole district)[16]	Reports		
		George's R. to C. Chidley	Ungava Bay	North coast
1872	**1,096**	(Ab.)	(Ab.)	..
3	512	..	..	..
4	217	..	..	..
5	1,432	..	+	..
6	**4,682**	..	+	..
7	[1,861*]	..	..	..
8	292*	..	..	..
9	**1,300**	..	..	..
1880	731*	..	..	..
1	753	..	..	..
2	**1,394**	..	..	..
3	498	..	V. Sc.	..
4	115	Ab.	Sc.	Ab.
5	**501**	..	Sc.	Ab.
6	306	..	..	..
7	**1,167**	..	**Ab.**	**Ab.**
8	628	Sc.	V. Sc.	Sc.
9	1,503	Sc.	+	..
1890	**2,585**	? Ab.	**Ab.**	..
1	1,119	V. Sc.	V. Sc.	..
2	979	Sc.	V. Sc.	..
3	**1,216**	..	(Ab.)	..
4	1,061	..	V. Sc.	V. Sc.
5	360	? Sc.	Sc.	V. Sc.
6	607	..	+	Sc.
7	**2,759**	V. Sc.	V. Sc. & **Ab.**	**Ab.**
8	796	V. Sc.	V. Sc.	V. Sc.
9	490	V. Sc.	V. Sc.	V. Sc.
1900	1,494	..	(+)	..
1	**4,489**	(Ab.)	**Ab.**	..
2	1,879	(Ab.)	Sc.	? Sc.
3	248	V. Sc.	V. Sc.	V. Sc.
4	3,237	+	Ab.	..
5	**5,019**	..	**Ab.**	..
6	1,189	V. Sc.	V. Sc.	V. Sc.
7	159	..	Sc.	Sc.
8	632	(? +)	Sc.	..
9	**3,502**	(+)	**Ab.**	(Ab.)
1910	547	..	Sc.	Sc./Ab.
11	78	V. Sc.	V. Sc.	? Sc.
12	131	..	..	..
13	**704**	..	..	..
14	429	..	Sc.	..
15	29	V. Sc.	V. Sc.	V. Sc.
16	344	..	Sc.	(+)
17	**1,607**	..	..	..
18	768	..	..	..
19	296	..	..	..
1920	2,397	..	..	..
1	**9,797**	..	..	..
2	1,806	..	Sc.	..
3	497	..	..	..
4	1,423	..	..	..

The fur-return figures that are available for study are not as satisfactory as those of the Moravian Missions. In a large ramifying organization like the Hudson's Bay Company, the fur returns are recorded in several ways according to the purpose for which they are required and we have to work from those records that happen to have survived. The natural unit of time in Ungava itself, and the one best suited for analysis of fur returns from the Arctic, is the ship-year. The furs taken out by the summer supply ship were practically all caught either in the previous winter trapping season, or in the one before that (the Northern Eskimo quota). But a good many of these furs were brought in after the trapping season was over, and officially in the next Outfit. For the Outfit was counted from 1 June (sometimes a little earlier, it seems, in the northern posts). When the furs reached civilization they were kept separate for accounting purposes according to the Outfits in which they were traded, whereas we wish to know the Outfit in which they were caught.

An example: after the ship left in 1881, 716 arctic foxes were brought to Ungava posts before the end of Outfit 1881. Between this date in the spring of 1882 and the arrival of the ship a further 56 arctic foxes were traded. After the ship left in 1882, and before the end of Outfit 1882, 1,338 arctic foxes were traded, and in the first part of Outfit 1883 another 94. The proper biological grouping would be 716 plus 56 for 1881–2, and 1,338 plus 94 for 1882–3. But the head-quarters accounts showed 56 plus 1,338 for 1882–3. The only long series of fur returns for the district that is available is one that was given to me for research in July 1929.[16] That is the series shown in Table 51. The figures are copied from an old record book until recently kept at Fort Chimo, but now in Winnipeg. But I have been able to trace a few other original fur returns,[15] from which the nature of the longer series can be ascertained. This comparison shows that they are rendered in the form of the standard Outfit, a form which, as has been explained above, resembles the head of one fox attached to the tail of the one in front. Table 52 gives the proof of this proposition. The long series is called 'H. B. Co. 1929' and the others are called 'H. B. Co. Archives 1937'.

Incidentally, the term 'Outfit' as used generally in the letters, journals, and reports of Ungava refers really to the ship-year, as is only natural in a district which could usually write home only once a year.

The arctic fox figures for Outfits 1879 and 1882 agree exactly, and those for 1881 are very close. The coloured fox figures agree less exactly, and this may be due to a category of 'kitt foxes' which forms a small variable fraction of the Ungava coloured fox returns. This must have been a complete error in naming, since the kitt fox is a prairie species. Probably it was locally used to describe young skins. There are, in addition, always a few small discrepancies in the fur accounts, presumably due to occasional confusion, delays, or the throwing out of bad skins.

We shall therefore take the 'H. B. Co. 1929' fur returns as being in accounting Outfits and not in ship-years. This means that there is a certain amount of slurring in the figures. For instance 48 per cent. of the arctic fox shown for Outfit 1878 were really caught in Outfit 1877. In other cases the fraction was quite small: 2 per cent. in 1879, 1·5 per cent. in 1880, 1 per cent. in 1881, 1·4 per cent. in 1882. Then we have to remember also that a large proportion of fox furs came from catches made two years before, on Hudson Strait. It follows that such fur figures, taken alone, are no good for defining the actual years of abundance and scarcity in Ungava.

TABLE 52

Analysis of Ungava Bay District fur returns, 1877–83, for arctic (white and blue) and coloured (red, cross, and silver) foxes

'H. B. Co. Archives, 1937'			'H. B. Co. 1929'		
	Furs			Furs	
'Outfit'	Arctic	Coloured	'Outfit'	Arctic	Coloured
2nd part '1877' . . . (aut. to spring, 1877–8)	1,861	318	'1877'	?	?
1st part '1878' . . . (summer, 1878)	139	26	..	..	..
2nd part '1878' . . . (aut. to spring, 1878–9)	153	87	..	..	..
Total '1878' . . .	292	113	'1878'	?	?
1st part '1879' . . . (summer, 1879)	5	13	..	..	..
2nd part '1879' . . . (aut. to spring, 1879–80)	1,295	681	..	..	..
Total '1879' . . .	1,300	694	'1879'	1,300	670
1st part '1880' . . . (summer, 1880)	31	9	..	..	..
2nd part '1880' . . . (aut. to spring, 1880–1)	700	590	..	..	..
Total '1880' . . .	731	599	'1880'	?	?
1st part '1881' . . . (summer, 1881)	48	4	..	..	..
2nd part '1881' . . . (aut. to spring, 1881–2)	716	438	..	..	..
Total '1881' . . .	764	442	'1881'	753	472
1st part '1882' . . . (summer, 1882)	56	5	..	..	..
2nd part '1882' . . . (aut. to spring, 1882–3)	1,338	362	..	..	..
Total '1882' . . .	1,394	367	'1882'	1,394	366
1st part '1883' . . . (summer, 1883)	94	10	..	..	..
2nd part '1883' . . . (aut. to spring, 1882–3)	?	?	..	..	..
Total '1883' . . .	?	?	'1883'	498	330

But when the run of figures is compared (Table 51) with the reports, a very close connexion is seen, which makes us suspect that the main Ungava contribution must usually have dominated the figures. The result of these processes which have affected the fur returns that we have before us now is a sort of smoothing effect such as statisticians apply to bring out the main trend of an irregular fluctuation.

Table 52 has a second use, as it supplies, by good luck, just those figures which are missing from 'H. B. Co. 1929'. The one for 1877 is, however, incomplete, but gives a minimum figure which is probably not far below the real mark. The general reliability of the other figures in the long series is evidently high (although it has not been possible to check them all independently), as they agree very closely with some that I have obtained from account books, for 1884, 1885, 1887, and 1897–1900.[15]

3

When the figures run into modern times, there are two new factors which may disturb them: competition and the creation of new posts or elevation of former outposts to independent status. These factors might affect the shape of the curve, e.g. the sudden loss of a post would pull the figures down, as well as altering the area of the district. The figures used in Table 51 are for a standard district throughout, with these exceptions: Wolstenholme was lopped off from 1909 onwards, and Stupart's Bay from 1914 onwards. The returns for Stupart's Bay in 1914 were 174 white foxes (not including blue, which would, however, be negligible). If these had been added to Fort Chimo, the total for 1914 would have come close to that for 1913. Wolstenholme in 1909 got very few furs the first year (see p. 408) so that the change probably caused no sudden dislocation.

The effect of competition can be tested by a comparison of the fur returns of Revillons with those of the Company. I have the figures of Revillon's arctic fox catch from 1913 to 1924,[17] though I am not at liberty to publish them. But it may be said that the two series run closely parallel and show the same years of peak and low.

The earlier Revillon figures are not to be had, but we can get a pretty good idea, from the archives, of the position between 1903 and 1912. The French Company came to Ungava in 1903, determined to break the monopoly that the older one held. This was a year of fox scarcity. Revillon 'did practically nothing that year [1903–4], though they secured a few Eskimo customers—some good men too; but the following year and the year after, quite a number of young men, lads and boys, went over to them'.[12(1)] These were Eskimos from the country between Leaf River and George's River, not Northerners.

The Hudson's Bay Company fur returns for arctic fox must have been pulled down somewhat by their intense competition, but there are independent reports of abundance which fix satisfactorily the peak year in 1905, and the great scarcity in 1906. In 1907–8 there was a definite interference with the trapping work of the Northerners. Boucher noted[14(1)] in 1908 that 'another reason . . . [than scarcity] for the poor Eskimo hunts was that all the Far North Eskimo from Hope's Advance, Stupart's Bay, and Apelook, were brought in here, spring before last [1906] by the Opposition. They were induced to remain here by them. . . . The result was that they, being in a strange part of the country, did not do anything [i.e. trap successfully]. Neither company got one skin from them.'

In 1908–9 the Hudson's Bay Company got most of the furs, and practically all the Northerners' hunt, from Hudson Straits (to which they had returned). In 1909–10:[14(2)] '1,200 foxes were obtained from Hudson's Straits: practically the entire hunt of that section.' It seems that the rest of the Eskimo trade was shared between the two companies. Again we have good independent reports to check the fur returns: these both give 1909 as peak for white foxes.

In addition to scarcity of foxes in 1910–11, Revillon Frères established a post at Wakeham Bay which effectually cut off the northern visitors from Fort Chimo. 'No trade was done with the natives from the Straits this year, as not a single hunter came in from there. . . . The white fox hunt from the Straits usually ranged between five to fifteen hundred pelts, so that if the natives had come here as usual, the total collection of white foxes would probably have amounted to about 1,000 skins.'[14(3)] These figures include both species of fox: even so the lower one must have been a rather high estimate for scarce years. We draw the conclusion that the fur figure for 1910–11 is lower than it would have been if these natives had not been cut off by opposition, but that they would still have been substantially lower than those for the previous year.

These facts show that the competition, although it changed the details of the Fort Chimo fur returns and altered the distribution of posts, did not produce enough effect to invalidate the main deductions we have made about the cycle in Ungava.

The elimination of Wolstenholme and Stupart's Bay from the figures after 1914 carries certain advantages, for it removes the lagging effect that the long trading journeys of the northern Eskimos caused. From 1914 onwards we have a fur curve that reflects largely the true catch of each Outfit, and from which the direct effects of competition can be eliminated. There were indirect effects which are more difficult to assess—interference with native stability and thrift, and with the traditional rhythm of hunting and trapping in the winter season, and also some movements of native bands not wholly due to the influence of competition.

4

This should be sufficient discussion of the background, and we may now leave the rather worrying jungle of critical analysis to draw some broad conclusions from the facts. But the study of cycles by biologists and practical men alike has hitherto been so light-hearted and comparatively superficial that no excuse need be put forward for the more than ordinary caution which has hedged these chapters.

Looking at Table 51 we see such close relation between the fur returns and the reports, especially those for Ungava Bay itself, that we may use the fur returns as an index of the number of cycles in those parts where reports are missing. This method gives fur peaks about the following years: 1872, 1876, 1879, 1882, (1885), 1887, 1890, 1893, 1897, 1901, 1905, 1909, 1913, 1917, and 1921. These up to 1913 are subject to an error of one year, e.g. 1872 might be 1871. On the whole the evidence is for them representing the real peak years of fur catch in Ungava. 1885 requires a note. It was a very small rise, and we know that in 1886 the Stupart's Bay Eskimos could not come in with their furs, because of the loss of dogs through epidemic.[14(4)] The figure for 1886 is obviously much below what it might have been with the Stupart's Bay furs. For these reasons we may eliminate 1885 as a maximum year, at any rate in Ungava Bay.

Summing the remaining years of abundance, which are confirmed by the reports (with a few disagreements in regions at a distance from Fort Chimo), we find 13 cycles in 50 years—an average of 3·85 years. This is almost exactly the same period as the coloured fox cycle in Labrador. The range in length of the cycle (though obviously less reliable from these figures) is much the same: 4, 3, 3, 5, 3, 3, 4, 4, 4, 4, 4, 4, 4.

5

These years of white-fox cycle are now about as good as we can expect to make them without a prolonged further search in the archives that is at present hardly justified. They are our yardstick for the four-year wild-life cycle in Ungava, with which we now wish to compare the one in northern Labrador. But that was for the coloured, not the arctic fox. There are two stages therefore that we have still to complete before the foxes can all be laid in row. First, to discover if the coloured fox has cycled in Ungava at the same time or at any rate with the same rhythm as the arctic fox. Second, to examine the arctic fox records down the coast of Labrador. To anticipate the result, we shall find in all the same strongly developed general four-year rhythm, from which we can deduce one general fox cycle for most of the northern part of Quebec Peninsula.

The Ungava coloured fox fur returns for Hudson's Bay Company from 1868 to 1924,[16] and Revillons from 1913 to 1924,[17] and the addition of both are given in Table 53. The Revillon figures for 1903 to 1912 have not been found.

These figures for coloured foxes are obviously on a much smaller scale than the white fox catches. This comes, one imagines, from the greater abundance of white foxes in northern Ungava, and the greater number of native trappers in white fox country. The smallness of the statistics gives cycle deductions correspondingly more errors due to chance sampling and local accidents of the trade. We expect therefore to find some discrepancies, which are either real or accidental—it is impossible to say which. That is, a small trapping sample cannot give a faultless index of population changes. On the other hand, these coloured foxes, with an exception, were taken by Indians over a vast inland country, as well as by Eskimos and white men near the coast. The sample, though small, tended to be well scattered, a distribution which would have a good influence on its statistical value. It is probably on this account that the cycle does, on the whole, stand out rather sharply, like that of the arctic fox.

TABLE 53

Ungava District Fur returns for coloured fox (red, cross, and silver), Hudson's Bay Company, 1868–1924; and the same for Revillon Frères, 1913–24

Compared with peak years of arctic fox cycle. Figure in brackets is incomplete; those with asterisks are from a different source, but comparable. Peak years follow reports for Ungava Bay (Table 51), except those in brackets which are from fur returns only. Wolstenholme omitted after 1908, Stupart's Bay after 1913.

Year	Arctic fox peak years	Coloured fox (H.B. Co.)[16]	Coloured fox (Revillons)[17]	Coloured fox (both companies)
1868	..	99	..	..
9	..	59	..	..
1870	..	65	..	..
1	..	405	..	..
2	(Peak)	455	..	..
3	..	504	..	..
4	..	174	..	..
5	..	474	..	..
6	(Peak)	617	..	..
7	..	[318*]	..	..
8	..	113*	..	..
9	(Peak)	670	..	..
1880	..	599*	..	..
1	..	472	..	..
2	Peak	366	..	..
3	..	330	..	..
4	..	257	..	..
5	..	189	..	..
6	..	177	..	..
7	Peak	211	..	..
8	..	175	..	..
9	..	262	..	..
1890	Peak	295	..	..
1	..	276	..	..
2	..	109	..	..
3	Peak	352	..	..
4	..	249	..	..
5	..	412	..	..
6	..	310	..	..
7	Peak	309	..	..
8	..	92	..	..
9	..	96	..	..
1900	..	94	..	..
1	Peak	293	..	..
2	..	151	..	..
3	..	43	..	..
4	..	99	..	..
5	Peak	200	..	..
6	..	192	..	..
7	..	45	..	..
8	..	173	..	..
9	Peak	270	..	..
1910	..	549	..	..
11	..	38	..	..
12	..	160	..	..
13	(? Peak)	224	176	400
14	(or ? Peak)	169	218	387
15	..	72	108	180
16	..	283	83	366
17	(Peak)	679	247	926
18	..	307	134	441
19	..	0	5	5
1920	..	17	6	23
1	(Peak)	76	17	93
2	..	87	31	118
3	..	55	17	72
4	..	108	52	160

The exception which has been mentioned is, however, important. It is the occurrence of poor years for the caribou, which kept the Indians from trapping where they wished or as much as they wished, since their energies were concentrated upon keeping their own skins on their backs. This factor must have caused some rather sudden errors here and there. But it seems hardly worth building up an elaborate discussion on this matter, where the fur figures are so small.

There is not very much direct reporting on the coloured fox (see Table 50), but what there is agrees in practically every instance with the fur returns. So the evidence is thereby slightly strengthened. Coming to analysis of the figures, we have to use one trick that seems legitimate, as a sort of smoothing to bring out the main trends. With the arctic fox peaks, we counted no differences of less than four skins. For the coloured fox we make this ten. Both are arbitrary, and if they seem like cookery, there is at any rate no secrecy about the recipe. In the later years we take the joint verdict of the two companies.

The peak years show as 1873, 1876, 1879, 1887, 1890, 1893, 1895, 1901, 1905–6, 1910, 1913, 1917, and 1922. The intervals are 3, 3, 8, 3, 3, 2, 6, 4 or 5, 5 or 4, 3, 4, and 5: that is 12 cycles in 50 years, a crude average of 4·17. If we average all but the long cycle of eight years, the result is 3·8, or exactly the same as we found for the arctic fox. But the variability is rather greater: there are not many straight fours. The results make it probable that the eight-year cycle was either really exceptional, or more likely two cycles whose centre peak was masked in the fur returns. Unfortunately Table 50 has no light on this period, as records were lacking.

In the years since 1900 the cycle stands out very well, showing equally in the catches of the two companies. The arguments developed earlier for the arctic fox apply also here. The later figures are the best, as the lag from distant tribal trading disappeared, and the areas of search became smaller and more standardized.

We also see that practically always the two species of fox went up and down together. The chief exceptions shown are in 1895 and 1897 and the period about 1883. Otherwise the connexion was very close, and can hardly be ascribed to purely trading influences, since there was such a wide difference in collecting grounds, and different bias in the Indian and Eskimo hunts. It is not necessary to flog any further the dead Ungava fox. I think that any reasonable panel of biologists would agree that Ungava had for these fifty-seven years a real, terrific, oscillation in foxes, that formed one of the chief themes of life of people living in that region; and that it had a cycle usually of from three to four years. The next chapter shows how the cycle rests on mice or lemmings, and a later one shows how it affects snowy owls and is also marked by outbreaks of epidemic nervous disease that devastate fox populations and appear also among sledge-dog teams, to the great detriment of Arctic travel. But we have still to make the final correlation with Northern Labrador.

6

Arctic foxes turn up at all the posts along the Northern Labrador coast, and also appear to be trapped inland to some extent. They are much more abundant in some years than in others, following the usual short cycle that obtains in Ungava. The best index is given by the Moravian Mission furs,[18] summarized in Table 54. As the stations are spread from the Arctic into the Subarctic forest belt, we need the details for each post, in order to be able to study the distribution of these white foxes.

An important question that will be discussed is whether the white foxes southwards occur chiefly in the years when the population has collapsed in the north; that is, whether these Labrador specimens are simply the surplus emptied out of a famine-stricken Arctic belt, just as in certain years the snowy owls emigrate *en masse* into Ontario and New England. There are other explanations which also have to be explored.

The figures in Table 54 are for white and blue foxes added together.

TABLE 54

Arctic (white and blue) foxes, Moravian Stations, 1834–1925[18]

Years are ship-years, i.e. 1834 means 1834–5. 'Southern stations' includes Makkovik, Hopedale, and Zoar only. Ramah has the earlier, Killinek the later series.

Year	Makko-vik	Hope-dale	Zoar	Nain	Okak	Hebron	Ramah, Killinek	Southern stations	Total
1834	..	6	..	4	3	66	..	6	79
5	..	18	..	32	37	140	..	18	227
6	..	25	..	82	72	123	..	25	**302**
7	..	4	..	27	37	84	..	4	152
8	..	15	..	41	181	257	..	15	**494**
9	..	34	..	106	92	84	..	34	316
1840	..	3	..	5	5	19	..	3	32
1	..	4	..	24	0	68	..	4	96
2	..	0	..	18	43	94	..	0	**155**
3	..	23	..	11	0	91	..	23	125
4	..	43	..	113	116	142	..	43	**414**
5	..	17	..	15	25	150	..	17	207
6	..	9	..	11	43	295	..	9	358
7	..	0	..	97	122	301	..	0	**520**
8	..	2	..	2	5	54	..	2	63
9	..	0	..	4	115	353	..	0	**472**
1850	..	6	..	10	42	156	..	6	214
1	..	4	..	39	49	125	..	4	217
2	..	11	..	0	0	0	..	11	11
3	..	0	..	5	30	299	..	0	334
4	..	140	..	353	464	1,307	..	140	**2,264**
5	..	0	..	133	147	560	..	0	840
6	..	8	..	11	25	294	..	8	338
7	..	1	..	0	7	256	..	1	264
8	..	70	..	56	274	905	..	70	**1,305**
9	..	131	..	106	97	702	..	131	1,036
1860	..	5	..	15	13	111	..	5	144
1	..	0	..	2	9	435	..	0	446
2	..	61	..	32	93	356	..	61	542
3	..	70	..	199	317	518	..	70	**1,104**
4	..	75	..	161	132	726	..	75	1,094
5	..	1	..	2	3	89	..	1	95
6	..	0	1	3	0	1	..	1	5
7	..	114	102	482	478	497	..	216	**1,673**

Year	Makkovik	Hopedale	Zoar	Nain	Okak	Hebron	Ramah, Killinek	Southern stations	Total
1868	..	28	13	18	45	21	..	41	125
9	..	0	1	0	5	0	..	1	6
1870	..	0	2	2	5	7	..	2	16
1	..	16	2	3	57	52	48	18	178
2	..	43	55	131	155	53	28	98	**465**
3	..	3	0	0	53	30	0	3	86
4	..	0	15	0	111	45	27	15	**198**
5	..	0	17	18	55	17	0	17	107
6	..	50	67	175	210	238	67	117	**807**
7	..	33	15	61	97	60	16	48	282
8	..	0	0	12	0	0	0	0	12
9	..	3	0	6	0	0	0	3	9
1880	..	10	20	33	58	49	57	30	**227**
1	..	3	17	5	6	7	2	20	40
2	..	9	27	24	6	11	9	36	86
3	..	10	43	61	139	300	43	53	**596**
4	..	1	8	3	7	13	6	9	38
5	..	6	0	3	8	29	17	6	63
6	..	22	10	5	27	40	43	32	147
7	..	30	21	114	153	171	19	51	**508**
8	..	1	..	6	3	3	0	1	13
9	..	2	..	37	56	55	0	2	150
1890	..	33	0	78	160	330	76	33	**677**
1	..	19	0	32	52	25	3	19	131
2	..	3	0	14	3	5	1	3	26
3	..	1	1	18	27	19	0	2	66
4	..	0	..	9	12	18	23	0	62
5	..	4	..	70	60	37	11	4	**182**
6	..	3	..	17	8	13	0	3	41
7	..	8	..	30	21	33	9	8	101
8	..	13	..	51	71	72	10	13	**217**
9	..	1	..	2	10	7	0	1	20
1900	1	4	..	12	3	0	0	5	20
1	55	144	..	22	76	126	0	199	423
2	28	23	..	151	252	160	35	51	**649**
3	1	0	..	5	8	4	0	1	18
4	0	16	..	8	14	18	3	16	59
5	32	69	..	593	332	387	127	101	**1,540**
6	20	60	..	132	134	132	123	80	601
7	1	0	..	1	0	4	1	1	7
8	1	0	..	1	0	0	87	1	89
9	9	37	..	114	28	74	538	46	**800**
1910	1	31	..	112	122	96	195	32	557
11	0	0	..	0	7	16	60	0	83
12	3	1	..	0	19	45	102	4	170
13	7	1	..	4	49	115	102	8	278
14	4	49	..	46	1	91	124	53	**315**
15	0	2	..	0	0	1	10	2	13
16	0	0	..	0	0	1	3	0	4
17	0	10	..	111	15	23	33	10	192
18	8	2	..	87	105	92	95	10	**389**
19	0	6	..	4	0	77	0	6	87
1920	15	2	..	356	45	20	260	17	698
1	237	284	..	891	84	347	411	521	**2,254**
2	75	242	..	319	64	250	308	317	1,258
3	4	9	..	26	0	11	47	13	97
4	32	36	..	71	24	105	..	68	268
5	17	32	..	291	0	121	..	49	461

The number of blue was always very low in proportion to white, only 1 or 2 per cent. These percentages, summed in ten-year periods, are given in Table 55. There is in them no progressive change through the century, and the figures are published here chiefly for geographical comparison with other regions in which (as in parts of Alaska and in west Greenland) the proportions are very different. If the theory previously put forward for the changing ratios of the coloured fox phases is correct, we must assume either that colour selection by man has been ineffective on the arctic fox, or that there has been none. The second explanation may be the true one, since all arctic foxes were of comparatively little market value until the twentieth century, so that selection, if it exists, has had little time to act. Low,[3](1) writing in 1906, gave the relative values as: white fox 1, blue fox 2, cross fox 5–15, silver fox 15–40. This was the scale in 'skins' of the Hudson's Bay Company's bartering tariff. That there is some difference in the nature of the colour-phase phenomenon in the coloured fox and arctic fox phases is suggested by the very great variation found in the blue-white ratio in different samples trapped. That is to say, the coloured fox averages show clearly on fairly small samples, but the arctic fox averages vary wildly even in quite large ones. This tendency is shown in Table 55 when different decennia are compared.

TABLE 55

Proportion of blue to white phases in arctic fox catches, Northern Labrador, all stations, 1834–1923, summarized in ten-year periods

(The totals of blue and white are given in Table 54.)

Years	Blue	White	Per cent. blue
1834–43	20	1,958	1·0
1844–53	38	2,772	1·4
1854–63	89	8,194	1·1
1864–73	47	3,696	1·3
1874–83	44	2,320	1·9
1884–93	43	1,776	2·4
1894–1903	20	1,713	1·2
1904–13	47	4,137	1·1
1914–23	23	5,284	0·4
Total	371	31,850	1·2

7

We may now draw a list of the peak years in the Labrador arctic fox catches, bearing always in mind that the figures are for foxes trapped and shot, and that they are not necessarily indicative of the real population. The peaks were in 1836, 1838, 1842, 1844, 1847, 1849, 1853 or 1854, 1858, 1863, 1867, 1872, 1874, 1876, 1880, 1883, 1887, 1890, 1895, 1898, 1902, 1905, 1909, 1914, 1918, and 1921. These dates give 24 cycles in 86 years, with a crude average of 3·6 years. The doubtful year for 1853 or 1854 is caused by the failure of the *Harmony* to bring all the furs back in 1853 (see p. 315). The actual series of intervals between the peaks was: 2, 4, 2, 3, 2, 4 or 5, 5 or 4, 5, 4, 5, 2, 2, 4, 3, 4, 3, 5, 3, 4, 3, 4, 5, 4, 3.

These arctic fox peaks agree very nearly with the coloured fox cycle along the same coast, and also with the arctic foxes in Ungava. This general correlation is brought out in Table 56, where the years are grouped in their cycles.

TABLE 56

Comparison of peak years in coloured and arctic foxes in Labrador (from fur returns) and arctic foxes in Ungava (from fur returns and field observations)

(Based on figures in Tables 17, 54, and 51.)

Coloured fox, N. Labrador	Arctic fox, N. Labrador	Arctic fox, Ungava
1835	1836	..
1839	1838	..
1842	1842	..
1844	1844	..
1847	1847	..
	1849	..
1851	..	..
1855	1853 or 1854	..
1859	1858	..
1863	1863	..
1867	1867	..
1871	1872	(1872)
1875	1874	(1876)
..	1876	..
1880	1880	(1879)
1883	1883	1882
1886	1887	1887
1890	1890	1890
		1893
1895	1895	..
..	1898	1897
1901	1902	1901
1905	1905	1905
1909	1909	1909
1914	1914	(1913 or 1914)
1917	1918	(1917)
1921	1921	(1921)

We can apply the same system of comparison used in the Labrador analysis. Taking the peak years of Labrador coloured fox as the standard, the Labrador arctic fox peaks fall as follows:

TABLE 57

Years			−3	−2	−1	0	+1	+2	+3
Numbers	.	.	0·5	1·5	3·5	13	6	0	0·5
Frequency %	.	.	**2**	**6**	**14**	**52**	**24**	**0**	**2**

Slightly more than half the arctic fox peaks coincided with coloured fox peaks, and 90 per cent. were either the year before, the same year, or the year after. This is sufficiently close agreement to indicate a connexion between the two cycles. Whether the differences in exact agreement are a result of chance influences or of real ecological differences in the species we cannot say. But we can reasonably suggest that the two cycles have a strong common denominator of some kind.

A rather similar result comes from a comparison of the arctic fox cycles in Ungava and Labrador (Ungava is taken as the standard):

TABLE 58

Years			-2	-1	0	$+1$	$+2$
Numbers .	.	.	0·5	0	7·5	5·5	1·5
Frequency %	.	.	**3**	**0**	**50**	**37**	**10**

The figures, owing to the shorter run in Ungava, are small for such analysis. But they show half in agreement, and 87 per cent. agreeing or falling a year later than Ungava.

Finally, we may finish by comparing Ungava arctic with Labrador coloured fox (the latter taken as standard):

TABLE 59

Years			-2	-1	0	$+1$	$+2$
Numbers .	.	.	1	3·5	5·5	3	1
Frequency %	.	.	**7**	**25**	**39**	**22**	**7**

Here there is less complete agreement. But the year before, the same year, and the year after, between them have (on small figures it is true) 86 per cent. In these comparisons we rely on two criteria, the extent of agreement between peaks combined with the average length of cycles, (which is practically the same in all series). They bring out quite conclusively the regional nature of the 'four-year' cycle in Labrador and Ungava, which is now seen to occur in two species of fox, in the marten, and in voles. Although there are exceptions, some of which must be real, it is very seldom that the cycles run in an inverse way.

The figures also contain a suggestion that the greatest arctic fox abundance in Labrador tends to come either in the same year as the maximum in Ungava, or in the year after, but never precedes it. Does this mean that there is a southern migration of foxes when their food disappears in the north ? Or is it due to a difference in vole years north and south ? The second explanation is contradicted by the greater agreement of the local Labrador coloured foxes with the Ungava cycle. But one doubts very much whether the figures will stand up to a refined discussion along these lines, and it is better to tackle the question from another angle.

8

If the arctic fox catch on the Labrador coast depended on a periodic emigration from the north, we should expect it to happen abruptly, and not to show a gradual increase to the peak.

The fur returns do not show any such abrupt incursion of arctic foxes along the coast, but, on the other hand, a steady cycle of increase each time towards the peak. The foxes are naturally more numerous at the northern stations (Killinek, Ramah, Hebron) than at the southern ones (Zoar, Hopedale, Makkovik). But even at the latter there was usually the same continuous cycle. This shows well if we group the successive cycles for the southern group in columns, with the minimum on the left and the maximum and descending value (if any) on the right. For this purpose only the series from 1869 to 1922 is used, because in the earlier years Hopedale was alone in the southern group, which was therefore more subject to random influences.

TABLE 60

1	2	18	98	..
3	15	17	117	48
0	3	30	..	..
20	36	53	9	..
6	32	51	..	..
1	2	33	19	3
2	0	4	..	..
3	8	13	..	..
1	5	199	51	..
1	16	101	80	..
1	1	46	32	..
0	4	8	53	2
0	10	10	..	..
6	17	521	317	..

The figures in heavy type indicate the position of the maximum for the *whole* coast. There is a substantial agreement between the southern group and the whole coast. Although the latter includes the former, it is much larger and the comparison is therefore reasonable. Much the same result comes, however, if we arrange the figures in other ways.

9

The next question is where these Labrador arctic foxes come from and how they come. No doubt those caught at Hebron and north of it can be foxes that live locally or in the hinterland and breed there. For all we know, there may also be a permanent, though small, arctic fox population inhabiting the southern regions down to Hamilton Inlet. The arctic hare is said to range as far south as that fjord, and the lemming also occurs on hills near it. On this question of the southern limits of the arctic foxes' breeding range I have no information. It is a fairly reasonable assumption that the species prefers the barren treeless country and avoids dense forest.

If all these arctic foxes were resident in Labrador, the figures would imply that they have the same cycle as their northern and western neighbours in Ungava, a reasonable hypothesis in view of the synchronizing also of Labrador coloured fox. But it is also quite possible that every year a certain fraction of the northern populations makes its way southwards and contributes to the Labrador trade. This theory explains the figures equally well. Neither explanation involves an abrupt emigration at the peak. But this also could occur sometimes, or to some degree.

A southern overflow of this kind probably does occur, replenishing constantly an arctic fox population that might otherwise die out without such a 'subsidy' to maintain its numbers. If so, both explanations would be true. Although we need extensive marking observations to discover how many come from elsewhere, there is some evidence about the way they get so far south.

Arctic foxes have shorter legs than their cousins and are smaller animals too. But their habit is to go out much on to the sea-ice in winter. Here they are believed to associate with polar bears, picking up the remnants of the seals they kill, and generally scavenging. Although seals excrete into the water, bears apparently do not. A Norwegian hunter, a shrewd observer, told me that when the bear has killed a seal he will often make a meal from the skin and fat, and then sleep. This gives a chance to fox, and there must also be many bits ultimately left behind for him. The story about the skin and fat is confirmed by several Spitsbergen bear stomachs I have cut open: these had skin and blubber, and not the meat. Foxes also kill young ringed seals on the bay-ice in spring, according to Kumlien and Soper.[10(1)]

There is another thing that may tempt the fox on to the frozen winter sea. Lemmings have frequently been recorded travelling out on to the ice, sometimes for long distances. (This had been noticed, for instance, by the Hudson's Bay Company post manager at Port Burwell.[19]) Then, foxes probably migrate a good deal in an exploratory way. The fast bay-ice, snow-covered, or the piled hummocks farther out, may not always be distinguishable from land, even to a fox. And yet the coloured fox seldom seems to make the experiment.

10

The movements of sea-ice may therefore be very important in transporting arctic foxes from one place to another. Fortunately these movements are rather well understood, through some scientific studies that justify a digression. For over a hundred years, Newfoundland fishermen, like the arctic fox, have turned to sealing in the early spring. These seals, harp (*Phoca groenlandica*) and hood (*Cystophora cristata*), come down every year on a long migration from the region of Baffin Bay to breed on the ice-floes that reach to Newfoundland. This astounding migration was estimated by Captain George Robinson to span some 840 miles and take about sixty days.[8] After breeding, the seals return (perhaps not all, for some may linger around the coasts between the limits of the journey). Of this southern influx the sealers take up to a quarter of a million, and kill a number more that lie to waste: an industry whose statistics Colman has recently reviewed.[2] He showed, among other things, an interesting fluctuation caused by the relation between seals and men.

These seals arrive just ahead of a huge stream of pack-ice formed originally in the high Arctic, assembled chiefly in Baffin Bay, and drifted southwards on the cold Labrador current. The most useful information on this whole subject of seals and ice and ocean currents I have found in two sources: the older (and little known) accounts published by Captain George Robinson,[6, 7, 8] harbour-master of St. John's, Newfoundland; and the more recent, scientific reports of the International Ice Patrol.[9] Robinson, living in the centre of the sealing trade, in touch with fishermen who had a profound experience of ice and winds, wrote several essays, published as blue-books. The Ice Patrol arose from the *Titanic* disaster in 1912, which galvanized a group of maritime nations into a planned international act which has continued ever since. As a committee cannot command a ship, the work was delegated to the United States Coast Guard. In recent years the mapping and reporting of icebergs has grown into part of a larger science concerned with the whole system of bergs, ice-pack, currents, and oceanography. The source of the danger lay ultimately far in the North, and the patrol has been drawn into regular Arctic surveying cruises. The results of all this work have been assembled by Lieut. Edward Smith, in particular in the results of the *Marion* Expedition in 1929, and of later expeditions of a similar kind.[9]

The trans-polar drift that brought Nansen in the *Fram* and, recently, the Soviet ice-floe party, across to the Atlantic, flows down east Greenland, and turns the tip at Cape Farewell, and follows north until it merges in other currents. But this floating ice plays no part in the Labrador story. It does not cross Davis Strait. The source of the Labrador and Newfoundland ice is threefold. A fair amount creeps down from among the Arctic islands into Baffin Bay. A little comes out of Hudson Strait, derived chiefly from Foxe Basin, only slightly from Hudson Bay. Most is formed in Baffin Bay itself. When the temperature falls in autumn, the ice forms in the north and accumulates chiefly in Baffin Bay. There is, through the rotation of the earth, which sends the ocean water south and piles it westward against the North American shelf, a strong southern cold current from Baffin Bay to Labrador and the Grand Banks. It runs at 12 to 14 miles a day past Northern Labrador.

This cold stream is remarkably self-contained, and the junction of it with the Gulf Stream (now called by specialists the North Atlantic Current) is often sudden and clearly marked. Ward says[11] that on one occasion, in 1922, the Ice Patrol's cutter lay across the dividing line, with the water at the bow 34° F. and at the stern 56° F. Smith[9(2)] actually gives a photograph of the junction of these two waters!

When the northern ice-factory starts to increase its output, the floes are carried down in large quantities. The pack begins to reach Northern Labrador in November, and by January it is off Newfoundland. The pack may cover the whole width of the continental shelf, which is about 80 miles wide between Cape Chidley and Hamilton Inlet, and up to 280 at St. John's. On the Grand Banks the maximum extension is in April.

All these figures are averages, for there is a good deal of fluctuation in quantity and in the dates of arrival. The seals bring forth their young on the southern ice in February or March. Although the ice round Newfoundland usually begins to diminish after April, there are some years in which the pack still encloses Northern Labrador until July or August. Smith says:[9(1)] 'As summer advances, the pack melts back towards its northern roots uncovering first the Newfoundland and then the Labrador coast lines.' In the north the ice production slackens. And another factor also comes into operation. The ice coming out in early summer from Hudson Strait may partly deflect the Baffin water and send it circling north again up West Greenland.

Smith's picture of the situation from March onwards is of a long procession of ice-floes 1,200–1,500 miles long, moving south, the supply diminishing in the north and melting back in the south, until by the summer most of it is turned to water.

11

The bearing of all this on arctic fox populations will be obvious. This ice may bring foxes down not only from Cape Chidley to Makkovik, but from Baffin Island or even farther north. And we know that it enables them occasionally to reach the Gulf of St. Lawrence and Cape Breton Island in Nova Scotia (see p. 239). It is a broad moving highway connecting, at any rate potentially, Baffin Island with Labrador. Whether such a connexion is of high significance to the fox trade we cannot assess without following marked foxes.

Robinson describes how bears and foxes appear with the ice. The first slob, or thin ice, apparently makes the bays, already full of slushy or thin ice, freeze at once. Then comes sheet-ice and later heavier drift-ice. In Newfoundland the heavy drift arrives by the end of January or middle of February. In Labrador it would come before the end of the year. 'As soon as this body arrives, and sometimes before, Polar bears and white foxes land from the ice and are killed by the inhabitants, and these animals have constantly been killed on the headlands between Aillik in Lat. 55° N. and Ferryland, in Lat. 47° N., in the early portion of ice obstruction. . . . About the year 1880, a bear 14 feet long was killed in Pistolet Bay, in the last week of January . . . it shows that these Arctic animals may be transported South at a very early date.'[7] Aillik is just north of Hamilton Inlet, Ferryland on the coast of the Avalon Peninsula in south-east Newfoundland, Pistolet at the north tip of Newfoundland, by Belle Isle Straits.

White foxes are often taken at Cartwright also, on mid-Labrador. The Hudson's Bay Company post there reported[13] in 1934–5: 'White fox not native to this vicinity, but come off the drift ice.' In 1935–6: 'In the absence of drift ice this spring, none were caught.'

Robinson also says that a few walrus and bearded seals float down on the heavy ice in June, even as far as Belle Isle Straits and northern Newfoundland. They were commonly seen in the Gulf of St. Lawrence before 1850. The older ice-masters of Robinson's time (the eighties and nineties of last century) believed that the ice was more intense before about 1850 or 1860:[6] and the Moravian Mission voyages certainly give the impression that heavy ice years were then more frequent. Robinson notes:[8] 'At least it is certain that Arctic animals frequented the Gulf of St. Lawrence and the east coast of this island in greater numbers than they do today. Polar bears, foxes, the walrus, the *Phoca barbata* rode the ice in much larger numbers.' It is rather interesting that the Eskimo race has also contracted a formerly larger southern range which reached to about the same point.

An insistent thought arises throughout this description of the ice-riding population. The fox depends on the polar bear, the polar bear on seals. The seals and the ice move south each year, and provide sustenance and foothold for the others. But the seals start *before* the ice. What sets them moving? Robinson has a theory also about this.[8] The cod caught off Cape Chidley at the end of July and August 'is emaciated to such a degree that the fishermen compare it to a lantern, or living skeleton'. He adds that the bone of a small octopus, abundant in Davis Strait, is the only food found in the stomachs of cod at Cape Chidley at that time. It seems likely, therefore, that the seals also find food scarce in the late summer and therefore emigrate. They are in fact thin when they leave Davis Strait in October and get to Cape Mugford, in the south. But how they find their way south is as much a mystery as the far movements of birds. Robinson's ecological wisdom resembles that of Cabot. Between them they set a list of probabilities and interrelations that challenges our scientific ignorance. There is in all this the likelihood of a wide connexion between the life of land and sea, and the almost certainty that the arctic fox population of Quebec Peninsula is not an independent, isolated unit. More evidence on this matter is to be found when we turn to conditions in Hudson Strait and Hudson Bay.

Colman has recently[2a] drawn attention to a still wider influence that these movements of seals and of sea-ice may have. If the seal herds that visit Newfoundland are the same as those that live on the west coast of Greenland, the welfare of the West Greenlanders is closely linked with the results of the Newfoundland sealing fleet in catching, and, it might be, depleting the seal herds. The Greenlanders may be catching the adults, and the Newfoundlanders the young of the same great herd. On this ground Colman calls for systematic marking experiments to be done on seals in order to settle this crucial question of the single integrity of the herd: there is a little evidence that some seals stay permanently on the coast of West Greenland. One can foresee here the growth of a huge, comprehensive investigation, in the course of which the movements of marked foxes would give a key to the drift of ice (no one has seriously tried yet to 'mark' the ice-floes themselves, though one cannot see why this too could not be done), and both would become related to the seals which bring with them also a following of bears on which foxes may depend.

12

The ice conditions in Hudson Strait have also a bearing on the arctic fox situation. Just as the Atlantic shipping has brought about an interest in bergs and currents, so the Hudson Bay grain route has directed attention to the navigability of Hudson Strait. An early report by Charles Bell[1] to the Winnipeg Board of Trade contains much interesting ice-lore, saved from the memories of experienced sea-captains at the end of last century. Mecking[5] has published extensive studies of the ice conditions, based on elaborate search of the records, and Smith[9] gives convenient summary in the *Marion* Expedition Report. Low's chapter[3(1)] in the *Cruise of the 'Neptune'* is also clear and valuable.

Hudson Strait is subjected to the influence of three different outside currents: from Hudson Bay, Foxe Basin, and Davis Strait. To these are to be added three other powerful influences: the contours of the land and the sea-bottom, the weather (especially the winds), and the tides. In Hudson Bay the water circulates anti-clockwise, so that the west coast of Quebec Peninsula is washed by waters with a northerly drift, unlike the east coast (Labrador) where the current passes southwards. The current passes out into Hudson Strait, where it is joined by one from Foxe Channel. Foxe Basin sends a second branch south that contributes to the circulation in Hudson Bay. This big bay does not become entirely covered with winter ice, which forms in a fairly narrow belt round the coast, leaving the centre free. The Belcher Islands, for instance (see p. 367), can only be reached on the ice in the early spring, when the ice sets hard across for a month or two (even so, it fails in certain years).

But Foxe Basin manufactures much heavy ice, which is the main component of the pack in Hudson Strait during the winter. A certain amount of the ice from Baffin Bay also gets into the eastern part of the Strait (a trend detectable by the occurrence of real icebergs here), but probably does not penetrate very far, and then mostly along the north shore.

The Strait is about 500 miles long, but the east entrance, between the Resolution Island group and the Button Islands, is only thirty-five miles across. There are, however, two inner channels between these islands and their respective mainlands (Baffin Island and Quebec–Labrador). In the middle part it widens, to about sixty miles; but the west entrance has several large islands (Salisbury, Nottingham) across a part of it; and farther into Hudson Bay there are Southampton, Coats, and Mansel Islands. The current tends to run westward along the north side and eastward along the south side of the strait.

This general scheme is greatly embroidered with variations brought about by winds and tides. The latter rise to 30 or 40 feet, and race at six or seven miles an hour. It is natural enough to find that the strait does not freeze entirely solid in winter, but remains a chaotic waste of ice-floes that move about, jam, free themselves, and move again. The strait becomes filled with ice during the winter to a large extent because there are two important supplies of pack moving into it, which tend to become jammed and confined at the narrow eastern end.

Captain William Kennedy, who led one of the Franklin Search Expeditions in 1850, and also had eight years' experience of Ungava Bay and the strait, stated:[1(1)] 'The Strait ice is never fast, and it keeps forming and breaking from shore during the winter months, covering it with moving ice more or less compact.' He also remarked[1(2)] that: 'The north shore of Hudson's Strait is sheltered from northerly winds. Southerly setting currents open a channel along the northern coast. If I was to give any directions for avoiding the thickest of the ice in Hudson's Strait, it would be to keep pretty near the north shore, for we always observed that side much the clearest. . . .' This refers chiefly to navigation in early summer. But the general effect of prevailing north and north-west winds in driving the pack to the south side was well known to many navigators.

McLean,[4] who did aerial reconnaissance of the strait, watched the development of winter-ice fulfilment. It came first at the western end, in November, and reached the east end two weeks later. By February there was only 15 per cent. of open water, and the ice remained thickly until about May. By July it has mostly cleared away in normal years.

13

We see that the waters that separate Ungava and Cape Chidley from Baffin Island in summer are for over six months almost choked with ice. But this ice is a moving chaos that leaves many large channels. How far it provides a highway for arctic foxes is hard to say: there is little to suggest that one side would get more foxes than the other, unless there are mass migrations south in certain years, as is believed by fur men. But the probability of interchange remains. Even if these movements tended to cancel out, they would be of great importance in the spread of disease or of colour mutations. There is no doubt that animals do get across sometimes. This is proved by records of the occurrence of coloured foxes and lynx in Baffin Island. Such records are rare enough to make it pretty certain that the animals are strays and not members of a permanent scarce breeding stock. Soper collected some notes on this subject during his stay in Baffin Island in 1924–6. (Incidentally, his expedition proved what rich possibilities await the trained naturalist who can make a long stay in the country.)

'John Hayward of the Hudson's Bay Company informed the writer that a few years ago, a black fox was captured by an Eskimo at Cape Dorset. The animal must have strayed there either on drifting ice from Ungava, in which case it might possibly be *Vulpes rubricosa bangsi* Merriam, the Labrador red fox, or by way of Southampton Island from Keewatin, in which case the animal undoubtedly would be *Vulpes fulva*. Mr. Hayward said that at least two red foxes have been taken on the south coast of Baffin Island. Sergeant Wight, R.C.M.P., is under the impression that either a red or a "cross" fox was taken in recent years [i.e. before 1928] in the Lake Harbour region. The following notes were made by F. Melton, Amadjuak Hudson's Bay Company's post: "March 28, 1923, a red fox traded at the post. January 31, 1924, red fox skin traded at the post." It is evident that the accidental occurrence of the red fox on Baffin Island is a comparatively common incident.[10(2)]

The zoological reports[13] of the Hudson's Bay Company post at Lake Harbour for ten years (1926–30 and 1932–6) contain only two records of coloured foxes. In 1934–5 there were 'more', but the species was 'very rare in this vicinity'. In 1936–7 some more were caught. 'Coloured foxes are never abundant here, but this year's catch . . . includes (I think for the first time in the history of the post) some cross foxes.'

Soper also got records of occasional lynx.[10(3)] 'John Hayward, of the Hudson's Bay Company post, Pangnirtung, informed the writer that a lynx was shot by an Eskimo, during the winter of 1918, at Lake Harbour. It was supposed that the animal was carried on moving ice, across Hudson Strait from the Ungava side. About the same time a lynx was caught on Coats Island, by Stephen J. Stewart, and another was shot by an Eskimo on ice-floes off Wakeham Bay on the south side of Hudson Strait.' Mr. James Cantley, of the Hudson's Bay Company's District Office in Montreal, told me in 1928 that a very few lynx had reached Baffin Land in 1918 or 1919, and that they were taken at Lake Harbour and Cape Dorset. There seems to have been an unusual incursion at this time. If coloured fox and lynx can be transported across the strait, the arctic fox must commonly be carried also.

Whereas the Labrador current takes a certain proportion of arctic foxes southward out of their natural home in the north, the currents up the west coast of the peninsula act in an opposite way, and the floating ice will tend to return the foxes north again. Of course arctic foxes do not all wander out on to moving ice. Soper remarked[10(1)] that in the spring they can be seen around tide-cracks near the shore, apparently eating seaweed that had been brought up. At this time they also attack and kill young ringed seals (*Phoca hispida*) in their snow dens on the first bay ice.

The fur returns of the Hudson's Bay Company and Revillon Posts agree with the ice conditions, in that large catches of arctic foxes are not made far south of the arctic zone, on this coast of the bay. From this survey of the Arctic fur cycle in Ungava we may now turn to a consideration of the causes underlying it, and in particular to the work of lemmings.

REFERENCES

* means that an abstract is deposited in the Bureau of Animal Population. Years are Outfits: 1908 means 1908–9. 'H. B. Co.' means Hudson's Bay Company.

1. BELL, C. N. (1884). 'Our northern waters: a report presented to the Winnipeg Board of Trade regarding the Hudson's Bay and Straits.' Winnipeg. Pp. 1–78. (1) 11. (2) 33.

2. COLMAN, J. S. (1937). 'The present state of the Newfoundland seal fishery.' J. Anim. Ecol. 6: 145–59.

2 a. COLMAN, J. (1938). 'The Newfoundland seal-fishery and its possible influence on the Greenlanders.' Polar Record, No. 16: 99–103.

2 b. ELTON, C. S. (1924). 'Periodic fluctuations in the numbers of animals: their causes and effects.' Brit. J. Exp. Biol. 2: 119–63.

2 c. ELTON, C. S. (1925). 'Plague and the regulation of numbers in wild mammals.' J. Hyg., Camb. 24: 138–63.

2 d. HEWITT, C. GORDON (1921). 'The conservation of the wild life of Canada.' New York. p. 223.

3. LOW, A. P. (1906). 'Report on the Dominion Government Expedition to Hudson Bay and the Arctic Islands on board the D.G.S. Neptune, 1903–1904.' Ottawa. p. 152. (1) 152. (2) Ch. 11.

4. MCLEAN, N. B. (1929). 'Report of the Hudson Strait Expedition.' Ottawa. pp. 1–221.

5. MECKING, L. (1907). 'Die Treibeiserscheinungen bei Neufundland in ihrer Abhängigkeit von Witterungsverhältnissen.' Ann. Hydrogr. Marit. Meteorol. 35: 348–55 and 396–409. (Discussed also in Smith's report.)

6. ROBINSON, G. (1889). 'A report on the movements of the ice, currents, and tidal streams of the Coast of Newfoundland and in the Gulf of St. Lawrence.' Blue-book, Hydrographic Office, Admiralty, London.

7. ROBINSON, G. (1891). 'Supplement (1891) to a Report on the movements of the ice etc., comprising the journey of the ice from Baffin Bay to the Banks of Newfoundland.' Blue-book, Hydrographic Office, Admiralty, London.

8. ROBINSON, G. (1897). 'Ice-riding Pinnipedes: a description of the migration and peculiarities of the *Phoca groenlandica* and *Cystophora cristata*. . . .' London.

9. SMITH, E. H. (1931). 'The *Marion* Expedition to Davis Strait and Baffin Bay . . . 1928. Scientific Results, Part 3: Arctic ice, with especial reference to its distribution to the North Atlantic Ocean.' U.S. Treasury Dept., Coast Guard, Bull. No. 19: 1–221. (1) 52. (2) 204. (Reviewed by W. L. S. Fleming (1938) in Polar Record, No. 16: 124–8.)

10. SOPER, J. DEWEY (1928). 'A faunal investigation of Southern Baffin Island.' Bull. Nat. Mus. Canada, No. 53. (1) 35–6. (2) 33. (3) 39.

11. WARD, R. DE C. (1924). 'A cruise with the International Ice Patrol.' Monthly Weather Rev. 52: 71–8.

*12. H. B. Co., Annual Reports on Fur Trade. MS. H. B. Co. Archives, London. (1) H. M. S. Cotter, Supplementary Rep. on Ungava Posts, 1910.

13. H. B. Co., Zoological Reports from Posts. MS. Bureau of Animal Population, Oxford.

*14. Ungava District (Fort Chimo), Correspondence. MS. H. B. Co. Archives, London. (1) 31 July 1908: G. B. Boucher to P. McKenzie. (2) Outfit 1910, Report on trade of Fort Chimo. (3) Outfit 1911, Report on trade of Fort Chimo. (4) 28 Sept. 1887: K. McKenzie to J. Wrigley.

*15. Fort Chimo (Ungava District), Fur Returns. 1877–83, 1884–7, 1897–1900. In account books, &c. MS. H. B. Co. Archives, London.

*16. Fort Chimo (Ungava District), Fur Returns. 1868–1924. Supplied by H. B. Co., Fur Trade Dept., Winnipeg.

*17. Fort Chimo, Revillon Fur Returns. 1913–24. Supplied by Revillon Frères, Winnipeg.

*18. Moravian Missions, Labrador Fur Returns, 1834–1925. MS. Moravian Mission, 32 Fetter Lane, London.

19. Information obtained by D. H. S. Davis in 1931, from the post manager at Port Burwell.

CHAPTER XXI
THE WORK OF LEMMINGS

Through the dazzling gloom
The many-coloured mice, that thread
The dewy turf beneath our tread,
In troops each other's motions cross,
Through the heath and through the moss.

SHELLEY, *Scenes from the Faust of Goethe.*

1

THE Russians have a convenient phrase for which our language has no graceful equivalent. They speak of 'mouse-like rodents' when they wish to describe the whole gallery of terrestrial rodents, smaller than a rabbit or a marmot, that are the key-animals in this book. The phrase helps to remind us that even in the barren lands of Ungava there are quite a number of rodent species, and at least seven of these are mouse-like rodents that are fit food for fox and hawk and owl.

Anderson[1] gives what is known of these species in Ungava. The lemming (*Dicrostonyx hudsonius*), two short-tailed voles (*Microtus pennsylvanicus labradorius* and *M. enixus*), a lemming-mouse (*Synaptomys borealis innuitus*), a 'false lemming-mouse' (*Phenacomys ungava ungava*), a red-backed vole (*Clethrionomys gapperi ungava*), and probably a white-footed or deer-mouse (*Peromyscus maniculatus maniculatus*). There is room among this varied rodent company for much complexity of interrelation, since each species will tend to differ in local abundance and in the course of its secular fluctuations. But, since scientific observers have so far been few and transient, and all long-continued field notes come from fur men and natives, we are compelled to confine our inquiries to animals which can most easily and safely be identified in the field. So we take the lemming and the voles (*Microtus*), but more especially the lemming, fully remembering that to do this is to make a simplified diagram or sketch of what is really a moving equilibrium of great subtlety. We try merely to detect the main theme amidst the infinite local and temporal variations, which must inevitably fall to experts to record and understand.

The most conspicuous member of this gallery is the lemming (*Dicrostonyx hudsonius*). It might almost be said to occupy, not the gallery, but the front stalls; with the various species of *Microtus*, which hold this position in Northern Labrador, relegated to the lesser affluence of the dress circle.

The lemming is much the largest member of the corps of Arctic mouse-like rodents, with substantial build, broad buttocks, a ridiculous short stumpy tail, a Roman profile, close-fitting grey fur with a dark dorsal stripe all turning to a whitish dress in winter, and a swift gait that denies the apparent intentions of its body. McClure called the lemming a diamond edition of the guinea-pig. Although it rivals the guinea-pig in bountiful power of increase, its blood runs close to that of the voles, and this resemblance extends to the great degree of fluctuation that lemming populations show.

Over most of the polar lands two genera of lemmings live together on the tundra, with almost unanimous ecology. But, whereas *Dicrostonyx* is greyish in summer and turns white in winter, when it also grows the specially long forked claws that give the name, *Lemmus* is brightly, even gaily coloured in rich browns and blacks, and keeps this costume throughout the seasons. Both are nocturnal, at any rate in the normal life of summer, and live under snow in winter. One may wonder, in passing, why two creatures living under identical conditions should differ in colour so profoundly, when one of the colour schemes is supposedly protective.

Soper[17] gathered some evidence that the two kinds of lemming, at any rate in southern Baffin Island, do not live quite together. *Lemmus trimucronatus*, which was much the commoner one, occurred in a wide range of habitats, but especially haunted low, often rather damp ground. It was also found sometimes quite high up on the hills. Of *Dicrostonyx groenlandicus* he noted:[17(1)] 'It evidently keeps to high, rocky ground, for none was taken in traps in lower country where *trimucronatus* was abundant.' *Dicrostonyx* was very scarce in Baffin Island; but a preference for the higher rocky or gravelly ridges was also noted by Preble,[15] surveying the fauna of the barrens north of Fort Churchill on Hudson Bay. And here *Dicrostonyx* was abundant and *Lemmus* scarce. The only *Lemmus* he found were on low ground with deep soil. Another thing that Preble noticed was the conspicuous difference between the runways of the two lemmings. *Lemmus* made a meandering network of tunnels joined into one general system, as did *Microtus*; while *Dicrostonyx* had small burrows from the surface with blind endings.

These two genera have each a series of species and races that inhabit different geographical zones of the Arctic. In nearly every part there are representatives of both kinds of lemming. But in Scandinavia only *Lemmus* occurs; in Quebec Peninsula and Greenland only *Dicrostonyx* has been found. Ungava has *Dicrostonyx hudsonius*; Baffin Island has *Dicrostonyx groenlandicus richardsoni* and *Lemmus trimucronatus trimucronatus*. The absence of *Lemmus* from Ungava simplifies the ecological problem of fluctuations a little, though most of the evidence for other regions suggests that all lemmings fluctuate together.

2

Before giving the evidence about Ungava lemming cycles the species deserves a little more description. The outstanding things about the lemming are its bulk, its voracity, its remarkably rapid powers of increase after scarcity, and its edibility. A small consignment of live *Dicrostonyx* arrived at Oxford from the Canadian Arctic in 1930 after a rather eventful journey. They were originally trapped at the Hudson's Bay Company post at Lake Harbour, sent to Port Burwell, where apparently local lemmings were put in to make up losses on the way, transferred to the care of the Hudson's Bay Company's doctor, in whose bedroom slippers they partly lived on board ship, reached England in a glass-fronted cage, and were discovered in the Oxford Parcels Office being worshipped by two thunder-struck porters. These lemmings were kept and bred by Mr. R. M. Ranson, and observed by us for several years.

Whereas a vole (according to its species) usually weighs something less than 50 grammes, a *Dicrostonyx* fully grown may weigh 75 grammes or even top a hundred. A guinea-pig, for comparison, weighs about 500–1,000. Since the exploitation value of a prey depends partly on its size, the pre-dator catching a lemming gets 50 to 100 per cent. more than if it catches a vole.

As to voracity the following experiment is instructive. A pair of captive *Dicrostonyx* were released inside a large pen that was kept for experimental work near Oxford. The pen covered 25 square yards, was deeply enclosed at the sides with sheet metal and wire, and overhead with more wire-netting. The ground had grown to a lush vegetation of grass (mostly a thick sprouting mat of *Holcus*) and a few buttercups and plantains. In this mat of vegetation, nearly 8 inches thick and covering all the ground, the lemmings were put on 30 March 1931. A note was made that this rich food should support them for some time. Under some artificial shelter a nest of grass was made by the lemmings, which produced five young about 14 April. By this time arterial roads had been made in the grass, and some of it had been nibbled and eaten. On 27 April the young were no longer in the nest, and one was seen to pop into a burrow—a small grey furry ball. By 28 May the lemming family of not more than seven had destroyed every vestige of vegetation in the pen, and the survivors had to be rescued and taken away. The ground was a desert: in eight weeks the lemmings had eaten right out 25 square yards of luxuriant herbage. On 8 June a little grass was sprouting again, and by September the pen had thick grass once more, though there were no plantains and buttercups.

One factor contributing to destruction was this lemming's habit of eating roots as well as stems and leaves. Freuchen[7(1)] says: 'In my opinion, a lemming burrows mostly for the sake of food—roots and, perhaps, grubs.' He found that lemmings in captivity ate all parts of the arctic willow, and also the long tap roots of *Silene acaulis*, an arctic-alpine pink cushioned campion. No doubt lemmings feed on a wide variety of plants, but this habit of digging roots is a direct assault on the capital value of vegetation which must greatly increase the influence of 'lemming pressure'.

Porsild[14] records an interesting result of this habit in the Northwest Territories of Canada. There is a leguminous plant, *Hedysarum boreale*, known in the north as 'liquorice-root', which has a large tap root. When cooked it tastes rather like carrot and is very good food for man. It is much sought after also by barren-ground bears. 'Several species of meadow mice and lemmings in the autumn "harvest" the roots and place them "en cache" for the winter. The caches are found in subterranean runways near the surface. The Eskimo, with the aid of a dog, has no difficulty in locating these mouse caches, and frequently obtains his own supply for the winter in this manner.' Von Wrangell[20] noted a similar thing in the Lower Kolyma region of Siberia, when he was travelling there in 1821–3: 'The Makarscha is a farinaceous root, which is used partly as an addition to the meat or fish cakes, to which it gives an agreeable flavour, and partly alone, as a kind of dessert before supper. The field-mice lay up in their holes large stores of this and other roots. The women are particularly expert in discovering these deposits.'

3

The lemming's continued survival is a little surprising when the host of his enemies is considered. Even for man lemmings are edible. When John Rae[16(1)] and his party were travelling in the north in 1851, they lost some stores and had to live for a day or two chiefly on lemmings, which were migrating then in hordes. These they roasted between thin plates of limestone, finding them fat and good. Peter Freuchen[7(2)] notes that: 'As a rule they are only eaten in cases of emergency, although I have met old people [i.e. Eskimos] who were fond of them because their flesh was so sweet. I met one man who ate lemmings "for the sake of a memory", as he said; I was unable to obtain any explanation beyond that.' Elsewhere he says: 'The Eskimos roast them between two flat stones, but [they] are not really nice; the flesh has a sweet, rather sickly taste.'

Several things can be suggested that tend to preserve the lemming in spite of its apparent vulnerability. Its largely subterranean habits set a limit to the chances of being caught before it can breed successfully. With the advantage of cover (from soil, rocks, vegetation, and, in winter, snow) goes a surprising swiftness and agility. 'The conies are but a feeble folk, yet make they their houses in the rocks.' Another factor is its powerful rate of increase. A fourth is to be found in the time-relations of the predator-prey fluctuation. The lemming crashes; the predators crash and migrate; the lemming begins to recover before the slower-breeding predators can catch it up. This is a rough description of a part of a phenomenon that is now known to be generally found in nature and is usually referred to as the Lotka-Volterra oscillation.

This is the animal whose part in the periodicity of fur fluctuations we hope to trace. Before studying the closer details of evidence it will be of assistance to notice the main headings under which it falls.

4

A persuasive general argument can be developed from the protracted observations of certain accomplished field naturalists outside Ungava itself who have studied the ecological life of *Dicrostonyx*. Especially one turns to the work of Manniche[12] in East Greenland, of Dewey Soper[17] in southern Baffin Island, and of Peter Freuchen[7] in Melville Peninsula (to the north of Hudson Bay and east of Baffin Island). To these we should add the patiently accumulated records of the Canadian National Museum, compiled by Anderson,[1] which give at any rate a skeletal framework for mapping lemming distribution, and discussing taxonomy and habits. These dovetail with Degerbøl's[6] museum studies in Copenhagen of the material that Freuchen brought back from the Fifth Thule Expedition.

The fox fur fluctuations in Ungava form the central phenomenon we seek to explain: these are derived, of course, from the Hudson's Bay Company and Revillons Frères statistics for 1925 to the present day. For trading reasons it is not considered desirable to publish the details of these at present, but a summary of the chief trends is given later. Then, from 1924 onwards a gradually increasing number of the Hudson's Bay Company's zoological reports enable the course of fluctuations in foxes to be traced at certain posts. From 1932 onwards this story is almost as complete as could be expected from the rough questionnaire methods used. After 1935 the Canadian Arctic Wild Life Enquiry,[3, 4] containing the joint contribution of the Government and the Company, takes up the tale more fully.

These various reports seek to supply a running record of the arctic fox, lemming, and snowy owl fluctuations, so that their interaction can be analysed. The record can be filled out here and there with odd observations made by other people, as in the reports of the Royal Canadian Mounted Police (which should be read by everyone who is interested in arctic wild-life questions or in native welfare: one prays that a hungry treasury will refrain from cutting down the volume of these extraordinarily useful notes).

The history of the periodic mass migrations of the snowy owl, which are a tremendously important part of the cycle story, has been assembled by the American ornithologist, Alfred Gross, and can be a little amplified by the sources already mentioned, and by the field observations of Hantzsch and others. This subject is treated in the next chapter.

In sifting this varied evidence we shall put together a story that almost exactly parallels that of the vole and coloured fox in Labrador, except that the snowy owl comes in prominently as well. But it should be remarked that the Ungava Arctic cycle, with its chain of lemming to arctic fox and snowy owl, epitomizes a phenomenon that is found all through the polar regions wherever lemmings occur and have been studied. A similar violent fluctuation, keyed to lemmings, with different species of lemmings, but practically the same species of owls and foxes, is found in Lapland, Novaya Zemlya, Arctic Siberia, Kamchatka, Alaska, the Western Arctic and the Arctic Archipelago of Canada, and in North and East Greenland. It is *the* short cycle of population on land in the Polar regions: and the vole cycles of Northern Labrador, of Scandinavia, and Great Britain are southern extensions of this generous rhythm of the north.

It is this wide extension that permits us to use, with due caution, the conclusions of workers outside Ungava—a fortunate privilege, since so few trained naturalists have been able to concentrate on land mammals within its territories. One begins with Manniche's monograph[12(1)] on 'The terrestrial mammals and birds of North-east Greenland', which gives the most entrancing, live account of arctic wild-life that I know. It is impossible not to refer to this work with enthusiasm, and Manniche must surely also deserve the title of 'incomparable observer' that Darwin bestowed on Fabre.

5

The scene of Manniche's survey was near Cape Bismarck, lat. 76° 46′ N. on the north-east coast of Greenland, where the Danmark Expedition under Mylius-Erichsen made its base in August 1906. Here Manniche studied, among other things, the critical stages of a lemming cycle, from its peak in 1906 to its decline in 1907 and beginning of recovery in 1908. The species was *Dicrostonyx groenlandicus*.

I shall give a good deal of space to a summary of Manniche's observations, since they hold some of the same vital quality that can be felt in William Cabot's essay on mice in Labrador: an intuitive understanding of the ordered stir of effort and contending forces that goes on among the small life of the Arctic. Mostly he worked on the low rolling rocky country near the coast, with its different types of ground: dry tundra carrying the arctic willow and *Dryas*; boggy stretches with moss and sedge; a little aquatic vegetation in the pools; stony tracts with small scattered plants; bare gravel; and the estuaries and shore. Whereas the arctic hare preferred the rocky slopes with plenty of coarse cover for refuge, Manniche found lemmings most numerous in the richer ground below. Here, besides a wide choice of plants, and soil to burrow in, the lemmings receive more protection in winter from the drifted snow.

In the autumn of 1906: 'The territory was here on long stretches . . . quite undermined by their passages and sown with their holes. The feathered enemies of the lemming, the snowy owl, the falcon, the arctic gull and the raven had their resort in great numbers to this territory during the autumn, and were living sumptuously on the abundance of the prey so welcome to them. In the same autumn I also met with great numbers of lemmings in other localities rich in vegetation. . . .'

In summer the lemmings made large round nests near the surface, sometimes lined with musk-ox wool. In winter they made others under the snow, by chewing up grass. Great piles of dung lay beside the nests. But the insulation of the nest was not enough to protect the lemmings against the severe winter cold (which averaged −25·9° in February: often the calm winter cold spells reached −40°). They stayed under the deeper snow patches. Only a few moments in this bitter cold would send the animals below again. Sometimes they were caught by the cold and frozen to death. In March a number of the lemmings migrated individually on to other places, and some went far out on to the sea-ice of the fjord. (In the spring of 1908 one of the sledge parties found that lemmings had journeyed 57 kilometres over the ice.)

'By nature the lemming is timid, suspicious not without reason, and as a consequence extremely cautious. This is the case especially when the animal is out in the light of day. The extraordinarily sensitive, much persecuted little creature, of which it has been said justly that its life hangs upon a thread, is the most nervous animal I know. Like a flash of lightning the lemming hurries from one hole to another. Wherever it goes, death is following on the heels of it, even when it has retired to its subterranean dwelling. The fox quickly makes its way to the secret passages of the defenceless animal, and the ermine personally pays its bloody visits there.'

6

The cycle in lemmings around Danmark Havn went like this. There was abundance in the late summer of 1906: lemmings were seen about, their traces were widespread in suitable ground, and enemies were having a feast. In the winter following, something happened that brought the population tumbling down with a crash. The causes of this crash are not the immediate question, though we shall have to consider them again later: April and May brought the snow melt, which disclosed deserted burrows and only a few lemmings left from the large population of the previous year.

'The great multitude of lemmings presented by the after-summer 1906, might seem to indicate that several successive favourable years have gone before and that winters like that in 1906–07, are rather unfrequent. In the summer of 1908 I might again meet with lemming in most of the tracts which I examined, but nowhere in anything like the number which was seen in 1906.'

We have here the crest, the trough, and the rising wave. The effects of these changes on the enemies of the lemming are of the greatest interest. It is not to be expected that the whole complicated situation would be revealed to a single observer, and we should not forget that Manniche was primarily an ornithologist who came freshly to the study of Arctic mammals. But the chief actors in the situation stand out very clearly from his notes.

First the arctic fox, noted as common in the lower ground where lemmings chiefly abounded. Here we have the fox at work during the boom of lemming prosperity:

'Its movements are at the same time graceful and swift as lightning. Like an India-rubber ball the nimble animal will jump up and down the steep snowdrifts, coated with a glazing of ice, and it sweeps across the snow-covered mountain side or over the sea ice, as if it were carried on wings. Under the difficult conditions of life the senses of the fox have been sharpened to the utmost. It is undoubtedly most beautiful to observe, when it is strolling about in pursuit of lemmings on a sunny autumn day. Like a tuft of cotton wool periodically carried along by the wind, it chases across the mountain slope or meadow land, always spying, listening and sniffing the air. Even when hurrying along at the utmost speed it discovers with never failing certainty the lemming which is hidden under the snow and quickly makes its way to it by means of its strong claws and fore limbs. With three or four powerful jumps the fox lets itself fall down into the snow pit, its body hanging down perpendicularly and the tail stiffly out-stretched behind, and it will go on in this way till it has got the dainty bit between the teeth. For some moments it tarries on the spot and then hastens on again. Soon it is seen once more occupied with its work of digging and its strange caprioles.'

Like the lemming, the fox was chiefly astir in the night hours. While the months of daylight lasted the fox had some other resources for its food. There were ptarmigan, the eggs of wading birds, and probably young hares. But in winter the lemming was the only abundant natural food. The birds had gone south, and the arctic fox hesitates to attack a full-grown arctic hare. In this region the story is even simpler than in Ungava, for *Dicrostonyx* is the only mouse-like rodent.

After the lemming crash, the foxes were seen to have turned in the emergency to other supplies. They followed the polar bear and shared its spoils of seal, not neglecting the bear's own dung. They visited tide-cracks in the ice, to pick up flotsam fish that might be thrown up there. They eagerly entered traps to take the bait, and then sometimes were torn to pieces and eaten by the other foxes. Though natural rations were so short, it seems quite likely that the Danish expedition saved, unintentionally, some of these foxes from starvation, because its depots of walrus meat were pillaged, and afterwards the foxes were found to be healthy and fat. Such subsidy may have altered somewhat the natural chances of survival during this crisis. A curious thing was that the foxes, even in scarcity, would never swallow the lemmings' stomachs, full of green stuff, but left them lying on the ground. All else they ate. But this habit does not seem to be universal.

The ermine (*Mustela arctica*) was not uncommon around Danmark Havn, and depended very closely upon the lemmings. It has an advantage over other predators in being thin and sinuous, so that it can hunt the lemmings in their runs beneath the winter cover of snow. But this close dependence carries a corresponding drawl..ck, for the ermine probably has few alternative resources for food in winter, except the hare, and a full-grown arctic hare is not an easy prey. Manniche noted little about any fluctuations in ermine, and the subject may be left aside now until we come to Peter Freuchen's notes. It may be rather important in certain ways.

The other predatory mammals can be passed in a word or two. Wolves were few, the hungry outriders of a population dependent on the muskoxen in other places farther off. The polar bear only comes into this story as a form of 'poor-relief' for the arctic fox.

7

Among the raptorial birds, chief lemming-hunter was the snowy owl (*Nyctea nyctea*), which also grabbed some ptarmigan and other birds in summer, and no doubt young arctic hares. But lemmings were its prop and stay. Hunting by day and night in the lemming territories, these owls had their nests hidden up on the higher rocky ground. Although the owls were seen throughout the year, their greatest numbers were on late summer

and autumn migration, when Manniche could see as many as seven during
a walk at night. But the great scarcity of lemmings in 1907 seemed to
have brought down their numbers, whether by death or emigration or
failure to breed as well as usual, was not known. In 1907 the autumn flight
was small.

The other large bird of prey was the gyrfalcon (*Falco gyrfalco*). Although
it was scarce as a breeder, a great number congregated on the lemming
grounds in the autumn of 1906. Manniche collected fifty for his museum:
great birds nearly 2 feet long, pale coloured. The stomachs and pellets of
gyrfalcons were full of lemming remains, though like the fox and owl, they
picked up a few ptarmigan, small birds, and arctic hares besides. But in
the autumn of 1907 very few gyrfalcons were seen at all.

Ravens (*Corvus corax*) were not uncommon during the months of light,
though they vanished during the heart of winter. Their head-quarters
were up among the rocks, but they hunted below. 'The lemmings absolutely form the principal food of the ravens in N.E. Greenland; they were
almost exclusively to be seen inland lemming hunting in the year 1906,
when lemmings were abundant. This year I found in every stomach
examined remnants of lemmings and almost nothing else. . . .' In 1907 the
ravens changed their habits, keeping attendance on the polar bears,
molesting tern colonies, hanging around the shore, and even visiting fox
traps for the bait. Raven and gyrfalcon often fought battles, with fairly
even success. These duels Manniche attributed to a hereditary impulse to
compete for a common food supply—the lemmings.

Finally, the long-tailed or Buffon's skua (*Stercorarius longicauda*), whose
addiction to lemmings was perhaps the most remarkable. In the first
autumn, thirty or forty pairs of skuas were counted in one part of the area
of the survey. Each of these couples had its own strictly guarded territory,
where they were bringing up usually a single chick on lemmings. 'A great
number of stomach analyses showed, that both the young ones and the
old birds fed on lemmings, which this summer occurred in vast multitudes.
The extreme fatness of the young ones gave evidence of the great "embar-
ras de richesse".' After a winter's absence the skuas returned, to find their
cupboard bare. The couples took up their usual territories, but, as Manniche
remarks, they seemed very disappointed, and after watching a long time
opposite empty lemming burrows, began to run after butterflies and other
insects. In June they flocked and flew away altogether without breeding.
In the spring of 1908 the birds that came were all adults. These stayed,
and with the rising tide of lemmings, bred once more. The long-tailed skua
is just a match for owl and falcon, by which it is occasionally attacked.

This should be enough to give a feeling of the ecological magnetic power
that lemmings exercise. They were, in this instance, the force that controlled directly the numbers and habits and movements of two kinds of
mammals and four kinds of birds. But the effects went probably far
beyond this immediate zone of influence. The abundance of lemmings
must have increased the chances of life for several other species: the

ptarmigan, snow bunting, turnstone, phalarope, and arctic hare, to mention only the ones for which some direct field information was collected about their enemies. During the lemming scarcity the conditions would be reversed. It would not be surprising to find that the central fluctuation started a huge chain of effects. In this way faint ripples of oscillation would reach to unexpected distances in the community.

8

We may already discern several principles at work in these periodic changes of numbers and habit. Lemmings must make very heavy inroads upon the vegetation, which sets definite limits to the amount of their increase and to their local distribution on the tundra. The ground that lemmings can occupy in winter is still further circumscribed by the depth to which snow lies and the configuration of hollows and ravines. There must be, in the winters of abundance, a formidable concentration of these fat, busy, agile mowing-machines that will deeply influence the quantity and composition of the plants. Growth of vegetation in the Arctic is slow, and the action of lemmings will tend to make its production jerky and always short of possible realization. But, like most other rodents, the lemming probably decreases before the vegetation is utterly ravaged, through the action of disease or other things.

On the whole, it is surprising that so good a crop of rodent flesh can be raised on so bare a vegetation. This first consideration has some general importance in fur-trade ecology, since, whatever measures might be taken to 'improve' the fur crop, i.e. to canalize it into the more valuable species, must fairly quickly run against hard limits set by the rate of plant productivity in the severe climate and barren soils of the Arctic. The farther north one goes, the more important this consideration becomes.

There are three common means by which predators react to the onset of lemming scarcity. They may simply die off in large numbers, like the lemming. The causes of death are various: starvation, exhaustion, cold, or disease. The fox certainly gets disease, and is not infrequently found near starvation (see Chapter XXII), and no doubt many deaths take place at these times in all the species that I have been describing. A second kind of reaction is to change the habits of feeding, and draw, as it were, upon various reserves that the country holds. Such change of habits has often been observed (as by Manniche), and it is at such moments that the Arctic community tends to become very closely drawn into a common interconnexion.

The unexpected range of foods that may be drawn upon is well illustrated by some stomach analyses of birds done by Cottam[5] from the materials of Captain R. A. Bartlett's expeditions to Greenland and the Canadian Eastern Arctic in the years 1931–3. These observations may usefully be set against the simplified picture of the lemming and its enemies, that was pieced together from Manniche.

From four stomachs of gyrfalcons: (1) 2 lemmings (*Dicrostonyx*). (2) 3 lemmings (*Dicrostonyx*), and a horned lark (*Otocaris*). (3) A red-backed vole (*Clethrionomys*). (4) A willow ptarmigan (*Lagopus*). Add to these the species noted by other observers: hares, ptarmigan, skuas, kittiwakes, eider ducks, common guillemots, and black guillemots.

From two stomachs of duck hawks (*Falco peregrinus anatum*): (1) A lemming (*Dicrostonyx*). (2) A phalarope (*Phalaropus*) and a red-backed sandpiper (*Pelidna*).

From a long-tailed skua: Ten sea-fish of two species, and three kinds of marine Crustacea (*Thysanoessa*, *Themisto*, and *Gammarus*). Løppenthin[9] in Greenland found the same species eating lemmings when these were abundant, but other diet in scarce years, e.g.: (1) A whelk (*Buccinum*). (2) A moth caterpillar; a fly larva and adult; 2 beetles (*Dasychira*), some crane flies (*Tipula*); and some remains of lemming. (3) Green berries.

From two ravens, Cottam got: (1) A bug (*Nysius*); bits of 5 horse-fly pupae (Tabanidae); fragments of birds' feathers, bones, and eggs; 'carrion' and hair of caribou; moss; 88 berries, also 125 seeds and bits of a plant (*Vaccinium*); 20 berries and also other remains of crowberry (*Empetrum*); bits of grass (two species), sedge, and heath. (2) Fragments of bird's egg; mammal 'carrion'; an insect; a mollusc; 9 berries and 11 seeds of crowberry; moss and plant remains. Cottam and Hanson[5a] give more analyses of the sort in another, later paper.

The problem is obviously not at all simple. When the dish of the day is not to be had, there are many side-dishes that predators can eat. Perhaps the most important plate is offered by the leavings of the polar bear, which is no doubt followed by the arctic fox in all years to some extent. The value to the fox of these food reserves, which vary greatly with the local character of the surroundings and the fauna, must be immense: and the polar bear alone must have an incalculable importance to the trade in this roundabout way, as well as by giving up its skin and meat.

Sometimes, it seems, starvation leads to cannibalism. This form of biological anarchy was mentioned by Manniche, and has been recorded by others. A more important change of behaviour, which forms the third principle, is migration, about which something was said in the last chapter. Changed feeding and changed movements often go together, as when the fox takes to the ice, or the snowy owl arrives in Massachusetts and feeds on rats. Starvation and other forms of death may also result from the emigration.

9

These general remarks lead on to an interesting speculation about the ermine's place in the fur trade. This creature in winter has practically no alternative food to turn to in the absence of lemmings, except the arctic hare. It is not likely that the hare is a sure and easy source of food, and one might expect that ermine, by concentrating upon the few remaining colonies of lemmings from which the next cycle of increase must develop, would intensify the scarcity. There is evidence that the ermine does not go far out on to the sea-ice, for both Manniche[12(2)] and Freuchen[7(3)] comment on its absence from islands a good distance out from land, islands where lemmings are numerous, and which can easily be visited in winter by the arctic fox. The ermine, in so far as it does not either emigrate from land or starve or change its food, may play an important role in the back scenes of the fur trade, by accentuating scarcity, reducing the power of lemming recovery, and therefore the size of the fox crop.

There is a practical expression of this idea in a report[21] for the season 1934–5, from the Hudson's Bay Company post at Lake Harbour, on the south coast of Baffin Island: 'The excessive scarcity of lemming and the abundance of ermine indicates that foxes will be scarcer next year than is usually the case after the big fox year.' Whether the ermine really controls at all the nucleus of numbers that lemming populations start from in the trough of every cycle is therefore a very interesting matter for research. If it does so, the production of arctic foxes may be lower than would otherwise be the case, and an enterprising fur dictator might trap the ermine deliberately and see if the fox cycle became appreciably more resilient. If he were wise he would ascertain first a few basic facts about the densities of ermine and lemming on chosen areas, and then handle the experiment with careful controls.

The ermine at present is not regarded as an important species to the trade. 'The ermine is not of much importance to the Eskimos. They have no use for the skin themselves and only keep it for trade, although no great value is set upon them at the store. As a matter of fact the animal is only an annoyance to the natives, for it often eats the bait out of their traps . . .' (Peter Freuchen[7(4)] for Melville Peninsula). 'While the species is widely distributed, there are few places in the northern regions where it is really common enough to be of great importance in the fur returns' (Anderson,[1(1)] for the Canadian Eastern Arctic and its islands). In the ten years 1918–27, the number taken at Fort Chimo was altogether only 2,655.[25]

10

Peter Freuchen's observations on Arctic wild-life have a peculiar authority and uniqueness, since they are made by a trained observer who had lived for many years in different parts of the Arctic and had the immense advantage of knowing Eskimos and their language and getting from them much hidden lore about animals. On Rasmussen's Fifth Thule Expedition a stay of several years in various parts of Melville Peninsula in 1921–4 produced abundant notes, some of which are relevant to the present discussion. But they deserve full reading, for their charm and interest.

In this region lemmings (*Dicrostonyx groenlandicus*) were not very numerous in 1921.[7(5)] Foxes and predatory birds were fairly scarce. 'In 1922, however, matters were quite different. There were lemmings everywhere, and there were traces of many more foxes, rough-legged buzzards and owls, more peregrine falcons, and more ravens. The Eskimos brought large numbers of ermine skins to the posts, but their catch of foxes was nothing extraordinary. . . . Both caribou and hares were left entirely in peace by the wolves, because there were lemmings enough.'

In 1923 lemmings swarmed in still greater numbers, even invading the tents, and gave everywhere a rich food for predators. 'Then suddenly they seemed to disappear. In December 1923, when we came to Danish Island . . . there was a remarkable difference. The lemmings seemed to have gone. The foxes we caught were not gorged with lemmings as had been the case the year before and that spring. The ravens we shot had no lemmings in them, and at most only a solitary individual was seen now and then.' The same thing had happened at other places: Igloolik, Pond Inlet, Admiralty Inlet, though a few lemmings were still seen that winter in the interior of Cockburn Land. Freuchen gives a great deal of information about the other foods of the arctic fox, to which it must turn entirely when lemmings fail. These are not dissimilar to the ones that Manniche and Soper[17(2)] mentioned: ptarmigan, wading birds, sea-fowl and their eggs, young hares, seal-cubs on the sea-ice in spring, the leavings of polar bears, carrion on the shore, other foxes in the traps, even (the Eskimos believe) new-born caribou calves. I have already quoted the observations of Weed round Nain, where it was reported that a local colony of arctic foxes had been able to survive the crash in rodents by catching fish (p. 324).

This preliminary disquisition on lemming fluctuations outside Ungava has served to show the dual nature of the food supplies of the arctic fox: on the one hand, lemmings while they are numerous, and on the other hand various alternatives during lemming scarcity. These alternative supplies are vital in supporting a remnant of foxes after every crash, and may have a more critical influence on the actual productivity of the fox crop in each cycle than the lemmings themselves. That is, the period of the cycle is caused by lemmings, but the amplitude, so far as it is controlled by food, is affected also by the size of the fox population at the bottom of the cycle, and this evidently depends to an important extent on food.

A survey of arctic fox ecology and fur production needs therefore to take a broad sweep. There is still an enormous amount of investigation to be done on the local distribution of these alternative food reserves: the location of sea-bird colonies of different kinds, the movements and activity and numbers of seals and polar bears in relation to marine animal communities and sea-ice, the occurrence and seasonal migrations of ptarmigan, arctic hare populations, and the caribou. An instance of these local differences was given me by Mr. T. H. Manning, who stayed and travelled in Southampton Island in 1933–5, living often in native fashion and on natural animal foods. In the region of Southampton Island and down the west of Hudson Bay the bears are not active much in the depth of winter, but den up on the land in snow-drifts. Both males and females hibernate in this manner, living on their summer fat. This local habit is confirmed by Freuchen,[7 (6)] who thought it might be because the bears are very well fed by the autumn and so can safely sleep. Mr. Manning believes that the severe winter cold prevents many seals from lying out on the ice, and therefore the bears have no easy food and leave fewer pickings for the foxes. But Freuchen gives many observations (for a different part of this large area) proving that both the ringed seal (*Phoca hispida*) and the bearded seal (*Erignathus barbatus*) are to be found on the ice all through the winter, and, furthermore, that polar bears can sometimes catch seals when they come up to breathe and haul them out on the ice. Southampton Island, Coats Island (the Eskimo name for it, Nanulik, means Isle of Bears), and Cape Wolstenholme are great places for bears. One only has to follow Freuchen's notes to see that the life and local movements of the polar bear are in themselves a huge ecological problem for study.

Another question connected with this one is the habit that arctic foxes have, at any rate sometimes, of making winter stores of food: lemmings, sea-birds or eggs, and other things. There are many records of fox caches, and the fox also carries inside its skin a store of fat which must also be of great value in sustaining the animal through the winter.

11

We have now got to this point: the foxes in Ungava (and Labrador) have a cycle in numbers; fox fluctuations outside Ungava have a relation to lemmings which cannot be denied; the lemming (and a similar array of predators) lives in Ungava, partly in company also with voles and mice; the Labrador fox cycle accompanies or follows a year behind one in voles: it seems highly probable therefore that lemmings (and other mouse-like rodents) in Ungava have a cycle which is responsible for the periodicity of the fox. It is the evidence for this lemming cycle and its connexion with fox fluctuations that we have to examine next. But first a short note on the distribution of lemmings and their enemies in Ungava. Actual museum specimens are scarce. We may take Anderson's official summary[1(2)] as general authority based on what little material exists. Of the Labrador collared lemming (*Dicrostonyx hudsonius*) he says: 'It is found throughout the barren grounds and treeless belts as far south as Hamilton Inlet.' Low,[10(1)] who was a good observer, noted it as 'common throughout the barren ground and southward to about latitude 54°. Specimen obtained from Lake Michikamau.' Strong,[18] for the barrens inland from Davis Inlet, says: 'From pictures by Louis Agassiz Fuertes they [the Naskapi Indians] identified the lemming (*Dicrostonyx*) and the meadow mouse (*Microtus*) by the same name *wit-sús-kwe*.' Bangs[2] found that in its southern limits at Hamilton Inlet, the lemming lived only on the treeless tops of the coast hills. No doubt if there was a spinal range of mountains reaching to the St. Lawrence, lemmings would be found there in an Alpine Zone, just as they are in Norway. As it is, the southern limits must be ill defined and scattered, depending on how height and latitude have moulded the forest belt. In the present survey I shall assume that the lemming occurs scattered over the whole of the Ungava barrens.

Except for small differences in race, Ungava has the same predator community depending upon the lemming as we have already described for

Greenland. There are, however, some additional species that introduce a greater range of complexity; for instance, the coloured fox and wolverine, the short-eared owl (*Asio flammeus*), the rough-legged buzzard (*Archibuteo lagopus*), also a growing company of woodland and semi-woodland species found as one goes southwards out of the true barrens.[8, 19, 19a] And we have already seen that there are half a dozen species of mouse-like rodents in Arctic Ungava, against only one in North-east Greenland.

Still, there is the essential nucleus of Arctic predators: arctic fox, ermine, snowy owl, long-tailed skua, gyrfalcon, and raven. Practically our only published local knowledge comes from Bernard Hantzsch, the German ornithologist who stayed at Killinek (near Port Burwell station) in 1906, explored parts of the coast of Ungava Bay, and later perished on his way back from a daring journey into Foxe Basin in Baffin Island. Of the snowy owl Hantzsch wrote:[8(1)]

'At Killinek, as a rule, the first Snowy Owls appear with the autumn migrations of the ptarmigan, which along with the not rare lemmings (*Dicrostonyx hudsonius*) and mice (*Peromyscus maniculatus*) make up their favourite food. From that time on, one sees them occasionally during the whole winter, sometimes several at a time in one region. . . . Along with the Ravens, the Snowy Owls are the only birds which regularly inhabit the waste mountain places during the whole winter.'

A few other local observations by outside visitors were made on Lieut. Gordon's expeditions in 1884–6. The best of these were by F. F. Payne,[13] the meteorologist left at Stupart's Bay in the season of 1885–6. Of the lemming he said: 'Apparently only inhabits the coast, where it is so numerous, that by turning over a few stones, one or more are sure to be found.' On a still winter night lemmings could be heard burrowing through the snow, and the arctic foxes used to listen too, and pounce. Payne thought the lemming was chief winter food of the arctic fox; but in the spring he saw foxes hunting young seals on the ice. Bears, caribou, wolves, and wolverines were scarce, but ptarmigan and arctic hares were frequently found. Among the raptorial birds he mentions rough-legged buzzards, numerous in 1886, and a few snowy owls (in the autumn of 1885).

12

The Fort Chimo traders seem to have had little realization of the relation between lemming fluctuations and fox numbers until fairly recent times: unless indeed they knew it and never mentioned it. But this is unlikely, since a great deal of correspondence is devoted to explanations of the fur scarcity that came so often. Any solid natural cause would surely have been mentioned by a prudent manager to his head-quarters. The earliest reference to lemmings in Ungava at all is by John McLean[11] in 1849, who noted that there was 'the lemming, in some parts of the interior'. But the rather full story of fox fluctuations related in Chapter XIX has no parallel in records of rodent cycles until quite recent years. Duncan Matheson, fully alive to fox cycles, made only a few references to rodents, and always from the point of view that they attracted foxes away from the baited traps.

In November 1895 he noted:[22(1)] 'Although the signs were numerous, the foxes don't seem to be hungry, and won't take bait.' And again, by his traps at False River:[22(2)] 'Signs were numerous, but as the mice are plentiful, the foxes are not hungry and the result is they won't take the bait: however, when the cold weather sets in it may be different.' At this time, coloured foxes, though not arctic, were abundant in the Fort Chimo district.

The next reference is to 1900–1, when foxes of all kinds were approaching a peak.[22(3)] 15 Dec. 1900: 'No foxes caught, but very good signs, the weather being too mild and too little snow for them to take the bait and the country overrunned with mice.' And in a letter[23(1)] about the season's work: 'Last fall the outlook was very promising and, but for the scarcity of deer, the hunt would, notwithstanding sickness and the plague of mice that infested the whole country, have been much more successful. Foxes, both colored and white, are reported to be very numerous inland and along the coast.' This was written in September 1901.

Still in January 1902, these 'mice' may have been abundant, for Wilson wrote that foxes were quite numerous in the George's River part of the country in January, but they would not take bait. 'The majority of those in the collection had been shot.'[23(2)] Note here the condition similar to that found in Labrador, where the biggest *trapped* number of foxes may come in the year after vole abundance, while a larger or at any rate very large quota may be *shot* in the year of maximum vole numbers. It may be remembered that this ratio between the numbers shot and trapped is probably an important and rather variable determiner of the cycle shown in fur returns. The 'mice' in question may have been lemmings or voles or both.

We see that the fur traders then had probably little idea of lemming cycles in Ungava, though they realized that a lot of 'mice' would hinder trapping. There is, however, one early description, by Payne, in 1885, which we have already quoted. It shows that scientists had noticed the connexion between fox and lemming. And Sir Frederick Stupart told me in 1928 that he also had noticed great abundance of foxes and lemmings at Stupart's Bay in 1884–5 (the season before Payne was there).

Louis Romanet, who served with Revillon Frères at Fort Chimo from about 1908–16 was fully aware of these cycles. In 1928 he told me something of the ideas he had gained from field observation, and which were embodied in a report to that Company which does not seem to have been preserved. He believed that the peak in numbers of arctic foxes was in the year after lemming abundance, that the lemming crash caused fox migration and disease, that the season of migration varied a good deal from one cycle to another and affected the catch according to whether the foxes were moving a great deal during the trapping time, and that the fox disease caused epidemics in the sledge dogs.

30

Although we need much more than opinion and casual observation to draw such inductions, yet these early records show that the traders were beginning, before 1910, to appreciate some of the underlying forces operating in the fox trade.

The next observation comes from the Royal Canadian Mounted Police at Port Burwell, in a report[24(1)] for the season 1920–1: 'The only animal life which the land seems to produce and sustain is a race of *mice*, which when very numerous induce the white foxes to come around and stay for a part of the winter. When mice are scarce, winter trapping is a complete failure. During the fall of 1920, the country was covered with signs of mice, with the result that about 900 foxes were trapped by natives, the best results that have been attained at this post, about 300 being the average catch for other years.'

13

With this observation we have the story much in the form in which we wish to test it from recent enquiries. Once fur-trade men have had their attention focused on the subject by properly drafted questionnaires (designed to avoid any sort of leading question, except to say that fluctuations matter to the trade), they begin to notice many useful facts. The gist of these questionnaire replies is given in Table 61, which contains the replies to standard questions, which are amplified by the additional remarks that are often added by the men.[21]

The questions follow (with slight variations) the form: were they *more abundant* or *less abundant* this season than last season; were they exceptionally *abundant* or exceptionally *scarce*; was their migration *greater* or *less*, and when was it noticed; did they have epidemic, and if so with what symptoms? The period was always a standard twelve months ending 31 May.

The table follows the fur posts round the coast of Hudson Strait and Ungava Bay. Taking this order, we may embroider the bare tabulation with explanation and additional field notes.

Port Burwell. When W. G. Kerr of the R.C.M.P. went from Port Burwell down to the east coast of Ungava Bay (that is through the territories of Port Burwell, George's River, and part of Fort Chimo Posts) in the spring of 1930, he noted[24(2)] that 'the fur catch was below normal, although a tremendous amount of lemmings were running around, their skins being marketable at the Hudson's Bay Company for a small price'. But in the season of 1930–1 and the summer of 1931, when F. Innes made a patrol from Port Burwell along the coast of Ungava Bay as far as Leaf River, he saw very few lemmings.[24(3)] 'In describing the game of the neighbourhood he refers to the lemming, saying that very few were seen; this is contradictory to former years, when the number of these peculiar creatures was very great.' There had been, therefore, a lemming crash between the spring of 1930 and the winter of 1930–1, in the country north-east of Fort Chimo.

The date of this turning-point is confirmed by some notes that Mr.

D. H. S. Davis communicated to me after a brief visit to Port Burwell in September 1931. The post manager of the Hudson's Bay Company told him that 1930 was a year of great abundance of lemmings in Ungava and Northern Labrador. Eight thousand skins were shipped to London as an experiment, and most of these were frozen lemmings that died above the snow and were picked up there by the Eskimos.

TABLE 61

Recent fluctuations in lemming, arctic fox, and snowy owl in Ungava
(1927–36)

Based on Hudson's Bay Company zoological reports from posts, except for a few R.C.M.P. and other notes, mentioned in the text.

M = More; L = Less; NC = No change; Ab. = Abundant (no comparative record); Sc. = Scarce (no comparative record); ML = More in summer, Less in winter season; heavy type means More (very ab.) or Less (very sc.).

Original records in Bureau of Animal Population, Oxford.

Post	Species	1927–8	1928–9	1929–30	1930–1	1931–2	1932–3	1933–4	1934–5	1935–6	1936–7
Port Burwell	Lemming	..	..	**Ab.**	L	Sc.	L	M	..	..	**M**
	A. fox	..	..	..	Ab.	?	L	M	..	..	M
	S. owl	..	..	..	..	..	?	M	..	..	M
George's River	Lemming	..	..	**Ab.**	L	Sc.	M	M	M	M	M
	A. fox	..	..	..	Ab.	..	L	M	M	L	L
	S. owl	..	..	..	?	..	?	M	M	M	?
Whale River	Lemming	..	..	**Ab.**	L	Sc.	M	M	..	..	L
	A. fox	..	..	..	..	..	L	M	Ab.	..	L
	S. owl	..	..	..	..	..	?	?	..	..	L
Fort Chimo	Lemming	L	M	**M**	**ML**	(Sc.)	M	M	M	L	L
	A. fox	ML	L	M	**M**	..	L	M	M	L	L
	S. owl	L	L	M	ML	..	M	M	M	M	L
Leaf River	Lemming	..	..	..	..	..	M	M	M	L	**M**
	A. fox	..	..	..	Ab.	..	L	M	ML	L	M
	S. owl	..	..	..	..	..	?	?	M	?	M
Payne Bay	Lemming	..	..	..	..	..	M	M	..	..	M
	A. fox	Sc.	..	..	..	..	L	M	..	..	M
	S. owl	..	..	..	..	..	?	M	..	..	M
Stupart's Bay	Lemming	..	..	..	..	..	M	M	L	L	L
	A. fox	..	..	..	..	..	L	M	M	L	L
	S. owl	..	..	..	..	..	M	M	M	L	L
Sugluk West	Lemming	..	..	..	..	..	M	? L	..	..	**M**
	A. fox	Sc.	..	..	..	..	M	M	..	..	M
	S. owl	..	..	..	..	..	Ab.	M	..	..	M
Wolstenholme	Lemming	..	..	..	..	..	M	M	L	L	**M**
	A. fox	..	..	..	..	..	M	M	L	L	M
	S. owl	..	..	..	..	..	?	M	L	L	M
Cape Smith	Lemming	..	..	..	..	..	?	M	NC	L	M
	A. fox	..	..	..	..	..	L	M	L	L	M
	S. owl	..	..	..	..	..	?	M	NC	L	M

In 1931 lemming traces were scarce; but it had been an abundant year for foxes, although a few dead ones were noticed. Similarly, when Innes made his spring journey in April and May 1931, he found[24(3)] that the Eskimo camps at George's River and along the coast as far as Leaf River had experienced a good fur season. The winter of 1932–3 at Port Burwell was very poor for fur. Stafford, of the R.C.M.P., reported[24(4)] that only twelve foxes were caught near the post, and that practically no other wild life was seen. The annual reports of the post (see table) show the change that occurred in 1933–4. Whereas lemmings and arctic foxes were less and scarce in 1932–3, they were on the increase again, with snowy owls, in

1933–4. These records cover one complete cycle and they show a general correspondence between the lemming and the arctic fox, with a lag of a year between their cycles.

George's River. We take the Police reports already mentioned as an index of conditions in the region of George's River Post in 1929–30 and 1930–1—lemming peak and crash. Kerr noted[24(2)] on his trip to George's River in February 1930 that: 'The natives . . . were having a fair year, alike as regards food and fur.' 1930–1 was also a good fur season.[24(3)]

In 1932–3 the Company's reports begin with lemmings and 'mice' increasing again and foxes of both kinds still decreasing and scarce. Next season, 1933–4, both rodents and foxes were increasing. The white foxes disappeared in mid winter, it was thought on account of storms and strong easterly winds that drove them for shelter inland; but they reappeared in spring, while coloured foxes showed a good sign all winter, both inland and on the coast.

In 1934–5 the increase in lemmings, mice, and foxes still continued; also snowy owls were reported fairly abundant and on the increase. 'Foxes around here the past fall [i.e. 1934] were very fat; but having plenty of snow and a rainstorm about the end of November, lemmings got frozen in and not so easily got at, and the foxes got much thinner. But towards spring, lemmings being plentiful, the foxes will soon fatten.' After the trapping season finished (i.e. after March 1935) a new influx of foxes was noticed, starving individuals, said to come from a north-west direction. Perhaps this deduction is not quite reliable: but it is possible that these foxes came from an area where the lemmings had already crashed.

In 1935–6 there was a crash in foxes, as these notes show:

'Coloured fox up to 31st December, 1935, was fairly plentiful, and in good condition, fat. In the first week of January, 1936, having some very cold spells, followed with heavy falls of snow, they suddenly disappeared. In the month of March they started to come round again, and at close of trapping season were fairly plentiful, these foxes coming from a north-west direction, were in very poor condition, thin, on the point of starving, in fact two had been picked up starved; seen where others had been killed and eaten by other foxes. White fox the past summer and fall (1935) has been exceedingly scarce, and no sign of them has been reported this spring.'

Lemmings were fairly plentiful in the summer and fall of 1935, and foxes were in good condition as long as they could get food. But the conditions of the previous winter were repeated, at any rate in March, and a hard frozen surface to the snow prevented the foxes digging for lemmings. The snow was so deep in the spring of 1936 that the post manager could not tell whether the lemmings had crashed as well. Snowy owls were reported fairly abundant, but there are no notes to say whether this was throughout the season. It seems possible that there was lemming decrease which accentuated the difficulty of finding them under the snow, though we cannot actually prove this from the evidence. At any rate, by 1936–7 we have the typical situation in the season after lemming and 'mice' scarcity:

lemmings going up, white and coloured foxes diminished in numbers. But in spring 1937 white foxes were noticed again, on the ice.

Whale River. Taking, as with Port Burwell and George's River, the lemming peak as probably 1930–1 followed by crash, we start in 1932–3, with the Company's reports. Lemmings and 'mice' were abundant, increasing, but foxes were scarce, both coloured and arctic. In 1933–4 lemmings and 'mice' and both foxes were on the increase, the rodents abundant. 'Lemming are greatly on the increase, and with the increase of these comes also the increase in foxes. When lemmings are scarce, foxes are also.' Though there is no Hudson's Bay Company report for 1934–5, a R.C.M.P. note[24(5)] fills the gap, recording 'a very good fur catch'. But there is no information about lemmings. Reports for the next season are lacking. In 1936–7 lemmings, mice, and both kinds of fox were scarce and decreasing, also snowy owls, of which it was recorded that 'a few white owls were seen in the fall, but seemed to have disappeared when the cold weather set in'. Evidently a crash occurred between 1934 and 1936.

Fort Chimo. This series of records is longer than the others. In 1927–8 lemmings and 'mice' were decreasing, as were snowy owls. White and coloured foxes, numerous in the summer and fall of 1927, were very scarce in winter and spring. 'White foxes did not travel during the winter, but remained in the one small neighbourhood of a radius of say, ten miles. Outside these particular zones natives reported no sign or tracks.' This is the sort of patchy distribution we might expect with the rodent cycle about to begin the recovery which was reported in 1928–9. But that season owls and foxes were very scarce.

By 1929–30 both prey and predators (including snowy owls) were on the increase. 'Lemmings extremely plentiful all fall and winter', with some mortality noticed in April 1930. The white fox movement was thought to be rather late and not noticeable until December 1929. The season of 1930–1 showed all the symptoms of a crash. Lemmings, abundant in summer and fall, were scarce in winter and spring. The actual crash was seen: 'Lemming observed dying and dead, E. side of Ungava Bay and up Koksoak River, October, 1930.' While foxes of both species were numerous all the season, snowy owls mostly departed after the lemming crash. 'No migratory movement amongst white foxes till late in April 1931.' The 'mice' (presumably meadow-mice, i.e. voles) were not noticed to decrease in winter and spring; conceivably this food, if it remained, may have kept the foxes.

In 1931–2 we have only the inference from the Police reports, already quoted, that the lemming cycle had gone down, at any rate in parts of the Fort Chimo territory. By 1932–3 rodents were increasing (Table 61), but foxes were less, though snowy owls were more abundant. Next year, 1933–4, everything was cycling up, and this increase went on through 1934–5. A Police report[24(5)] noted that Chimo had 'the best fur catch in fifteen years'. In 1935–6 there was apparently the periodic crash in lemmings and mice, with white foxes utterly vanished, but coloured fox and snowy owls reported more. In 1936–7 lemmings and mice were still said to be on the decrease, also snowy owls and both sorts of fox.

Leaf River. In the spring of 1931 the Police patrol from Burwell reached as far as Leaf River, and found[24(3)] that the people had done well in fur, that is, in foxes. There is no detailed record for 1931–2, but sometime occurred the crash in white foxes, which showed in 1932–3. That season lemmings and mice were on the increase and abundant. Next year this recovery continued, and included white and coloured foxes. There was no information about snowy owls.

In 1934–5 increase continued, and all forms (including now snowy owls) were very abundant, at any rate up to the beginning of winter. White foxes, numerous in fall, almost disappeared after the freeze-up. This disappearance was correlated with sheet-glaze in the middle of November, which cut off their access to lemmings. At this time there were signs that coloured foxes (which remained abundantly until the spring) were attacking arctic foxes and devouring them. By 1935–6 lemmings had decreased and were very scarce: also arctic foxes, though there were still some numbers of coloured foxes.

In 1936–7 lemmings had recovered to some abundance, and white foxes, as well as snowy owls, were more than in the previous year. But coloured foxes were scarcer.

Payne Bay. The Hudson's Bay Company record begins in 1932, but a special patrol of the R.C.M.P. attached to the air survey expedition at Wakeham Bay left some notes. J. Murray travelled eastwards in February 1928 to Payne Bay, in order to get news of the two missing airmen.[24(6)] At Burgoyne Bay (on the way) the Eskimos complained about the very poor winter for fur, 'very few foxes having been caught'. At Payne Bay itself the same was said: 'Very few foxes have been caught this past winter.' There is no mention of lemmings.

In 1932–3 lemmings were on the increase; but both kinds of foxes were decreasing and scarce. Next year, 1933–4, lemmings and arctic foxes were increasing. 'White owls and hawks have been exceedingly abundant this spring (1934) and according to past observations this is a very good sign of the fox cycle reaching its peak next year.' After a two-year gap in the records, which probably saw the crash that other posts experienced, we find the cycle showing increase in 1936–7.

Stupart's Bay. There are records only from 1932 onwards. The cycle in lemmings and 'mice' was going up in 1932–3, and with them snowy owls, but foxes were decreasing and scarce, and lemmings themselves were reported scarce. In 1933–4 all members of the cycle complex were increasing abundantly. In 1934–5 the rodents seem to have crashed, white foxes remained abundant up to the fall of 1934, as also did coloured foxes and snowy owls. The last two, but not the white foxes, were numerous again in the spring of 1935. The inference is that the disappearance of lemmings sent all predators away in the winter, and the white foxes did not return. Next season, 1935–6, everything was cycling down, and 'mice' and white foxes, at any rate, were scarce. 'It is notable that whilst white foxes have been excessively scarce, coloured foxes, although decreased, were not scarce.' In 1936-7 the lemmings and mice were still reported decreasing and scarce, but 'early in June [1937] mice were reported plentiful and white fox signs good'. White foxes and snowy owls were scarce, but coloured foxes said to be abundant and on the increase.

Sugluk West. There are a few notes from here, not continuous. They help in the geographical mapping of the cycle. Murray visited here on his Police patrol in February 1928, and made some notes.[24(6)] The people had caught very few foxes that winter. At a free-trader's post near here: 'Foxes are very scarce, the worst year for them for some time.' There is no word of lemmings.

The records now skip five years. In 1932-3 increase of lemmings and arctic foxes. Snowy owls, together with hawks, were very numerous in the spring of 1933. In 1933-4 all predators, also 'mice', were abundantly cycling up. Lemmings, it was reported, were scarcer during the winter, but got more plentiful towards the spring. There is a gap in records during the crash that probably followed. In 1936-7 we find lemmings, 'mice', both foxes, and snowy owls increasing—the rodents and coloured foxes numerous.

Wolstenholme. Reaching this post at the north-west corner of Quebec Peninsula, we have traversed from Cape Chidley (that is from Port Burwell) the whole south coast of Hudson Strait. In 1932-3 both lemmings and arctic foxes were on the increase, but coloured foxes were less abundant than in 1931-2. The manager remarks: 'A more abundance of lemming always precedes a rise in the fox cycle.' In 1933-4 the lemmings and 'mice' reached a peak of abundance, accompanied by foxes (both kinds) and snowy owls. 1934-5 found the rodents scarce, also white foxes and snowy owls. But coloured foxes were still increasing, and were numerous. In 1935-6 the cycle struck the bottom. All life was scarce, including lemmings, and the white fox harvest was the lowest since the post was established in 1909. But next season, 1936-7, lemmings were increasing ('mice' still scarce), also foxes of both kinds and snowy owls. The last were numerous in the fall of 1936.

Cape Smith. This is the last post in Quebec Peninsula for which I shall give details: there is a mass of information still to be collated, which would carry us down round and up Hudson Bay, along the northern coast nearly to Alaska, not to speak of the Arctic Archipelago and Baffin Island. But a book must be published.

In 1932-3 'mice' were increasing, abundant. 'During the fall and winter, white fox signs were very scarce on the shore line; but during the end of April some of the natives who went approximately 100 miles inland reported fox signs innumerable in that vicinity.' In 1933-4 lemmings, white foxes, and snowy owls were cycling up. 'During the winter and spring white fox signs inland and on the shore line were very plentiful.' In 1934-5, 'for the first two months of the season, white foxes were nearly as plentiful as last year; after that they were practically non-existent'. There is only a cautious record of 'no change' for lemmings and snowy owls, which may have been due to lack of information. Coloured foxes were reported increasing, however. Next season, 1935–6, lemmings were less, but 'moderately abundant'. 'Fox signs were observed all along the coast-line during the summer and early fall. Toward the beginning of November, foxes were known to migrate inland, and became exceptionally scarce until the beginning of April, when they became a little more plentiful. Very few snow-owls were found in this locality until towards spring.' Coloured foxes were scarce. 1936–7 saw lemmings increasing, also the three predators. 'Lemming and white fox were very scarce during the summer and early fall, along the coast-line. Round the beginning of December, signs [presumably of foxes] were observed in more abundance, followed by a migration toward the coast-line during the months of March and April. An unusual increase also became very noticeable from the last of April on toward the end of May. Snowy owls seemed to follow the same line, and it was not until late in May that they became unusually abundant. On the other hand, red foxes were unusually abundant during the early part of the winter, but became very scarce after the beginning of March.'

14

From these records (which are all that I have been able to collect for northern Ungava in these years) and Table 61 the following conclusions can be drawn. They depend, of course, on the assumptions that the observations are honestly made and that they are correct. The data are, no doubt, liable to a certain amount of error on these counts, errors that cannot be checked scientifically. I take the information to be mostly based on careful and honest observation made by men who have much time to observe their surroundings, and yet few kinds of things to observe and these often relevant to their trade. Also the post managers are in constant touch with the unrivalled naturalists that primitive hunting races are. From one point of view the data seem limited and partly gained by subjective estimations. From another they are priceless bits of ecological history, rescued from oblivion by a rough-and-ready system of questionnaires. On the whole, it is the fact that they were ready that matters here more than their roughness. The results make out a prima-facie case for the importance of the lemming cycle in Ungava, and are confirmed by every other line of experience outside Ungava itself.

Taking the conclusions, then, as a working hypothesis for which we should seek confirmation and definition by improved field methods of census, the lemming fluctuations at all the ten places studied are marked, and agree in most respects. The peak years in lemmings, so far as they can be deduced, are shown in Table 62, p. 461.

The detailed fur returns for these recent years have been made available to me by the Hudson's Bay Company, though not for publication. They kindly allow me, however, to give the main years of the fur cycle at each post. To a certain extent the knowledge of fur-trading results will have influenced post managers in the reports that have already been analysed. But these reports also contain information about abundance, gained from signs and other observations by the trader or by natives. The fur returns, as has already been shown in the Labrador story, are not necessarily a direct measure of population. But their great value as an index of some kind lies in their continuity.

TABLE 62

Port Burwell . . .	1929–30	?
George's River . .	1929–30	? 1934–5
Whale River . . .	1929–30	?
Fort Chimo . . .	(1929–30)	1934–5
Leaf River . . .	?	1933–4
Payne Bay . . .	?	?
Stupart's Bay . .	?	1933–4
Sugluk West . . .	?	?
Wolstenholme . .	?	1933–4
Cape Smith . . .	?	1933–4 or 1934–5

The arctic fox fur cycle at these posts is analysed in Table 63. The cycle shown by the original figures is clear at each individual post, offering no difficulties to a summary of this kind. Figures for the first years are not available for all posts.

TABLE 63

Cycle at Ungava posts; summarized from arctic fox fur returns of H. B. Co.

Dates are maxima, dates in brackets minima. Years are outfits.

Port Burwell .	1926	(1928)	1930	(1932)	1934	(1935)
George's River .	. .	(1928)	1930	(1932)	1934	(1936)
Whale River .	. .	(1928)	1930	(1932)	1934	(1935, 1936)
Fort Chimo . .	1926	(1928)	1930	(1932)	1934	(1936)
Leaf River . .	. .	(1928)	1930	(1932)	1934	(1935)
Payne Bay . .	. .	(1928)	1930	(1932)	1934	(1935)
Stupart's Bay .	1926	(1928)	1930	(1931)	1933	(1935)
Sugluk West .	. .	. .	1930	(1931)	1933	(1935)
Wolstenholme .	1926	(1928)	1930	(1931)	1933	(1935)
Cape Smith .	. .	(1928)	1930	(1932)	1933	(1935)

There was a general peak in 1930, but in 1933 the western area came up a year sooner than the eastern one with its peak in 1934. It is interesting that three of the four western posts had their *minimum* a year before the rest—giving them a start in recovery. The same difference between the western and eastern parts of the area came out of the analysis of reports.

In the reports, the fox and snowy owl peaks mostly came in the same years as the corresponding peaks in lemmings, though in other instances the predators lingered a year longer. We find the same relationship between lemming peaks and fur return peaks: four of them (Port Burwell 1929, George's River 1929, Whale River 1929, Leaf River 1933) preceded the peak in furs by one year; three of them (Fort Chimo 1934, Stupart's Bay 1933, Wolstenholme 1933) coincided. These correlations are based on scanty lemming data, subjective reports that may have errors in them. But as far as they go, they confirm the general belief that lemming and fox cycles go closely together. And the fox records show the extraordinarily regular and wide regional behaviour of the cycle.

A proper analysis of this relationship needs larger data, and more exact information about the months in which lemmings have their crash. A difference of a month or two might make a whole season's difference in the maximum fox fur returns. All this is for future research, with several resident ecologists carrying out census and marking work. Perhaps the most immediate needs are a convenient and easy census index for lemmings, and the marking of young foxes and owls. There is a very close parallel between the fur trade and sea fisheries, since both are trades that started with uncontrolled exploitation but are driven to adopt management and conservation, which in turn can only be applied on the basis of real scientific knowledge. The fisheries use marking methods now for studying fish numbers and movements. They are also beginning to use standard plankton indicators, which show the distribution of herring food and of areas unfavourable to the fish. The same advance in the Arctic fur trade would use some standard census as index of the lemming situation from month to month, while marking experiments would throw light on the range and local shifting of predator populations.

The questionnaire system is still the only method which gives quickly and conveniently a general picture of fluctuations over vast areas of the north. It should be continued and strengthened by sample censuses and other studies done at permanent biological stations. In the last few years the questionnaire enquiries originally confined to the Hudson's Bay Company's posts have been greatly extended to cover the whole of the occupied Canadian Arctic. This extension has been made possible by the Canadian Government, which started the Canadian Arctic Wild Life Enquiry,[3, 3a, 4] the first report of which covered the season 1935–6. This enquiry is co-operative between the Northwest Territories Administration and the Hudson's Bay Company, and the results are all mapped in the Bureau of Animal Population at Oxford (Chitty and Elton, 1937; and Chitty, 1938, 1939). The advantage of such co-operation is obvious: for instance, the Government has few or no observers in northern Ungava, while there are police but no traders in Ellesmere Island. The mapping is done in such a way as to show visually the situation of four species every season: lemming, arctic fox, snowy owl, and sledge dog (that is, sledge dog disease). These staff maps can also be divided into smaller regions for which statistics can be expressed. Three examples of these staff maps (for 1935–6) are reproduced here. They show the first upward turn of a lemming cycle, followed closely by the snowy owl. But the arctic fox (which always shows this marked lag in recovery) was still at the bottom of the cycle. From later reports the progress of the cycle can be observed.

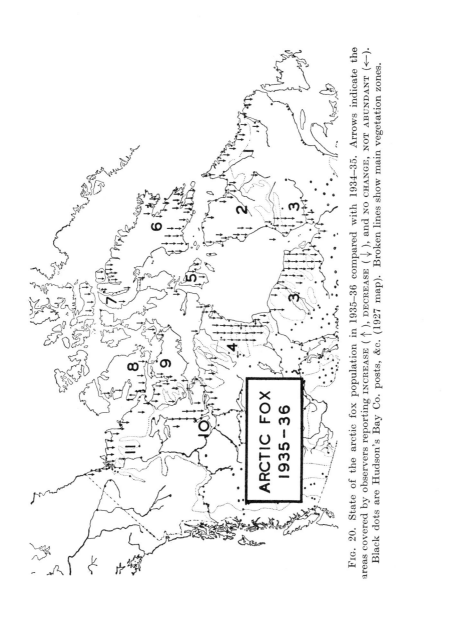

Fig. 20. State of the arctic fox population in 1935–36 compared with 1934–35. Arrows indicate the areas covered by observers reporting INCREASE (↑), DECREASE (↓), and NO CHANGE, NOT ABUNDANT (←). Black dots are Hudson's Bay Co. posts, &c. (1927 map). Broken lines show main vegetation zones.

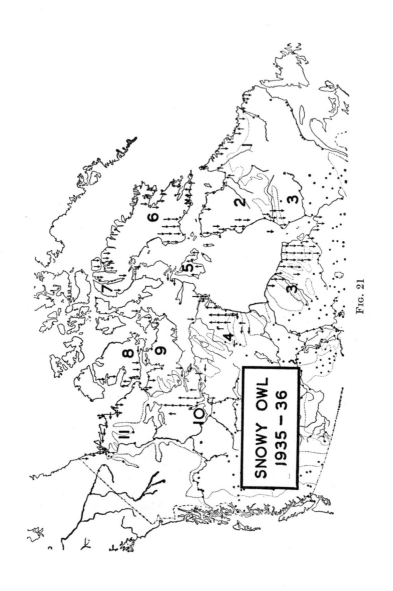

SNOWY OWL
1935 – 36

Fig. 21

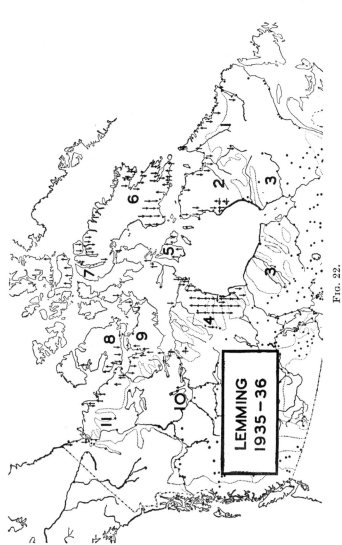

Fig. 22.

Figs. 21 and 22. State of the lemming and snowy owl populations in 1935–36 compared with 1934–35. Arrows indicate areas covered by observers reporting INCREASE (↑), DECREASE (↓), NO CHANGE, ABUNDANT (→), and NO CHANGE, NOT ABUNDANT (←). Black dots are Hudson's Bay Co. posts, &c. (1927 map). Broken lines show main vegetation zones. (From Chitty and Elton[1].)

If lemmings do cause the arctic fox cycle in the northern part of Quebec Peninsula, then the conclusions about fox periodicity in earlier years can be extended to the lemming. That is to say, there must be a cycle averaging four years in length in all the chief mouse-like rodents (voles and lemmings) which has continued for a great number of years over a vast area of the peninsula, and which happens more or less simultaneously in different places.

REFERENCES

* means that an abstract is deposited in the Bureau of Animal Population. 'H. B. Co.' means Hudson's Bay Company.

1. ANDERSON, R. M. (1934). 'Mammals of the Eastern Arctic and Hudson Bay.' In 'Canada's Eastern Arctic.' Ottawa. Pp. 67–108. (1) 86. (2) 100.

2. BANGS, O. (1897). 'On a small collection of mammals from Hamilton Inlet, Labrador.' Proc. Biol. Soc. Washington, 11: 235–40.

3. CHITTY, D. (1938). 'Canadian Arctic Wild Life Enquiry, 1936–37.' J. Anim. Ecol. 7: 381–94.

3 a. CHITTY, D. (1939). 'Canadian Arctic Wild Life Enquiry, 1937–38.' J. Anim. Ecol. 8: 247–60.

4. CHITTY, D., & ELTON, C. (1937). 'Canadian Arctic Wild Life Enquiry, 1935–36.' J. Anim. Ecol. 6: 368–85.

5. COTTAM, C. (1936). 'Food of Arctic birds and mammals collected by the Bartlett Expeditions of 1931, 1932, and 1933.' J. Washington Acad. Sci. 26: 165–77.

5 a. COTTAM, C., & HANSON, H. C. (1938). 'Food habits of some Arctic birds and mammals.' Field Museum of Natural History, Chicago, Zool. Ser. 20, No. 31: 405–26.

6. DEGERBØL, M. (1935). 'Mammals. Part I. Systematic notes.' Rep. Fifth Thule Expedition, 1921–4, vol. 2, No. 4.

7. FREUCHEN, P. (1935). 'Mammals. Part II. Field notes and biological observations.' Rep. Fifth Thule Expedition, 1921–4, vol. 2, No. 5. (1) 86. (2) 89. (3) 191. (4) 195. (5) 79–92. (6) 105–7.

8. HANTZSCH, B. (1908). 'Beitrag zur Kenntnis der Vogelwelt des nordöstlichsten Labradors.' J. für Ornith. 56: 175–202 and 307–92. (Translation by M. B. A. & R. M. Anderson, in Canad. Field-Nat. vol. 42, No. 1 (1928) to vol. 43, No. 3 (1929), has been used.) (1) Vol. 43, p. 32.

9. LØPPENTHIN, B. (1932). 'Die Vögel Nordostgrönlands zwischen 73° 00′ und 75° 30′.' Copenhagen. P. 93. Cited by Cottam (1936).

10. LOW, A. P. (1896). 'Report on explorations in the Labrador Peninsula. . . .' Ann. Rep. Geol. Surv. Canada for 1895, 8: 1–387 L. (1) 321 L.

11. McLEAN, J. (1849). 'Notes of a twenty-five years' service in the Hudson's Bay Territory.' London. Vol. 2, p. 108.

12. MANNICHE, A. L. V. (1910). 'The terrestrial mammals and birds of North-east Greenland.' Meddelelser om Grønland, 45, No. 1: 1–199. (1) Numerous citations throughout. (2) 81.

13. PAYNE, F. F. (1887). In 'Report of the Hudson's Bay Expedition of 1886 under the command of Lieut. A. R. Gordon, R.N.' Blue-book, Dept. of Marine and Fisheries, Ottawa. pp. 70–83.

14. PORSILD, A. E. (1937). 'Edible roots and berries of Northern Canada.' Nat. Mus. Canada. p. 3.

15. PREBLE, E. A. (1902). 'A biological investigation of the Hudson Bay region.' N. Amer. Fauna, No. 22: 54–7.

16. RAE, J. (1890). 'Notes on some of the birds and mammals of the Hudson's Bay Company's Territory. . . .' J. Linn. Soc. (Zool.), 20: 136–45. (1) 143.

17. SOPER, J. DEWEY (1928). 'A faunal investigation of Southern Baffin Island.' Bull. Nat. Mus. Canada, No. 53. (1) 55. (2) 35–6.

18. STRONG, W. D. (1930). 'Notes on the mammals of the Labrador Interior.' J. Mammal. 11: 1–10.

19. TAVERNER, P. A. (1922). 'Birds of Eastern Canada.' Canada, Dept. of Mines, Geol. Surv. Mem. No. 104. (2nd ed.).

19 a. TOWNSEND, C. W., & ALLEN, G. M. (1907). 'Birds of Labrador.' Proc. Boston Soc. Nat. Hist. 33: 277–428.

20. VON WRANGELL, F. (1844). 'Narrative of an expedition to the Polar Sea in the years 1820, 1821, 1822 & 1823.' (Transl. by E. Sabine, London, p. 67.)

*21. H. B. Co., Annual Zoological Reports from Posts.

*22. Fort Chimo (Ungava District) Journal. MS. H. B. Co. Archives, London. (1) 14 Nov. 1895. (2) 16 Nov. 1895. (3) 15 Dec. 1900.

*23. Ungava District (Fort Chimo) Correspondence. MS. H. B. Co. Archives, London. (1) Sept. 1901: D. Matheson to the Commissioner, H. B. Co. (2) 20 Jan. 1902: J. A. Wilson to P. McKenzie.

24. Royal Canadian Mounted Police, Reports. Ottawa. (1) Rep. for 1920–1: 32. (2) Rep. for 1929–30: 75. (3) Rep. for 1930–1: 80, 83. (4) Rep. for 1931–2: 100. (5) Rep. for 1935–6: 82–3. (6) Rep. for 1927–8: 85–7.

*25. Fort Chimo Fur Returns. H. B. Co. Winnipeg.

CHAPTER XXII

THE DOWNFALL

'Therefore all they that devour thee shall be devoured.' Jeremiah 30: 16.

1

AS the cycle in population mounts steadily for several years, it reaches a breaking-point and crashes. The danger-signals are not long delayed in a community dependent upon the exiguous supplies of a northern land. Vegetation is denuded of the reserves built up in the previous time of lemming scarcity. Lemmings tend to concentrate in the better ground, and that means in hollows where the soil and the snow are deepest. Foxes and owls multiply to numbers which can little withstand the stress of famine. And just when the trader feels that business is spinning along well at last, his furs stop coming in.

We can see clearly enough the sort of limits imposed by nature on the fruitfulness of the barren grounds, which only seem fruitful at all in fur because so few men trap there.. But we are far from understanding exactly how the downfall comes about, what makes the lemmings crash, where the snowy owls depart to and how many ever return, what causes disease in foxes, whether this is caught from them by sledge dogs or develops in them independently, and how it is that the crash is seen over such enormous tracts of country and on islands away from the mainland.

Something was said in Chapter X of the epidemics that Norwegian lemmings suffer, though there are many obscure points about them still. In Canada no pathological studies have been done on lemmings, and the only studies ever made were on the *Dicrostonyx* stocks that the Hudson's Bay Company sent to Oxford. One of the reasons why this stock died out was that it developed a kind of encephalitis—an infection of the brain, that was studied experimentally by Dr. G. M. Findlay and Dr. Edward Hindle in the Wellcome Bureau of Scientific Research, in London. The creatures would get ill, shiver, and chatter their teeth, become partly paralysed and very weak and eventually die. The brain condition, seen microscopically, showed a meningo-encephalitis (with infiltration of leuco-cytes from the blood-vessels into the surrounding tissues) not unlike that caused by virus diseases in silver foxes. But the experiments were not complete or conclusive. Also the disease may have been caught by the lemmings from some other animal after they reached England. It was first noticed a year after the first stock had been obtained. For the present the incident only shows that *Dicrostonyx* can die with symptoms of encephalitis, possibly due to virus infection. It is mentioned because no other evidence exists and because arctic foxes seem to die of a kind of encephalitis, which might be caught from lemmings.

Although Canadian lemmings do not undertake the impressive treks that those on the Norwegian mountains do, yet they have often been seen migrating on a smaller scale, and these migrations seem to occur most conspicuously at the peak of abundance.

One of the biggest migrations recorded was seen by John Rae[19] in June 1851 when he was searching for Franklin's relics along the west bank of the Coppermine River. He met thousands of lemmings trekking northwards and swimming the river. He noticed that, like the Norwegian species, they mostly travelled at night. Dr. R. M. Anderson has kindly allowed me to draw upon notes that he in turn got from Arctic travellers in more recent years. Mr. Herodier, of the Hudson's Bay Company, was crossing Queen Maud Sea, from Perry River to King William Island, in the early part of May 1926, and he saw great numbers of grey lemmings (just changing from their white winter dress) going north across the sea-ice. Many were dead in pools on the ice, and some were as far as thirty-five miles from land. Captain J. Berthé, a shipmaster who worked with Revillon Frères for many years, saw a big migration on land, near Baker Lake, in May 1926. These were probably *Lemmus*, or most of them.

There are a good many published records also, by Freuchen and others, proving that Canadian lemmings emigrate in certain years. The three factors that spring at once to the mind—food shortage, epidemic, and emigration—probably all play a part in the lemming crash. There must be other, subtler factors also, especially the overbearing weight of predator pressure on a lemming population already dwindling through other reasons.

2

The emigration of snowy owls after the lemming downfall is one of the most remarkable features of the Arctic cycle and also affects the equilibrium of animal populations thousands of miles south of the tundra and barren grounds. Probably this periodic exodus happens to some extent over the whole circumpolar zone, though not of course in the same years in all parts of it. There is a very large literature about the fluctuations of snowy owls, mostly arising from the observations of expeditions that have stayed several years in the field. From this literature one gets an overwhelming impression of the predominant importance of lemmings for the snowy owl. They are its anchor to the Arctic lands, and when this anchor is removed, the snowy owl population drifts away, seeking other means of subsistence.

Because there are so many observers to the south we hear mostly of the great southern flights in certain years. But there is no reason to suppose that all starving owls move south; some at any rate fly far out to sea, where ocean steamers pick them up. Also we must assume that a considerable nucleus of owls either remains in some parts of the North or else returns there after the migration, otherwise there could hardly be the quick recovery that is so often noticed.

31

For Ungava the reports from various posts given in the last chapter are an index of the periodic emigration and its connexion with lemmings. A much greater body of evidence could be added, from Hudson's Bay Company reports covering other parts of the Canadian Arctic in these years. This material still awaits full analysis and publication, but we can say with assurance that in all parts of this region short periods of high abundance of snowy owls alternate with short periods of great scarcity. Since these periods do not synchronize over the whole region, there is probably a good deal of transference of snowy owls to areas of favourable lemming abundance within the northern country itself. Movements of this kind must often take place. But there are some years in which, by chance coincidence of different fluctuations or by widespread ecological conditions affecting the populations, there is almost unvaried scarcity of predators from eastern Alaska to Baffin Island and Labrador. In such years the mortality or emigration or both must be tremendous.

At the other end of the migration we have observations made in the settled regions of Canada and the United States recording the arrival of the snowy owls in great numbers in certain years. The best information about these southern flights we owe to Alfred Gross,[13, 14, 15] who, while engaged on the New England Ruffed Grouse Investigation, also found time to organize a wide inquiry into the snowy owl. In the autumn of 1926 reports of big white owls began to be received, not only from the eastern United States but also from Ontario and Quebec. The earliest arrival recorded was on 26 October, in Northern Ontario, and the maximum influx was reached in November, after which the numbers diminished during the winter months until few were noticeable by February 1927.

Unfortunately, the owls arrived during the height of the shooting season, and a huge number were shot as soon as they were seen. Taxidermists were flooded with orders to mount dead snowy owls. 'A Boston dealer in glass eyes received so many orders for owl's eyes that he cabled to Europe for 250 additional pairs.'[8] This sorry slaughter was made very easy by the fact that most of the owls showed no fear of man. In Ontario twenty-six taxidermists reported a total of 517 owls among them, and in Quebec there were 271 from twelve taxidermists. One firm in Boston alone received 143 snowy owls.

In addition to taxidermists, various other sources of information were used. Through radio appeals, the ornithologist readers of the *Auk*, the observers of the Ruffed Grouse Investigations, museums, State departments, and lighthouses, an intelligence system was quickly arranged, by means of which the first real map of a 'snowy owl year' in eastern North America was produced. This showed a main area of invasion in the east, extending from the Atlantic coast west to the edge of Manitoba, the Great Lakes, and Ohio and Pennsylvania. The southern limits of the main invasion were roughly along a line from the southern tip of Lake Michigan to New York. Beyond these lines the records were fewer, and the invasion may be assumed to have come down chiefly or entirely from the Eastern

Arctic. This conclusion is backed by the strong concentration of snowy owls along the Atlantic coast, by their occurrence in Newfoundland also, and by records obtained by ships hundreds of miles out in the Atlantic. The distribution of records in New England shows a very remarkable grouping actually on the seaboard and up certain of the river valleys, and by large lakes.

Altogether from Canada and the United States at least 2,500 records were tabulated. Most of these owls were killed and would not have been counted twice. Gross concludes: 'From estimates made of conditions in Maine and from reports received from elsewhere I feel that 5,000 is a conservative estimate of the number of snowy owls killed in the United States and Canada during the 1926–7 flight. It would be most interesting to know how many snowy owls succeeded in returning to the northland to breed after having passed the gauntlet of fire arms on their visit to civilized America.' It is sad to consider this mass of transfigured lemming taking flight to civilized America in search of food, seeing the open fields and marshes that look like tundra, settling confidently as on an empty land, falling to innumerable guns, and finally adding its barred white beauty to a thousand triumphant farms and urban homes. As Job said (though without satire): 'The stranger did not lodge in the street: but I opened my doors to the traveller.'

Mostly these exiled owls seem to have lived on small rodents such as rats and field-mice; but they also were seen to pick up wild-fowl, especially along the coast. Little is known of any return flight north in the spring and it is likely that most of the snowy owls that arrived in the autumn had died or been destroyed. Whether man's actions thus affect in any way the arctic fox crop by relieving 'owl pressure' on the lemmings cannot yet be answered. The question turns on whether owls that were shot on migration would in any case have died through natural causes, and if not whether they could have found their way home again. At any rate the owls must have an appreciable influence upon rodents and birds in the countries they visit. Beamer[1] kept a captive snowy owl in Ontario, and found that it ate 2 lb. of beef in a week, and that in four days it devoured from thirty to thirty-five voles. An owl like this is a pretty good engine of destruction. The southern flights occur also in western America, and Couch[4] records that during the winter of 1922–3 large numbers of snowy owls appeared in the valleys of Okanogan and Wenatchee in the State of Washington. At this time orchards, and fields of alfalfa, were suffering severely from a plague of voles (*Microtus*) which it was thought the owls played some part in checking.

Four years later Gross gathered notes on another invasion. It was not so large as the previous one, but covered nevertheless a wide front from south-east Canada through New England to the Atlantic coast. 1,313 snowy owls were reported altogether. Places in the Middle West of Canada also had a good many owls. In the east there was again a grouping along the sea-coast and some were seen far out to sea. As before,

November saw the height of the movement. Hicks[16] did a careful inquiry on the Ohio part of this 1930–1 invasion.

Gross, who realized the cyclical nature of these movements and their relation to the Arctic cycle, collected the previous dates of influx of the snowy owl, which are contained in Table 64. To them I have added his subsequent note of a repetition in 1934–5, which affected Quebec, the

TABLE 64

Correlation between snowy-owl migrations and the Arctic cycle

The arctic fox peaks have been corrected from data in Chapter XX; but they remain the same as those published by Gross, 1931, except that '1913' is now given as '1913 or 1914'. 1934 has been added. Dates in brackets are based on fur returns alone. Lemming peaks from Chapter XXI, voles from Chapter XIV. Dates in brackets indicate great abundance without proof that peak had been reached.

Snowy owl, E. Canada & U.S.A.	Arctic fox, Ungava	Lemming ab., Ungava	Vole ab., N. Labrador
. .	(1872)	. .	. .
1876	(1876)	. .	(1874, 1875)
. .	(1879)	. .	. .
1882	1882	. .	. .
. .	1887	. .	. .
1889	1890	. .	(1888)
1892	1893	. .	. .
1896	1897	(1895)	. .
1901	1901	(1901)	. .
1905	1905	. .	1905
. .	1909	. .	1909
. .	(1913 or 1914)	. .	(1913)
1917	(1917)	. .	(1916, 1917)
. .	(1921)	(1920)	(1920)
1926	(1926)	. .	. .
. .	. .	[sc. 1927]	[sc. 1927, 1928]
1930	1930	1929	. .
1934	1934	1933, 1934	1933, 1934

Maritime Provinces of Canada, and New England (and probably also regions farther west that he does not mention). Gross used the dates of maximum arctic fox catch in Ungava (supplied by the Hudson's Bay Company through me) to make a very interesting correlation between the owl migrations and the Arctic cycle. These dates have been critically checked in the light of Chapter XIX, but remain substantially as he used them. There is an obvious connexion between the Ungava fox peaks and snowy owl irruptions southwards. Of the eleven owl migrations eight coincided with fox peaks, and three occurred the year before. In so far as the year that precedes maximum fur catches is always a fairly good one, the correlation suggests that snowy owl flights into eastern Canada and United States are an invariable index of good white fox harvests in the same winter.

If the table is studied further, there can be seen a close connexion between the abundance of mouse-like rodents in the North and the snowy owls. The owl influx is an autumn event, and it is likely that lemming decrease in the winter of 1929–30 would not send the owls southwards until the following autumn, because there are various alternative foods in summer, but little else than lemmings in the winter. No doubt there is a good deal of southward drift of owls every winter, but as the rodent cycle happens over the whole of northern Quebec, the owl population is driven farther south.

A great deal remains to be found out about the manner of the migration. We have only these correlations and general probability to prove that the snowy owls do come from the Eastern Arctic. And it must be remembered that our correlation includes only the Ungava and Labrador region. Many owls must come also from Baffin Island and perhaps the western side of Hudson's Bay. The fur figures show that the whole of this vast region, including at any rate southern Baffin Island, Melville Peninsula, Baker Lake, and Chesterfield Inlet, tends very strongly to follow the same cycle as Ungava. Considering, therefore, that we are using Ungava as an index of this larger reservoir of snowy owls, the correlation stands astonishingly well.

A periodic phenomenon which operates over millions of square miles, is an index of the chief Arctic fur crop, influences game management and agriculture in the temperate zone, and doubtless has innumerable minor effects, deserves a more steadily organized research than it has received. For such a study three different things are needed. The first—an annual record of the Arctic cycle at posts throughout the North—is already in existence through the Canadian Arctic Wild Life Enquiry.[2] This needs strengthening and calibration by lemming census studies at fixed stations. The second, which could be combined with the special lemming work, is the ringing of snowy owls on as large a scale as possible, in order to settle the origin of the emigrants. The third thing needed is a permanent staff intelligence ready to record and map the periodic appearance of snowy owls in the south.

3

Emigration and death also bring each arctic fox cycle to a decline, though probably fewer foxes leave the Arctic before death overtakes them than do snowy owls. This is only natural since the fox is wingless and has many hundred miles of desolate country to negotiate. I have suggested in Chapter XIV that an appreciable fraction of the coloured foxes in Quebec Peninsula is killed by trappers, and that the animals may enter traps in larger numbers when they are hungry through scarcity of voles. Probably quite a large fraction of the arctic foxes that are stranded without food when lemmings get scarce also falls to the trapper. This fraction should now be greater than it was in the nineteenth century, owing to the expansion

of the white fox fur trade. However, although much greater induce-
ment to trap comes from the higher prices in recent years, the number of
hunters may not have increased, and some of them will have gone to
grounds not previously trapped intensively for fur. The very vagueness
of the comments that one can make on these questions suggests the need
for more inquiry into the trapper-territory-fox relationship.

What happens to those foxes that do not fall to the hunter's trap or
gun ? As was seen in Chapter XX, some migrate. There is also evidence
that epidemic disease attacks them, disease with nervous symptoms which
show a curious similarity to those seen in epidemics among sledge dogs in
the same northern regions. The nature of the evidence makes it convenient
to consider the fox and dog disease together. We shall find that this
problem is not just one of Ungava and Labrador, but is part of a circumpolar phenomenon, which has implications for other regions as well. Its
elucidation cannot be complete until a great number of pathological and
nutritional experiments have been done, and some of these await the
establishment of adequate field stations in the Canadian Arctic.

A list of sledge dog epidemics in Northern Labrador (with references)
was given in Chapter XV, and this showed no obvious connexion with the
cycle in coloured fox, so that one could infer that the occasional crippling
of native transport does not introduce any cyclical trend into the fur
returns and is therefore not a cause of the cycle in them. Unless otherwise
indicated, the notes below come from the Mission reports.[27] Some of these
epidemics were very severe indeed. An 'infectious distemper' in 1835
killed 200 dogs at Nain; in 1836–7 about 280 out of 300 dogs at Okak died
of disease or starvation. In 1858–9 about 95 per cent. of the dogs all down
the Moravian Mission coast died. We are not told much about the symptoms of this epidemic, except that 'in its general type it seems to have had
much similarity to the canine madness of Europe'. But the dogs showed
no disposition to attack man, either European or Eskimo, only other dogs
(this observation was made by the Hebron missionary). Okak station
recorded that 180 dogs died: 'Those which were attacked ran about in a
kind of stupefaction till they were exhausted.' At this place an interesting
thing was noted: one of the dogs accidentally fell through the roof of a
house on to two Eskimos, who were bitten but developed no illness. A
party of Eskimos from the north, who visited Hebron in February 1860,
'stated that the distemper which raged among the dogs all along the coast
had also extended to the reindeer and even to the wolves and foxes'.
We shall find this interesting suggestion cropping up again, both in the
Eastern and Western Arctic, also in Baffin Island and Alaska.

In 1863–4 it was noted that: 'The natives call the disease by a name
signifying "want of sense". . . . In May two foxes actually came into our
garden, an occurrence almost unheard-of at a season of the year when
hunger does not drive them into the close neighbourhood of human dwellings.' Here again we find a reference to the native observation or belief
that the disease occurred also in reindeer and foxes. The severity of these

occasional outbreaks among the sledge dogs is shown by a record for 1898: 'Between New Year and Easter a fatal epidemic broke out among the Okak dogs, an epidemic which . . . spread southward as far as Makkovik, and carried off many of the best dogs on the coast.' At Okak, in the winter of 1898–9, on the Eskimos' spring reindeer hunt, 'some even dragged their sledges themselves, all their dogs having been killed'. The journals of Davis Inlet Post[20] contain a few references to the nature of the disease in dogs. On 9 February 1875, the manager wrote: 'One of our dogs got mad and had to be hanged. . . . Another of the Esqx. dogs got mad.'

These Northern Labrador records are scanty, yet give us a clear picture in outline, of epidemics that decimate the dog populations at long intervals, sometimes affecting the whole coast from Hebron nearly to Hamilton Inlet, with symptoms of madness or hysteria, ending in death with exhaustion, but with no danger to man. And a suggestion that the same disease breaks out at these times among wild animals, of which fox, wolf, and caribou are specifically mentioned. The early Ungava archives do not contain much information on this subject, but what there is agrees with this picture from Labrador, and is amply reinforced by more recent inquiries. In the season of 1886–7 the Stupart's Bay Eskimos were unable to visit Fort Chimo with their furs, because their dogs had 'all died of distemper'.[25(1)] On 15 December 1897 we read in the journal of that post that the cooper (who had gone trapping) had broken up his camp and returned, because his dogs had 'distemper', of which three of them had died.[24] And in his review of the trade for Outfit 1901, Wilson wrote[25(2)] from Fort Chimo: 'The Esquimaux from Stupart's Bay and Wolstenholme did not come out in such numbers as usual on account of the difficulty they experience in obtaining sufficient dogs to make up teams. There was an enormous loss of dogs through the epidemic of "sickness" which periodically breaks out among them, and which this winter has proved very fatal.' Wilson's remark rather implies that dog disease was well known to be recurrent in Ungava, although so little record of it occurs in the archives.

4

Several accounts of mortality among wild foxes (in one case specifically arctic foxes) have already been included in quotations about the Ungava fox cycle in Chapter XIX. These were in 1888–9, 1891–2, 1892–3 (possibly referring to the same deaths in the year before), and 1898–9. In the first of these there is also mention of deaths among wolves.

In 1928 (before I had investigated any of these archives) Professor William Rowan drew my attention to the existence of the dog disease in the North, of which he in turn had been told by Mr. Louis Romanet. Romanet, who had been at Revillon Frères' fur-trade post in Ungava Bay from about 1908 to 1916, later on became district manager of the Athabasca-McKenzie District of the Hudson's Bay Company, with headquarters in Edmonton, where I discussed this question with him in October 1928. He had made many observations on the cycles in fur-bearing animals in Ungava (upon which he wrote a full report to his firm that I have not been able to trace). Among other things he had observed that the white fox suffers from epidemic disease in its peak years, with symptoms of dizziness and sudden rabies-like attacks. These symptoms were also seen in sledge dogs. A meeting with Mr. W. O. Douglas in London in January 1929 provided further evidence of the great importance of the disease. Douglas was then post manager of the Hudson's Bay Company post at Baker Lake, in Chesterfield Inlet, north-west Hudson Bay, and he knew the fox and dog disease and had noticed it to be more or less cyclical. It seemed not unlikely that the dog disease might arise from the foxes, and in any case the phenomenon was of obvious interest if it affected the cycle in white fox fur supplies and the means of hunting and transporting them. Accordingly, a questionnaire inquiry was organized through the Hudson's Bay Company to posts round Hudson Bay, in Ungava, and in Baffin Island, and the results (with information from other sources) published in 1931.[6] There is no need to repeat the details given in that paper; they confirm and amplify the general picture from the archives. The disease in dogs had been observed at the posts of George's River, Fort Chimo, Leaf River, Stupart's Bay, and Wolstenholme; at posts around Baffin Island; at the posts of Baker Lake, Chesterfield, and Eskimo Point (on north-west Hudson Bay); and at some more southern posts around the bay and in James Bay. Disease in the arctic fox had been noted at George's River, Fort Chimo, and Wolstenholme; also in Baffin Island, and at Baker Lake (Chesterfield Inlet).

The symptoms, both in dog and fox, are evidently protean, yet one can also perceive in them certain common denominators. They are manifestations of some grave derangement of the central nervous system, the mortality is usually very high, there is strong evidence of infectiveness, yet in spite of the crazy behaviour man is seldom attacked, or if he is, with no pathological results, and no instance of human hydrophobia has been recorded. From these features we can infer an infection of the central nervous system that is not ordinary rabies and is usually quite different from ordinary dog distemper. A single instance, not necessarily typical, will illustrate its startling and highly fatal nature. Fort Chimo (John Blackhall, manager) reported that there had been two outbreaks in dogs in the years 1922-9.[22]

'In some cases, slight foaming at the mouth, apparent giddiness, snapping at any noise close at hand as if they were blind, vomiting, and except in rare cases, dying in the course of a few days. In other cases, loss of power of the hind quarters, continual snapping at all approaching, whether man or beast, and very savage. . . . Or savage at any restraint, absolutely wild, liable to attack people, run at a tree, house, or large object that crosses their vision, or a mad desire to gallop. These three sets of symptoms may be separate, or intermingled to a varying extent.'

The natives at this post believed that the disease appeared at the lemming peak, and was exactly similar in dogs and arctic foxes.

Natives at Pond Inlet Post in Baffin Island asserted that a severe epidemic some years before had killed dogs, foxes, and wolves, and that it had spread very rapidly; while Indians at Fort George Post on Hudson Bay had observed similar nervous disease in the coloured fox.[6] We shall see that there are also reports about the disease in dogs and in wild animals, from the Western Arctic of Canada, Alaska, Greenland, Novaya Zemlya, and Siberia. Here is an extraordinary Arctic phenomenon, the pathological derangement of behaviour in certain years, in several species, usually with fatal results. The fact that most of these species form the basis of man's Arctic economic arrangements is an accidental circumstance that has drawn attention to a problem of wide biological interest.

However, the effects of the outbreaks on native welfare and the fur trade are often very serious indeed, and on this ground alone, there is need for a full investigation. Witness such reports as the one from Clyde River Post in northern Baffin Island in 1931:[23]

'This winter a fatal sickness broke out that killed about 80 % of the dogs in this part of the country. Practically all the Post dogs were destroyed, having now only three dogs left out of eighteen. Every native lost, on an average, twelve or fourteen and they are now reduced to three or four dogs each, four natives having lost their whole team. . . . This dying out of the dogs has been very disastrous to the year's trade, as with the few dogs the natives have now they cannot go bear-hunting nor can they carry fat etc. from their camps to the Post. The sickness has died down now but it has left all the natives in a very poor condition as far as dogs are concerned.'

Since 1931 a good deal more information has been collected about dog epidemics in Quebec Peninsula and elsewhere. The chief sources are further reports from Hudson's Bay Company posts, the recent Canadian Arctic Wild Life Enquiries[2] (which combine the Company's results with those obtained by the Northwest Territories Administration), and notes collected during the Matamek Conference on Biological Cycles in 1931.[26] I shall not try to present here a complete arrangement of this raw material, as it has not yet accumulated sufficiently to tell a conclusive story. It will also be noticed that I have not cited details about the actual years of epidemic outbreaks in recent times. One reason is that, in spite of a good many general statements to the effect that the disease is associated with the cycle (as indeed it seemed to be in the early Ungava fox mortalities of 1888–9, though not in northern Labrador), analysis of the actual dates for recent times does not afford any clear general correlation either between fox and dog outbreaks, or between dog disease and fox cycle. Leaving aside the possibility that the correlation does not exist, there are several reasons why it is difficult to arrive at it by such methods. First, the records are few and incomplete. Secondly, there are difficulties in deducing the exact peak in fox populations from fur returns. Thirdly, the dog disease often starts at one or two centres and spreads by the travel of dog-teams to other posts, so that there is a progressive lag introduced, which cuts at the basis of correlation. To study the subject on this plane, we need continued and very completely mapped records, such as the Canadian Arctic Wild Life Enquiry is handsomely providing.

A fourth reason is that we do not really know how far all these different outbreaks are the same disease. We can say, with absolute certainty, that illness with strongly marked nervous symptoms breaks out at intervals in northern regions, and that the disease is unlikely to be any ordinary type of rabies. The protean symptoms that have been referred to make it particularly difficult to integrate the story. But even if the disease were homogeneous in its symptoms, we could not deduce its course without experiment, which is at present lacking. Nearly every disease that has been profoundly studied is found to manifest itself in a great many atypical forms that cannot at first be recognized from the average text-book description. Especially in nervous epidemic diseases, such as encephalitis, are found great variations in the symptoms. These considerations have made one realize the futility of speculating too far in field epidemiology, without a solid corpus of experimental evidence.

5

Since the 'silver' variety of the coloured fox was turned into a domestic animal, a great deal of attention has been devoted to the diseases of this species, and in particular by R. G. Green and his associates since 1925 to epidemics on the huge silver fox farms of Fromm Brothers in Minnesota and Wisconsin. Here disastrous outbreaks killed up to 40 per cent. of the foxes in certain years. The chief disease has been proved to be a form of encephalitis, on which these workers have produced a fine series of reports[12] in the *American Journal of Hygiene* from 1930 to 1936. The cause is an invisible virus that attacks especially the central nervous system, but is also present in the respiratory tract, from which it spreads from one animal to another in the breath. It produces distinctive intranuclear bodies in the endothelial cells of the central nervous system, which shows microscopic haemorrhages as a characteristic lesion. These intranuclear bodies are not seen in distemper, which also differs in that it is highly infectious to ferrets, whereas this fox encephalitis is not.[10] The virus can be transmitted from fox to fox by inoculation of material from the spinal cord or brain of an infected animal. It can also be obtained from other organs such as the spleen. Coyote and dog have proved susceptible in experiments, but not mink or cat or ferret, or rodents. The disease in dogs was studied thoroughly and found to be similar in symptoms and pathology to that in the silver fox, but with certain differences. The illness in the fox often starts rather suddenly: loss of appetite, convulsions, excitability, then a sort of 'sleep-walking' or lethargic stage when the animal walks about with its eyes closed—often in circles, then more convulsions. There is usually some paralysis, and great weakness, turning to

coma and death. Some, however, die suddenly. There is often some discharge from the nose and eyes, but the latter remain clear. In dogs, on the
other hand, a purulent discharge from eyes and nose often develops; the
nervous symptoms take the form of a kind of running fit, with great
excitability, but without the sleep-walking stage. Convulsions are less
frequent. Coma and death develop as in the fox. This comparison is, of
course, based on the results of tests with particular strains of the virus,
and should not be taken as applying in all the varied circumstances in
which epidemics might occur.

There is a great general resemblance between Green's dog and fox
encephalitis and the 'crazy disease' reported from sledge dogs and arctic
foxes. But a proof of identity can only be obtained by controlled experiments. Attempts have been made by me several times to obtain infected
brain material from dogs, through the Hudson's Bay Company's northern
posts. The fact that the virus of encephalitis of fox will remain alive for
several years in 50 per cent. glycerin makes such long-distance study
theoretically practicable. A little material was actually obtained in this
way in 1934 and examined by G. M. Findlay in London, but without
conclusive results. The importance of following this subject energetically
through is obvious, especially as Green and his associates have immunized
silver foxes against the disease.

The symptoms of dog distemper are ordinarily rather different from
those of encephalitis, in that the nervous symptoms are not developed in
the same extreme manner; though the two diseases have a good deal in
common in some other external symptoms, and in the death from weakness. Also convulsions may occur. But distemper is primarily a 'dog
influenza' and not a disease of the central nervous system. If our records
from the North were all made by pathologists, it would probably be easy
to sort out the 'physiognomies' of different outbreaks. As it is, the
accounts are often incomplete. With the increase in volume of transporta-
tion to the Canadian North in recent years (itself partly a consequence of
the development of white fox fur trade), there has come an increasing risk
of the introduction of dog diseases from the south. Also, losses of the
northern sledge dogs have often been made up by mongrels from outside.

An apparent instance of a pandemic starting outside the normal range
of the 'crazy disease', but spreading far northward, occurred in the years
1930–2, when the North Shore of the Gulf of St. Lawrence, other parts of
Canadian Labrador north of this, and the Moravian Mission coast of
Northern Labrador, were ravaged by epidemics among the dogs. I have
received through the courtesy of Dr. Harrison F. Lewis of the National
Parks Bureau of Canada a very full account of this pandemic, by Dr. D. G.
Hodd of the Grenfell Mission. Among other things he writes:

'It has been possible to trace the origin of the disease locally during the recent
epidemic, as far as Deer Lake, Newfoundland. In the winter of 1929–30 a team
of dogs travelled by way of the west coast of Newfoundland from Deer Lake to
Flower's Cove. It is reported that these dogs on arrival at their destination

showed signs of illness and some of the team died. Within a short period other dogs that had been in contact with them showed signs of illness and the condition very rapidly assumed epidemic proportions in that neighbourhood. The following summer, dogs from Flower's Cove and other settlements in Northern Newfoundland found their way across the Straits of Belle Isle to the Labrador coast, and during the following winter and spring the disease spread rapidly east and west, killing and devitalizing hundreds of teams. This epidemic continued until the latter part of 1932, reaching its peak in the winter of 1931–32. Since then there have been sporadic cases, showing somewhat similar signs but with much less fatal results.'

Reports from the Moravian Missions and the Hudson's Bay Company suggest that the same pandemic penetrated at least as far north as Davis Inlet (1930–1), and that possibly it was the same disease at Nain and Nutak (Okak) in 1932–3. The important feature of this pandemic, apart from its destructiveness, is that Dr. Hodd's description of the symptoms (with loss of appetite, vomiting, high temperature, purulent discharge from eyes and nose, blindness, weakness, in some cases paralysis of the legs) belongs distinctly to the distemper picture, not to that of encephalitis. Another pandemic in sledge dogs, resembling distemper and not the 'crazy disease', has been very clearly mapped by Chitty[2] for the western Arctic, 1938–9,

6

It seems evident that we are now faced with at least two different problems in northern dog disease. On the one hand, there is the endemic disease, known for over a hundred years, resembling or identical with the encephalitis of ranch foxes, which occurs both in dogs and in wild foxes, especially the arctic fox. On the other hand, there is a disease resembling or identical with distemper of dogs, which is probably penetrating the Canadian North in a series of pandemics from the south. Incidentally, Green and Dewey[10] have shown experimentally that the virus of dog distemper is fatal to red foxes: also that infections from encephalitis or from distemper do not establish cross-immunity. It would seem therefore that science must find a way of immunizing arctic sledge dogs against both types of virus.

The same connexion between epidemics with nervous symptoms in dogs and wild animals is found at points right round the Arctic region. In 1908 the Danish veterinarian Hjortlund published a monograph[18] on epidemics that had been ravaging West Greenland dog populations at intervals for at least a hundred years. It affected the arctic fox also. He believed it to be a form of rabies that was harmless to man, but the symptoms are just those of the 'crazy disease'. Clarke's recent report[3] upon the Thelon Game Sanctuary in the Western Barrens of Canada assembles some records of dog disease in that region, and draws attention to evidence of the same type of epidemic among wolves. Since wolves depend chiefly upon the caribou herds, any disease that checks their numbers is an important factor in conservation. A Hudson's Bay Company report[21] from Baker Lake Post (Chesterfield Inlet) for 1930–1 supports Clarke's evidence: 'During December, January and February, crazy foxes were seen inland in the Beverly Lake region, and during December and January wolves were noted running around in a demented condition.' In 1937 Clarke[3] watched a wolf on the bank of the Hanbury River 'running around in circles and howling in a manner identical with dogs at Reliance in the "hysterical" stage'. The Canadian Arctic Wild Life Enquiries are accumulating much evidence about dog diseases in the Western Arctic.

Hadwen[6] has reported the dog and fox disease from Alaska, where it is well known; and Anderson[26] also mentions a dog epidemic in northern Alaska associated with the same crazy disease in foxes. 'One crazy fox came right into the dog house and was killed by the men. Another crazy fox came into an Eskimo house and tried to bite an Eskimo woman and she killed him. . . . There are three diseases with the same [Eskimo] name: mollycolly. There is a mollycolly dog, and a mollycolly fox, and a drunken man is also called mollycolly.'

Bergman[6] noticed the crazy disease among foxes in Kamchatka. From references kindly given me by Dr. A. N. Formozov of Moscow University, it appears that the same symptoms have been observed among foxes in the region of Anadyr in north-western Siberia, where, according to the observations of Gondotti (1897): 'A disease of some kind attacked foxes; they ran into houses, hurled themselves upon men and dogs, without, however, injuring them, and a multitude of foxes perished at this time.' He also found records of the dog and fox disease in other parts of Siberia: Turukhansk Province in the Lower Yenisei region, on the Lower Pechora, in the Yamal Peninsula.

The disease also occurs in Novaya Zemlya, as shown by the observations of Gorbunov[9] and of Dubrovskii,[5] published in Russian. The latter has a particularly interesting note on a 'rabid' arctic fox which was caught in a trap and there killed and eaten by the trapper's leading sledge dog. At the end of that month the dog went mad and had to be shot. Gorbunov mentions that in 1927 'an epidemic of rabies raged in Novaya Zemlya among the arctic foxes, and during the attacks of the disease the arctic foxes ran into villages and bit the dogs. The dead bodies of arctic foxes with their winter coat, which we found in summer, completely corroborated the information from the hunters quoted above.'

There is, finally, something more to be said about the conditions in which such disease breaks out. A good deal is becoming known about the effects of food deficiency in producing nervous symptoms and paralysis in dogs and foxes. The essays of a Norwegian veterinarian, Baashus-Jessen,[17] contain many interesting arguments based upon a reading of the literature on polar travel. He points out the extraordinarily widespread occurrence of diseases, especially outbreaks with nervous symptoms, in the dog-teams of expeditions, both in the Arctic and Antarctic. His chief theory is that these symptoms are caused by a deficiency of fat, that dogs fed on a straight protein or carbohydrate ration develop such diseases. He has no experimental verification to offer, nevertheless he has made out a sound case for considering the environmental, especially the feeding, conditions as a contributing, or even sometimes a dominant cause of the outbreaks. In this connexion we may note Findlay's verdict[7] about the canine hysteria that has puzzled the owners of English dogs in recent years: 'The evidence for virus or other infective agent is slight; hyperinsulinism, vitamin B_1 deficiency, or the action of phytotoxins from a too-exclusively vegetarian diet, have been suggested as possible causes, but experimental evidence is lacking.'

Quite recently Green and Evans[11] have announced some experiments on a curious deficiency disease in ranched silver foxes, caused by feeding them with 10 per cent. or more of fresh fish in their diet. This diet soon brings about a condition of weakness, unsteady gait, nervous movements, and even convulsions, followed by death in a few days. The brain has characteristic microscopic lesions that resemble closely those in the human disease called Wernicke's polioencephalitis. This human disease is caused by vitamin B_1 deficiency, and it is suggested that the fresh fish somehow destroys or immobilizes this vitamin in the foxes' food.

When we remember the very poor conditions in which many northern sledge dog teams are kept, especially as regards summer food, and at the same time consider the effects of periodic starvation on foxes (and perhaps dogs also) caused by the lemming crash, we can perceive that food factors may greatly complicate and vary the manifestations of virus infections. We leave the subject at this stage: a dog and fox disease or diseases of circumpolar distribution; often pandemic; showing affinity with the encephalitis of virus origin that ravages ranched silver foxes in temperate countries; probably complicated by varying natural and human food supplies; with a southern problem of a disease resembling distemper now invading northwards; some connexion with the lemming cycle not yet scientifically proved; a huge problem that can only be cleared up by work in the North itself. Surely this huge panorama of Arctic ecological fluctuations deserves at least as much money, trained scientific workers, field stations, and continuity of attention as has been given to the study of malaria or fish or whales or sleeping sickness.

It is to be hoped that the reader of this book will by now have seen that we stand on the near shore of an ocean larger than any that Columbus explored, in which we can at present discern only a few islands rising out of the mist. Let us hope that wise governments will train navigators and equip them to explore more closely the Islands of Vole, Mouse, and Lemming; and that they will do so not only in order to round Cape Fox and cross Dog Deep, but with some idea of understanding, not for power alone, but on account of its own wildness and interest and beauty, the unstable fabric of the living cosmos.

REFERENCES

* indicates that an abstract or copy is deposited in the Bureau of Animal Population, Oxford. Dates of archives are those of the 'Outfits'. H. B. Co. means Hudson's Bay Company.

1. BEAMER, L. H. (1937). 'Observations on the food habits of the snowy owl.' Canad. Field-Nat. 51: 59–60.

2. CHITTY, D. (1940). 'Canadian Arctic Wild Life Enquiry, 1938–39.' J. Anim. Ecol. 9: 227–42. (Contains references to the three previous inquiries.)

3. CLARKE, C. D. H. (1940). 'A biological investigation of the Thelon Game Sanctuary.' Bull. Nat. Mus. Canada, No. 96 (Biol. Ser. No. 25).

4. COUCH, L. K. (1928). 'Relationships of predatory mammals and birds to rodent life.' J. Mammal. 9: 73–4.

5. DUBROVSKII, A. N. (1937). ['The arctic fox (*Alopex lagopus* (L.)) and arctic fox trapping in Novaya Zemlya.'] Trans. Arct. Inst., Leningr. 77: 7–31. (In Russian; English translation in Bureau of Animal Population.)

6. ELTON, C. (1931). 'Epidemics among sledge dogs in the Canadian Arctic and their relation to disease in the arctic fox.' Canad. J. Res. 5: 673–92.

7. FINDLAY, G. M. (1940). 'Nervous affections in man and animals.' Proc. R. Soc. Med. 33: 161–8.

8. GILBERT, A. W. (1926). Commonwealth of Massachusetts, Dept. Agric., Items of Interest, No. 68, Dec. 8.

9. GORBUNOV, G. P. (1929). ['Materials on the mammal and bird fauna of Novaya Zemlya.'] Trans. Institute for Scientific Exploration of the North, No. 40: 169–237. (In Russian; summary in German. Translated passage, p. 174, supplied by A. N. Formozov.)

10. GREEN, R. G., & DEWEY, E. T. (1929). 'Fox encephalitis and canine distemper.' Proc. Soc. Exp. Biol. 27: 129–30.

11. GREEN, R. G., & EVANS, C. A. (1940). 'A deficiency disease in foxes.' Science, 92: 154–5.

12. GREEN, R. G., and others (1930–6). Series of 8 papers under general title: 'Epizootic fox encephalitis.' Amer. J. Hyg. 12: 109–29; 13: 201–23; 14: 353–73; 18: 462–81; 19: 343–61, 362–91; 21: 366–88; 24: 57–70.

13. GROSS, A. O. (1927). 'The snowy owl migration of 1926–27.' Auk, 44: 479–91.

14. GROSS, A. O. (1931). 'Snowy owl migration—1930–31.' Auk, 48: 501–11.

15. GROSS, A. O. (1935). 'Snowy owl migration—1934–35.' Auk, 52: 310.

16. HICKS, L. E. (1932). 'The snowy owl invasion of Ohio in 1930–1931.' Wilson Bull. 24: 221–6.

17. JESSEN, J. BAASHUUS- (1935). 'Arctic nervous diseases.' Skandinavisk Veterinärtidskrift: 310–45. (Also printed in Norges Svalbard- og Ishavs-undersøkelser (1935), No. 28.)

18. HJORTLUND, S. R. (1908). 'De smitsomme hundesygdomme i Grønland.' Maanedskrift for Dyrlaeger: 1–77.

19. RAE, J. (1890). 'Notes on some of the birds and mammals of the Hudson's Bay Territory . . .'' J. Linn. Soc. (Zool.), 20: 136–45.

*20. Davis Inlet Post, Journals, 1869–76, 1879–98, 1901–9. MS. H. B. Co. Archives, London.

*21. H. B. Co., Annual Zoological Reports from Posts.

*22. H. B. Co., Dog Disease Enquiry, 1929. (Partly summarized by Elton, 1931.)

*23. H. B. Co., Dog Disease Enquiry, 1931.

*24. Fort Chimo Post (Ungava District), Journals, 1866–72, 1874–6, 1883–5, 1895–6, 1898–1900. MS. H. B. Co. Archives, London.

*25. Ungava District (Fort Chimo) Correspondence, 1869, 1871–3, 1882–97, 1899–1912. MS. H. B. Co. Archives, London. (1) 28 Sept. 1887: P. McKenzie to J. Wrigley. (2) Sept. 1902: J. A. Wilson to P. McKenzie.

*26. Matamek Conference on Biological Cycles, 1931. Full Report of Proceedings. (Copies in Bureau of Animal Population, Oxford; in New York Zoological Society and several other American institutions.)

*27. Periodical Accounts of the Moravian Missions. London.

APPENDIX

EVIDENCE ABOUT THE OPENING AND CLOSING OF POSTS IN NORTHERN LABRADOR AND IN THE REGION OF HAMILTON INLET

In this note the 'year', unless otherwise defined, invariably means the 'ship-year' or 'Outfit'. Thus '1834' means 1834–5, '1835' means 1835–6, and so on. The exact month in which this period began or ended was variable. The Moravian Mission year was roughly July of one year to August of the next. In old days the Labrador posts of the Hudson's Bay Company followed a similar year; but later on (cf. Davis Inlet Post fur returns, 1872 onwards) they adopted, at any rate for fur and other accounting purposes, the usual 'Outfit', which ran, and still runs, from June 1st of one year to May 31st of the next. The term originated with the 'outfitting' and sending out of the Company's ship about June, for the voyage through Hudson Strait to the posts in Hudson Bay. Thus 'Outfit 1834' would mean the twelve months June 1st, 1834, to May 31st, 1835, i.e. including the winter fur season of 1834–5.

However, as the annual relaxation of ice-conditions in these northern waters really determines the annual cycle of trade, the ship-year still remained for most practical purposes the important thing, and has been used in all the fur-return lists for Labrador that occur in this book. In some instances this involved adding in a few furs which are put under the next Outfit, but were in fact collected during the same winter season.

The main authorities for the following details are

(1) The *Periodical Accounts* of the Moravian Missions ('P.A.': allusion being to the date the account refers to, not the date of publication).

(2) Dr. S. K. Hutton, recognized authority on Moravian Missions in Labrador, who has kindly supplied some information ('S.K.H.').

(3) Hudson's Bay Company archives, MS. in London; copies of abstracts in Bureau of Animal Population, Oxford ('H. B. Co. Archives').

(4) James White, *Forts and Trading Posts in Labrador Peninsula and adjoining territory* (Ottawa, 1926, 67 pp. and map), prepared as part of the evidence before the Privy Council during the Labrador Boundary case ('White').

(5) Voorhis, E. (1930). *Historic Forts and Trading Posts of the French régime and of the English Fur Trading Companies.* Natural Resources Intelligence Service. Dept. of the Interior, Ottawa.

(6) The Reports of the Labrador Boundary Case before the Privy Council.

A. *Moravian Mission Stations.*

Nain, Okak, and *Hopedale* were established in 1770, 1776, and 1782 respectively (Labrador Boundary Case vol. 3, pp. 1335–6: letter from B. La Trobe and J. Hutton, Moravian Mission, to Lord Sydney, May 26th, 1784). Nain and Hopedale have been in continuous existence ever since (P.A. 1791 onwards; fur returns 1834–1925). Okak was more or less abandoned after the disastrous influenza epidemic of 1919, but fur returns continued to be recorded until 1925.

Hebron was established in 1830 (P.A. Hebron narrative, August 1830 to July 1831) and has been in continuous existence ever since (P.A. 1830 onwards; fur returns 1834–1925). The native name for the place was Kangertluksoak (P.A. Hebron, 1831, where the site is described).

Zoar was established in 1866. In the summer of 1865 the missionaries began to set up the station, at Takpangayok (P.A. Nain, July 1865). The first narrative in P.A. and the first fur returns are for 1866. White states, on the authority of D. A. Smith, that the station was founded in 1863. This is incorrect, and probably Smith was referring simply to the decision to found Zoar. Except for one fox in 1893, the last fur returns were for 1887, but there are several references to the people at Zoar in the years after this (P.A.), and the station was finally abandoned in the summer of 1895 (P.A.). The general P.A. narrative for 1889 states that 'at New Year there were only 39 inhabitants at Zoar, the rest having moved to other stations or to the neighbourhood of H.B.C. posts'.

Ramah was established in August 1871 at Nullatartok Bay (P.A.). The fur returns run from 1871 to 1899. The station continued for a few years after 1899. The Ramah diary for 1906 announces that the station will probably be given up in the summer of 1907, the natives to go to Hebron and Killinek (P.A.). The general narrative for 1907 records the first steps towards abandonment. S. K. Hutton in an article called 'The last of Ramah' (*Moravian Missions*, vol. 7, pp. 88–9, 1909) states that there were 45 Eskimos there in the summer of 1908 (when it was abandoned. S.K.H.). A Hebron letter dated 20 February 1909, mentions that the Ramah people had a good seal hunt in 1908 autumn, so that a small native population evidently stayed on, at any rate for a short time.

Makkovik was established in 1896 (S.K.H.). The P.A. mention the building materials for this station being sent out in 1896. Owing presumably to competition, the first fur returns do not appear until 1900. Makkovik has existed continuously up to the present day.

Killinek was established in 1905 (S.K.H.), the first report being for this year (P.A.). An earlier general account (June, 1904) discusses the proposed new station which was to be 'known in future by its Eskimo name, Kikkertaujak, which means Peninsula. At present the place is called either Killinek, or Port Burwell, or Bishop Jones' Village. "Killinek" is quite a misnomer for this particular spot, for it is a name already in use not only for the whole of a large island at the northern extremity of Labrador, but also, locally, for the Cape otherwise known to us as Cape Chidley or Chudleigh.' But in 1905 it was decided to use Killinek rather than the correct, but jaw-breaking Kikkertaujak (P.A.).

Stewart, of the Colonial and Continental Church Society, had already been working here; but he moved south to Ungava Bay, leaving a clear field for the Moravians (*Moravian Missions*, vol. 2 (1904), p. 112). The fur returns begin in 1905 and run until 1924. The Report of the Royal Canadian Mounted Police for 1925 (1926), p. 42, notes that no missionary had been stationed there since 1923.

There are no more Moravian Mission fur returns after 1925, when the Hudson's Bay Company took over the surviving posts of *Nain*, *Okak*, *Hopedale*, *Makkovik* (and *Killinek*). *Okak's* name was changed to *Nutak*; and *Killinek* disappeared, as the Company already had a rival post at *Port Burwell*.

B. *Hudson's Bay Company posts on the coast of Northern Labrador.*

Aillik was established between 1836 and 1839, but I have not been able to find the exact date. In these early days it was called Eyelik or Eyeleck (various other spellings also occur). It cannot have existed before 1836, because it was in that year that North West River and Rigolet were founded, and Aillik was more or less the outpost of these. A letter from the Company to D. Finlayson dated 4 March 1840, gives the Esquimaux Bay District posts as 'Rigoulette, North West River, Kibocock and Eyeleck' (H. B. Co., London Outward Letter Book; mentioned also by White). The post appears, from scattered references in the archives of other posts, to have operated more or less continuously until 1875. After 1876 it was not mentioned in the Company's Minutes of Council, which gave a list of appointments (White); but this is only a rough criterion. A letter from G. McTavish (H. B. Co. Rigolet, 6 May 1876) to James Scott at 'Eyelicke' (H. B. Co.) evidently assumes the continuance of the post. It is not quite certain when the post was finally closed, but probably about this date, for there is a letter from M. Fortescue (H. B. Co. Rigolet, 15 July 1879) to John Ford at 'Kibikok', telling him to find out whether Captain Bartlett would be disposed to rent the buildings at 'Eyelick'. Had the post still been running, this request would presumably have been sent to the Aillik manager. It appears, then, that Aillik was established between 1836 and 1839, and abandoned between 1875 and 1878.

The evidence quoted by White and Voorhis, that it was reopened in 1891, is not relevant, as it refers merely to the transport of mails by the Company to this neighbourhood, to the settlement of Makkovik, at which the Moravian Mission station was founded a little later, in 1896. This station never had any direct competition with any Hudson's Bay Company post at the same point (P.A., S.K.H.).

Kaipokok (usually called 'Kibokok' or 'Kibocock' in the old days) was acquired by the Hudson's Bay Company in 1837 from a previous trader, D. R. Stewart. It appears to have been operated more or less continuously until 1878 (White, H. B. Co.). In the summer of 1879 M. Fortescue wrote (H. B. Co. Rigolet, 1879) to John Ford at 'Kibokok' conveying the Company's decision to close the post. The dates are therefore 1837–78.

Lampson was established in 1867 (White.) It had a rather uneven history. It formed part of the northern competition against the Moravian Missions in those years. A letter from G. McTavish (H. B. Co. Davis Inlet, 19 April 1876— he was on a visit there from Rigolet) to John Olsen at Nachvack refers to opera-tions at Lampson, which was then evidently Nachvack's outpost. A letter from M. Fortescue (H. B. Co. Rigolet, 3 July 1878) to James Bissett at Montreal states that 'the small vessel at Lampson employed at carrying the returns of that place to Nackvack, was totally wrecked last fall'. Another from Fortescue (H. B. Co., Rigolet, 1 August 1878) to 'James Lane, Hudson's Bay Company, Lampson', instructs him, on account of the loss of his own small vessel, to abandon Lampson, and take all his goods on board the *Labrador* to Nachvack. The post was therefore open for eleven years, 1867 to 1877.

Nachvack (spelt variously, as Nachvak and Nackvak) was established by D. A. Smith in 1868 (White). The journal began on 25 September 1868 (H. B. Co.). It ran probably continuously until 1905, as shown by scattered references in the Company's archives. White quotes evidence that the post was due for abandonment in the autumn of 1905. This was so, but the Nachvack Post journal runs until 18 September 1906 (H. B. Co.). The explanation is contained in an entry in the journal for 26 October 1905: 'The "Pelican" made her appearance . . . Nachvak Post was to be abandoned; but as Mr. Ford had no notice of it, things were not ready, and the Post is (to) run for another year, then close up for good.' (H. B. Co.) The dates are, therefore, 1868–1905.

x32

Davis Inlet was bought by the Company in 1869, from A. B. Hunt and Co., who also sold another post on St. Paul Island (White), that was probably used to some extent as an outpost for Davis Inlet (H. B. Co., Davis Inlet Post journals). Davis Inlet has operated ever since (H. B. Co., Davis Inlet Post journals and fur returns).

Port Burwell was established in 1916. 'The Hudson's Bay Company have put up a dwelling house and store, ten minutes walk from the Mission House. . . .' (P.A. Killinek, 1916). It has operated ever since (H. B. Co. fur returns).

The status and history of posts said by White to have existed at '*North River*' and '*Zoar*' are doubtful. They certainly existed for a very short time, and may have been only temporary outposts.

The taking over of the Moravian Mission stations by the Company in 1926 has already been mentioned. From that time to the present, the Company has operated *Hebron, Nutak* (= *Okak*), *Nain, Hopedale,* and *Makkovik. Nutak* was moved locally.

C. *Hudson's Bay Company posts around Hamilton Inlet and in Sandwich Bay.*

The Northern Labrador posts, considered in section B, formed in the nineteenth century part of Esquimaux Bay District, whose head-quarters lay in Hamilton Inlet. It is not necessary here to give a detailed history of the Hamilton Inlet posts, about which some information is published by White. The chief posts have always been *Rigolet* and *North West River*, both of which began in 1836. The Company put up these posts to compete with those of a trader, D. R. Stewart, who was already established there. In 1837 the Company bought up Stewart's property (White). Both posts have operated ever since (H. B. Co.). In Sandwich Bay, east of Hamilton Inlet, *Cartwright* was bought from A. B. Hunt and Co. in 1873 (White). It has operated ever since (H. B. Co.). It used to be in Esquimaux Bay District.

Certain other posts were established inland from Hamilton Inlet. These are not considered here.

INDEX

References to literature and other sources are put in alphabetical order at the end of each chapter. The authors' names are not repeated in this Index, which, however, includes a few names mentioned in the text but not to be found in the references. *Fluctuations of voles and mice in different countries* will be found under sub-headings of 'Vole and mouse plagues and fluctuations'. (The countries are defined by their position in 1930.) So far as possible, *names of species* are indexed under their Latin names, even when the latter are not mentioned in the text. There are cross-headings for the English names. For a good many of the names of animals, fur trade posts, &c., that occur in Parts III and IV, separate page references are not given, only chapter numbers. Various *acknowledgements* to people and organizations, scattered through the text, are not indexed; but the *chief organizations* actively concerned in the study of fluctuations are included. Some *main page references* are italicized.

Roman numerals refer to Chapters, unless preceded by 'Part'.
M.M. = Moravian Mission.
H.B.Co. = Hudson's Bay Company.

Accipiter nisus, 137, 223, 226.
Achorion quinckeanum, 101.
Acomys, 96.
Activity rhythm, 179, 186–8.
Aelian, 5.
Age distribution, 170–4, 180, 201; *see also* Life, length of.
Agrikulturbotaniśche Anstalt, Munich, 53–6.
Aillik post, H.B.Co., 262–3, 486.
Akpatok Island, 401, 403, 405.
Alactaga, 79, 96.
Alopex lagopus: Canada and Labrador, 157, 160, 239, 253–5, 341, 351, xix, xx, xxi, xxii; ditto, fur returns, 254, xix, xx (esp. 415–20, 424–6), 460–1; ditto, alternative foods, 324, 445, 447–8, 450; N.E. Greenland, 444–5; Norway, 223; U.S.S.R., 71, 296, 481.
Alsomys, see *Apodemus major*.
Antagonism, social and sexual, 205, 214.
Apodemus 85, 96; *agrarius*, 30, 49, 51, 75, 78; *flavicollis*, 75, 78–9; *fulvipectus*, 75–6; *major*, 75–6; *sylvaticus*, 15–17, 37, 49, 51–2, 60–1, 75, 78–80, 85, 162–73, 186, 195, 199, 205–6, 211, 222.
Apollo, mouse-god, 5–6, 9, 65.
Aquila chrysaëtus, 135, 137, 223.
Archibuteo, see *Buteo*.
Aristotle, 3.
Arsenious oxide, 29.
Arvicola, 96; *amphibius*, 71–2, 75–6, 161, 222, 229; *monticola*, 15; *terrestris*, 49.
Asio flammeus, 111, 121–2, 134–5, 150–2, 191–2, 452; *otus*, 10, 60, 135, 192.
Astur gentilis, 223, 226.
Australia, rabbit control in, 29–30.
Avian cholera, 29–30.

Bacillus murisepticus, 115; *rhusiopathiae*, 115; *typhi-murium*, 30.
Bacterium pitymysi, 63; *typhi-murium*, *aertrycke*, *enteritidis*, &c., iii (esp. Sect. 3), 102.
Badger, 116; see also *Meles meles*.
Bamboo, periodic flowering, 99.
Bandicoot-rat, see *Nesokia*.
Bank-vole, see *Clethrionomys glareolus*.
Barium carbonate, 29.
Barley, *see* Cereals.
Bear, black, see *Ursus americanus*.
Bear, brown, see *Ursus arctos*.
Bear, polar, see *Thalarctos maritimus*.
Beaver, see *Castor canadensis*.
Beetle, parasitic, 167.
Beetroot, *see* Sugar-beet.
Belcher Islands, 366–8.
Bergen Museum, 226.
Berry crops; and Eskimos, 334; and foxes, 326; and grouse, 227; and voles, 334.
Bersimis District, H.B.Co., 247.
Berwickshire Naturalists' Club, 131.
Big River, *see* Eastmain.
Biological control, *see* Control measures, diseases.
Biologische Reichsanstalt für Land- und Forstwirtschaft, Berlin, 48–9, 55.
Bird Lore, Christmas Bird Census, 335.
Birds, effect of poison on, 29.
Bitterns, 116.
Bounties, *see* Control measures, bounties.
Breeding season, *see* Reproduction, rates of.
Bridge-grafting, 117.
Bubo bubo, 223, 225–6.
Buckwheat, *see* Cereals.